Shooter's Bible

ABOUT OUR COVER

The Parker shotgun featured on our front cover marks the return of what generations of American sportsmen have referred to affectionately as "Old Reliable." First produced at Meriden, Connecticut, following the Civil War, Parker's gun makers pioneered such innovations as the hammerless type of lock mechanism and the automatic ejector. In 1903, they also produced the first 28 gauge gun, followed by the development of the combination bolt and top level action.

In 1922, Parker perfected the single trigger, and a year later the first beavertail forends were fitted to Parker's double barrel guns. The ventilated rib for doubles followed in 1926, and soon the first .410 gauge was added to the line.

Now, after nearly half a century, Remington has revived and improved the "Old Reliable" and made it available once again to the shooting fraternity. For further details, see p. 324. We also invite your review of Wayne van Zwoll's fine article on the history of the Remington Arms Company (p. 20).

Shooter's Bible

STOEGER PUBLISHING COMPANY

Copyright © 1990 by Stoeger Publishing Company

Published by Stoeger Publishing Company
55 Ruta Court
South Hackensack, New Jersey 07606

Library of Congress Catalog Card No.: 63-6200

International Standard Book No.: 0-88317-157-0

Manufactured in the United States of America

Distributed to the book trade and to the sporting goods trade by Stoeger Industries, 55 Ruta Court, South Hackensack, New Jersey 07606

In Canada, distributed to the book trade and to the sporting goods trade by Stoeger Canada Ltd., Unit 16/1801 Wentworth St. P.O. Box 445, Whitby, Ontario, L1N 5S4, Canada

Shooter's Bible

NO. 82
1991 EDITION

EDITOR:
William S. Jarrett

PRODUCTION EDITOR:
Charlene Cruson Step

FIREARMS CONSULTANTS:
Bill Meade, Vincent A. Pestilli,
Paul Rochelle, and
Robert A. Scanlon

COVER PHOTOGRAPHER:
Ray Wells

PUBLISHER:
Paul G. Emberley

PRESIDENT
Brian T. Herrick

Contents

FOREWORD

We welcome our readers once again to this, the 82nd edition of *Shooter's Bible*. As always, the book has been updated and improved to provide you with as much accurate and relevant information as we can cram into 576 pages.

Our article section this year leads off with an impressive array of Stephen Irwin's gun poster collection from a bygone era. We featured another Irwin pictorial essay two years ago—"The Golden Age of Sporting Art"—on the subject of illustrated gun covers. His sampling of poster art in this edition (see pp. 8–19) may well inspire a revival of this nearly extinct art form.

We are also pleased to introduce in this edition a new series of company "biographies," starting with Remington Arms (p. 20). You'll note that one of Remington's many fine products—the Parker shotgun—graces the front cover of this edition. Future editions will tell the stories of other great and famous American and European gun and ammunition makers.

We welcome several old friends back to our article section, including Ralph Quinn ("Shotguns and Game Shooting"), Stan Trzoniec ("Classic Handguns"), Jim Casada ("Fred Etchen") and Norman Johnson ("The Art of Buying Used Guns"). We also welcome a few newcomers, namely Wayne van Zwoll, who wrote the Remington piece, Sam Fadala ("The Mannlicher-Schonauer Rifle") and Charlene Cruson Step ("Camp Cooking"). Charlene has played a role for several years in the editing and production of this book and many other well known gun publications, including *The Gun Trader's Guide*.

The catalog and detailed specifications section offers nearly 400 pages of illustrated, up-to-date descriptions and prices for more than a thousand guns of every type, plus scores of scopes, sights and mounts. Included in this section for the first time are such gun makers as Auto-Ordnance, Chinasports, Francotte, Grendel, IAI, K.B.I. (formerly Kassnar), Maverick and Antonio Zoli. Extensive coverage of ammunition suppliers, ballistics tables, and reloading equipment (including bullets, powders, primers and cases) round out a very full catalog section.

The reference section once again includes a complete listing of gun-related books in print (along with the names of addresses of leading gun book publishers), discontinued models, a directory of manufacturers and suppliers, and a general index. And if you're looking for a gun or caliber in particular, we've made it easy for you with our unique Caliberfinder and Gunfinder features.

Change means progress, and as always there have been many welcome changes for us to pass along to you in 1991 as the new decade of the 90's gets underway. Whether you're just browsing or studying in earnest, we feel this new edition of *Shooter's Bible* will both enlighten and entertain you in the months ahead.

William Jarrett
Editor

Articles

The Wonderful World of Gun Posters

by R. Stephen Irwin, M.D.

From about 1890 until the 1930s, the firearms industry gave birth to smokeless gun powder, repeating (and eventually automatic) rifles and shotguns, and brass and cardboard fixed shotshells that rendered the old muzzleloaders obsolete. During that same period, the emphasis on hunting for the pot shifted gradually to sport hunting. A lucrative market for the new and improved sporting arms and ammunition products was at hand, if only it could be reached.

The solution was an outpouring of strikingly illustrated posters and calendars distributed nationwide to hardware stores, sporting goods stores and other retail outlets. With movies still a rarity, with television a distant dream, and with sporting

---

DR. STEPHEN IRWIN, an avid big game hunter and sport fisherman, has been writing for many years on the history of hunting and fishing, including such specialized areas as antique fishing lures, duck decoys and firearms. His articles have appeared in most of the major outdoor publications. He is also the author of a book, The Providers: Hunting and Fishing Methods of the Indians and Eskimos.

---

magazines still restricted to black and white illustrations only, these lavishly illustrated promotions, most of them printed in full color, exerted a powerful influence on young and old alike. A sampling of this poster and calendar art, commissioned by such prominent companies as Winchester Repeating Arms, E.I. duPont, Remington Arms, Union Metallic Cartridge and Marlin Firearms is reprinted on the following pages for your enjoyment and enlightenment.

The message conveyed in the typical gun poster was implicit in the illustration itself. Aside from the name of the company sponsoring the ad, captions were seldom used. The only exceptions were those that said, simply and to the point, something like: "Winchester's Big Game Rifles and Ammunition;" or, "The Kind That Gets 'Em."

The artists hired to illustrate these advertisements were quite simply the best and finest of their day. Among them were Carl Rungius, Phillip R. Goodwin, Edmund Osthaus, Frank Schoonover, Frederic Remington, C. M. Russell, Lynn Bogue Hunt, and the incomparable A. B. Frost. More than a few artists made their reputations by creating these sporting scene illustrations. Other, already established artists accepted commissions from gun companies but refused to sign their work for fear

(text continued on p. 19)

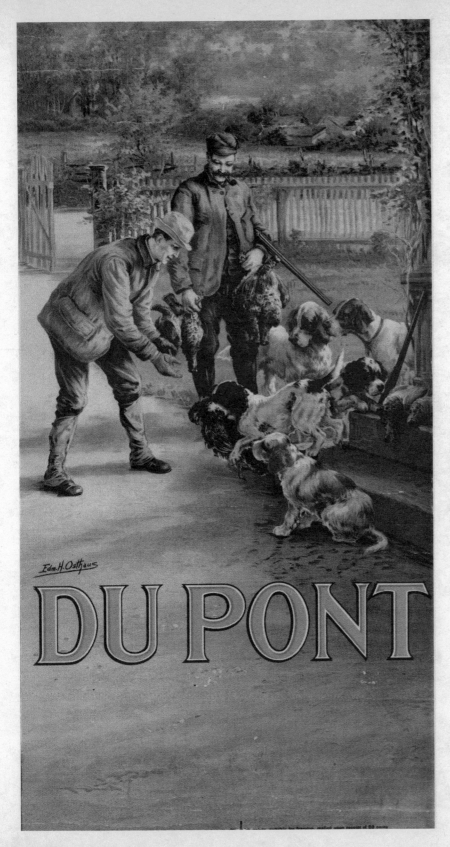

A note at the bottom of this 1900 DuPont poster by Edmund M. Osthaus states that "an exact reproduction without advertisement" can be acquired for only fifty cents. The vibrant eagerness of the setters shown here characterizes the upland game dog paintings of this fine artist.

This dramatic advertisement from Remington-Union Metallic Cartridge Co. emphasizes the need for reliability in firearms and ammunition. No artist's credit is given here, but the style and color in this painting are suggestive of Phillip Goodwin or perhaps Frederic Remington.

DuPont tried hard to bridge the generation gap in promoting its gun powder. This Edmund Osthaus poster has survived in greater numbers than its contemporaries because it was reproduced on tin.

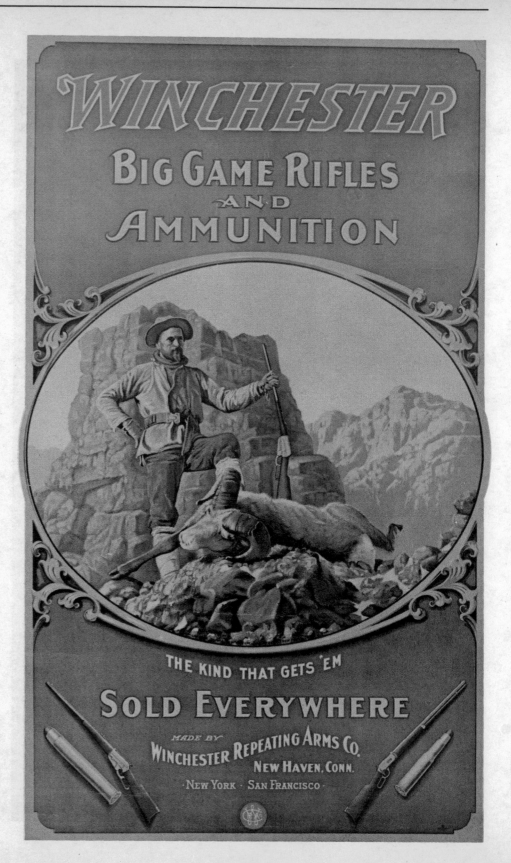

Winchester's 1904 poster features a triumphant hunter posing with his trophy ram and boasting of the rifles and ammunition ''that got 'em.''

This poster, entitled "Going In," is typical of P. R. Goodwin's Northwoods scenes. Remington's 1906 autoloader Model 8 big game rifle is featured prominently in the foreground.

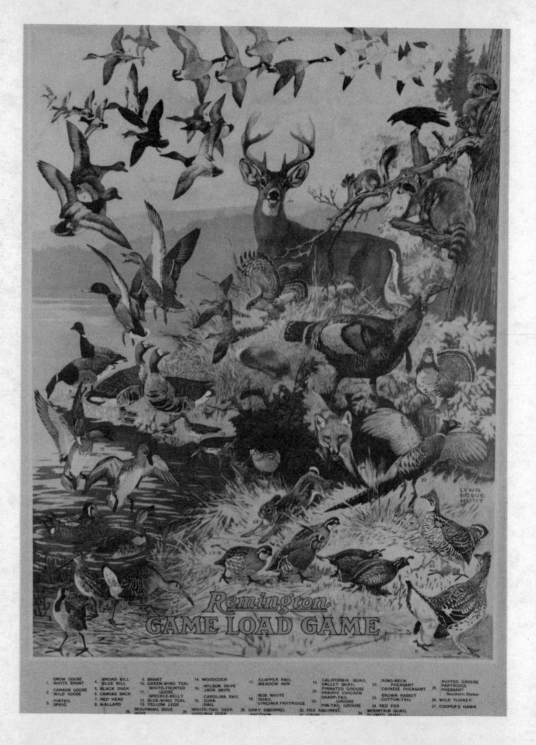

In an attempt to illustrate as much North American game as possible in this 1923 poster, Lynn Bogue Hunt probably did his artistic genius a mild disservice.

"Opportunity!"

SHOT-SHELLS US CARTRIDGES

UNITED STATES CARTRIDGE CO.   111 BROADWAY, NEW YORK

This painting by William Harden Foster, called "Opportunity," is a takeoff on the popular grandfather series created by A. B. Frost.

Lynn Bogue Hunt was commissioned by DuPont to create this artistically pleasing 1913 poster.

Parker Brothers used this broadside to promote its famous shotguns.

*"The Cock of the Woods,"
copyrighted in 1905, is
among a few Winchester
broadsides still available. The
concealed hunter can barely
be seen behind the log in the
background. No artist's credit
is given.*

that doing such "calendar art" might ruin their reputations.

The rugged and daring characters portrayed on these early gun posters looked like men who knew how to get the job done, no matter what the odds. Often the subjects were caught in the midst of a fracas or desperate situation. Whether the hero was being chased by a bear, or was about to be pounced upon by a marauding mountain lion, you sensed that somehow he would come out on top. There was always the strong suggestion that the subject could not have escaped certain disaster were it not for his trusty Winchester rifle or the Winchester ammunition he carried.

Gun and ammunition posters did not emphasize big game and exotic places only; local small game favorites were also well represented. An illustration by Lynn Bogue Hunt showing a covey of bobwhites made one yearn for the bird season long before the end of summer. Another scene on a Parker shotgun poster, depicting a scene of some gray squirrels scurrying through an oak tree, made a hunter's finger itch with anticipation. Still others dispensed with the fast-paced outdoor action and emphasized instead more idyllic subjects, such as an old gentleman painting and repairing his decoys for the next season, with his favorite retriever asleep in front of the fireplace.

Not infrequently, gun posters carried humorous themes. William Harden Foster, who illustrated many calendars for U.S. Cartridge Co., created a popular "Grandfather" series, featuring a be-whiskered old gent who kept getting into amusing situations with his ever reliable, sure-nosed beagle. Some ads tried to shorten the generation gap by showing an older, grandfatherly figure, obviously well acquainted with the ways of outdoor life, counseling a younger person. The caption under one such illustration stated that, "Generations have used Dupont Powder."

By the advent of World War II, gun posters had become almost extinct. Still, wartime did produce a few with poignant messages. A popular 1943 Hercules Powder calendar showed a uniformed lad marching off to war with his trusty rifle and his hunting dog eagerly following. The soldier looked back tearfully at his faithful companion and said, according to the caption, "Not this time, old pal."

Today, most of these old firearm advertisements rest unseen in private collections. Some are sold through gun and advertising shows, auction houses and specialized dealers. We invite your inspection of the splendid examples of this sadly outmoded art form on the preceding pages.

> Wayne van Zwoll's history of Remington Arms, which follows, is the first in a series of articles featuring the world's greatest gun makers. Future editions of Shooter's Bible will include similar company "biographies" tracing the development of guns, ammunition and related products of interest to gun owners and shooters everywhere.

Remington: Armsmaker for America

by Wayne van Zwoll

In August of 1816, at the age of 22, Eliphalet Remington II built his first gun from iron scrap. He and his wife, Abigail, lived in his father's stone house on Staley Creek in upper New York State four miles from the Mohawk River. "Lite," as he was known, fashioned his .45 caliber barrel from a half-inch square iron rod he had hammered into shape by hand, then heated red and wound around an undersize mandrel. Vigorously pumping the bellows in his father's forge, Lite next fired the barrel white-hot, sprinkled it with powdered Borax and sand, and pounded it against the stone floor

> *Wayne van Zwoll is a hunter and competitive rifleman whose gun writing has been widely published. An experienced handloader and amateur ballistician, he serves on the technical staff of* Rifle *magazine and writes a column on elk rifles and cartridges for* Bugle. *Wayne's first book, "Mastering Mule Deer," was published in 1988. He is now at work on another, called "Shooter's Notebook." Van Zwoll currently serves as Pacific Northwest Field Director for the Rocky Mountain Elk Foundation.*

to seat the coils. After letting it cool, he checked the barrel for straightness, then ground eight flats. Because he had no rifling equipment, Remington took his barrel to nearby Utica and, according to legend, paid about one dollar to have that work done.

Remington completed that first gun himself, forging and shaping the breechplug and lock parts, brazing priming pan to lockplate, drilling the touchhole, shaping and fitting a walnut stock. Metal parts were finished with hazel-brown, a mixture of uric acid and iron oxide. The wood was smoothed with sandstone, then sealed with bees-wax. Lite Remington took his rifle to a local match and, as history records, was asked by a fellow shooter to build him another just like it. Lite agreed to deliver one in 10 days for the price of 10 dollars. Soon he had more orders and began working full time to fill them. Thus was America's first gun-making company born.

Meanwhile, the young gunsmith built himself a house and foundry on Staley Creek. But when the Erie Canal was completed in 1825, he decided to move closer to port. Reluctant as he was to leave the quiet, religious atmosphere of his rural home, Lite know too well how drastically the new canal had cut shipping costs between New York and

Eliphalet Remington, founder of the Remington Arms Company.

The original Remington homestead in Ilion, New York, built by Eliphalet Remington in 1799.

Buffalo. This prompted him to buy 100 acres along the Mohawk from one John Clapsaddle in 1828. This land is now part of Ilion's business district.

When Lite and his growing family moved to what was then called Morgan's Landing, they comprised 20 percent of the town's population. But soon his new foundry drew other families to the area. In summer, Remington employed 20 machinists; and in winter, when ice idled his water-powered equipment, he hired almost as many workers to assemble the guns. Wrapped in bundles, the finished firearms were carted to a bridge on the canal and dropped on the cabin roofs of passing freighters for shipment to New York.

In 1832, Remington doubled production capacity with his first true factory building, then traveled east on the Erie Canal to promote his guns. The 300-mile trip from Albany to Buffalo cost him $14.33, meals included. Later, the Schenectady and Utica Railway began its eight-hour service to Albany as an all-weather alternative.

Remington's plant in Ilion, New York, as it appeared in 1828.

By 1841, Lite had become a partner in a nearby smelting plant that, in addition to gun parts, produced farm and sawmill equipment. Lite's eldest son, Philo, had by now entered the gun business too; his job was installing steel facings on trip hammers to reduce manufacturing tolerances. By then, Remington was using a scaled-down cannon drill to bore barrel blanks (instead of wrapping bar stock around mandrels). Philo also pioneered the use of reflected light to replace plumb lines as a measure of bore trueness.

On August 12, 1841, tragedy struck the Remington family. It happened on the same road where Lite's father had been killed back in 1825. A carriage horse, spooked by a lady's parasol popping open in the wind, galloped through a stream, causing the cart behind to smash into a large, unyielding oak. Abigail Remington was killed instantly.

His wife's sudden death profoundly affected Lite, and he began working even harder to build his business. In 1845, he bought a government contract for 5,000 Harpers Ferry percussion muskets. An impending war with Mexico spurred production, and soon another Remington factory was built. Needing still more capacity, Lite next bought the N. P. Ames Company, a cutlery firm in Chicopee Falls, Massachusetts, and hired William Jenks, a Welsh designer whose work with an experimental carbine had aroused Lite's interest. With the help of Remington's top engineer, Riley Rogers, Jenks revamped his carbine, incorporating a Maynard lock with tape-fed primers. The barrels, tinned for protection against salt spray, were the first drilled steel barrels sold by contract to the government, which then shipped the guns to Veracruz for use by Commodore Matthew Perry's U.S. fleet.

Next, inspired by Colt's stunning success with revolvers, Lite marketed in 1849 an improved Beals revolver in calibers 31, 36 and 41. He then paid designer Joseph Rider 12 pairs of revolvers and 400 acres of land in Ohio for partial rights to his latest gun. Another designer, William Elliott, contributed a 41 caliber Derringer and a Four-barrel, zig-zag pistol (in which the firing mechanism bounded from one barrel to another in turn). By 1850, the Remington company was supplying thousands of rifles and barrels to pioneers heading across the Great Plains. In 1852 alone, some 1,475 barrels were shipped. The company was now known officially as "E. Remington & Sons." New

plant machinery was added, including a 500-horsepower Corliss steam engine that remained in service until 1935.

When it became apparent that Springfield Armory could produce only a small portion of the rifles needed by Union troops during the Civil War, Lite Remington immediately geared up his Ilion plant. Eventually it fulfilled Army and Navy gun contracts totaling nearly $30 million, and by war's end his plant capacity had reached 1,000 rifles a day.

Meanwhile, Remington responded to the growing demand for revolvers by converting Utica's Hamilton Hotel into a factory, where his workers made 200 pistols a day. They also manufactured 18,000 Maynard percussion locks for antiquated 1842 muskets, drop-forged bayonets to put on Harpers Ferry rifles with a mount designed by Hiram Berdan, made various reloading tools, and assembled nearly 10 million rounds of ammunition. Unfortunately, this frantic pace drained Lite Remington. A month after the Battle of Bull Run, he was hospitalized with "inflammation of the bowels," and on August 12, 1861, Eliphalet Remington II died at the age of 67.

The Sons Take Over

By this time, Philo and his younger brothers, Samuel and Eliphalet III, had joined forces and managed to keep wartime production on schedule, even loaning Savage Arms some equipment to build 20,000 of its Geiger carbines for the government. As demand spiraled, the Remington brothers added more machinery and factory space. Then, just as the expanded plant reached its capacity, the war ended. Suddenly, as the nation rejoiced at the advent of peace, Ilion's workers sat forlornly by their silent, heavily mortgaged machines.

To counter the market's slump, E. Remington & Sons introduced to sportsmen an improved version of the Geiger split-breech rifle. Designed by Joseph Rider, the new mechanism had been passed over by wartime ordnance officials who found the hurriedly submitted prototype less than appealing. Rider quickly corrected the gun's weaknesses, and his rotating breechblock soon found a ready market in the West. One of its first field tests came in October, 1866, when hostile Sioux warriors under Red Cloud and Crazy Horse attacked 30 drovers moving cattle through Wyoming. Vastly outnumbered, the cattlemen fired their rolling block rifles so fast they had to cool the barrels by pouring water on them. The circling Indians, finding no pause in the deadly volleys, were forced to retreat.

That same year, Sam Remington replaced Philo as company president and set out to increase domestic and European gun sales in a market glutted by military surplus arms. By 1870, E. Remington & Sons, with its 15 acres of floor space and 400 milling machines, could routinely produce 350 rough barrels a day. While Remington's biggest seller was the efficient rolling block, Winchester's fast-firing 73 had quickly become popular as a saddle gun. But its .44-40 cartridge was anemic compared to the cigar-size rounds chambered in

the rolling block. Buffalo hunters got rich with the Remingtons, including Brazos Bill McRae, who once downed 54 buffalo with as many shots from one position with his .44-90-400 Remington and a Malcolm scope. Shamelessly, these hunters stripped the native American of their food supply and littered the plains with bones.

In 1874, at the peak of this slaughter, Remington designer L. L. Hepburn was busy engineering a target rifle. Built on the proven falling-block principle, the new gun was designed to equip the American long-range team in a shooting match against the favored Irish team, to be held on a new Long island facility called Creedmoor. The Amer-

The Union Metallic Cartridge Company plant in Bridgeport, Connecticut, as it looked prior to the merger of Remington and UMC in 1912.

icans used Sharps breechloaders and the Remington-Hepburn .44-90 rifle firing 550 grain conical bullets to defeat the Irish with ease.

When Sam Remington died in 1880, his surviving brothers had neither the acumen nor resources to bolster sagging gun sales. The company faltered and, in 1886, was forced into bankruptcy. Two years later, Marcellus Hartley of the Union Metallic Cartridge Company joined with Thomas Bennett, son-in-law of Oliver Winchester, in the purchase of E. Remington & Sons for $200,000.

Hartley, an astute businessman, had founded the International Banking Corporation and nego-tiated the sale of the struggling New York *Times* to Chattanooga publisher Adolph Ochs. He wisely continued bringing bright young inventors to Ilion, including Arthur Savage, who in 1892 developed a lever rifle with a spool magazine—the now famous Model 99.

The Boy President Takes Charge

On the same day that Marcellus Hartley died in 1902, two men—John and Moses Browning—had visited his office. Upon learning of Hartley's death, they left and took their invention instead to Fabrique Nationale de Guerre at Liege, Belgium.

Shown here admiring a portrait of the company's founder, Eliphalet Remington, during the 1930s are (left to right): Charles K. Davis, president and general manager, M. Hartley Dodge, chairman of the board, Franklin Remington, the founder's grandson, and Henry B. du Pont, member of Remington's Board of Directors.

Their contract regulated only the European sales of Browning guns, however, and the brothers returned to the U.S. to call on Remington once again. By then, Hartley's 21-year-old grandson, Marcellus ("Marcy") Hartley Dodge, while still a student at Columbia University, had taken control of the company. He wisely accepted the Brownings' high royalty demands and contracted with them for $1 million in services over a 10-year period. Thus did John Browning travel to Ilion one day to begin overseeing production of America's first autoloading sporting guns.

A few years later, in 1907, Danish designer J. D. Pedersen developed Remington's first slide-action shotgun, the Model 10. It was followed by the Model 12 (22 rimfire) and the Model 14 centerfire rifle. Meanwhile, Marcy Dodge managed to acquire all his family's stock in Remington and the Union Metallic Cartridge Company and became sole owner of both companies. When World War I erupted in 1914, England was suddenly in need of a million guns or more. Quickly, Dodge quadrupled production to 2,000 rifles a day. More orders came piling in. To stretch capacity, the company leased an auto plant at Eddystone, Pennsylvania, where 450,000 Enfields were produced. Still, the demand for arms was insatiable. When Russia asked for a million more rifles and 100 million cartridges, Marcy Dodge responded by ordering construction of 25 factory buildings, five forges, and a huge power plant in Bridgeport, Connecticut. To finance this work, he sold $15 million in company bonds, borrowed another $15 million against his own

stock, and raised $14 million more in personal loans. Within a year, Remington had created a million feet of new floor space and a production capacity of 5,000 rifles a day. Cartridge capacity doubled with the addition of 160 buildings and 24 acres of floor space. Within one 10-month span, a rented factory spewed out 2½ million rounds of ammo per day.

When Tsar Nicholas II lost control in Russia, the new government there canceled all existing arms contracts, leaving Remington with 750,000 rifles. France bought 600,000 of them at bargain rates (and later resold them to Russia's White Army), but still the loss sustained by Remington in the deal was to affect the company adversely long after the war had ended. Meanwhile, Remington turned to other, more urgent business. America's arsenals had only 700,000 Springfields on hand at the time and a manufacturing capacity of 350,000 a year, forcing the company to modify its Enfield to take the 30-06 cartridge. Production peaked at over 4,000 rifles a day, totaling 1.6 million by war's end. In all, Remington made 69 percent of the rifles used by U.S. forces in World War I, plus half of the Allied ammunition, causing Remington's payroll to jump from 1,400 to 15,000 men and women.

Peace in 1917 brought a predictable nose dive in the arms and ammunitions market. Even after closing three plants, Remington still made too much of everything, so it moved into cutlery and cash registers. A few years later, the company introduced its Model 30 and 30S bolt action rifles; and

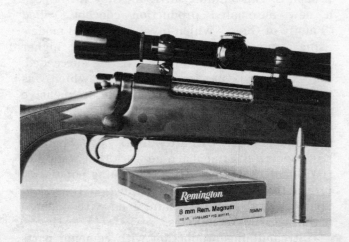 

Introduced in 1978, the 8mm Remington Magnum (left) is based on a full-length .375 H&H case, necked down and blown out. Results using a Model 700 shown at right demonstrate its exceptional accuracy.

in 1926 it offered the first noncorrosive priming made in the U.S. By 1929, Remington's sales were in excess of $21 million; but when the stock market collapsed in 1929, so too did sales. By 1932, Remington registered only $8 million in sales and suffered a million-dollar loss. A new company president, Charles Davis, managed to stop the free-fall in 1933, and by 1936 Remington was paying stock dividends once again. It also bought the Peters Cartridge Company and the Parker Gun Company, a 100-year-old firm started by Charles Parker. As prosperity accelerated industry, Remington introduced a steady stream of new products from its plant in Ilion, including the 141 center-fire pump rifle and 241 rimfire autoloader in 1935. The 81 centerfire autoloader and 121 rimfire pump followed in 1936; the 37 target rifle arrived in 1937, and the 510, 511 and 512 bolt-action rimfires came into production in 1939 and 1940. In 1941, the 550 autoloader became the first 22 autoloader to handle mixed loads of short, long and long rifle cartridges without adjustment.

When Germany's blitzkrieg swept across Holland and Belgium in 1940, Europe was woefully unprepared. England had fewer than a million rounds of rifle ammunition, and when Winston Churchill asked the U.S. for Enfields, he was forced to accept Springfields instead. Remington quickly broke ground for a new munitions plant in Denver, Colorado, and seven months later it was producing more than a million rounds a day. The Bridgeport plant was overhauled so its 14,000 workers could make not only 30 and 50 caliber rifle and machine gun rounds, but 22 rimfire training cartridges and shot-charged 45 ACP cases for airmen as well. Remington plants also produced 20 mm cannon shells, frangible practice bullets, and an incendiary Spitfire machine gun bullet developed by the British. The company also designed a grenade launcher for the Garand, electrically fired primers, and a 12 gauge shell to start torpedo gyroscopes.

When copper grew scarce during the war, Remington began making steel cartridge cases in a converted cotton mill in Massachusetts. The Peters plant at Kings Mills in Ohio produced up to two million 30 carbine cartridges a day, and during the war it tallied 125 million shotshells for aerial gunner training. To fill orders, Remington bought (through Lend-Lease) 27,300 machines worth $200 million, thereby expanding its operations by 2,000

Remington's Model 37, a top-flight .22 rimfire target rifle, was named for the year of its inception. Among its many features was a machine-steel, detachable magazine. This model was replaced in 1955 by Model 40X, but many of the original 37's remain in use.

percent. The company payroll, which totaled 4,000 in 1939, grew to 82,500 in 1943. In all, the company delivered more than a million rifles and 16 billion rounds of ammunition in a production frenzy that claimed "perishable" machine tools at the rate of 30,000 a day.

The Post-War Period

The return to peace in 1945 brought with it plant closings, throttled production lines and slumping profits. But Remington's innovative managers stemmed the downturn using a new approach to gun-building. In 1948, they introduced a new automated production concept, called "Family of Guns," which involved several models using common parts. Fewer parts meant higher production capacity, and the program succeeded. For example, Remington's Model 870, which was introduced in 1950, proved much less expensive to produce than Winchester's Model 12. As higher costs gnawed at the Model 12's marketability, the dependable Model 870 ate into its sales. Shooters still savored the fine machine work that went into the Model 12, but the 870's continuing popularity proved that high standards for function, finish and "pointability" could be maintained with updated manufacturing techniques.

Streamlining production with common parts might have yielded dreary uniformity, but new models were quick to come. In 1956, Remington

A production technician monitors the automated cutting operation inside the completely enclosed T-10 machining center, part of Remington's new Flexible Manufacturing System (FMS). In this operation, a constant spray serves as a cooling, lubricating and removing agent (for metal chips).

announced its Sportsman 58, the first gas-operated shotgun made in the U.S. A year later, it offered an autoloading 22 and the Nylon 66 with the first successful synthetic stock. In 1962, the Model 700 suceeded Remington's 721/722 centerfires and became one of the most popular bolt rifles ever made. That was followed in 1963 by the Model 1100 shotgun, the all-time, best-selling autoloader with a production run to date of nearly four million. In 1987, Remington offered a new gas-operated shotgun, the 11-87, which could for the first time handle all 2¾- and 3-inch shells without adjustment.

Two years later, the autoloading SP-10 10 gauge was unveiled, and recently the company introduced its first single barrel trap gun, the 90-T. Other post-war products at Remington include the 40X target rifle, XP-100 pistol, 600 carbine, Model Seven lightweight centerfire rifle, 788 and 78 economy class rifles, Special Field shotguns, REM Choke shotgun choke tubes, 700-series Mountain and Classic centerfire rifles, 572 pump and 552 autoloading rimfire rifles, and stocks made of Kevlar, Rinite, Arylon and wood laminates.

Some of the company's guns are available only

222 Remington (1950)

244 Remington; 44 Remington Magnum (1955)

280 Remington (1957)

222 Remington Magnum (1958)

22 Remington Jet (1961)

7mm Remington Magnum (1962)

6mm Remington; 221 Remington Fireball (1963)

223 Remington; 444 Marlin; 41 Remington Magnum (1964)

22-250 Remington; 350 Remington Magnum (1965)

6.5mm Remington Magnum (1966)

25-06 Remington; 5mm Remington Rimfire Magnum (1970)

17 Remington (1971)

"Accelerator" sabot cartridges in 30-30, 308 & 30-06 (1977)

8mm Remington Magnum; 22 BR Remington (wildcat) (1978)

6mm BR Remington (wildcat); 22 Rimfire Yellow Jacket & Viper (1979)

7mm-08 Remington; 7mm BR Remington (wildcat) (1980)

357 Remington Maximum (1983)

7mm BR Remington (1986)

35 Whelen (1988)

6mm BR Remington (1989)

Unmachined shotgun receiver blanks are loaded four deep on four sides of a pullet fixture for robotic delivery to Remington's T-10 automatic machine center.

by special order, among them a remarkable re-creation of the Parker shotgun. Introduced in 1988, Remington's Parker is built by its Parker Gun Works division at Ilion. Although modern materials and machinery are used, the guns are handfitted and faithfully detailed in keeping with the original Parkers, which have been called the best shotguns ever made in America. [Editor's Note: The front cover of this edition features Remington's Parker shotgun].

Remington's history as an ammunition manufacturer dates back to 1867 with the 50 Remington pistol. Several black powder rifle rounds followed in the 1870s and 1880s, and in 1906 the company brought out its 25, 30, 32 and 35 Remington cartridges, followed in 1934 by the 257 Remington Roberts. After World War II, a flurry of new rounds appeared, including the following:

Three years after its introduction of the first plastic shotshells in 1960, Remington announced its "Power Piston" one-piece plastic wad and shot column. Now, in addition to its economical Shurshot field loads, the company markets lead pellets in buckshot, "Express," and buffered "NitroMag" shells. In 1988, Remington broke tradition with a duplex field load (two sizes of shot in one shell) that was both buffered and copper-plated. An unbuffered, chilled-shot duplex target load followed in 1989.

While Du Pont has held controlling interest in Remington Arms since 1933, Remington became the chemical giant's wholly-owned subsidiary in 1980. Five years later, company headquarters were moved to Wilmington, Delaware, home of Du Pont. In 1989, Remington was detached from the Fabricated Products Department and set up as the Sporting Goods Division, which includes Remington clothing and Stren fishing line.

A Remington research designer uses a computer-aided design system (CAD) to detail a receiver for the new SP-10 Magnum 10 gauge shotgun, which was introduced in 1989.

As part of a volatile industry, Remington survives as one of only a few companies still producing sporting guns in the U.S. In a highly competitive business complicated by legal and political constraints unimagined by Lite Remington more than 150 years ago, the company remains strong and healthy. Its founder would be delighted to know that new guns and cartridges are still being developed by America's oldest gunmaker.

Mannlicher-Schoenauer: Rifle for Adventurers

by Sam Fadala

The famous Mannlicher-Schoenauer rifle was born in Steyr, Austria, once known as the "Iron City." It was there, in the 16th century, that the "Society of Barrel and Riflemakers of Steyr" began. The city produced an abundance of arms and accouterments for the Austrian army during that period, and in time the Iron City became the gunmaking center of Europe and the "Arsenal of the World."

In the early 1800s, Leopold Werndl, an independent gunmaker, established himself in Steyr as a successful manufacturer of carbine barrels, steel ramrods, lance points, shoes and other commodities. On February 26, 1831, Werndl's son, Josef, was born, and he later surpassed his father in the

art of gunmaking. Josef's big dream was to invent a strong, machinable action with superior locking ability. The result of his labors was a bolt-action rifle, for which the Steyr-Werke factory earned a large Army contract. Other countries followed with orders and Werndl's turn-bolt design soon gained global fame. With the advent of smokeless powder, Werndl's bolt actions were ready to harness this powerful new propellant. By 1880, the demand for hunting and luxury firearms caused Werndl to begin work on various sporting rifle designs. Josef passed away on April 29, 1889, but his dream did not die with him. A great hunting rifle emerged from the Steyr plant, and it was called the Mannlicher-Schoenauer.

The father of this new rifle, which began production in 1900, was Ferdinand von Mannlicher, a true gun genius. Born in Mainz (Germany) in 1848, he became known throughout the world as Ritter von Mannlicher. For a while, he was chief engineer for the Austrian Northern Railway, but his work with Oesterreichische Waffenfabriks-Gesellschaft (OWG), the armory famed for magazine rifles, earned von Mannlicher immortality. Between 1875 and 1904, he invented numerous gun designs, more than either John Moses Browning or Paul Mauser, and he was responsible for 150 repeating and automatic arms blueprints, including

In addition to his work as Technical Editor for Rifle *and* Handloader *magazines, Sam Fadala contributes often to many other leading outdoor and firearms publications. He is also the author of 14 books, including* The Book of the Twenty-Two, *published in 1989 (Stoeger Publishing Co.). In all, Fadala has been hunting and shooting for the past 30 years throughout the U.S., Mexico, Canada and Africa.*

Ferdinand von Mannlicher, a true gun genius.

straight-pull, bolt-action rifles, which were copied directly from his 1884 design.

While no one is accusing Browning of copying Mannlicher's patterns, the operating principles of the former's automatic firearms are much like Mannlicher's, including the use of an accelerator housing, locking action, reciprocating parts associated with the barrel, and in the unlocking, cocking and harnessing of recoil energy. By 1885, Mannlicher had perfected an automatic rifle, a light machine gun that embodied five moving parts (which were later used in the Browning machine gun).

The man who was responsible for perfecting Mannlicher's magazine concept, in which the cartridges are held in a circular pattern on a star rotor, was Otto Schoenauer. He was Werndl's arms technician and a director of the OWG. The Mannlicher-Schoenauer sporting rifles, which one gun writer described as the "most legendary of European rifles," are still admired by knowing hunters and honored by the Mannlicher's Collectors Association, one of the finest organizations of its kind in the world.

Ernest Hemingway often carried a Mannlicher and wrote about the little rifle in his books and articles. Vilhajalmur Stefansson, the Arctic explorer and hunter, preferred a Mannlicher Model 1903 for his adventurous exploits. The carbine served him with total reliability during 12 cold winters on the northern ice. Roy Chapman Andrews, the famous scientist, used a 250 Savage and 6.5mm Mannlicher in his arduous quests for big game. Andrews hunted not only the Chinese tiger, but also the Marco Polo sheep. And Elmer Keith, noted for his devotion to big bullets, found the Mannlicher 6.5mm deadlier than the size of its bore. He wrote in *The American Rifleman* (June 1950) that the rifle was entirely reliable, and that the 6.5mm cartridge performed well beyond its caliber. The famous gun house of Abercrombie and Fitch called the rifle the most accurate and dependable firearm for long-range shooting and all-around use, recommending it "without reserve."

A. F. Stoeger, Inc., which imported Mannlichers for years, was most responsible for putting the Mannlicher rifle in the hands of American shooters. The company's 1932 catalog lists several models, including the famous carbine in its equally famous 6.5mm Mannlicher caliber. While the 6.5mm came with an 18-inch barrel, the hunter could opt for an 8mm, 9mm or 9.5mm Mannlicher

the first production semi-automatic military rifle. His 1886 Mannlicher clip-fed 11mm black powder cartridge rifle, with its straight-pull bolt, was adopted by the Austrian army. Later, the caliber was reduced to 8mm, but it still used black powder.

While in the employ of OWG, Mannlicher adapted the Model 1886 for smokeless powder cartridges and earned a British patent for his bolt-action rifle with a rotary magazine in its buttstock. He and Werndl both worked to perfect the Mannlicher magazine, but without commercial success. But finally, in 1900, a refined Mannlicher-Schoenauer bolt-action rifle was unveiled at the *Exposition Universalle* in Paris, and Mannlicher's name became famous at last. Unfortunately, he received no credit later for the M-1 Garand, which copied liberally from Mannlicher's gas bleed-off system, nor for the Canadian Ross or Swiss Schmidt-Ruben

The author (right) poses with a 30-06 Mannlicher rifle with a 24-inch barrel. It belonged to his hunting companion, Ivon du Plessis (left), from whom the author borrowed the rifle during an African hunt.

carbine, all with 20-inch barrels. The 30-06 was also available in either 20-inch or 24-inch rifles. In 1932, Stoeger sold the 6.5mm, 8mm, 9mm and 9.5mm for $82.50, with the 30-06 fetching $99.00 for the rifle ($107.25 for the carbine). By comparison, Winchester's Model 54, forerunner of the Model 70, sold for $53.40, while its Model 94 cost less than $40.00. By 1939, Stoeger was selling the 6.5mm for $140.00 and the carbine for $175.00. That same year, Winchester's Model 70 (standard version) cost $61.25.

The heart of the M-S rifle, many fans believe, is not its action, but rather its magazine. Cartridges do not touch each other in this system; instead, they stand around a pivot pin in a circular fashion on a star rotor. As each cartridge is pushed into the magazine, the force of its entry rotates the spool. Detractors claim the M-S action is weak, while its admirers say the action is slick as a

greased ball bearing. Neither opinion is entirely correct.

More noteworthy than either the magazine or the action, however, are two distinctive Mannlicher features: a butterknife bolt handle and a full-length stock (carbine only). The two-piece bolt cocks on opening, but full pressure upon the mainspring is not realized until the bolt handle is turned down as far as it will go. The cocking knob extends rearward in the cocked position, similar to various military rifles, including our own Springfield. Lock time is admittedly slow compared with that of a Model 700 Remington, but you won't notice this in the hunting field. The butterknife bolt handle, which is positioned ahead of (rather than directly above) the trigger, may seem at first to slow down the action; but once you get used to it, the Mannlicher action is fast enough.

The M-S carbine also features a slim forearm

Neil De Lapp, a Wyoming rancher and skilled hunter, poses with the author's Model 1905 carbine. The gun's flat-sidedness, thanks in part to the butterknife bolt handle, allows easy entry and exit in a horse scabbard.

The magazine of the Mannlicher-Schoenauer rifle can be removed with the point of a cartridge. It snaps back into place readily. Cartridges are held in a circle around the center pin of the magazine. Rounds do not touch each other.

and a slight buttstock, which many hunters find delightful. A heavy forearm may be ideal for the bench, but it is totally useless in the game field. Strangling the forend with a white-knuckle grip does nothing for marksmanship, especially on a running target where the rifle must be free to flow. The Mannlicher, remember, is a guitar, not a hammer. You don't pound with it—you strum it.

It's impossible to describe a Mannlicher rifle generically. A typical M-S carbine is the Model 1905, which weighs seven pounds and two ounces (unloaded). Its 20-inch barrel is long enough to realize cartridge potential and short enough to deliver a compact unit with an overall length of 40½ inches. The blued nose cap dresses the full-length stock up front, while a blued-steel, serrated buttplate adorns the other end. A wraparound checkering pattern embellishes the forend, with two checkered panels on each side of the wrist. The buttplate contains a trap door, designed to hold a

The metal buttplate of this Model 1905 Mannlicher is serrated with broad grooves. It also contains a trap. The upper hole is for a take-down cleaning rod. The other holes are for extra cartridges.

The butterknife bolt handle is a distinctive Mannlicher feature. Note the shiny, knurled magazine release pin; depressing this pin allows the magazine to be emptied without running cartridges into the chamber.

take-down cleaning rod and two spare cartridges. The cartridge stalls are contoured to the shape of the round, preventing bullets from being driven back into the cartridge case.

The rotary magazine is removed by pushing a bullet tip against the forward hole in the floorplate, then turning the floorplate 90 degrees, thus freeing the magazine. The trigger guard levers into the rear of the floorplate and is held by a screw at the back tang. The slight pistol grip is fitted with a metal cap. The underside of the butterknife bolt handle is serrated. The magazine release catch is located in front of the bolt handle; by pushing the release catch, the cartridges roll up out of the magazine and into your hand without having to work them through the action.

The safety on this Model 1905 is military-like. A wing over the cocking piece revolves upward to lock the bolt and deactivate the sear. A quick thumb-push moves the wing to a left-hand posture, putting the rifle into battery. You'll know immediately if the safety is on, because it blocks the view through the aperture of the receiver sight. The safety can be switched to full right, or you can carry the rifle with the safety in the upright position. M-S rifles could be purchased originally with single trigger ($14) or double trigger ($20). The triggers were interchangeable; a single rifle could switch from one to the other. For its American and Canadian markets, Stoeger demanded alterations on the M-S, including a change in stock design and a side safety. Furthermore, the bolt handle was swept back for quicker handling (but failed to do so). The new stock design was better suited to scope mounting, however, and proved a positive change overall for North American shooters.

Chamberings for the original-style Mannlicher

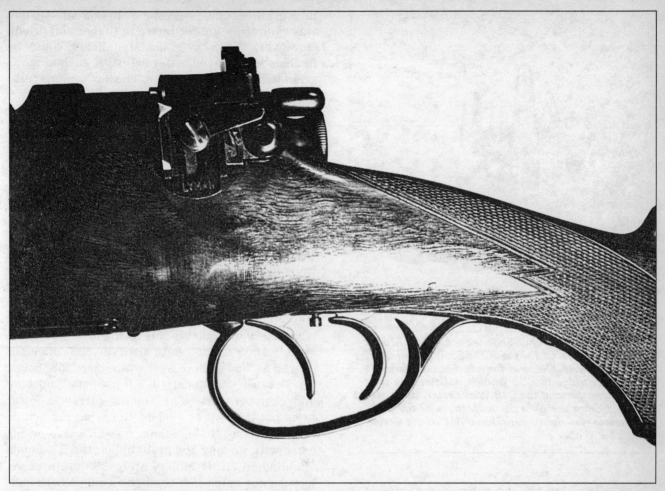

Behind the Lyman receiver sight shown here is the bolt release button. The double set triggers are tuned with the set screw located between the two triggers.

rifles numbered as many as 30, including the following:

Pre-WWI
{
  6.5mm
  8mm
  9mm
  9.5mm
}

1917–1939
{
  7 × 57 Mauser
  7 × 64 Brenneke
  30-06 Springfield
  8 × 60mm
  9.3 × 62mm Mauser
  10.75 × 68mm
}

Post-WWII
{
  243 Win.
  257 Roberts
  257 Weath. Mag.
  6.5 × 68mm
  264 Win. Mag.
  270 Win.
  308 Win.
  8 × 68S
  338 Win.
  458 Win. Mag.
  30-06
  6.5 × 54mm
}

Current interest lies in the 6.5, 8mm, 9mm and 9.5mm, because each represents a specific M-S model. The 6.5mm is associated with Mannlicher Model 1903; the 9 × 56mm came in with the 1905 Model; the 8 × 56mm Mannlicher cartridge was added for the 1908 Model; and the 9.5 × 57mm Mannlicher cartridge was chambered for Model 1910. The 6.5 × 53mm Mannlicher was also called the 6.7 × 53mm and 6.5 × 54mm. Oversize bores were possible. Some 6.5's had groove diameters of .2665″ and others .2660″. Among different brands of 6.5mm ammo, the cartridge head size might vary as much as .009″, enough discrepancy to promote a ruptured case or case head separation in some rifles. But all in all, the 6.5mm gave great satisfaction to its owners.

The first Models 1903 carried 17½-inch barrels, but this length was extended to 18 inches af-

The author's Mannlicher-Shoenauer carbine, Model 1905, is chambered for the 9 × 56mm Mannlicher cartridge, shown above at far left. For comparison, the next cartridge is a 35 Whelen, followed by the 358 Winchester and the 348 Winchester. Ballistics of the 9 × 56mm are on a par with those of the 348 Winchester (far right), considered one of the better rounds for timber elk.

ter World War II. The small 6.5mm cartridge was deadly because of the high sectional density of the 160-grain bullet. This property increased penetration and retained downrange energy. Modest velocity actually aided bullet performance; it's difficult, after all, to make a bullet behave at 3,000 feet per second or more. At 2,300 feet per second, bullets tend to retain their jacket/core integrity. The round nose configuration of the long 6.5mm bullet may have helped in creating straight wound channels. As for recoil, the 6.5 was gentle on the shoulder, enabling hunters to put bullets where they belonged. Bullet placement may not be everything, but it's far better to drive a 26 caliber 160 grain bullet through the vitals of a big game animal than to hit it in the hoof with a 30 caliber 220 grain projectile.

The 8mm Mannlicher proved excellent in the hunting field as well. With bullets of about 170 grains travelling at more than 2,400 fps mv, it was adequate for any North American big game. A 200-plus grain weight projectile at over 2,100 fps mv was even more authoritative in timber and brush. Moreover, the 8 × 56mm Mannlicher could be handloaded for even better ballistics, such as a 227 grain bullet at 2,300 fps mv. The 9.5 × 56mm (also known as the 9.5 × 57mm, 9.5 × 56.7mm or 375 Nitro Express Rimless) is another interesting and capable cartridge. A bullet weighing over 260 grains at about 2,150 fps mv provided enough power for all North American big game as well as African fauna.

The least loved and most maligned cartridge among Mannlicher collectors is the 9 × 56mm. One expert declared that the 9 × 57mm Mauser was adequate for all North American big game, while the 9 × 56 Mannlicher was not acceptable for anything larger than a deer. Ballistically speaking, the 9 × 56mm is everything that the 9 × 57mm Mauser was. But there were problems. The 9 × 56mm Mannlicher was supposed to shoot 9mm bullets; but a true 9mm bullet is .354″ in diameter and many Models 1905 carried bore sizes of .356″ diameter as well as .354″. There were even some .358″ bores.

Because the Model 1905 9 × 56mm had bore and chamber variations, it now carries a lower price tag than other models. But what a machine it has become. If the 6.5mm was effective on big game with its long 160 grain bullet, the 9 × 56mm Mannlicher, firing bullets up to 286 grain at velocities not much less than the smaller cartridge, proved equally effective.

Meanwhile, times change. Charles Sheldon wandered the lonesome territory of the Denali wilderness for months on end. Today's hunting seasons are relatively brief. Most hunters have a weekend or perhaps a week's vacation in which to fill their bags. Under such conditions, modern scoped shooting machines make sense for the average hunter. On the other hand, going afield with a 9mm Mannlicher isn't exactly like being undergunned. The Model 1905 is surprisingly accurate. Scopeless, it can drill three shots into about an inch and a half group at 100 yards. Trajectory of the 225 grain Sierra bullet, starting at 2500 fps mv allows for 200- to 250-yard shooting. For elk in black timber, it's deadly. On whitetails in the creek bottoms, the fast little rifle is a fine performer.

Over a 47-year period, the Steyr factory produced only 74,000 original-style Mannlicher rifles,

The author's prized Mannlicher-Schoenauer Model 1905 carbine in 9 × 56mm Mannlicher chambering. The 1905 is the least sought after of the collectibles because of its chambering discrepancies.

or 3.5 per working day. That's not a lot of rifles. But the Mannlicher-Schoenauer was a special firearm for the serious world class hunter. To hunt with one of the old-style rifles now is to relive the past—and sometimes that's not such a bad thing to do.

Ballistics of Mannlicher Cartridges (from *Shooter's Bible, 1932*)

Cartridge	Grain	Muzzle Velocity (feet per second)	Muzzle Energy (foot-pounds)
6.5mm Mannlicher	157.5	2313	1873
6.5mm Mannlicher	123.4	2575	1815
8mm Mannlicher	200.8	2138	2032
8mm Mannlicher	169.8	2428	2220
9mm Mannlicher	247	2083	2393
9.5mm Mannlicher	261.7	2148	2783

Author's Handloads for 9 × 56mm Mannlicher Cartridge:

Cartridge	Grain	Muzzle Velocity (feet per second)	Muzzle Energy (foot-pounds)
9mm Mannlicher	225 grain Sierra bullet	2425	2939
9mm Mannlicher	250 grain Hornady/Speer	2235	2774

Camp Cooking— Keeping The Wilderness Wild

by Charlene Cruson Step

Camping is a timeless activity. It can occur every day, every season, in every type of terrain, in almost every country of the world. Not every type of person camps, however. Even so, in the United States the number of visitors who engage in "backcountry land use" has mushroomed from about 4 million in 1965 to over 15 million in the mid-1980s. A few decades ago, the only decent guide to campsites in this country was a thin book with meager offerings. Today, the Rand McNally RV Park & Campground Directory is a hefty 1½ inches thick and contains healthy information on 18,000 public and private campsites.

"Camper" became a popular word when

A Stoeger editor for the past 10 years, Charlene Cruson Step is an avid outdoor person. She began camping over 20 years ago and has enjoyed, from a tent, much of Canada, Alaska and many northern U.S. states. Always the chef on an expedition, she is interested in cooking and cookware. She was the editor of Jerry Steindler's revised Game Cookbook (Stoeger Publishing Co., 1985) and was responsible for its redesign.

RV's—recreational vehicles (usually 4-wheel drive, some with trailers of varying design and dimensions)—made their debut not too long ago. But "camper" also encompasses all the people who venture out—the hikers, backpackers, bicyclers, mountain climbers, fishermen, hunters, vacationers, RVers, you name it—and who sleep and eat outdoors. And for as many motivating interests as exist for camping, there are as many camping styles in sleeping and eating. You can, for example, travel "light" on a mountain bike with just a sleeping bag, folding mini-stove, Swiss Army knife and dried foods. At the other end is the Holiday Rambler-type recreational vehicle complete with bed, bath and fully stocked gourmet kitchen.

To satisfy the wide variety of camping preferences, manufacturers have responded with an equally incredible array of products. In 1988, Americans spent an estimated 900 million dollars plus on camping equipment, according to the U.S. Department of Commerce. Let's take a look at just the eating segment of the camper's day and some of the cooking gear available in 1990. Manufacturers are meeting the challenge of making products that are usually lightweight, easy to pack and carry, easy to use, and require low maintenance. With growing emphasis on minimal-impact camping, one important element is that if used properly, their equipment can be carried from the campsite, leaving little or no adverse effects on the environment.

A Million Ways to Heat the Meat

Well, maybe not a million, but certainly more than Early Man could ever have imagined. Forget twig-foraging and circling a fire with rocks. The American Camping Association recommends not disturbing the woods—an endangered resource—rather bring your own fire-making devices and learn to use alternate fuels. Here's some of what's available for campers in 1990 that meet that objective.

Mini-Stoves. For the light traveler today, Safesport Manufacturing Company of Denver, Colorado, offers the "Kwik Cook Stove." At 6½ inches square, it folds flat for efficient packing and stands only 5 inches high when opened. It is sturdy enough to support a large pan filled with your favorite fixings, while wind shields underneath protect the heat source. That can be sterno, other canned heat, or solid fuel, such as Hexamine or Trioxane. Sold for about $7 retail, this heating unit is compact, efficient and well-liked by backpackers. Safesport markets other small units, including the veteran wing stove and several other Mountain Climber's stoves.

As for heat sources, Sterno has been in use for a long time, most memorably under the fondue pot

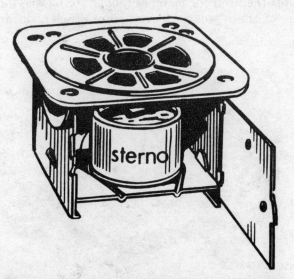

The Kwik Cook Stove by Safesport Manufacturing affords the light-traveling chef a compact, yet sturdy heating unit that stands only 5 inches high when assembled.

or chafing dishes at fancy house parties. It is the tradename for gelatinized methyl alchohol (mixed with nitrocellulose). In solid form, it looks like wax, burns with moderate heat (virtually no smoke), travels well and is inexpensive at about $4 per package of three 2⅝-ounce cans. It is also offered in liquid form as "Fondue Fuel," obtainable in larger containers for a bit more in price. Its only drawback is that it is slow-burning when compared to other fuels.

Another mini-unit, the "Whisper Lite International Stove," was developed by Mountain Safety Research of Seattle, Washington. It is a three-pronged multi-fuel stove (about 4 inches high) that requires liquid fuel, such as kerosene, white gas or Coleman Fuel, and Chevron Blazo, and the like. Made of brass and stainless steel, it weighs under 12 ounces, including the pump that accesses the fuel from a 22-ounce MSR Fuel Bottle. This stove will boil a quart of water in about 4½ minutes; total burn time is 3 hours 10 minutes. Winner of the Backpacker Design Award, this unit sells for around $55. Mountain Safety Research also offers additional models, some using isobutane, a particularly clean-burning fuel.

For the outdoor chef who can handle a slightly larger, yet efficient single unit, Peak 1, a division of Coleman—the king of camping equipment—also markets a Multi-Fuel Stove. This small, four-footed burner uses either white gas (Coleman Fuel) or kerosene (converter materials provided). The newest improved Multi-Fuel model has a leveling ring used to adjust the leg height of the stove. No more wedging rocks or sticks under it to make it level. Another new feature is the lanyard that keeps the fuel cap attached to the tank or base of the stove. This prevents the cap from dropping on the ground, thus keeping the fuel free of moisture and debris. The stove weighs a little over a pound without fuel. Full, it will burn 1½ hours on high power, six hours on simmer. Suggested retail is about $85. What most campers like about this stove and others like it is not only its fuel versatility, but also the fact that the flame is adjustable. If you want boiling water for tea, you turn it to high; if you're frying eggs for breakfast, you can set it lower. Ultimately, it provides for more culinary possibilities.

Here's the type of dish you can fix on a single-burner unit. A meal-in-itself, it is tasty, nutritious and requires only one pan.

Peak 1's improved Multi-Fuel Stove offers camp cooks an efficient, versatile unit, with a leveling ring that allows for adjustment of the legs on uneven surfaces.

Hunter Trail Beef

Sauce:
1 package (1.1 oz.) Hunter Sauce Mix
 (Brown Sauce with Mushrooms)
3 tablespoons fortified nonfat dry milk
1/2 teaspoon dried minced onion
1/4 teaspoon dried crushed basil
Freshly ground black pepper

1 5-ounce package dried beef
1 1/2 cups cold water (for Sauce)
1/4 cup couscous (precooked semolina pasta)

Before your trip, prepare the basics of the Sauce by combining dried Hunter Sauce Mix, nonfat dry milk, minced onion, basil and black pepper. Place in an airtight, sealable plastic bag.

When ready to prepare the dish, open dried beef and cut up (or shred) into bite-size pieces, using all or a portion of the package. Soak in cold water (in the pan you're going to cook in) for 2 minutes to remove excess salt; rinse well, discarding all salt water. Place meat in lid of pan.

Empty prepared Hunter Sauce Mix into pan and add 1 1/2 cups cold water, stirring to dissolve. Simmer over medium heat about 5 minutes until sauce starts to thicken. Add beef and heat through. Stir in couscous, cover and let sit for 5 minutes. About 15 minutes from start to finish. Serves 1-2.

Mid-Sized Models. Coleman Outdoor Products, Inc., of Wichita, Kansas, has been manufacturing its famous lanterns since 1914, its portable stoves since the 1920s. Today the company offers a wonderful assortment of outdoor equipment that is renown for quality, convenience, reliability and value. Talk to campers who have been at it for any length of time, and you'll find a Coleman Stove among their gear.

The favorite is the two-burner model, especially for groups of larger than two who like to eat well on the trail. It's efficient, easy to carry, and does the job. One outdoorsman, a close friend who hates to spend a dime more on equipment than he has to, invested in this model just before he and three buddies took off on a recent fishing trip to Canada. When the fish were brought back to camp fresh from the lake, that Coleman stove went to work serving up meals those fishermen will savor for a lot of summers to come.

An improved propane stove was recently introduced by Coleman that provides larger shields, or baffles, to protect against the wind; a better lid latch with more positive closure; a redesigned hand hold for easier carrying; a removable grate for faster clean-up; a regulator stored in the cook top; and new graphics for a more contemporary appearance. All this in the Standard green propane model (about $50), plus a piezo ignition in the Electronic Ignition propane model, which eliminates the need for matches (about $68). Carrying one of these stoves is even more efficient in an

Coleman's Two-Burner Propane Stove—"Old Faithful"—now with larger wind baffles, improved lid latch and easier carry hand hold. In standard or electronic ignition versions.

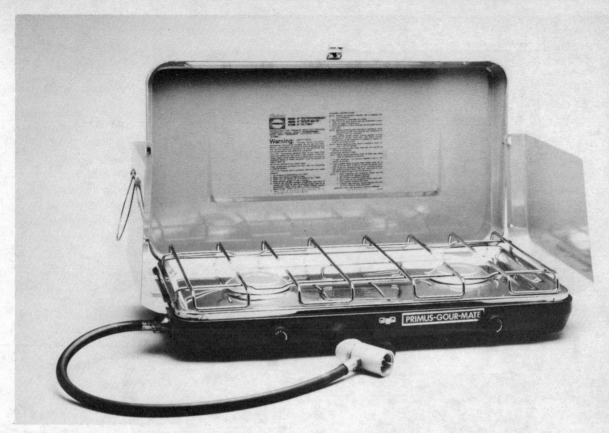

A sleek two-burner propane stove—Century Tool & Mfg.'s "Gour-Mate"—boasts a secure locking device, full wind baffles, chrome-plated spill tray and screw-out burners for easy clean-up, plus an optional lantern hook-up.

optional nylon case that also houses two 16.4-ounce propane cylinders. (You wouldn't want to backpack this bundle, however.)

A rival to the Coleman two-burner propane unit—and a very attractive one—is the Century Primus "Gour-Mate." Made by Century Tool and Manufacturing, a 46-year-old company based in Cherry Valley, Illinois, it is a little more sleek in design than the Coleman, with a brown base and beige top. It has a very secure locking device; the wind baffles fold up from the base and hook into the top; the interior surface, including the grill, is chrome-plated, which makes it easy to clean, and the burners screw out, also adding to ease of clean-up. The rectangular unit measures roughly 21 inches × 11 inches and retails for about $45, a good value. Century Tool & Mfg. also offers a variety of other single, double and triple-burner models, as well as propane lanterns and other camping equipment.

Propane, by the way, is a petroleum by-prod-

uct. It produces a blue flame, no smoke, and an even, adjustable heat in the stoves discussed. It is easier and safer to transport than the gasoline-type fuels, (white gas and kerosene) and can be purchased in 16-ounce cylindrical tanks for about $2.75 or so per cylinder. Propane performs well at low temperatures and receives high ratings from virtually all users (except those who must carry their stoves manually, since the propane cylinders are heavy).

In autumn of 1989, Coleman introduced new camp stoves and lanterns that burn ordinary unleaded automotive gasoline. The Unleaded Powerhouse™ Stove, and its smaller brother, the Unleaded Two-Burner Stove, both boast a technologically advanced generator that can accommodate the residue that results from burning unleaded gas. Coleman engineers redesigned coil placement and increased the size of the chamber that stores the residue created by the additives and impurities found in unleaded gas. Ultimately,

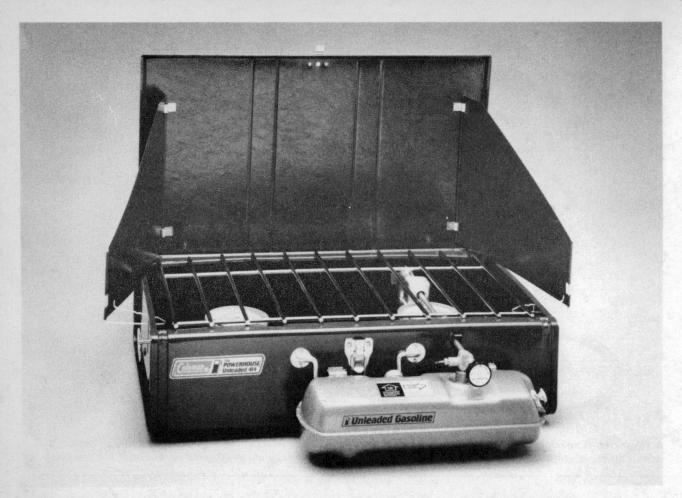

Coleman's newest entry in the camp cookware field is its Powerhouse® Unleaded Gasoline Stove that burns regular unleaded automotive fuel. Innovative engineering, a new filtering funnel and fill-stop feature enhance this economical model.

this innovation should inhibit clogging and increase vaporization, thereby ensuring efficient burning of the easily accessible fuel. The Unleaded Two-Burner Stove, at suggested retail of about $70, has $9\frac{5}{16}$-inch centers and holds $2\frac{1}{2}$ pints of fuel, while the Powerhouse™ model, at about $80, incorporates 11-inch centers to support larger pots and handles $3\frac{1}{2}$ pints of fuel. Either stove will burn with both burners on high for approximately two hours. At $1.20 per gallon, the smaller stove operates at a cost of about 16¢ per hour, the larger, at 19¢ per hour. That's about 1/4 the cost of other camp fuels and about 1/20 the cost of propane. Incidentally, these stoves will burn other Coleman camp fuel as well. (Don't try unleaded gas in stoves that call for other fuels, however).

In addition to the familiar features seen on the traditional Coleman models, these units come packaged with a new filtering funnel created to improve ease of filling, while filtering out water and impurities from the unleaded fuel. There's also a fill-stop feature that reduces the chance of overfilling and spillage. While these stoves retain the customary green color, the fuel tanks are silver and stamped with red "Unleaded Gasoline" markings to distinguish them from other fuel containers. One objection campers have voiced about unleaded fuel in outdoor equipment (which has been tried before, by the way) is the strong odor it emits. Coleman assures campers that "there are no increased odors from the unleaded stoves" when they are in operation.

Cooking outdoors on a stove with two burners is almost like being at home—only better. And nothing beats fried fish fresh-caught. Try these simple variations next time you're at the lake.

Herb-Fried Fish

Depending on the ingredients you usually take with you, you can do this recipe two different ways and achieve similar results.

Herb vinaigrette dressing
Flour or bread crumbs (or a combination of both)
Or:
Milk or mayonnaise
Flour/bread crumbs seasonsed with black pepper, garlic powder, tarragon, dill, and/or thyme, or your favorite herb combination such as oregano, basil and parsley.

Cleaned and boned fresh fish filets
2 - 4 tablespoons vegetable or olive oil

Dip fish filets in vinaigrette dressing, then in flour/bread crumb mixture. *Or* dip in milk or spread lightly with mayonnaise on both sides, then cover with seasonsed flour/bread crumbs.

Heat oil in skillet and fry filets a few minutes on each side.

Brown rice is a first choice in our family as a complement to many meals and now you can buy fast-cooking brown rice that takes only 10 minutes to prepare. You could have that simmering on the second burner while you're frying the fish.

Venison Fajitas

2 pounds venison round, cut into thin strips about 2-3 inches long
Fajitas Marinade (see below)
Olive oil
3 cloves garlic, peeled and left whole
1 large green pepper, cut into thin slices
1 large onion (Spanish preferred), thinly sliced
2 large tomatoes, cut into wedges, then halved
8 or more flour tortillas
Shredded cheddar cheese
Guacamole and sour cream (optional)

Fajitas Marinade: Combine in a large glass or ceramic (nonmetal) dish, 4 tablespoons fresh lime juice, 2 tablespoons wine vinegar, 2 tablespoons light brown sugar, 1/4 teaspoon ground coriander, 1/4 teaspoon oregano, 1 clove pressed garlic, freshly ground black pepper, 1/2 cup light vegetable oil. (Can be prepared ahead of time in a small container.)

Place venison in marinade and let sit, covered, at least two hours, if possible. Overnight is preferable.

To prepare, remove meat and drain; reserve marinade. Heat oil in large, heavy skillet. Add garlic to pan and brown lightly on all sides; remove. Add onion, green pepper and tomato and sauté lightly; remove from pan. Now brown the meat on all sides. Return the garlic and some of the marinade to the pan to cover the bottom; cover and simmer over low heat for about 45 minutes or so, until tender, adding more marinade and water, if necessary.

In the meantime, roll two tortillas together and enclose them in aluminum foil, making 4 wraps total. Warm on the grill over very low heat. Or place all, flat, in another heavy skillet, cover pan and slowly warm over the other burner (add a few drops of water to bottom of pan).

When meat is tender, return the onion, green pepper and tomato to pan. Stir until heated through. To serve, spoon meat mixture into the center of each tortilla. Top with cheddar cheese and, if available, sour cream and guacamole. Fold up and enjoy. Serves 4, depending on your appetite.

It's a crisp autumn day and you've brought your birds back to camp. Mesquite-smoked quail is going to taste mighty fine, especially on one of the portable grills available today. Weber, the famous gas grill company of Palatine, Illinois, has produced a number of smaller easy-carry versions—the "Go-Anywhere" Grills. The Gas Go-Anywhere model is rectangular, with wooden handles on the lid and base. Nickel-plated folding feet attached to either side wrap up and around the stove to lock the cover in place when not in use. A cylindrical propane tank attaches at the side of this black porcelain-on-steel oven, which boasts direct or indirect cooking with natural convection over bright nickel-plated 160 square-inch grill

Weber, famous for quality grills, accents its line of small models with the "Go-Anywhere" grills. The gas version (above) uses a propane tank at its side; the legs pivot up and lock the cover in place for easy carrying. The Smokey Joe Tuck-N-Carry (below) is a popular "kettle" unit.

(about $45). The Smokey Joe Tuck-N-Carry™ model, introduced a few years ago, is a round black "kettle" grill. It stands only 16¾ inches high on zinc-plated steel legs. The lid and bowl are made of porcelain-sealed heavy-gauge steel to prevent rust, fading and burning. At 14½ inches in diameter, the grill affords 150 square inches of cooking area over charcoal. It is relatively light to carry with wooden handle and retails for about $35.

Coleman's improved Cookin' Machine™, made of rust-resistant aluminized steel, is still larger. It stands on sturdy tri-pod legs, features two 170-square-inch cooking grids, a stainless steel burner, stay-cool handles, a five-foot hose, bulk propane system adapter, and an enamel water pan for steaming and smoking. It's available in either standard or electronic ignition at a suggested retail price of about $90.

For people who enjoy outdoor life at a more leisurely pace, there are the charcoal models. Charcoal briquets are easily obtainable, even at your local grocer, are inexpensive, and must al-

ways be used out-of-doors because of the toxic fumes they emit. They are also slow to heat up (as much as an hour), but give off even heat that would make any venison steak melt in your mouth. United States Stove Company (USSC) of Chattanooga, Tennessee, produces the "Campmate" and

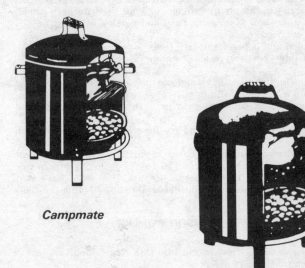

Campmate

L'il Smoker

United States Stove Company (USSC) markets easy-to-carry smoker/grills, the Campmate and the Li'l Smoker, both of which will accommodate about 15 pounds of meat at one time. Using slower-burning charcoal, they can smoke, roast, steam or barbecue your favorite fixings.

"Li'l Smoker" smoker/grills that smoke, roast, steam and barbecue. Both have a 15-pound food capacity, feature built-in skewer notches, porcelain water pan, charcoal pan and lid latch for easy carrying (Campmate). The Campmate, in black matte, weighs about 12 pounds, while the Li'l Smoker, in flame, weighs about 15 pounds. USSC's smoker/grills range from these small models to the larger, deluxe stainless steel versions, spanning a price range of $40 to $125.

The following barbecue sauce I adapted for Jerry Steindler's revised *Game Cookbook*, a Stoeger publication that appeared a few years ago. Great with big game steaks, country ribs, you name it, this sauce is Versatility Plus—outdoors or in—on any type of grill.

For larger groups and leisurely cooking, Coleman's Cookin' Machine features two 170-square-inch cooking grids, a stainless steel propane burner and an enamel water pan for steaming and smoking.

B-B-Q Sauce with a Zip

(2 cups)

1/2 cup ketchup
1/4 cup apple cider vinegar
1/4 cup light salad oil
2 tablespoons light brown sugar
1/2 envelope dry onion soup mix
1 tablespoon prepared country mustard
   (stone ground with horseradish)
1/4 teaspoon garlic powder
1/2 cup water
Optional:
1 tablespoon liquid smoke
Prepared hot pepper sauce

Combine all ingredients in a small saucepan and bring to a boil; lower the heat and simmer about 10 minutes. Cool before using. Sufficient to marinate about 2 pounds of meat, this sauce also freezes well.

For tastebuds that enjoy a little more kick, try this *Texas Style,* with the liquid smoke and a few dashes of hot pepper sauce.

Mesquite-Smoked Rabbit

(serves 4)

2 cottontails, cut into serving pieces
2 cups Bar-B-Q Sauce with a Zip (above)
Enough Mesquite chips for one charcoal fire

Prepare Bar-B-Q Sauce (above), lacing it with drops of hot pepper sauce, but not the liquid smoke. Marinate rabbit pieces overnight, if possible; two hours at least.

Soak Mesquite chips according to package instructions and place on charcoal grill. When fire is hot, place rabbit on grill, browning on all sides and turning often until tender, about 1/2 hour, depending on heat. Scrumptious with buttermilk biscuits, stuffed Spanish Onions (see below) and mixed salad. Try the marinade with squirrel or frogs' legs, too.

Stuffed Spanish Onions

(serves 4)

4 large Spanish (or Bermuda) onions
1 16-oz. container prepared baked beans
1/4 teaspoon dry mustard
1/2 teaspoon dried onion
1 tablespoon molasses
2 tablespoons tomato ketchup

Peel onions and lower into boiling water; parboil 5 minutes to soften slightly. Drain and cool. With a small, sharp knife core out the centers, leaving the walls thick enough so they don't collapse. Take aluminum foil and shape it around the bottom of each onion and about halfway up, leaving a collar around each to catch drippings.

Prepare filling by combining remaining ingredients. Fill the onion cavities with the baked bean mixture. Place onions on grill and cover to steam through, about 20 minutes depending on how high the heat is.

These are a wonderful complement (you'll receive compliments, too) with most barbecue menus.

Whichever stove you ultimately choose, make sure you try it out before you embark on that long-awaited trip. Cook on it before you leave, making certain that all parts work properly and that you feel confident using it. You don't want to find yourself out at camp, floundering around with knobs and grills that don't fit right, feel right or work right.

Regarding the prices indicated, these are retail price tags suggested by the manufacturers and may vary depending on what section of the country you're in. Some retailers are able to allow larger discounts than others, so shop around if you've got something specific in mind to add to your gear. Most of the stoves described are obtainable in sporting goods stores, certain hardware chains and retail outlets where outdoor equipment is sold.

Most important, try to remember when shopping that the wilderness you enjoy so much really is shrinking. The 200 acres of woods that once comprised my backyard have become a thriving neighborhood of 35 homes. The place where my husband's once-favorite hunting stand existed is now in somebody's driveway. So take good care of what's left. Use equipment that will keep whatever wilderness still exits, natural and unspoiled.

Classic Handguns: Six Models That Have Stood the Test of Time

by Stanley W. Trzoniec

The word *classic* is hard to define. As applied to handguns, it means to shooters everywhere a particular model that has become the standard by which others are judged. Included in this category are the famed Colt .45 automatic and Single Action Army, Smith and Wesson's magnum revolvers, Ruger's hefty .44 Super Blackhawk, and Browning's 9mm Hi-Power, all of which form the subject of this piece. Since their introductions, these guns have been improved, of course, but the rich, overall designs that have set them apart from the other centerfire models have remained unchanged.

Smith and Wesson Model 27

Let's turn first to Smith and Wesson. Two guns come immediately to mind: one set the world afire 53 years ago with its power back, while the other helped to launch many a shooter into big-bore .44 caliber shooting. The first was Model 27, chambered in the hot .38 caliber .357 magnum, and it showed up at the right place at the right time. During the early 1930s, law enforcement officials and sportsmen alike longed for something bolder than standard .38 Special loadings. Largely through the efforts of Phil Sharpe, a noted ballistician, the dream became a reality. For the first time, a gun had been designed to handle pressure readings almost double those of previous revolvers. With its unprecedented velocity of 1,515 feet per second (fps), the new .357 magnum (which became known as Model 27 in 1957) could not only withstand this new threshold, it offered shooter comfort and safety as well.

Smith and Wesson's new gun was first produced on a custom basis, including a numbered registration certificate that was sent to each new owner. Retail pricing at that time was $60, or $15 above anything else in the Smith and Wesson line at the time. The gun could be ordered with the following options: barrel lengths from 3½″ to 8¾″ (the longer the barrel, the greater the velocity); and any one of seven sight blades with fully adjustable rear. As a finishing touch, each gun was sighted in with the owner's choice of factory ammunition at any distance up to 200 yards.

Stanley Trzoniec is a veteran firearms writer and photographer who has long specialized in the reporting of all modern weapons. An accomplished handloader, he has written on that subject for virtually every major firearms journal. Currently Special Projects Editor for Harris Publications, he is also the author of several books and has written over 500 articles on firearms and the outdoors.

Model 27 is a popular handgun offering many variations. Shown here is a collector's gun featuring a 5″ barrel in nickel finish.

Caught completely by surprise, the Smith and Wesson factory was hard-pressed to finish its quota of about 120 guns per month. Just three years after its introduction, the Springfield plant completed its 5,500th revolver. Because of the demand, registration of both gun and certificate were discontinued. In 1941, with wartime demands at an all-time high, production of the .357 magnum ground to a complete halt. It would not begin again until 1948, at which time new improvements included a short throw hammer, a new safety, and barrel lengths of 3½″, 5″, 6″, 6½″ and 8⅜″. Engineering changes continued through the ensuing years, among them the elimination of the extra side plate screw; the use of a left-hand thread on the extractor (to keep it from backing out); and the addition of a target hammer, trigger and extra fancy checkered Goncalo Alves grips.

Whether it's used for target shooting or competitive sports, Smith and Wesson's Model 27 remains one of the most sought-after double action revolvers.

Smith and Wesson Model 29

Hardly a day goes by among serious revolver enthusiasts without some mention of the .44 magnum cartridge. Its success is due in part to the work and creativeness of three men, all of whom made history in the shooting world with Smith and Wesson's Model 29.

Elmer Keith, that grand old man of the bigbore, got the ball rolling initially. In magazine ar-

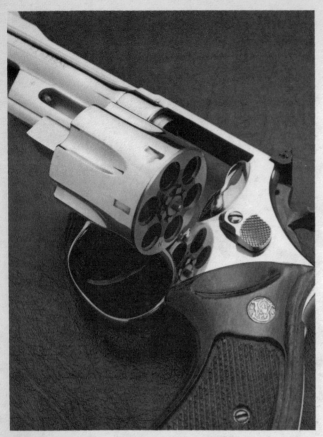

Some years back, cylinder counterboring was eliminated in order to streamline production. Modern cartridge cases, similar to the Smith and Wesson model shown here, are strong enough to take on decent pressures, hence there's no need for any case support within the cylinder.

Close on the heels of the cartridge was the gun itself; in fact, that is what made the picture complete. Planned originally as a specially heat-treated .44 hand ejector, further testing indicated that the gun should be slightly heavier. Increasing the weight by 7½ ounces seemed to be the best compromise, and so in late 1956 the first 6½″ double action, barreled guns rolled down the assembly line. About six months later, a 4″ magnum was introduced (for collectors, it should be noted that a special run of about 500 units was also made in the highly desirable 5″ barrel length). The primary features of this model were its target sights and grips, all snuggled down within a black presentation case.

Today, Smith and Wesson's Model 29 is still in great demand. Current variations include 4″, 6″ and 8⅜″ guns in both carbon and stainless steel. A brand new version—called the "Classic Hunter"—has been introduced recently. It comes complete with a nonfluted cylinder, heavy barrel underlug, and neoprene grips. Smith and Wesson has also bowed to the field hunter by supplying scope rings with its longest barrel gun. Hikers and campers can also order a 3″ barrel model featuring a round grip frame for easy portability.

Ruger Super Blackhawk

As the story goes, Sturm, Ruger got into the .44 caliber revolver race by way of a single cartridge case. It seems that someone found the case in a factory trash pile, handed it over to Bill Ruger, the company president, who did some heavy arm-twisting in order to obtain pertinent information on the new .44 magnum. Whether this story is entirely accurate depends on who tells the story, but nevertheless it propelled Ruger into the big-bore business.

In 1956, Ruger, still capitalizing on Colt's infrequent production of its fine Single Action Army, introduced the .44 magnum Flat-Top revolver (Model BKH4). Conservative in style, this model was designed to keep the flow going for all those buyers who were still intent on shooting single action revolvers. Now a very collectable firearm, this gun was made in six different versions up until 1962.

Superseding Model BKH4 was the Super Blackhawk, perhaps the best .44 caliber single action revolver in existence. The Super Blackhawk, first produced in 1959, has since been stylized somewhat to reflect Sturm, Ruger's continuing de-

ticles and personal appearances at various arms factories, he had for several years strongly advocated the use of heavy loads in the popular Smith and Wesson .44 hand ejector pistol. Blessed with enough common sense not to push his luck with over-pressurized handloads, Keith urged both Smith and Wesson and Remington Arms to produce a combination of cartridge and handgun. The result was a legend that lives even today.

By 1954, the dream had turned to reality. C. R. Hellstrom, then head of Smith and Wesson, and R. H. Coleman, Remington's chief, finally got their resources together. Remington's cartridge featured a case with dimensions of about .10″ longer than previous examples of the .44 Special, thus preventing the chambering of .44 magnum cases in weaker (and much older) .44 Special revolvers. This cartridge was indeed a major step forward in the history of American handgunning.

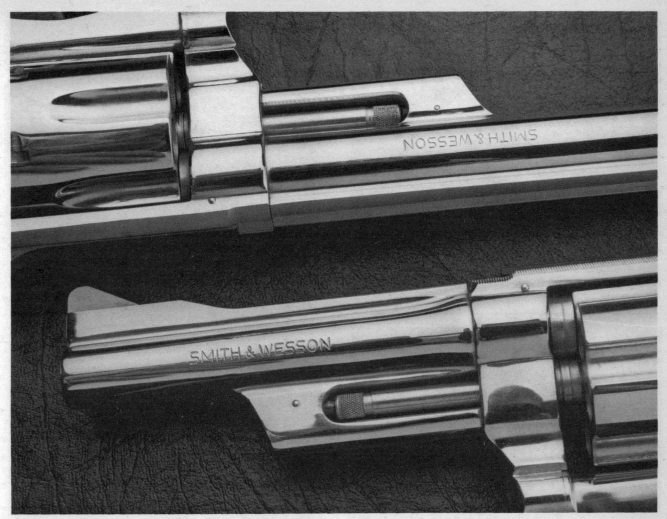

This photo shows the comparison between a .44 magnum barrel (top) and the slimmer Model 27 barrel (bottom).

sire to provide shooters with strong, reliable firearms. For many shooters, this gun broke tradition. With its high gloss finish, nonfluted cylinder and "dragoon"-styled trigger guards, the Super hardly represented guns of the Old West. And yet, for the modern enthusiast, this model was the ultimate in high-performance wheelguns—especially for shooters who were active in handloading and field hunting.

When first marketed, the Super Blackhawk was sold in Ruger's mahogany case complete with red lining. Later, all long frame guns (fewer than 500 were made) were shipped in these cases. This gun featured a grip frame that measured about three-sixteenths of an inch longer than the current standard Blackhawks.

The Super Blackhawks also had fully adjustable rear sights encased in streamlined (and very functional) integral sight ribs. This feature, which helped protect the sight fixture, also eased the gun in and out of leather gear that much better. A wide, serrated hammer was incorporated for ease of cocking, and a wider trigger was fitted in to aid in let-off. Combined with a 7½" barrel, this model has been in constant demand by both big-bore aficionados and hunters in general. While the .44 magnums produced by Sturm, Ruger and Smith and Wesson were introduced in the same time frame, the price difference between them amounted to exactly $44—the same caliber number for which they were chambered!

In their concern for safety, Ruger's engineers

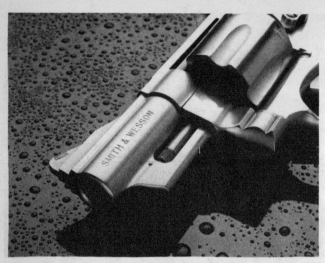

This stainless steel version of the Model 29 series features a 3" barrel. It's ideal for backpackers and military personnel.

At top is an older model of Ruger's famous Super Blackhawk, and at bottom is the New Model in stainless steel. Both are chambered for the hard-hitting .44 magnum cartridge.

The .44 magnum (top) is a nickeled Model 29 with a 6¹/₂" barrel. The new Classic Hunter (bottom) comes complete with unfluted cylinder and heavy underlug barrel.

To load this Super Blackhawk, simply open the loading gate, eject the spent rounds, and insert new ones.

brought on line the first revolution within single actions since the 1830s. Now, once and for all, it was possible to carry six loaded rounds in the cylinder without fear or danger of setting one off accidentally. Heretofore, the accepted practice was to carry five loaded rounds with the unloaded chamber under the firing pin. With this new system, a transfer bar was placed between hammer face and firing pin. When the hammer was at rest, it never touched the pin; instead, the uppermost part of the stepped hammer lay on the frame proper. Cocking the hammer raised the bar; when released, the two were united. Releasing the trigger dropped the transfer bar downward. This also alleviated another problem, that of loading the gun with the hammer back. To charge the weapon, you must open the cylinder gate; while in this mode, the hammer cannot be brought back. It's a very safe and effective system.

The words "New Model" are stamped on the side frame of Ruger's Super Blackhawk. The massive unfluted cylinder has been stylized in the single action format.

This Colt Government Model is dressed up in stainless steel and highly polished in what Colt calls its "Ultimate" finish.

In recent years, a stainless Super Blackhawk with an optional 10″ barrel was introduced, and now a much heralded 5½″ gun is also available.

Colt Forty-Five Automatic

How many times have you heard the phrase, "If only I had a dollar for every one made, I . . . ." If ever there was a gun to which you could relate that phrase, Colt's timeless .45 caliber automatic definitely ranks among the top contenders. With production figures fast approaching four million or more, this gun has become familiar to just about everyone. If you didn't experience it in the Army, you have probably shot it on the range. For targets, combat shooting games, police work, or even close range hunting, this old reliable .45 caliber pistol is hard to beat.

The U.S. Army certainly agreed, for it adopted the gun for service use way back in 1911. Embarrassed by its choice in .38 caliber sidearms and its subsequent problems in the Philippine Campaign, the Army decided to adopt this .45 caliber automatic for general service use. After several years of careful consideration, tests were made in 1906

Note the adjustable rear sights and trigger on this Gold Cup model in highly polished stainless steel.

In this side view of Colt's Government Model, note the slide release, safety lever and combat-type sights. Magazine release is just behind the trigger.

to determine if the Army was on the right track in considering a .45 caliber pistol. In 1907, it was finally concluded that, yes, this automatic was indeed the right gun for armed forces use—on the condition, however, that it be not less than .45 caliber.

Both Colt and Savage Arms submitted guns to the Army for testing, but none proved worthy. Given additional time for making the necessary improvements, the two competitors met for a final test on March 15, 1911, with Colt emerging the victor. Human fatigue was a major consideration in the testing. Savage's model lost in part because the Army's testing team discovered it could fire the Savage about 500 times against the Colt's 2,000 rounds before the pounding of the Savage weapon left the shooters too tired to continue. Since that time, Colt's Model 1911 has become a standard by which other larger caliber automatics are judged.

Over the years, this big Colt has proved itself in many different fields. Target shooters have "accurized" the gun to shoot the better part of a full magazine into one hole from a machine rest. Stoked with mild wadcutters, this big, hand-held gun excelled at matches all across the country. With practical or combat shooting having taken shooters by storm in recent years, the Colt has demonstrated its ability to perform against the clock in simulated combat situations. Especially effective in such competition is the Gold Cup, a highly tuned Colt automatic modified by the factory for target shooters or gamesmen. Equipped with fully adjustable sights, a crisp trigger and numerous other features, this gun is one of many successful variations in the famous auto's lineup.

Colt offers the straight Government Model, Gold Cup, Officers ACP and Commander, all with finishes ranging from regular stainless to steel to nickel, blue, mirror blue and Ultimate. Many private distributors of Colt products have introduced

This photo illustrates why Colt's Single Action Army never seems to die. Classic lines, beautiful engraving, fit and finish are hallmarks of this classic gun.

limited editions of Colt automatics. These rare guns are still around and gain value each year as collectors' items.

Meanwhile, internal modifications have improved safety, especially with the now popular firing pin lock on all Series 80 guns. Sights have been improved somewhat, with a higher, more visible sight picture. Special editions made by Colt for combat shooters include two-toned finishes and higher combat-type sights. The list of options goes on; indeed, there seems no end to the possibilities of this famous and popular weapon.

Colt Single Action Army

"THE GUN THAT WON THE WEST." That saying has become synonymous with Colt's most famous handgun. It all began in 1872, when the U.S. Army was testing Colt's older Open Top .44,

which proved totally inadequate for the job at hand. Colt raced back to the drawing board and within a few short months returned with a solid frame gun that combined most of the practical features of both the Open Top and Navy-sized weapons. Among the important steps in propellants that helped father this gun was the abandonment of black powder in favor of the higher pressurized smokeless. This method of securing the cylinder and barrel with a wedge was not the right way to go, both in design and shooting effectiveness; hence the introduction of the solid top revolver. The U.S. Army adopted the Single Action Army (SAA) as its official service weapon in 1873, and by 1891 more than 37,000 revolvers had been produced under contract.

The Peacemaker, as it was known then (and still is), was produced in so many varieties, calibers

Here the author demonstrates the wrong—and dangerous—way to handle a fine gun such as this Colt Single Action Army model.

Note the comparison between Browning's Hi-Power and a pair of ordinary reading glasses. A lot of firepower is packed into this small package.

and custom orders that it's difficult to pin down specifically. Calibers ran from .22 to .476 Eley, with the most popular being .32-20, .38-40 and .44-40. And for good reason—they were well suited to the popular Winchester Model 73 rifles, giving frontiersmen and scouts alike the advantage of complete interchangeability. A man could now use the same cartridge in his pistol or long gun. Other notable calibers included the .32 Colt, .38 Colt, .41, .44 Rimfire and the ever popular .45 Long Colt. In fact, over 30 different chamberings were offered at one time or another, with the .45 Colt by far the most popular. For the serious collector, this gun can cost plenty. Aside from its chamberings, various barrel lengths, finishes, serial numbers and recent commemorative Models only heighten the confusion. Engraved guns, both past and future,

can be a large part of any collection, and here Colt's .45 will not disappoint you. For modern shooters, brand-new Colt SAA's are available from Colt's Custom Shop. For more details, call or write Colt (Hartford, CT).

Browning 9mm Hi-Power

It's ironic to think that John Browning's last pistol development proved to be his greatest achievement. In fact, history books tell us that a patent on his 9mm semiautomatic filed in 1923 was finally granted on February 22, 1927, just three short months following his death.

Browning always believed that the autopistol was the handgun of the future, especially for the military. He wasn't interested in long range facts or figures; his primary concerns were stopping power and decent accuracy at close (combat) ranges. He seemed to have gotten his wish; not only did his 9mm Hi-Power reach production figures of more than 1.5 million, but the U.S. Army took his .45 automatic under its wing. The rest is history.

The Hi-Power is a semiautomatic pistol that operates with short recoil combined with a locked breech. Its capacity is 13 rounds plus one in the chamber (if desired). What some consider the "father of the modern super-nine" gun, it's known as a high volume (or high capacity) automatic. We see them on the market today—the Smith and Wessons, the Berettas, and the Rugers—all of which can be traced one way or another back to the beginnings of Browning's 9mm Hi-Power. It's available currently in two versions. One is the basic Hi-Power in a blue polished finish and walnut grip panels, with or without adjustable sights. The other model is slanted toward the military or SWAT units, with its plastic grips, ambidextrous safety lever and special matte finish.

Of all the so-called high volume automatics on the market today, this 9mm ranks highest. Even though it holds 14 rounds, the grip is not bulky or hard to manage for shooters with smaller hands. The backstrap is gracefully arched so as to afford a consistent placement in the hand. The trigger needs some fine tuning, but then we are talking primarily about a service revolver, not a target gun. Sights are always a problem for some people, but this can be solved by having a set of fine Bo-Mar's installed by a good gunsmith. They are low profile in style and hug the slide in such a way that they neither hinder the sighting picture nor delay a hasty withdrawal from leather gear.

Over the years, we have seen various collectors or special editions put out by Browning; there was even a fancy engraved gun produced on a regular basis, but it was later dropped because of high production costs. And at one time you could also find a nickle-finished gun.

The handguns described in this article represent only a small slice of the so-called classic pie. If you are fortunate enough to own one, be sure to check your backstops, be safe, shoot what you have, and most of all, enjoy it.

The Shotgun and Game Shooting

by Ralph F. Quinn

Learning how to become a skillful and proficient upland game shot is not an easy assignment. It's much more difficult than, say, achieving the magical "25 straight" in trap or skeet. Even though both sports are similar—you release one thing (the

shot pattern) to intercept another (the clay target or game bird)—the similarity ends there. In competitive shooting, the exact distance to the trap or skeet house is known and the speed of the target is fixed. When the clay bird is called for, the shooter has his gun mounted and aligned. All that remains is to track the pigeon and press the trigger.

Not so in upland gunning. Even with the aid of a classy pointer, the shotgunner never knows when or where the bird will appear. The speed of the target is another big handicap; we may know that a ruff grouse rockets away at 65 feet per second, but there's always the late season beater that's slow to get in gear, thus throwing off our timing. Another problem relates to unusual angles; instead of flying straight, a quail may rise up behind the gunner, then circle. Toss in an unmounted gun and is it any wonder why so few game birds are bagged?

All scattergunning, whether wing or competition, is basically a sport of *coordination*. Feet, legs, hips, shoulders, hands and eyes, all must be put together into one fluid movement to achieve

Ralph Quinn is an award-winning, full-time freelance writer specializing in shooting and outdoor subjects. A television and film producer, lecturer and book author, he travels throughout the U.S. and around the world in search of new material. A longtime participant in trap, skeet and sporting clays events, he contributes regularly to various upland shooting publications. His current work in progress is a book, Gunning Upland Birds, *scheduled for publication in 1992. The advise he offers there and in this article derives from over 30 years of game shooting experience.*

the goal, whether it's breaking the target or bagging the game. The only difference between a mediocre shotgunner and an expert is *controlled mental development*. The best shots are those who thrive on pressure and are not flustered by it. They are slick, smooth and quick beyond belief. Developing such dexterity and smoothness comes from hours of practice until form and motion become second nature. By acquiring easy rhythm and flow, the gunner is able to follow the target freely and with little wasted motion. Once you can follow the bird and discharge the shot column, while at the same time keeping the barrel swing smooth, you have mastered one of the most difficult problems in game shooting.

Sticking to the Basics

Because it has become so difficult to gain practical experience in the field, shooters today must rely on clay target sports to develop the all-important *feel* for the shotgun, its weight and balance. After that, it becomes a matter of concentrating on the basics.

The proficient shotgunner stands with feet apart at shoulder width, facing 45 degrees to the point where he expects the bird or target to appear. For right hand shooters, body weight is concentrated over the left leg and forward to absorb recoil. With this solid foundation, the gunner is able to move hips and shoulders laterally, covering the field, left or right. When swinging from right to left, most of the weight is kept on the right leg; while from left to right, the weight shifts to the left leg. Should a premature shift occur, the swing will be interrupted momentarily, causing the shot to pass in all likelihood behind the bird.

Mounting the gun is relatively simple, yet few shooters execute it properly. When the bird or target appears, the successful gunner centers both eyes on the target or bird and pushes the gun out and back in a straight line, with the comb of the stock meeting the cheek (not cheek to stock). Once the butt hits the shoulder, the shooter's eye must align automatically with the barrel. The eyes are essentially the shotgunner's rear sight; any devia-

An expert shotgunner mounts his gun by pushing out in a straight line, then back, with comb meeting cheek. Note the author's controlled stance and head position in the photo above.

Rising targets, such as the pheasant shown above, are ideal for the swing-through method. The shooter must concentrate and focus on the head only.

tion of the head on the comb will cause the shot to hit high or low.

As the bird or target approaches, the gunner's task is to "point" the muzzle of the gun in the right direction, track the target smoothly, press the trigger, and follow through. When an untrained shooter consciously tries to "aim" the front sight on the target, his concentration suffers. The slightest shift in focus from barrel to bird and back interrupts the swing and leaves the pattern behind the target.

Good gunners are well aware of the barrel's position, but they center their attention on the bird. When the primer pops, the shooter knows exactly where the muzzle is in relation to the target. Only by analyzing each shot can he tell whether it was behind, in front, high or low. Expert shots automatically go through the mechanics of stepping into the shot, getting the head down, firing and following through. Once you've mastered these basic steps, you are well on your way to developing the proper *rhythm* needed to be a success in game shooting. Mental or physical strain interrupts the delicate balance between the mind and eye, causing coordination to suffer. Concentration and attention to detail are the keys to

The British/Orvis system relies on the shotgunner to "point out," supplying an unconscious lead. The muzzle follows the path of the bird instinctively.

successful shotgunning—plus practice, practice, PRACTICE.

On Getting Ahead

In developing the correct mental approach to upland shooting, two schools of thought exist. One is the British system as taught in the Orvis Shooting School (a modified form of the Holland & Holland system); the other is the American system. Both are designed to reduce the amount of lead required to intercept a flying target, and both call for controlled movements of body and gun.

The British system relies heavily on an individual's instinctive ability to "point out" a target and hit it without giving conscious thought to lead. In practice, the gunner sees the target, centers, and in one fluid motion mounts and fires the instant the butt stock touches cheek and shoulder. This so-called "unconscious lead" technique requires the gunner to have a clear view of the bird. Since the eyes are the shotgun's rear sight, the pattern must strike where the eyes are centered. If the eyes are too low, the shot will be low; if the eyes are too high, the result is over-shooting. Any conscious adjustment of the cheek on the stock comb will compromise the entire process.

In the U.S., birders use a method or technique called "pointing out." It's similar to the British system, in that the shooter centers the target, swings the muzzle left or right in one fluid movement, fires and follows through. The English system relies more on instinct to move the gun faster than the apparent speed of the target. According to theory, when the gun fires, overthrow or gun momentum will place the shot column ahead of the target, resulting in a bagged bird. Conversely, in "pointing out" the muzzle moves at the same rate of speed as the target. The trigger is pulled while the gun is in full motion, with the shooter maintaining a *conscious* lead all the while.

American shooters use other systems as well, including "snap shooting," in which the shooter points at a spot ahead of the target. Another calls for a sustained lead, with the shotgun moving a "guess-timated" distance ahead of the bird. Then there's the swing-through method, in which the shooter tracks, swings through the target, and fires when the muzzle passes the bird's head. The lag between trigger squeeze, shell function, and the

Using a try gun to match the customer's personal measurements (as the scene above illustrates) is an essential part of the British/Orvis system. The shotgun comb must fit, or the entire tactic will be compromised.

The American system is a combination of sustained lead and swing-through. The shooter tracks the target and fires just as the muzzle passes the bird's head.

moment the shot leaves the barrel will, according to theory, automatically place the barrel ahead, creating the necessary lead. The faster the swing, the greater the lead. If there is an "official" American technique, it's a combination of the last two methods, individualized to suit both shooter and shotgun.

Exactly how much do you lead the target? If it's an overhead on duck, quartering grouse or driven pheasant, only experience will define the amount needed to intercept the game. The biggest advantage of the American method is that sighting takes place *on the bird*, not on a point ahead of the target, as in sustained lead. Its main drawback is the necessity for changing the pace of the swing to compensate for changes in direction and speed

Because ruff grouse inhabit brushy terrain, shooters will benefit from the balance and quick handling of doubles, either over-under or side-by-side.

not so much on form and fit (although most of today's fine doubles are indeed works of art) but on function. To such side-by-side notables as Robert LeFever, George "Bird" Evans, Guy De La Valdene, and Michael McIntosh, a side-by-side double is the greatest scattergun in the entire universe.

On the plus side, the double with a standard 26″ barrel is 3″ shorter on average than a repeater with the same length tube. With a reduced receiver, the weight is distributed between the hands, making the gun a joy to swing and shoot. This built-in balance and liveliness make the side-by-side a prime candidate for any number of up-

of the bird. Also, the shooter gets so tied up in cognitive functions, he commits one of the principal sins of shotgunning: *head lifting.* When that happens, even though the lead may be calculated perfectly, the shot will go high.

Shotgun Selection

Historically, shotgun selection has been more a matter of *availability* than one's shooting style. In the early 1900s, the overwhelming choice was a double made by one of the fine old gun firms— Parker, Baker, Ithaca, L. D. Smith, Winchester and the like. Two decades later, the repeater made its mark, first with Winchester's Model 97, then Model 12, followed by Remington's Models 29 and 31. Shortly after World War II, automatics from Browning and Remington rose from the ashes, and sometime during the 1950s the over-under came on the scene.

Today, with an international gun market in operation, upland specialists have their pick of wandlike doubles, side-by-sides and over-unders, plus slick pumps and featherweight automatics. The limiting factor today is no longer availability, but how willing a shotgunner is to lay out the required cash.

Actually, the current reintroduction of the double gun into the American birding scene by Parker Reproductions, Classic Doubles, Remington and others reflects a shrewd marketing plan, based

Bobwhite quail (above) are the "bombshells" of the uplands, requiring fast-pointing shotguns. Whichever gun or gauge is chosen, center the bird and follow through.

land targets, including ruff grouse, bobwhite quail, woodcock and doves. In any upland situation where a fast-handling, true pointing gun is needed, a straight-wrist 20 gauge with 25″ or 26″ barrels is ideal.

For students of the English system, the side-by-side is a good choice as well, simply because the method relies heavily on a fitted gun that patterns exactly where the shooter is looking. Since most quality doubles manufacturers offer custom stock dimensions (i.e., drop at comb, length of pull, pitch), the shooter is assured of centering the target each time.

To conduct your own impact test, step off 25 yards and, without giving conscious thought to aiming, fire each shot as the butt stock touches cheek and shoulder. If the pattern is consistently off the mark, some stock adjustment may be needed. Since most grouse, woodcock and quail shooting is on rising targets at modest ranges, shotgunners will benefit from a straight stocked double, which places the eye high on the comb and prints the pattern high.

Another advantage of double guns is instant choke selection. The shooter armed with a side-by-side choked IC/M, and who takes his first bird at 25 yards and his second at 35, has exactly the boring needed. A dove shooter, for example, can use his full choke barrel for pass-shooting birds to 40 yards and his modified boring for decoyed birds.

Like the classic side-by-side double, the over-

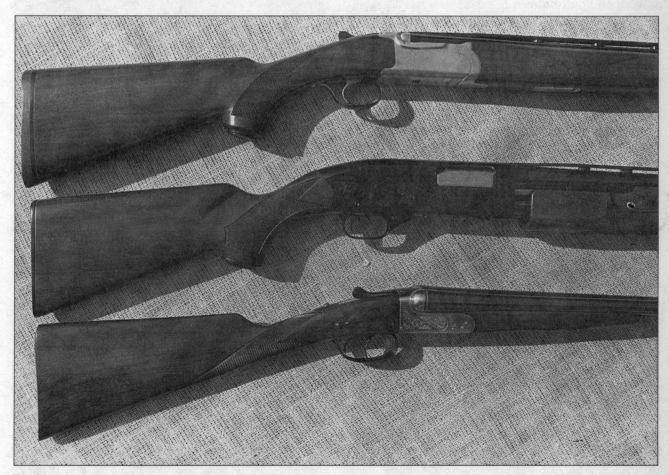

Doubles—over-under (top) and side-by-side (bottom)—are trim, lightweight, natural pointers suited to grouse, quail and woodcock. The repeater (center) is 3″ longer, heavier, and highly recommended for passing shots using the swing-through or sustained lead method.

under has many of the same handling qualities: balance, liveliness, fast pointing, tang safety, and instant choke selection. And yet, for many shooters, a single sighting plane is considered a major plus, especially with the sustained lead system. For gunners who were raised on single barrels, it's a strange sensation to throw up a side-by-side only to survey the broad plane of two barrels. Actually, there's little difference in gunning for gently rising or angling birds, such as grouse, quail or woodcock, with either double.

On passing shots, right or left, the author, based on personal experience, recommends an over-under. The single sighting plane provides the correct sight picture for sustained lead gunning, thereby increasing his confidence. Conversely, with a side-by-side it is often difficult to know how much you're ahead.

Repeater fanciers, whether pump or automatic, have the same single barrel picture, plus the added advantage (in case a bird is slow to get up) of a third shell. If the barrel is fitted with a screw-in choke system, pattern selection becomes another advantage. Even though repeaters weigh an average of one full pound more than double guns, those additional ounces can translate into a smoother swing and follow-through; also, second and third follow-up shots are steadier.

When using a repeater on wild flushing pheasants, driven grouse or passing geese, it's amazing how little lead is required to bag birds using the American swing-through method. The reason is, in part, the gun's forend design and the shooter's hand placement. Instead of extending the forward hand, as in the British system, the shooter grips the forend near the receiver, thus shortening the fulcrum and, in effect, speeding up the swing. A greater amount of energy is needed to start the barrel in motion, true, but once underway the swing is smooth and uniform.

In the past, both pumps and autos were unsightly things and slow to respond. But all that has changed. Today's generation of repeaters with their bobbed barrels, straight stocks and alloy receivers are a joy to look at, carry and shoot—especially the gas-operated automatics. Over the last decade, automatics have made steady gains vs. pump guns, and the trend is continuing into the 1990s. Some of the best and fastest quail shooting

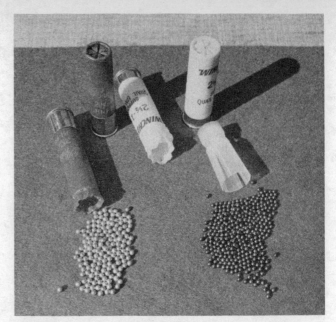

Using copper-plated shot (left) and protective shot cups (right), shotgunners can raise the choke one level without loss of performance.

has been accomplished with Winchester's Model 12 and Remington's Model 1100. In the hands of an accomplished upland shot, both guns are worth serious consideration.

Gauges and Loads

Whatever the advantages or disadvantages of a particular shotgun design, each hunter should use the gun that fits and handles best. Whether it's a side-by-side 20 or 12 gauge pump, so be it. It is *shot load*, not gauge, that produces clean kills. Properly loaded, the new 20s are equal in performance to standard 12s, especially at 25 to 35 yards. In recent years, many shooters have opted for the smaller gauge, simply because it performs well and the shells are easier to lug around. Over the course of a long day afield, the lightened load can make any gunner perform better.

If one must choose a particular shotgun for all-round use, it would probably be a 12 gauge over-under, weighing 6½ to 7 pounds, and equipped with a screw-in choke system. By manipulating shot load and boring, the 12 gauge can

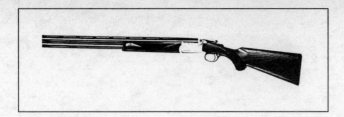

An ideal, all-round shotgun for upland use is a 12 gauge over-under equipped with screw-in chokes (below) such as this Ruger "Red Label" model (top). By manipulating shot load and boring, it becomes a versatile and pleasant gun to shoot.

be quite versatile as well as pleasant to shoot. Using reduced trap loads—Federal's Extra-Lite or Winchester's AA Super Light, for example—big shell performance with mild recoil is definitely attainable.

For gunners who seek wider than normal patterning from an IC boring, try Winchester's Special Skeet or Federal's Sporting Clays loads. For tighter loads, use trap 7½'s or 8's. Hard or copper-plated shot and cup protectors reduce patterns even further. And for really long range gunning, plastic-buffered magnums are just the ticket.

Aficianados of the 20 gauge are somewhat limited with hard shot options, but manufacturers are now increasingly attuned to load weights and shot sizes. Prime examples are Winchester's 20 gauge Xpert loads and Federal's Premium rounds (using copper-plated shot). These sweetened loads in an IC/M bored under-over and side-by-side are excellent for gunning long range doves or sharptail grouse, enabling the shooter to raise the choke one level without sacrificing performance.

Over the years, both the 28 gauge and .410 have been considered pop guns, suited more for skeet ranges than game fields. With modern loads, however, both gauges make fine choices for upland game. One must realize their limitations, though, and use more choke to gain the pattern density needed for clean kills.

Many shooters labor under the misconception that small gauges throw smaller patterns than do similarly bored 12 or 20 gauges. Not so. A modified 28 throws just as large a pattern, but it's less dense (measured at 25 yards). The same applies to the .410. By using Winchester's $^{11}/_{16}$-ounce 3″ sleeved magnum with extra hard shot, the .410 can be elevated to 28 gauge performance. And with Federal's Premium with copper-plated shot, the 28 pushes into the 20 gauge performance level.

Regardless of your gauge choice, the bottom line in all upland gunning is determined by whether or not you use a shotgun efficiently and effectively. It must be a shotgun that points naturally, fits you to a tee, and gives clean kills. Unfortunately, many shooters believe that acquiring a new, elegantly engraved shotgun will somehow make them better game shooters. The fact is, the man who shoots well afield is one who practices often throughout the year and pays particular attention to details. Remember, the skills you acquire at clay target sports are easily transferred to game shooting. From that point on, it's only a matter of trigger time—and you can count on that.

Fred Etchen: Master of the Shotgun

by Jim Casada

Perhaps no one in 20th century shotgunning is better known and yet less heralded than Fred Etchen. A competitive marksman of exceptional ability, his feats on ranges around the globe were enough to assure him a secure niche within sporting posterity. Yet there was much more to this talented, multi-faceted man than the ability to hit targets. An outdoor writer of some note, he contributed regularly to *True* and other popular magazines for men. His only book, *Commonsense*

Shotgun Shooting, has become a classic; indeed, many still consider it the finest work of its kind. Add to these accomplishments his role as founding father of the Amateur Trapshooting Association, his ability to teach and coach great trapshooting champions, his innovative development of the Etchen pistol grip, and countless other feats of note, and you begin to understand why Frederick Rudolph Etchen was a shotgunner for all seasons.

He was born in Coffeyville, Kansas, in 1884, the seventh son of John Etchen and his wife, Elizabeth. The senior Etchen was a farmer who had recently settled on remote land in Coffeyville. There he set about the formidable task of wresting a living from the untamed prairies of southeastern Kansas. From the outset, Etchen supplemented his income with extensive market hunting in the Indian territory. Because his large brood required economic support wherever it was available, Etchen's boys became intimately familiar with guns at a very tender age. Before moving to Kansas, John Etchen had competed successfully in live pigeon and glass ball matches, once reputedly holding his own against the great shooter, Captain Bogardus. So there was little doubt that paternal tutelage

Jim Casada teaches history at Winthrop College (Rock Hill, SC) and contributes to outdoor publications on a variety of subjects. He is currently Editor at Large for Sporting Classics, *Field Editor for* Sporting Clays, *and Contributing Editor for* Fly Fishing Heritage, The Flyfisher, *and* Flyfishing News & Reviews. *He also writes three weekly newspaper columns and is at work on a book about great African hunters, entitled* Africa Was Their World.

Fred Etchen was inducted posthumously into the Trapshooting Hall of Fame in 1979 and became a charter member in 1960 of the Kansas State All Sports Hall of Fame.

en's mode of market hunting required such a balance, for it enabled the brothers to fire from both sides of their father's wagon as it rolled across the prairie, affording clear shots at quail, plover, prairie chickens, and other birds.

Fred Etchen's tales of the abundance of birds carry us back to a world long since past. He tells of shooting thousands of wood ducks, and of spending half an hour or more just to pick up the ducks and geese killed in a single volley. There were no game laws then except, as Fred put it bluntly, "To kill all we could and get the money for our take." The only rule John Etchen enforced was, "Not to shoot unless we could kill." After all, by the harsh standards of the Etchen household, shells were expensive at a quarter-penny per shot.

With this kind of apprenticeship, it was not surprising that Fred Etchen developed into a superior marksman long before he reached manhood. In fact, two of Fred's brothers, Charlie and Frank, participated successfully in regional and national competitions. It was young Fred, though, who made the transition from Kansas farm boy to international shooting fame. A good friend of his was the immortal Nash Buckingham, who ranks among the finest of all American writers on hunting with the shotgun. He once wrote: "Fred Etchen came up from market hunting days on midwestern prairies and sloughs to achieve trapshooting immortality in every part of North America and in the live bird and inanimate target money matches of Europe. He was a skilled wing shot before he knew trapshooting existed."

Buckingham goes to the heart of Etchen's abilities. As a superb marksman himself, "Mr. Buck" knew that a man who honed his skills afield normally made the transition to the skeet or trap range with comparative ease (whereas movement in the opposite direction was not always so simple). After endless days of hunting nature's bounty in the sea of grass and extensive wetlands near his home, the predictability of trapshooting came almost naturally to Etchen. By his own account, "What really made me the shot I later became was continued wing shooting under varying conditions and at many types of game birds and wildfowl."

After watching his father compete in some local competitions, Fred convinced his father one day that he could outdo the adults in a trapshooting match. Armed with his trusty Model 1897 Win-

played an important role in his children's prowess with the shotgun.

Almost from the cradle, young Fred enjoyed the support and guidance he needed, not only from his father, but from his older brothers as well. By the age of six, he was handling guns on a daily basis, and by the time he reached 12—an age when most boys of his day received their first gun—he was already accompanying his father on market hunting expeditions. All seven boys joined their father on these forays, and a standard family joke focused on the fact that half of them shot left-handed while the other half fired from the right side (the seventh boy died in infancy). John Etch-

The annual Spring Shoot in 1921 at Coffeyville (Kansas), where Etchen got his competitive start.

chester pump, the teenager proceeded to break eight out of 25 clay pigeons. As he laughingly recalled, the young man went home a "chastened spirit."

That dismal performance, far from dulling his appetite for competitive shooting, only increased Fred's determination to excel. His training, his dogged desire to succeed, plus helpful hints from several experts, all combined to turn Etchen into an accomplished clay target shooter by the time he was 21. Soon he was shooting with the likes of Frank Butler and his famous sharpshooter wife, Annie Oakley, whom Etchen fondly remembered as a "grand person [who was] unselfishly helpful to a youngster."

Young Fred made his first real breakthrough in 1905, beating the great O. N. Ford to win the

Fred and Ethyl Etchen at Studebaker's corporate offices in South Bend, Indiana, where they picked up a new 1941 Studebaker President and showed off a few of their favorite shotguns.

Oklahoma State Shoot. That same year, he placed second in the 1905 Kansas State Shoot, all of which encouraged him to take up trapshooting for keeps. It was not until the early 1920s, however, that Etchen reached the pinnacle of his trapshooting career. That year, he won the first of a whopping eight Kansas State Singles championships, plus 11 Kansas State Doubles victories. Over the next two decades, countless regional, national and international laurels came Etchen's way.

A Son is Born

Meanwhile, the young man faced the essential task of earning a livelihood. With the energy and determination that marked his path throughout

Rudy Etchen, photographed in 1982 at the Shreveport Gun Club, where he took the Grand American championship with the same Remington 870 he won with 32 years earlier.

Etchen displays the ''Etchen pistol grip,'' which became virtually synonymous with his name.

life, Etchen set about establishing the first Studebaker automobile dealership in Coffeyville. His timing was as perfect as the smooth swing he displayed on a fleeting clay pigeon. The opening of the business coincided with a big boom in oil production at the nearby Indian Territory, and the resultant upsurge in the local economy caused Etchen's automobile business to prosper. He soon became the biggest Studebaker dealer in the entire country. Cars rolled in—80 to 120 at a time—by rail, and they were sold almost as soon as they could be unloaded and prepped. Indians, flush with oil money, were his primary customers, and they demanded nothing but the finest.

Eventually, Etchen reached a point where he could afford to be a serious competitor on the national trapshooting scene. The results were little short of spectacular. During the decade of the 1920s, he participated in meets almost constantly. In 1920, he was captain of the U.S. Olympic trap-shooting team, and both before and after the Olympics he shot in matches all over western Europe, winning the British Open championship with what was then an almost unheard of 200 consecutive hits. From then on, his exclusive "Etchen pistol grip," which he had designed especially for the Olympics, gained widespread popularity. Two years later, he won the International Live Bird championship outright (live birds were then commonly used in Great Britain and on the continent); and the following year, in 1927, he tied for first in the same event.

Even as he began to fill the shelves and walls of his den with trophies, Etchen demonstrated what became the hallmark of his shooting career: he consistently gave far more to the sport than he took from it. In 1923, he became one of the first life members of the Amateur Trapshooting Association (ATA). That same year, Etchen, who was now 40, became the father of his only child, Frederick Rudolph ("Rudy") Etchen, Jr., who was to become an outstanding marksman in his own right. In later years, Fred liked to tell friends about how his wife, Ethyl, and their good friend, Jimmy Robinson, wheeled the two-week-old baby out to watch his father compete against the country's best at the 1923 Grand American Shoot. As Fred had learned market hunting almost from the cradle, so did the incomparable tang of gunpowder become familiar to Rudy from his birth on.

In truth, shooting was and continued to be the focal point of activity for all the Etchens. As Fred later reminisced, his 1920 victory in the Kansas State Shoot led him to a momentous decision: "Flushed with victory," he recounted, "I decided to teach my wife to shoot. I had seen enough to believe she could become a first-rate shot and, besides, I didn't want to go to [all those] tournaments alone. . . . What a shot she turned out to be!"

Ethyl Etchen went on to win a British Open championship, eight state championships, the women's Western Amateur championship, and a host of other competitions. Her success, along with young Rudy's, confirmed Fred Etchen's rare natural talent as a teacher. Rudy's apprenticeship, in fact, represented another successful try at "practice teaching" by his father. Fred later acknowl-

Ethyl Etchen, who was not only a devoted partner to her husband but an outstanding shooter in her own right.

edged that he "set a lot of store [in] remembering how, step by step, I trained our lad to shoot. . . . Beginning with a diminutive twenty-two and a tiny shotgun I cut down to eight inches in length, I got him off on the right shoulder."

Those words, reprinted in Etchen's book, *Commonsense Shotgun Shooting*, which he wrote in 1946, were a real exercise in understatement. By that time, Rudy, now in his early 20's, had al-

This wild antelope often came down from the hills overlooking the Sun Valley (Idaho) Gun Club to visit Etchen. No one else could even come close to the animal.

ready compiled a record requiring a full page in the back of his father's book. Yet there was far more to this father-son camaraderie than a shared interest in competitive shooting. As much as Fred Etchen loved the trials and occasional tribulations of trapshooting, he never forgot the prairie roots that underlay his career, and throughout his life he hunted whenever possible. His son fondly recalls countless days spent afield in pursuit of ducks, quail and other upland birds. Together with their hardworking Pointers and Labradors, father and son hunted extensively throughout the South, the Midwest, and West, along with regular forays into Manitoba, Canada.

The two men also shot together in many competitive meets during the 1930s, a period that found Fred at the top of his form. Among his many championships were the 1932 International All-Around championship, the 1938 National Doubles championship, and 11 World Doubles championships, not to mention an unprecedented run of 472 consecutive hits.

The Teacher Emerges

The ominous clouds of World War II brought dramatic changes for the Etchens, as they did for all Americans. Recognizing full well what war, with its shortages of gas and oil, would mean to an auto dealer, Etchen sold his highly successful Studebaker business in 1939 and decided to turn his favorite hobby into a profit center by starting up a chain of shooting schools. But first, even

a standard part of the curriculum at Army Air Corps gunnery schools all over the country.

Once the war was over, Etchen was able to turn his full attention to developing the shooting schools. Thus did teaching become the focal point of the last 15 years of his life, during which he trained literally thousands of shooters in shotgun basics. "The most wonderful thing in the world to me," he once remarked, "is to take young women or middle-aged men who never fired a shotgun before in their lives and be around when they broke their first twenty-five at skeet."

In his book, *Commonsense Shotgun Shooting*, Etchen's endearing personality and abundant common sense shine through. He begins this work appropriately enough with a 35-page chapter called "Handle This Shotgun Safely!," an approach he took as well with his school pupils, many of whom were women and children. As a "gun professor," he was—and remains—without peer. Dozens of his students went on to become state,

Fred Etchen poses at the Grand American following the 1938 North American doubles championship with his M31 Remington pump.

though he was too old to see active service, Etchen served his country during the war years as a gunnery instructor. He taught in aerial gunnery schools and also trained military personnel who went on to teach the basics of shooting to others. Ever the innovator, Etchen developed an unusually effective technique for giving gunners a feel for movement. Realizing that all the lectures in the world could not instill a real understanding of range and lead, he taught his students how to shoot from fast moving flatbed trucks on special ranges equipped with traps. This novel approach proved remarkably successful—so much so that it became

A smiling, youthful Rudy Etchen, who followed in his father's footsteps from an early age.

regional or national champions. As patient as he was practical, Etchen looked at each student as an individual, eschewing the tiresome and often ineffective concept of "Do as I do." Many of his pupils, in fact, ended up in the Trapshooting Hall of Fame. Foremost among them, of course, were Fred himself and his son, Rudy. The two were elected to the Hall of Fame in 1979 and 1980, respectively; and in a touching deviation from the rules, the Hall placed the framed portraits of father and son side-by-side.

Unfortunately, Fred Etchen did not live to attend his induction into the Hall, nor did he witness Rudy's rise to the pinnacle of shooting fame. He died in 1961, leaving behind a rich legacy as a teacher, master shooter, and writer. Even today, more than a quarter of a century later, his family and the wider world of trapshooting and shotgunning still miss his presence. Without doubt, Fred Etchen left this world richer for his being here; indeed, his endeavors became a key part of the foundation on which today's shotgunning is built.

The Art of Buying a Used Gun

by Norman E. Johnson

Buying a used gun can be a waste of time and money, or it can be just the opposite. It depends largely on how you go about it. Learning the art of buying a previously owned gun need not be complicated, either, so long as you do your homework and know how to evaluate a gun's worth with care and confidence.

Learning how to evaluate a used gun before making a commitment to buy will obviously give you a decided advantage; but first, you need to consider some reasons why you've decided to buy a previously owned gun in the first place. You should then be ready to go through the step-by-step process of deciding where and when to buy it, how to evaluate it, how to estimate its worth, and finally, how to conclude the transaction. If you play your cards right, here's what you can expect.

Why Buy a Used Gun?

You probably have your own good reasons for buying a used gun, but there are several others that you probably share with everyone else in this field. Substantial savings in cost rank high among these. Some discontinued models are sought after for obvious reasons, including superior workmanship. Few things bother a gun owner more than to see his favorite gun join the ranks of the discontinued. Then too, cartridge chamberings can seemingly vanish overnight, or gun styles can change, leaving you with unsatisfied needs. Tradition also motivates many of us to search for fine older guns.

Some shooters find it desirable to buy a much used gun with the idea of restoring it. Such guns can often be found, purchased and restored at modest cost. This can become an enjoyable hobby in its own right, involving considerable pride and personal satisfaction. Even a relatively cheap used

Norman Johnson has been writing for most of the major shooting and hunting publications for more than 20 years and currently serves as Shooting Editor for Outdoor Sports & Recreation. *He also owns and operates the Plum City Ballistics Range (Plum City, Wisconsin), where he tests and researches firearms, ammunition and related subjects.*

This Browning Model 78 Single Shot (top) and Savage Model 219 in caliber .22 Hornet (bottom) were found by a lucky buyer at an estate sale.

gun can be satisfactory for occasional hunters who require only infrequent use of their firearms. The key question here is: does the gun have enough life left in it to take care of your limited needs?

When and Where to Buy a Used Gun

Buying a quality used gun is something like horse trading. The buyer may know exactly which gun he wants, or he may not. Likewise, the seller may know exactly how much money he wants for the same gun, or he may not. So where and when you look for a gun is important. A really fine gun is always in demand, but there is definitely an off-season for buying current models or those that are not so much in demand. Spring and summer, or a month or so following the peak hunting season, are usually good times to buy a used gun. A quick tour through your local gun shops or a glance at the local want ads will bear this out. Most gun shops will mark down their used gun prices at these times, so get out there and deal while the time is right.

Where to find that special gun you're looking for presents no real problem if you can keep an open mind. For starters, watch the local newspaper ads. Check the gun magazines, or subscribe to such publications as "Gun List" or "Shotgun News,"

where literally thousands of guns are routinely listed for sale. Don't overlook the possibility of listing your own "Gun Wanted" ad in newspapers or other outlets for such ads. It's not uncommon to find a seller who didn't realize he wanted to sell a gun until he saw your ad. Estate sales or even garage sales can also uncover good used guns at reasonable prices. Gun auctions and gun shows offer possibilities as well, but the prices will be higher. Be careful in any case not to let your desire for a particular used gun run too strong. Act in haste and you could pay dearly for it.

Inspection and Evaluation of Used Guns

It's likely that only a small percentage of buyers really knows how to inspect and evaluate a used gun. You'll find an equally large percentage of sellers, some dealers included, who are also in the dark about what their guns are worth. It behooves you, following your own logical evaluation process, to be the best judge of a gun's worth. To do this, you must first be aware of certain quality standards commonly used in the arms trade, all of which correctly describe the condition of a used gun. These standards, which are described in "Gun List" and similar gun sales publications, include the following:

PERFECT:	The gun is in like-new condition in all respects.	FAIR:	In safe working condition but well worn, perhaps requiring replacement of minor parts or adjustments (which should be indicated in the ad); no rust (there may be corrosion pits that do not, however, render the gun unsafe or inoperable).
EXCELLENT:	In like-new condition with no noticeable marring of metal or wood; bluing is perfect except perhaps at the muzzle.		
VERY GOOD:	In perfect working condition; no appreciable wear on working surfaces; no corrosion or pitting; only minor surface dents or scratches.	POOR:	Major and minor parts need replacement and/or extensive restoration is required; metal is deeply pitted; letters, numbers and designs are obliterated; wood is badly scratched, bruised, cracked or broken; the gun is mechanically inoperative and generally undesirable as a collector's firearm.
GOOD:	In safe working condition with minor wear on working surfaces; no broken parts; no corrosion or pitting that can interfere with proper function.		

To locate and learn the value of a used gun, buyers and sellers alike can turn to a number of good reference books, including "Antique Guns" and "Gun Traders Guide" (above).

Tenth Anniversary Edition

Blue Book of Gun Values

By S. P. Fjestad

The "Blue Book of Gun Values" (above) provides gun buyers with a wealth of valuable information about buying used guns. The prices listed are all based on percentage ratings of each gun's condition.

These guidelines, when properly used, can greatly assist the buyer in the evaluation process, which demands a good, sharp eye and a minimum of cleaning and inspection. For the latter, you'll need a cleaning rod, bore solvent, cleaning brush and patches, bore scope, and wiping cloth. Unless a bore is clean and dry, proper inspection cannot be completed. Don't try to evaluate a gun under poor light conditions; many a buyer has been stung by giving a used gun a quick onceover, trusting the seller's description of the gun. Let the buyer beware!

With the presentation of any used gun, you should first give it a good visual inspection. Does it match the seller's description and claims? Does it meet your needs? Answering these questions alone may help you decide if the gun is worth the price. This is also the time to inspect the gun carefully for external blemishes or damage. If you're buying the gun as a collector's item or for possible resale at a later date, make certain everything on the gun is original or unaltered—*if that is what you are paying for.* You must learn how to recognize a refinished and reblued gun, both of which detract from its value. A dead giveaway in a gun that has been buffed and reblued is the rounding of sharp metal parts or the blurring of numbers and letters. The gun stock or wood grips must also get a close inspection. Shortened stocks or recoil pads that have been added on can ruin an otherwise fine piece. To help detect dents or buffed out defects, sight down the surface of the stock and barrel. Move your hands over the stock and barrel to discover an undetected bulge or dent—especially when you're inspecting an expensive gun.

After the gun has passed its first external inspection (and you've made sure it's unloaded), work the action a few times to check on its smoothness and general functioning. And if you are really serious about it, check the headspace (i.e., the distance from the bolt face to that part of the chamber where the forward thrust of the cartridge stops). Headspace gauges come in sets of three, including GO, NO-GO, and Field. A gun with excessive headspace could be all but worthless; and it may be dangerous to shoot as well.

While checking the outside of the gun, look for stripped or damaged threads in the receiver (assuming it has been drilled and tapped for scope mounts). These screw holes are sometimes cross-threaded or completely stripped out. Keep in mind, too, that some collectable used guns of older vintage were never drilled and tapped for scope mounts (pre-World War II Model 70 Winchesters are examples). Also, look for marred or rounded screw slots, especially the guard screws. Sloppy gun owners have been known to ruin good guns with these screws.

The heart of any gun is the *bore*. This is particularly true where fine accuracy is expected. Bore evaluation is not always easy unless you know exactly what to look for; so clean and dry the bore thoroughly before you examine it. Watch out for sharp, clean lands and grooves at the breech and muzzle. Using a bore scope, look for throat erosion; it will show up as rounded or dam-

A good, well stocked gun shop can be an excellent source for used guns. Here a prospective buyer discusses a transaction with his local gun dealer.

aged lands with sandpaper-like appearance. Some high-power rifle barrels can be badly eroded even though the rest of the rifle appears to be in perfect condition. Poor cleaning techniques can also damage the bore at either end.

Bore rust, pits and other visible scratches and damage are often found in used gun bores. Shotgun barrels can develop bulges from repeated use of incorrect loads. Removing a gun from its stock can reveal most of these nasty defects. A sloppy barrel channel that's free-floating can sometimes look like it was attacked with a chisel. You may also find that a former owner has glass-bedded the gun or tried to improve the inletting and botched it. Be-

fore attempting to remove a barreled action from its stock, however, be sure you have the owner's permission—particularly if it's a rifle, where screws are involved. The same applies to test firing a gun. To evaluate a target rifle thoroughly, a few test groups and additional bore study may be in order. Special tools are available to gauge a bench-rest-quality bore; pushing a soft, closely fitting lead slug through the bore from chamber to muzzle should reveal any variations in bore diameter.

Obtaining some history about a used gun can also be to your advantage. How has the gun been used in the past? How many times has it been fired? You may not always get an accurate history

Because it was in production for only a short time, Smith & Wesson's Model 651 Stainless Kit gun in caliber .22 MRF (above) now sells for more than it did when new.

from the owner, and your interpretation of a gun's condition may vary widely from that of the seller, but it's worth asking the questions. Sometimes

when a meeting of the minds proves impossible, a gun may have to be appraised by a professional, but take that step only as a last resort.

How Much Should You Pay?

Several factors are involved in establishing the selling price of a used gun. These include demand, availability, collector's value, overall physical condition and, of course, the amount which the seller feels the gun is worth. Sometimes, despite a gun's real or apparent value, a seller will hold the price too high, and this can unfortunately ruin a sale. As a buyer, you have some control, of course, but only if you can evaluate the gun intelligently and can convince the seller precisely where the gun ranks pricewise. No hard feelings should be involved in this process, particularly if the gun is listed currently in sellers' guides together with its overall condition and price. In any event, don't even consider making an offer before you've arrived at the gun's fair value. And don't come armed with stacks of publications showing the price you

These three guns were all bought used at modest prices. From top: Savage Model 112V in caliber .220 Swift; Remington Model 700 Varmint Special; and Winchester Model 70 (pre-1964) in caliber .220 Swift.

When the action was removed from the stock of this Winchester Model 70, it revealed an extremely poor forend free-floating job that greatly detracted from the gun's true value.

Pushing a .22 bullet into the muzzle of a .22 rifle, as shown here, will often reveal serious muzzle damage. When such a test fails to show engraved markings on the bullet, the bore is defective and the gun devalued as a result.

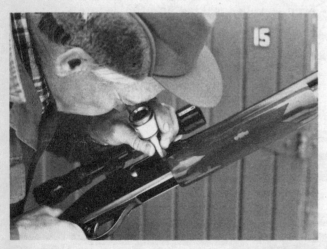

This careful buyer is shown inspecting a bore for rust and other damage using a bore scope.

expect to pay (who knows, the seller may be willing to settle for less!). Chances are, should you spot a gun similar to the one you've been considering listed in "Gun List" or "Shotgun News," you'll have a pretty good indication of its real worth.

Often a used gun is sold together with various accessories that may be of value to you; i.e., scopes, mounts, gun cases, reloading equipment, ammunition, and the like. Scoped guns are usually sold as a package deal. If you know the value and condition of such equipment, but aren't convinced you need it, you might consider selling it at a later date. The price you receive could reduce the total purchase price significantly. In some cases, a good rifle scope can be worth as much as the gun; in fact, a top name-brand scope is usually worth three or four times that of a cheaper grade, even though they may look the same.

If you like the gun in question and have decided in your mind what you can pay for it, don't hesitate to make an offer. But do so only after you've evaluated the gun in accordance with the advice provided in this article. Whatever happens, don't let your enthusiasm force you into paying more than the gun is worth. It's like buying a used car or anything else—once the buyer knows you must have what he's selling at all costs, you're in deep trouble.

A Word of Warning

As a used gun buyer, you must be aware of certain caveats. For example, be wary of the cheap, quick sale. The gun in question could be "hot," and you certainly don't want to be stuck with a stolen gun. If in doubt, ask a few questions. Where did the seller get the gun? How long has he owned it? Why is he selling it now? Questionable sales like these are almost always made by single, often younger individuals, so beware.

Also be sure to get a bill of sale for any gun you buy, even when it's bought by direct mail. It's

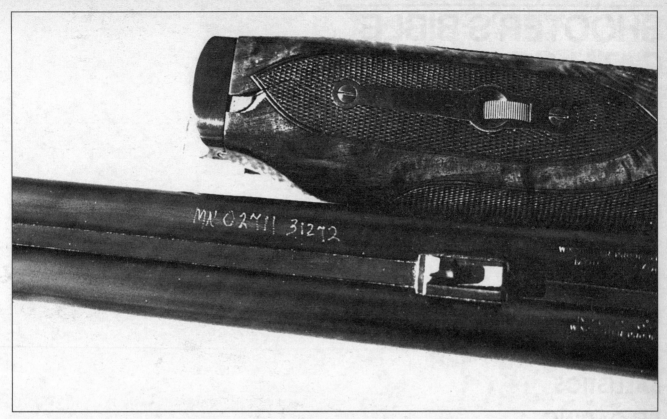

This very expensive Winchester Model 21 has a crack in the forend wood and the owner's I.D. number scratched on the barrel. Such defects reduced the value of this fine used gun by several hundred dollars.

customary as well for the buyer to have a three-day inspection period for guns received by mail or other shipping methods. Your evaluation of a particular gun may differ entirely from that of the seller, so before the gun is shipped always arrange for a reasonable inspection clause, finalize shipping and insurance charges, and know precisely who will be paying these costs—you or the seller.

Under the Federal Gun Control Act of 1968, a non-licensed person cannot ship a gun across state lines to a private party or a dealer. If you're thinking of buying a gun through an ad from a seller in another state, you'll have no problem doing so *if* proper arrangements are made between the out-of-state seller and a licensed dealer in the buyer's own state, delivery to be made by the dealer direct to you, the buyer.

Nothing in the gun control act prohibits sales between residents of the same state provided such sales are not in violation of any state laws or local ordinances. In general, a single sale, unattended by other circumstances, does not require that a buyer or seller be licensed as a gun dealer. Thus, a non-licensee can ship a rifle or shotgun—*but not a handgun*—to another non-licensee in the same state. Multiple sales and trading of firearms by a non-licensed person may, however, constitute unlawful dealing in firearms as viewed by the Bureau of Alcohol, Tobacco and Firearms. This is particularly true where such sales and transactions are profit-oriented; i.e., purchased for resale.

Don't let all of these warnings and precautions discourage you from seeking that special gun you've been searching for. This whole process of search-and-find can add a whole new dimension to your shooting and hunting pleasure. Any other rewards are strictly frosting on the cake.

SHOOTER'S BIBLE
CATALOG SECTION

Complete Illustrated Listing of Guns, Specifications & Accessories

HANDGUNS

RIFLES

SHOTGUNS

BLACK POWDER

SIGHTS & SCOPES

AMMUNITION

BALLISTICS

RELOADING

Handguns

FOR ADDRESSES AND PHONE NUMBERS OF MANUFACTURERS AND DISTRIBUTORS INCLUDED IN THIS SECTION, SEE *DIRECTORY OF MANUFACTURERS AND SUPPLIERS*

ACTION ARMS PISTOLS

Crafted by the British, this new double-action handgun is available in two sizes and calibers: 9mm and the new .41 Action Express. It can also be used cocked and locked.

AT-88S

AT-88S

SPECIFICATIONS
Operation: Locked breech, inertial firing pin
Ammunition: 9mm or .41 Action Express
Barrel length: 4.6″
Overall length: 8.1″
Weight: 35.3 oz. (empty)
Magazines: 9mm—15 rds.; 41 A.E.—10 rds.
Safety system: Thumb safety; cocked and locked or double action
Sights: Fixed blade front; drift adjustable rear
Stock: Checkered walnut
Finish: Blue or chrome
Price: $595.00

AT-88P

AT-88P

SPECIFICATIONS
Operation: Locked breech; inertial firing pin
Ammunition: 9mm or .41 Action Express
Barrel length: 3.7″
Overall length: 7.3″
Weight: 32.1 oz. (empty)
Magazines: 9mm—13 rds.; 41 A.E.—8 rds.
Safety system : Thumb safety; cocked & locked or double action
Sights: Fixed blade front; drift adjustable rear
Stock: Checkered walnut
Finish: Blue or chrome
Price: $595.00

Also available: **AT-88H**
Same specifications except:
Barrel length: 3.4″
Overall length: 6.9″
Weight: 30.5 oz. (empty)
Price: $595.00

AMERICAN ARMS PISTOLS

MODEL PK-22 DA SEMIAUTO
$199.00

MODEL P-98 SEMIAUTO
$225.00

MODEL PX-22 DA SEMIAUTO
$189.00

Also available:
MODEL CX-22—$179.00
MODEL EP-380—$449.00

MODEL WOODMASTER
$159.00

SPECIFICATIONS

MODEL	PK-22	PX-22	EP-380	P-98	Woodmaster
Caliber	22LR	22LR	380	22 LR	22 LR
Barrel Length	3⅓″	2¾″	3½″	5″	5⅞″
Overall Length	6⅓″	5⅓″	6½″	8⅛″	10½″
Weight (empty)	22 oz.	15 oz.	25 oz.	25 oz.	31 oz.
Magazine	8 clip	7 clip	7 clip	8 clip	10 clip
Grip	Black Polymer	Black Polymer	Wood Checkered	Black Polymer	Wood Checkered
Action	Straight Blowback Double Action	Straight Blowback Double Action	Delayed Blowback Locking Breech Double Action	Straight Blowback Locking Breech Double Action	Straight Blowback Locking Breech Single Action
Finish	Blued	Blued	Stainless	Blue/Black	Blue/Black
Safeties	Hammer & Firing Pin Block	Hammer & Firing Pin Block	Hammer & Firing Pin Block	Hammer Block	Magazine Disconnect
Front Sights	Blade Fixed	Blade Fixed	Blade Fixed	Blade Fixed	Blade Fixed
Rear Sights	"V" Notch Fixed	"V" Notch Fixed	Square Notch Adjustable	Square Notch Adjustable	Square Notch Adjustable

AMERICAN DERRINGER PISTOLS

Also available:
Ultra Lightweight (7½ oz.) Model 7

22 LR	$195.00
32 Magnum, 32 S&W Long	169.95
38 Special	195.00
380 Auto	169.95
44 Special	500.00

Model 10 (10 oz.)

45 Colt	$295.00
45 Auto	225.00

Light Weight (11 oz.) Double Derringer Model 11

38 Special	$169.95

Lady Derringer (Stainless Steel Double)

38 Special, 32 Magnum, 32 S&W	$225.00

MODEL 1

SPECIFICATIONS
Overall length: 4.82″
Barrel length: 3″
Weight: 15 oz. (in 45 Auto cal.)
Action: Single action w/automatic barrel selection
Number of shots: 2

Calibers	Prices
9mm Federal, 32 Magnum, 32 S&W Long, 32-20	$200.00
22 LR, 22 Rimfire Magnum	250.00
30 M-1 Carbine, 10mm Auto, 357 Mag.	235.00
38 Special Shot Shell	212.00
357 Maximum	250.00
380 Auto, 9mm Luger	187.50
45 Colt, 44-40, 44 Special	307.00
45 Colt (2½″ .410), .410 x 2½″ (45 Colt)	310.00
45 Win. Mag., 44 Magnum, 41 Magnum, 30-30 Win., 223 Rem. Comm. Ammo only	375.00

DOUBLE ACTION 38 DOUBLE DERRINGER
(38 Special & 9mm Luger; 3″ Barrel)
$235.00

MODEL 3 (Stainless Steel Single Shot Derringer)
(not shown)

SPECIFICATIONS
Calibers: 32 Magnum, 38 Special
Barrel length: 2.5″
Overall length: 4.9″
Weight: 8.5 oz.
Safety: Manual "Hammer-Block"
Grips: Rosewood
Price: $100.00

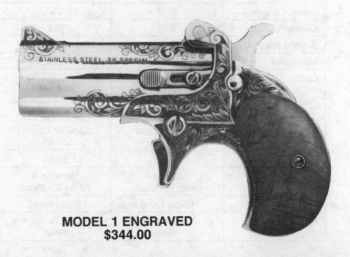

MODEL 1 ENGRAVED
$344.00

AMERICAN DERRINGER PISTOLS

MODEL 4 (Stainless Steel Double Derringer)

SPECIFICATIONS
Calibers: 45-70 upper barrel, 45 Colt or 3″ .410 lower barrel
Barrel length: 4.1″
Overall length: 6″
Weight: 16.5 oz.
Number of shots: 2
Finish: Satin or high polish stainless steel
Price:. **$375.00**

Also available in 45 Auto, 45 Colt, 44 Special, 357 Magnum, 357 Maximum, 50-70 (single shot only) **$345.00**

MODEL 6 (Stainless Steel Double Derringer)

SPECIFICATIONS
Calibers: 357 Magnum, 3″ .410, 45 Auto, 45 Colt
Barrel length: 6″
Overall length: 8.2″
Weight: 21 oz.
Number of shots: 2
Price: Grey matte finish **$337.50**
Satin finish **357.00**
High polish finish **375.00**

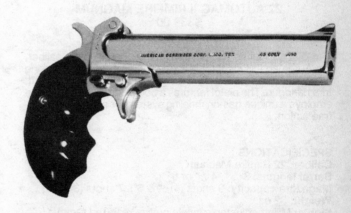

SEMMERLING LM-4
VEST-POCKET

SPECIFICATIONS
Caliber: 45 ACP or 9mm
Action: Double action
Capacity: 5 rounds
Overall length: 5″
Price: Blued finish (manual repeating) **$1250.00**
Stainless steel **1500.00**

AMT PISTOLS

22 AUTOMAG II

AMT 380 BACKUP

22 AUTOMAG II RIMFIRE MAGNUM
$339.00

The only production semiautomatic handgun in this caliber, the Automag II is ideal for the small-game hunter or shooting enthusiast who wants more power and accuracy in a light, trim handgun. The pistol features a bold open-slide design and employs a unique gas-channeling system for smooth, trouble-free action.

SPECIFICATIONS
Caliber: 22 Rimfire Magnum
Barrel lengths: 3³/₈;″, 4¹/₂″ or 6″
Magazine capacity: 9 shots (4¹/₂″ & 6″), 7 shots (3³/₈″)
Weight: 32 oz.
Sights: Millett adjustable (white outline rear; red ramp)
Features: Squared trigger guard; grooved carbon fiber grips

AMT 380 BACKUP
$250.00

SPECIFICATIONS
Caliber: 380
Capacity: 5 shots
Barrel length: 2¹/₂″
Overall length: 5″
Weight: 18 oz.
Width: ¹¹/₁₆″
Sights: Open
Grips: Carbon fiber

1911 GOVERNMENT MODEL and
HARDBALL VARIATION
(not shown)
$504.00

SPECIFICATIONS
Caliber: 45 ACP Gov't
Capacity: 7 shots
Barrel length: 5″
Overall length: 8¹/₂″
Weight: 38 oz.
Sights: Fixed (1911 Gov't); Millett adjustable (Hardballer)
Features: Matte rib (Hardballer); long grip safety; rubber wraparound Neoprene grips; beveled magazine well; wide adjustable trigger; rounded slide top (1911 Gov't)

45 ACP LONGSLIDE (not shown)
$539.00

SPECIFICATIONS
Caliber: 45 ACP
Capacity: 7 shots
Barrel length: 7″
Overall length: 10¹/₂″
Weight: 46 oz.
Sights: Millett adjustable
Features: Wide adjustable trigger; Neoprene wraparound grips

ANSCHUTZ PISTOLS

EXEMPLAR

EXEMPLAR
$395.00

SPECIFICATIONS
Calibers: 22 LR and 22 Magnum
Capacity: 5-shot clip
Barrel length: 10″
Overall length: 19″
Weight: 3$\frac{1}{3}$ lbs.
Action: Match 64
Trigger pull: 9.85 oz., two-stage adjustable
Safety: Slide
Sights: Hooded ramp post front; open notched rear; adjustable for windage and elevation
Stock: European walnut

Also available:
EXEMPLAR LEFT featuring right-hand operating bolt.
Price: $405.00.

EXEMPLAR XIV
$419.50

SPECIFICATIONS
Calibers: 22 LR and 22 Magnum
Barrel length: 14″
Overall length: 23″
Weight: 4.15 lbs.
Action: Match 64
Trigger pull: 9.85 oz., two-stage
Safety: Slide

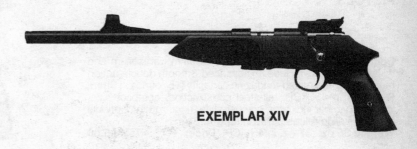

EXEMPLAR XIV

EXEMPLAR HORNET

EXEMPLAR HORNET
$744.50

A centerfire version with Match 54 action.

SPECIFICATIONS
Trigger pull: 19.6 oz.
Barrel: 10″
Overall length: 20″
Weight: 4.35 lbs.
Features: Tapped and grooved for scope mounting; wing safety

ASTRA PISTOLS & REVOLVERS

ASTRA BIG-BORE REVOLVERS

These large-frame, big-bore revolvers feature forged steel construction, large cylinders, magnum-sized bolts and recessed chambers (full 360 case-head support). A four-position adjustment for main spring tension tailors the trigger pull to the shooter's own specifications.

Designed around the popular lines of the 357, its forerunner, Astra's 44 Magnum model features wide-spur target hammers and a four-position main spring adjustment device that allows for custom tuning of trigger pull. Includes oversized, beefed-up frame and target-style grips to provide balanced weight distribution and minimize recoil. The revolver, finished in stainless steel only, is available with 6-inch barrel that features integral sight ribs and shrouds for the ejector rods. Grooved trigger, ramp front sight and fully adjustable rear sight are standard.

Calibers: 357 Magnum, 44 Magnum. **Capacity:** 6 rounds. **Barrel lengths:** 3″ in 357 Mag.; 6″ in 44 Mag. **Overall length:** 8½″ in 357 Mag.; 11½″ in 44 Mag. **Weight:** about 2½ lbs. The 9mm/357 Magnum model is fitted w/two interchangeable cylinders to handle either 9 mm Parabellum or 357 Magnum.

Prices:
9mm/357 Magnum Convertible (Blue) $395.00
44 Magnum (Stainless Steel) 450.00

9mm/357 MAGNUM CONVERTIBLE

PISTOLS

ASTRA MODEL A-90

Double-action, semiautomatic pistol in 9mm Parabellum and 45 ACP. Features include an advanced, smooth double-action mechanism, increased magazine capacity (15 rounds in 9mm, 9 rounds in 45 ACP), all-steel construction, compact size, loaded chamber indicator, combat-style trigger guard, optional right-side slide release. **Barrel length:** 3¾″.
Weight: 36 oz. (37 oz. in 45 ACP). **Price:** $500.00

MODEL A-90

ASTRA CONSTABLE 22 L.R. & 380 ACP

The Astra Constable is a double-action, all-steel, small-frame auto, so you can safely carry it fully loaded with a round in the chamber and the safety off. A single pull of the trigger then cocks and fires the pistol without the necessity of cocking the hammer manually, as is necessary with most autos. The thumb safety completely blocks the hammer and actually locks the firing pin in place until released. The barrel is rigidly mounted in the frame for greater accuracy and the gun features quick, no-tool takedown, integral non-glare rib on the slide, push-button magazine release and a round, non-snagging hammer spur. **Barrel length:** 3½″. **Weight:** 37 oz. (380 ACP) and 28 oz. (22 LR). **Capacity:** 10 rds. (22 LR) and 7 rds. (380 ACP).

Prices:
22 LR Blue $365.00
22 LR Chrome 375.00
380 ACP Blue 350.00
380 ACP A-60 (13 rds.) 435.00

CONSTABLE

AUTO-ORDNANCE PISTOLS

**MODEL 1911A-1 THOMPSON
(9 mm)**

MODEL 1911A-1 THOMPSON

SPECIFICATIONS
Calibers: 45 ACP, 9mm and 38 Super
Capacity: 9 rounds (9mm & 38 Super); 7 rounds (45 ACP)
Barrel length: 5″
Overall length: 8¹/₂″
Weight: 39 oz.
Sights: Blade front; rear adjustable for windage
Stock: Checkered plastic with medallion
Prices:
MODEL 1911A-1 45 ACP **$368.95**
   Same as above in 9mm & 38 Super **404.25**
   Satin nickel finish (all models) **390.80**
PIT BULL MODEL (45 ACP w/3¹/₂″ barrel) **404.25**

**MODEL 1911A-1 THOMPSON
PIT BULL**

MODEL 1927A-5 (not shown)

SPECIFICATIONS
Caliber: 45 ACP
Capacity: 30 rounds
Barrel length: 13¹/₂″ (finned)
Overall length: 26″
Weight: 7 lbs.
Sights: Blade front; adjustable open rear
Stock: Walnut rear grip, vertical forend
Price: **$660.00**

BEEMAN PISTOLS AND REVOLVERS

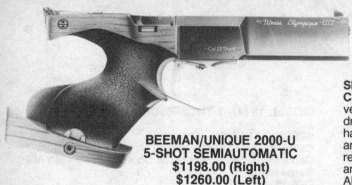

**BEEMAN/UNIQUE 2000-U
5-SHOT SEMIAUTOMATIC**
$1198.00 (Right)
$1260.00 (Left)

SPECIFICATIONS
Caliber: 22 Short. **Weight:** 2.7 lbs. **Features:** This improved version of the 823-U includes a reshaped grip, a redesigned dry-firing mechanism that is easier to use and a faster falling hammer. Trigger weight is only 3.5 oz.; special light alloy frame and solid steel slide and shock absorber; five vents reduce recoil; three removable vent screws adjust for jump control and velocity; counterweights available.
Also available: **Beeman/Unique DES/32** (32 LG) **$1235.00.**

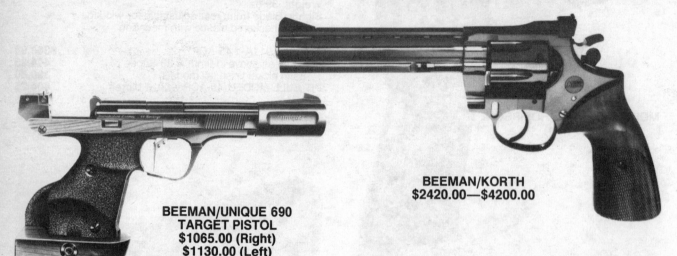

**BEEMAN/UNIQUE 690
TARGET PISTOL**
$1065.00 (Right)
$1130.00 (Left)

BEEMAN/KORTH
$2420.00—$4200.00

SPECIFICATIONS
Caliber: 22 LR. **Capacity:** 5-shot magazine. **Sight radius:** 8.7″. **Weight:** 2.2 lbs. **Grips:** Adjustable, anatomically shaped. **Features:** Trigger adjusts for position and pull weight; several barrel counterweights available; dry-firing device; meets all U.I.T. requirements.

SPECIFICATIONS
Calibers: 357 Mag. or 22 LR w/interchangeable combo cylinders of 357 Mag./9mm Para or 22 LR/22 WMR. **Barrel lengths:** 3″, 4″, 6″ (Combat or Target). **Features:** The metal parts of these revolvers are hammer-forged steel super-hardened to high tensile strength; cylinder gap of .002″ eliminates stretching of the frame while firing, reduces flash and increases velocity.

MODEL MINI-P08
$389.00

MODEL P08
$389.00

SPECIFICATIONS
Caliber: 380 ACP. **Barrel length:** 3.5″. **Overall length:** 7.4″. **Weight:** 1.4 lbs. **Grips:** Checkered hardwood.

SPECIFICATIONS
Caliber: 22 LR. **Barrel length:** 3.8″. **Overall length:** 7.8″. **Weight:** 1.9 lbs. **Grips:** Checkered hardwood. **Features:** Toggle-joint mechanism and magazine safety device.

BEEMAN/HÄMMERLI PISTOLS

MODEL 150 FREE PISTOL
$1885.00 ($1998.00 Left Hand)

SPECIFICATIONS
Caliber: 22 LR
Overall length: 17.2″
Weight: 45.6 oz.
Trigger action: Infinitely variable set trigger weight; cocking lever located on left of receiver; trigger length variable along weapon axis
Sights: Sight radius 14.8″; micrometer rear sight adj. for windage and elevation
Locking action: Martini-type locking action w/side-mounted locking lever

Barrel: Free floating, cold swaged precision barrel w/low axis relative to the hand
Ignition: Horizontal firing pin (hammerless) in line w/barrel axis; firing pin travel 0.15″
Grips: Selected walnut w/adj. hand rest for direct arm to barrel extension
MODEL 150L: Same as above but w/left-hand adjustable grips

MODEL 152 ELECTRONIC PISTOL
$1998.00 ($2055.00 Left Hand)

SPECIFICATIONS:
Same as **Model 150** except trigger action is electronic. Features short lock time (1.7 milliseconds between trigger actuation and firing pin impact), light trigger pull, and extended battery life.

MODEL 280 SPORT PISTOL
$1330.00 ($1420.00 in 32 S&W)

SPECIFICATIONS
Calibers: 22 LR and 32 S&W
Capacity: 6 rounds (22 LR); 5 rounds (32 S&W)
Barrel length: 4.58″
Weight: (excluding counterweights) 34.92 oz. (22 LR); 38.8 oz. (32 S&W)
Sight radius: 8.66″
Also available:
Conversion Kit: $720.00 ($872.00 in 32 S&W)

BEEMAN/HÄMMERLI PISTOLS

MODEL 208 TARGET PISTOL
$1615.00

SPECIFICATIONS:
Caliber: 22LR
Barrel length: 6″
Overall length: 10.2″
Weight: 37.3 oz. (w/accessories)
Capacity: 8 rounds
Sight radius: 8.3″
Sights: Micrometer rear sight w/notch width; standard front
   blade

MODEL 215 TARGET PISTOL
$1420.00

SPECIFICATIONS
Same as **Model 208** except it has fewer "luxury" features.
Also available: **MODEL 212 Hunter's Pistol** featuring safety
catch, nonslip slide and optimal balance. **Price: $1525.00.**

MODEL 232 RAPID FIRE PISTOL
$1435.00

SPECIFICATIONS:
Caliber: 22 Short
Barrel length: 5.2″
Overall length: 10.5″
Weight: 44 oz.
Sight radius: 9.6″
Capacity: 5 rounds
Grips: Adjustable (add **$40** for wraparound grips)
Wraparound grips and left-hand version also available.

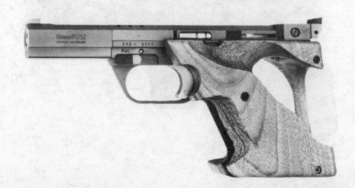

BERETTA PISTOLS

MODEL 21 DA SEMIAUTOMATIC
$215.00 ($237.00 Nickel)

A safe, dependable, accurate small-bore pistol in 22 LR or 25 Auto. Easy to load with its unique barrel tip-up system.

SPECIFICATIONS
Caliber: 22 LR or 25 Auto. **Magazine capacity:** 7 rounds (22 LR); 8 rounds (25 Auto). **Overall length:** 4.9″. **Barrel length:** 2.4″. **Weight:** 11.5 oz. (25 ACP); 11.8 oz. (22 LR) **Sights:** Blade front; V-notch rear. **Safety:** Thumb operated. **Grips:** Walnut. **Frame:** Special alloy.
Also available:
Model 21 Engraved $255.00

MODEL 21

**MODEL 950 BS
(22 Short)**

MODEL 950 BS
Single Action Semiautomatic

SPECIFICATIONS
Calibers: 25 ACP and 22 Short. **Barrel length:** 2½″. **Overall length:** 4½″. **Overall height:** 3.4″. **Safety:** External, thumb-operated. **Magazine:** 8 rounds (25 cal.); 6 rounds (22 Short). **Sights:** Blade front; V-notch rear. **Weight:** 10.2 oz. in 22 cal.; 9.9 oz. in 25 cal. **Frame:** Special alloy.

Model 950 BS	$161.00
Model 950 BS Nickel	189.00
Model 950 EL Engraved	230.00

MODEL 92F (9mm)

This 9mm Parabellum semiautomatic pistol is specifically designed for use by law enforcement agencies. It has also been adopted as the official sidearm of the U.S. Armed Forces. Its 15-round firepower combines with flawless reliability and safety to make it the ideal police and military sidearm. Its firing mechanism will handle thousands of rounds without malfunction. And the ambidextrous triple-safety mechanism features a passive firing pin catch, a slide safety that acts as a decocking lever, plus a unique firing pin to ensure that a falling hammer can never break safety and discharge accidentally.

SPECIFICATIONS
Caliber: 9mm Parabellum. **Overall length:** 8.54″. **Height:** 5.4″. **Barrel length:** 4.9″. **Weight** (empty): 34 oz. **Magazine:** 15 rounds, removable floorplate. **Sights:** Front, blade integral with slide; rear, square-notched bar, dovetailed to slide. **Slide stop:** Holds slide open after last round, manually operable.

Model 92F	$600.00

(Wood grips **$20.00** additional).
Also available:

Model 92F Compact (13 round)	620.00
Same as above with wood frame	625.00

MODEL 92F (9mm)

BERETTA PISTOLS
MEDIUM FRAME PISTOLS
Calibers 22 LR and 380

MODEL 84

MODEL 85

This double-action semiautomatic pistol features walnut grips, blued steel slide, ambidextrous safety, and anodized alloy frame with a single line 8-round magazine.

SPECIFICATIONS
Caliber: 380 Auto. **Barrel length:** 3.82″. **Weight** (empty): 21.8 oz. **Overall length:** 6.8″. **Overall height:** 4.8″. **Capacity:** 8 rounds. **Sights:** Blade integral with slide (front); square notched bar, dovetailed to slide (rear).
Also available: **MODEL 85F** w/8-round straight-line magazine.
Price: $467.00

BERETTA MEDIUM FRAME PISTOLS

MODELS	PRICES
Model 84 Plastic (13 rounds)	$479.00
Model 84 Wood	505.00
Model 84 Nickel	545.00
Model 85 Plastic (8 rounds)	440.00
Model 85 Wood	467.00
Model 85 Nickel	500.00
Model 87 Wood (22 LR)	447.00
Model 87 (Long barrel, SA)	460.00
Model 89 Target	620.00

MODEL 87

MODEL 84

This pistol is pocket size with a large magazine capacity. The lockwork is of double-action type. The first shot (with hammer down, chamber loaded) can be fired by a double-action pull on the trigger without cocking the hammer manually.

The pistol also features a favorable grip angle for natural pointing, positive thumb safety (uniquely designed for both right- and left-handed operation), quick takedown (by means of special takedown button) and a conveniently located magazine release. Black plastic grips. Wood grips available at extra cost.

SPECIFICATIONS
Caliber: 380 Auto (9mm Short). **Weight:** 1 lb. 7 oz. (approx.). **Barrel length:** $3^3/_{44}$″. (approx.) **Overall length:** $6^1/_2$″. (approx.) **Sights:** Fixed front and rear. **Magazine capacity:** 13 rounds. **Height overall:** $4^1/_4$″ (approx.).
Also available: **Model 84F** w/matte black Bruniton® finish.
Price: $505.00

MODEL 85

MODEL 89 TARGET (not shown)

This sophisticated single-action, target pistol features an 8-round magazine, adjustable target sights, and target-style contoured walnut grips with thumb rest.

SPECIFICATIONS
Caliber: 22 LR. **Barrel length:** 6″. **Overall length:** $9^1/_2$″. **Height:** 5.3″. **Weight:** 41 oz.

BERNARDELLI PISTOLS

P018 STANDARD

P018 COMPACT

MODEL P018

SPECIFICATIONS
Caliber: 9mm
Barrel length: 4.88″; 4.08″ Compact Model
Overall length: 8.52″; 7.68″ Compact Model
Weight: 35 oz. (empty); 33 oz. Compact Model
Frame: Steel
Sights: Welded blade front; notched bar rear, adjustable for
   windage
Finish: Blue
Grips: Plastic
Price: W/standard grips $499.00
       With walnut grips   539.00
       P018 COMPACT w/walnut grips 519.00

MODEL 69

MODEL 69

Also available:
MODEL 69 COMPETITION/TARGET PISTOL
   (22 Long Rifle) $459.00
MODEL AMR (22 LR and 380) 309.00
MODEL USA (22 LR and 380) 289.00

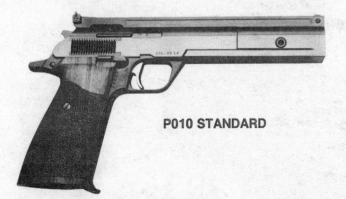

P010 STANDARD

MODEL P010 STANDARD

SPECIFICATIONS
Caliber: 22 LR
Barrel length: 5.9″.
Weight: 40.5 oz.
Magazine capacity: 5 and 10 shot
Sight radius: 7.5″.
Features: Matte black reflection-preventing finish; walnut grips
   for right- and left-hand shooters; interchangeable front and
   rear sights; external hammer with safety notch; pivoted
   trigger adjustable for pull weight and take-ups; external
   slide catch for hold-open device; manual safety; inertia safe
   firing pin.
Price: $519.00

BERSA AUTOMATIC PISTOLS

MODEL 23 DOUBLE ACTION
$263.95

SPECIFICATIONS
Caliber: 22 LR
Barrel length: 4″
Action: Blowback
Sights: Front blade on barrel; rear, square-notched adjustable for windage
Capacity: 10 + 1 in chamber
Grips: Custom wood
Finish: Blue
Also available in nickel finish: **$291.95**

MODEL 23 DOUBLE ACTION

MODEL 83 DOUBLE ACTION
$263.95 ($366.95 in 13-Shot)

SPECIFICATIONS
Caliber: 380 Auto
Barrel length: 3$\frac{1}{2}$″
Action: Blowback
Sights: Front blade sight integral on slide; rear sight square notched adjustable for windage
Capacity: 7 + 1 in chamber or 13 + 1 in chamber
Grips: Custom wood
Also available:
MODEL 85 in blue or satin nickel finish (13-shot): **$374.95**

MODEL 83 DOUBLE ACTION

MODEL 90 SINGLE ACTION (not shown)
$383.95

SPECIFICATIONS
Caliber: 9mm
Capacity: 13 rounds
Action: Single
Grips: Hand-carved checkered walnut
Frame: Precision-machined, high-strength one-piece steel
Finish: Blue

BROWNING AUTOMATIC PISTOLS

**9mm HI-POWER
SINGLE ACTION**

The Browning 9mm Parabellum, also known as the 9mm Browning Hi-Power, has a 14-cartridge capacity and weighs 2 pounds. The push-button magazine release permits swift, convenient withdrawal of the magazine.

The 9mm is available with either a fixed-blade front sight and a windage-adjustable rear sight or a non-glare rear sight, screw adjustable for both windage and elevation. The front sight is a ¹/₈-inch wide blade mounted on a ramp. The rear surface of the blade is serrated to prevent glare. All models have an ambidextrous safety.

In addition to the manual safety, the firing mechanism includes an external hammer, making it easy to ascertain whether the pistol is cocked.

Prices:
Standard with matte finish and molded grip **$436.95**
Polished blue with adjustable sights **517.95**
Polished blue with fixed sights **473.95**

9MM SEMIAUTOMATIC PISTOL (SINGLE AND DOUBLE ACTION)

	SINGLE ACTION FIXED SIGHTS	SINGLE ACTION ADJUSTABLE SIGHTS	DOUBLE ACTION FIXED SIGHTS
Finish	Polished Blue, Matte, or Nickel	Polished Blue	Matte
Capacity of Magazine	13	13	14
Overall Length	7³/₄″	7³/₄″	7³/₄″
Barrel Length	4²¹/₃₂″	4²¹/₃₂″	4²¹/₃₂″
Height	5″	5″	5″
Weight (Empty)	32 oz.	32 oz.	32 oz.
Sight Radius	6⁵/₁₆″	6³/₈″	6⁵/₁₆″
Ammunition	9mm Luger, (Parabellum)	9mm Luger, (Parabellum)	9mm Luger, (Parabellum)
Grips	Checkered Walnut	Checkered Walnut	Polyamide
Front Sights	¹/₈″	¹/₈″ wide on ramp	¹/₈″
Rear Sights	Drift adjustable for windage.	Screw adjustable for windage and elevation.	Drift adjustable for windage.

BROWNING AUTOMATIC PISTOLS

BUCK MARK PISTOLS

SPECIFICATIONS
Caliber: 22 LR. **Magazine capacity:** 10 rounds. **Action:** Semiautomatic, blowback operated. **Sights:** Ramp front; rear screw-adjustable for windage and elevation. **Sight radius:** 8". **Grips:** Standard; black molded composite with skipline checkering; contoured, laminated wood grips on Buck Mark Plus.

BUCK MARK 5.5 TARGET

BUCK MARK PISTOLS

Model	Finish	Sights	Barrel Length	Overall Length	Overall Height	Weight Unloaded	Mag. Cap.	Price
Standard	Matte Blue	Adj.	5 1/2"	9 1/2"	5 3/8"	32 oz.	10	$218.95
Plus	Matte Blue	Adj.	5 1/2"	9 1/2"	5 3/8"	32 oz.	10	265.95
Silhouette	Matte Blue	Target	9 7/8"	14"	5 5/16"	53 oz.	10	370.95
Varmint	Matte Blue	*	9 7/8"	14"	5 5/16"	48 oz.	10	334.95
Target 5.5	Matte Blue	Target	5 1/2"	9 5/8"	5 5/16"	35 1/2 oz.	10	353.95

* Full length scope base, beveled and grooved for scope rings (rings and scope not included).

MODEL BDA-380

MODEL BDA-380

A high-powered, double-action semiautomatic pistol with fixed sights in 380 caliber.
Nickel Finish $499.95
Standard Finish 474.95

CHARTER ARMS REVOLVERS

**357 MAGNUM REVOLVER
BULLDOG "TRACKER"**

**BULLDOG PUG
44 SPECIAL**

357 MAGNUM REVOLVER BULLDOG "TRACKER"

SPECIFICATIONS
Caliber: 357 Magnum. **Type of action:** 5-shot. **Barrel length:** 2½". **Overall length:** 7½" (2½ bbl.). **Height:** 5⅛". **Weight:** 21 oz. **Grips:** Hand-checkered walnut, square butt design. **Sights:** Ramp front; adjustable square-notched rear; elevation reference lines; definite click indicator. **Finish:** Service blue.

Price:
Blue finish and Neoprene or Bulldog grips $240.00

BULLDOG 44 SPECIAL

SPECIFICATIONS
Caliber: 44 Special. **Type of action:** 5-shot, single- and double-action. **Barrel length:** 3". **Overall length:** 7¾". **Height:** 5". **Weight:** 19 oz. **Grips:** Neoprene or American walnut hand-checkered bulldog grips. **Sights:** Patridge-type, 9/64" wide front; square-notched rear. **Finish:** High-luster Service Blue or stainless steel.

Also available: **44SPL Bulldog Pug Model** with 2½" barrel and ramp front sight. **Overall length:** 7¼".

Prices:
Blue finish (2½" Bull or 3")	$222.00
Blue finish (Pug)	240.00
Stainless steel (2½" Bull or 3")	275.00
Stainless steel Pug	288.00

**POLICE BULLDOG
32 MAGNUM**

POLICE BULLDOG

SPECIFICATIONS
Calibers: 32 Magnum, 38 Special, 357 Magnum. **Type of action:** 5-shot and 6-shot (38 Special only), single and double action. **Barrel lengths:** 2" and 3½" (32 Magnum only); 4" (38 Special & 357 Mag. only). **Overall length:** 6½" (32 Mag.), 8¼" (3½" 32 Mag.) and 9" (4" barrel). **Weight:** 20 oz. (2" 32 Mag.); 26 oz. (3½" 32 Mag.); 20-23½ oz. (38 Spec. & 357 Mag.).

NEW POLICE BULLDOG (not shown) 44 SPECIAL

SPECIFICATIONS
Caliber: 44 Special. **Type of action:** 5-shot single and double action. **Barrel length:** 2½" and 3½". **Overall length:** 7" (Bulldog grips); 7¼" (Neoprene grips); 8" (3½" barrel). **Height:** 5". **Weight:** 19½ oz. (2½" Bulldog); 21 oz. (2½" Neoprene); 23 oz. (2½" stainless); 23½ oz. (3½"). **Grips:** Bulldog and Neoprene. **Finish:** Stainless steel and Service Blue (2½" barrel only).

Price:
44 Special	$250.00
In Stainless steel	302.00

Prices:
32 Mag. & 38 Special (w/3½" shrouded barrel) ...	$240.00
Same as above in stainless steel	280.00
32 Mag. & 38 Special (w/4" tapered or bull barrel) .	223.00
32 Mag. & 38 Special (w/4" shrouded barrel, stainless)	274.00
Same as above w/adjustable rear sight	288.00
357 Mag. (stainless steel only w/adj. rear sight) ...	296.00

CHARTER ARMS REVOLVERS

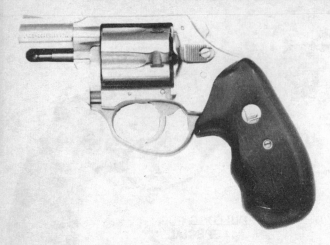

POLICE UNDERCOVER

SPECIFICATIONS
Caliber: 32 H&R Magnum and 38 Special. **Type of action:** 6-shot, single and double action. **Barrel length:** 2″. **Height:** 4¹/₂″. **Weight:** 17¹/₂ oz. (2″ barrel) and 19 oz. (4″ barrel.) **Grips:** Checkered walnut panel. **Sights:** Patridge-type ramp front; square-notch rear. **Finish:** Blue.

Price **$240.00**
Stainless steel and checkered walnut panel 270.00

UNDERCOVER 38 SPECIAL

SPECIFICATIONS
Caliber: 38 Special (Mid-Range & Standard). **Type of Action:** 5 shots, single and double action. **Barrel length** (with shroud): 2″. **Overall length:** 6¹/₄″. **Height:** 4¹/₄″. **Weight:** 16 oz. **Grips:** American walnut hand-checkered. **Sights:** Patridge-type or standard ramp front, square-notched rear. **Finish:** High-luster Service Blue or stainless steel.

Prices:
Blued finish with checkered panel grips **$206.00**
Stainless steel with checkered panel grips 261.00

PATHFINDER
22 L.R.

SPECIFICATIONS
Caliber: 22 LR. **Type of action:** 6-shot, single and double action. **Barrel length:** 3″ or 6″. **Overall length:** 7³/₄″ (3″ bbl.); 10⁵/₈″ (6″ bbl.). **Height:** 4³/₄″ (3″ bbl.); 5″ (6″ bbl.). **Weight:** 20 oz. (3″ bbl.); 22¹/₂ oz. (6″ bbl.). **Grips:** Hand-checkered square butt or checkered walnut panel. **Sights:** Patridge-type ramp front sight; fully adjustable notch rear sight. **Finish:** High-luster Service Blue.

Prices:
With 3″ barrel **$220.00**
With 6″ barrel 223.00
With 3″ barrel in stainless steel 280.00

OFF-DUTY 38 SPECIAL

SPECIFICATIONS
Calibers: 22 LR and 38 Special. **Type of action:** 5-shot, single and double action. **Barrel length:** 2″. **Overall length:** 6¹/₄″. **Height:** 4¹/₄″. **Weight:** 16 oz. (matte black); 17 oz. (stainless). **Grips:** Select-a-grip (9 colors) or Neoprene. **Sights:** Patridge-type ramp front (with new ''red dot'' feature); square-notch rear on stainless.

Prices:
Matte black finish **$176.00**
Stainless steel 230.00

CHARTER ARMS REVOLVERS

BONNIE

CLYDE

BONNIE AND CLYDE

This matching pair of handguns in 32 Magnum and 38 Special are designed for couples who like to go to the shooting range together. Both guns come with their own "gun rug" identified by name. Each model also offers a scrolled name on the barrel and features Select-A-Grip color-coordinated grips. The fully shrouded barrels are 2½" long with an attractive blue finish.

Price: (per set) . . . . **$256.00.**

PIT BULL

Actual target group at 40 feet.

PITBULL

SPECIFICATIONS
Calibers: 9mm, 357 Mag., 38 Special. **Capacity:** 5 rounds. **Barrel lengths:** 2½", 3½", and 4". **Overall length:** 7", 7¼", 8¼", 8½", and 8¾". **Height:** 5". **Weight:** 21½ oz. (357 Mag. w/2½" barrel); 24 oz. (38 Special w/4" barrel); 25 oz. (9mm

TARGET BULLDOG

TARGET BULLDOG

SPECIFICATIONS
Calibers: 357 Mag., 9mm FED, 44 Special. Barrel length: 5½". Overall length: 10". Height: 5". Weight: 28 oz.; 27 oz. in 44 Special. Grips: Target. **Finish:** Stainless steel.

Price: **$360.00**

w/2½" barrel); 26 oz. (9mm w/3½" barrel); 26½ oz. (38 Special w/4" barrel); 28 oz. (357 Mag. w/4" barrel). **Finish:** Stainless steel; 2½" 357 Mag. and 4" 38 Special in Service Blue only.

Prices:
Service Blue finish **$276.00**
Stainless finish **360.00**

CHINASPORTS

TYPE 54-1 TOKAREV
$239.00

SPECIFICATIONS
Caliber: 38 Super or 7.62×25mm
Action: Single semiauto
Capacity: 8 rounds
Barrel length: 4½″
Overall length: 7.7″
Weight: 29 oz.
Sights: Fixed

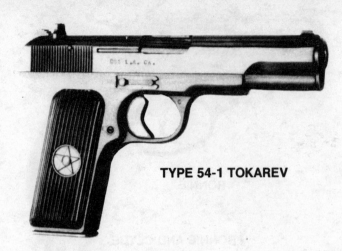

TYPE 54-1 TOKAREV

TYPE 59 MAKAROV
$329.00

SPECIFICATIONS
Caliber: 9×18mm
Action: Single and double
Capacity: 8 rounds
Barrel length: 3½″
Overall length: 6.3″
Weight: 24 oz.
Sights: Fixed and adjustable

TYPE 59 MAKAROV

NORINCO TYPE M1911 PISTOL

NORINCO TYPE M1911 PISTOL
$439.00

SPECIFICATIONS
Caliber: 45 ACP
Capacity: 8 rounds (7+1)
Barrel length: 5″
Overall length: 8½″
Weight: 39 oz.
Sights: Blade front; square-notched rear
Finish: Blued

TYPE 77B (not shown)
$399.00

SPECIFICATIONS
Caliber: 9mm×19mm
Action: Single
Barrel length: 5″
Overall length: 7½″
Weight: 34 oz.
Sights: Adjustable rear
Features: Trigger guard cocking

COLT AUTOMATIC PISTOLS

MKIV SERIES

DOUBLE EAGLE

SPECIFICATIONS
Action: Double action
Calibers: 45 ACP and 10mm
Capacity: 8 rounds
Barrel length: 5″
Overall length: 8½″
Weight: 39 oz.
Grips: Checkered Xenoy stocks
Sight radius: 6½″
Finish: Stainless steel
Price: $679.95 (45 ACP only; price not set for 10mm)

DOUBLE EAGLE

COMBAT COMMANDER

The semiautomatic Combat Commander, available in 45 ACP, 38 Super or 9mm, boasts an all-steel frame that supplies the pistol with an extra measure of heft and stability. This outstanding Colt also offers fixed square-notch rear and fixed blade front, lanyard-style hammer, thumb and grip safety and firing pin safety.

Caliber	Weight	Overall Length	Magazine Rounds	Finish	Price
45 ACP	36 oz.	7¾″	7	Blue	$624.95*
45 ACP	36 oz.	7¾″	7	Stainless	669.95
38 Super	37 oz.	7¾″	9	Blue	629.95
9mm	37 oz.	7¾″	9	Blue	629.95

*Add $45.00 for Stainless steel

COMBAT COMMANDER
4¼″ barrel only

LIGHTWEIGHT COMMANDER

This lightweight, shorter version of the Government Model offers increased ease of carrying with the firepower of the 45 ACP. The Lightweight Commander features alloy frame, fixed-style sights, grooved trigger, lanyard-style hammer and rubber stocks; also thumb and grip safety, and firing-pin safety.

SPECIFICATIONS
Weight: 27½ oz.
Barrel length: 4¼″
Overall length: 7¾″
Magazine rounds: 7
Finish: Blue
Price: $624.95

LIGHTWEIGHT COMMANDER
4¼″ barrel only

COLT AUTOMATIC PISTOLS

MKIV SERIES 80

GOLD CUP NATIONAL MATCH

SPECIFICATIONS
Caliber: 45 ACP
Capacity: 7 rounds
Barrel length: 5″
Weight: 39 oz.
Overall length: 81/2″
Sights: Colt Elliason sights; adjustable rear for windage and elevation
Hammer: Serrated target hammer
Stock: Checkered walnut
Finish: Colt blue or stainless
Price: $799.95 Blue
      859.95 Stainless steel
      924.95 Bright stainless
Also available:
COMBAT ELITE 45 ACP; features 3 dot front and rear combat sights, extended grip safety. **Price: $759.95.**

GOLD CUP NATIONAL MATCH

GOVERNMENT MODEL

GOVERNMENT MODEL

These full-size automatic pistols, available exclusively with 5-inch barrels, may be had in 45 ACP, 9mm and 38 Super. The Government Model's special features include fixed military sights, grip and thumb safeties, grooved trigger, rubber combat stocks.

SPECIFICATIONS
Overall length: 81/2″
Capacity: 9 rounds; 7 rounds (45 ACP)
Weight: 39 oz.; 38 oz. (45 ACP)
Price: $624.95 45 ACP blue
      659.95 45 ACP stainless
      729.95 45 ACP bright stainless
      629.95 9mm and 38 Super (38 Super only in stainless steel. **$669.95**)

GOVERNMENT MODEL 380 AUTOMATIC

This scaled-down version of the 1911 A1 Colt Government Model does not include a grip safety. It incorporates the use of a firing pin safety to provide for a safe method to carry a round in the chamber in a "cocked and locked" mode. This provides for a consistent trigger pull rather than the double-action style of a heavy first pull. 380 Auto caliber. Now available in matte stainless steel finish with black composition stocks.

SPECIFICATIONS
Barrel length: 3.25″
Height: 4.4″
Weight (empty): 21.8 oz.
Overall length: 6″
Magazine capacity: 7 rounds
Sights: Fixed ramp blade in front; fixed square notch in rear
Grip: Composition stocks
Price: $399.95 Blue
      449.95 Satin nickel
      429.95 Stainless steel

**GOVERNMENT MODEL
380 AUTOMATIC**

COLT PISTOLS

MKIV SERIES 80

DELTA ELITE 10mm

The proven design and reliability of Colt's Government Model has been combined with the new powerful 10mm auto cartridge to produce a highly effective shooting system for hunting, law enforcement and personal protection. The velocity and energy of the 10mm cartridge make this pistol ideal for the serious handgun hunter and the law enforcement professional who insist on down-range stopping power. Available in stainless steel and "Ultimate" bright stainless finish.

SPECIFICATIONS
Type: 0 Frame, semiautomatic pistol
Barrel length: 5″
Overall length: 8½″
Weight (empty): 38 oz.
Magazine capacity: 8 rounds
Sights: 3-dot, high-profile front and rear combat sights; new Accro rearsight adj. for windage and elevation
Sight radius: 6½″
Grip: Rubber combat stocks with Delta medallion
Safety: Trigger safety lock (thumb safety) is located on left-hand side of receiver; grip safety is located on backstrap; internal firing pin safety
Rifling: 6 groove, left-hand twist, one turn in 16″

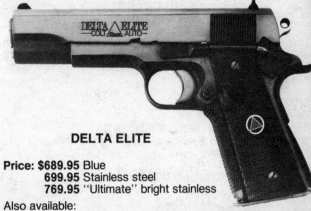

DELTA ELITE

Price: **$689.95** Blue
699.95 Stainless steel
769.95 "Ultimate" bright stainless

Also available:
DELTA GOLD CUP. Same specifications as Delta Elite, except 39 oz. weight and 6¾″ sight radius. **Price: $889.95.**
FIRST EDITION STAINLESS STEEL DELTA ELITE. Limited edition (1,000) from Colt's Custom Gun Shop. Complete with serial number and compact carrying case. **Price: $889.95.**

COLT MUSTANG .380

This new backup automatic has four times the knockdown power of most 25 ACP automatics. It is a smaller version of the 380 Government Model.

SPECIFICATIONS
Caliber: 380 Auto
Capacity: 6 rounds
Weight: 18.5 oz.
Overall length: 5.5″
Height: 3.9″
Price: **$399.95** standard blue
449.95 in nickel
429.95 stainless steel

Also available:
MUSTANG POCKETLITE 380 w/aluminum alloy receiver; ½″ shorter than standard Government 380; weighs 12.5 oz. **Price: $399.95.**
MUSTANG PLUS II combines full grip length of 380 Government Model with shorter compact barrel and slide of the Mustang. **Price: $399.95. ($429.95** in stainless steel).

MUSTANG .380

COLT OFFICER'S 45 ACP

SPECIFICATIONS
Caliber: 45 ACP
Barrel length: 3½″
Overall length: 7¼″
Weight: 34 oz.
Price: **$605.50** matte finish
659.95 stainless steel
624.95 standard blue
729.95 Ultimate stainless

Also available:
LW Officer's ACP w/aluminum alloy frame (24 oz.): **$624.95**

MUSTANG POCKET LITE

COLT REVOLVERS

KING COBRA
357 MAGNUM

This "snake" revolver features a solid barrel rib, full-length ejector rod housing, red ramp front sight, white outline adjustable rear sight, and new "gripper" rubber combat grips. All stainless steel.

SPECIFICATIONS
Caliber: 357 Magnum
Barrel lengths: 2½", 4", 6", 8" (stainless)
Weight: 36 oz. (2½"), 42 oz. (4"), 46 oz. (6"), 48 oz. (8")
Price: $395.95 (blue)
       419.95 (stainless)
       456.95 ("Ultimate" Bright Stainless)

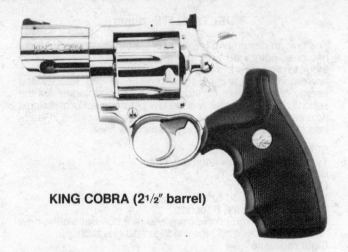

KING COBRA (2½" barrel)

ANACONDA

SPECIFICATIONS
Action: Double action
Caliber: 44 Magnum
Barrel length: 6"
Overall length: 11⅝"
Weight: 53 oz.
Sight radius: 7¾"
Capacity: 6 rounds
Grips: Black neoprene combat-style with finger grooves
Finish: Matte stainless steel
Sights: Red insert front; adjustable white outline rear
Price: not set

ANACONDA

PYTHON

PYTHON
357 MAGNUM (shown with 8" barrel)

The Colt Python revolver, suitable for hunting, target shooting and police use, is chambered for the powerful 357 Magnum cartridge. Python features include ventilated rib, fast cocking, wide-spur hammer, trigger and grips, adjustable rear and ramp-type front sights, ⅛" wide.

SPECIFICATIONS
Caliber: 357 Magnum
Barrel lengths: 2½", 4", 6", 8"
Overall length: 8" to 13½"
Weight: 33 oz. (2½"), 38 oz. (4"), 43½ oz. (6"), 48 oz. (8")
Stock: Rubber combat or rubber target

Finish: Colt royal blue, stainless steel and "Ultimate" bright stainless steel
Prices:
Royal Blue $759.95
Stainless steel 849.95
"Ultimate" bright stainless steel 879.95

DAVIS PISTOLS

MODEL D-22 DERRINGER

MODEL D-22 DERRINGER
$64.90

SPECIFICATIONS
Calibers: 25 Auto, 22 LR, 32 Auto, 22 Mag.
Capacity: 2 shots
Barrel length: 2.4″
Overall length: 4″
Height: 2.8″
Weight: 9.5 oz.
Grips: Laminated wood
Finish: Black teflon or chrome
   (32 Auto in chrome only)

MODEL P-32
$87.50

SPECIFICATIONS
Caliber: 32 Auto
Barrel length: 2.8″
Overall length: 5.4″
Height: 4″
Magazine capacity: 6 rounds
Weight (empty): 22 oz.
Grips: Laminated wood
Finish: Black teflon or chrome

MODEL P-32

MODEL P-380
$98.00

SPECIFICATIONS
Caliber: 380 Auto
Capacity: 5 rounds
Barrel length: 2.8″
Overall length: 5.4″
Weight: 22 oz.

DETONICS PISTOLS

All Detonic pistols include the following features:
- Patented, self-centering cone barrel system
- Beveled magazine well
- Hand-turned trigger pull
- Patented counter-wound dual spring system

- Built-in adjustable sights
- Blackened stainless slide
- Serrated front slide
- Extended beavertail grip safety

COMBAT MASTER™ 45 ACP (Stainless Steel)
$768.00

SPECIFICATIONS
Calibers: 45 ACP, 6-shot clip; 38S and 9mm available on special order.
Barrel length: 3¹/₂″
Weight: 29 oz. (empty)
Overall length: 6³/₄″
Stock: Checkered walnut
Sights: Combat-type, fixed; adj. sights available
Features: Self-adjusting cone barrel centering system, beveled magazine inlet, ''full clip'' indicator in base of magazine; throated barrel and polished feed ramp.

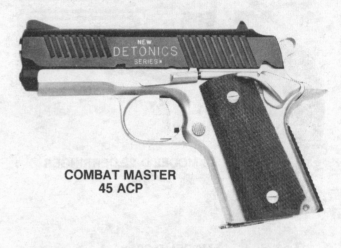

**COMBAT MASTER
45 ACP**

SERVICEMASTER
$998.00

SPECIFICATIONS
Caliber: 45 ACP
Capacity: 7 shots
Barrel length: 4¹/₂″
Overall length: 7⁷/₈″
Weight: 32 oz.
Height: 5¹/₄″
Sights: Adjustable combat sights

SERVICEMASTER

SCOREMASTER
$1178.00

SPECIFICATIONS
Caliber: 45 ACP
Capacity: 7 shots
Barrel length: 6″
Overall length: 9³/₈″
Weight: 43 oz.
Height: 5¹/₄″

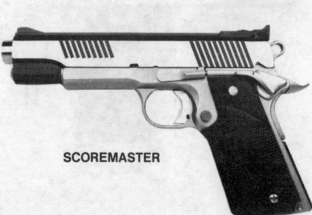

SCOREMASTER

DETONICS PISTOLS

COMPMASTER
$1650.00

SPECIFICATIONS
Caliber: 45 ACP
Capacity: 7 shots
Barrel length: 6″
Overall length: 9¾″
Weight: 47 oz.

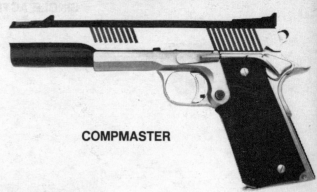

COMPMASTER

EMF/DAKOTA

SINGLE ACTION REVOLVERS

CUSTOM ENGRAVED
NICKEL SINGLE ACTION REVOLVER
$690.00

SPECIFICATIONS
Calibers: 22, 45 Long Colt, 357 Magnum, 44-40. **Barrel lengths:** 4⅝″, 5½″ and 7½″. **Features:** Classic original-type scroll engraving.

1873 PREMIER SINGLE ACTION REVOLVER
$520.00

SPECIFICATIONS
Caliber: 45 Long Colt. **Barrel length:** 4⅝″ or 5½″. **Finish:** Blued, casehardened frame. **Grips:** One-piece walnut. **Features:** Set screw for cylinder pin release; parts are interchangeable with early Colts.

HARTFORD MODELS

EMF's new Hartford Single Action revolvers are available in all calibers and barrel lengths. They feature steel back straps, trigger guards and forged frame. Identical to the original Colts. **Price: $595.00**

HARTFORD MODEL "CAVALRY COLT"

This Model 1873 Government Model Cavalry revolver is an exact reproduction of the original Colt made for the U.S. Cavalry. Caliber is .45 Long Colt and barrel length is 7½″. **Price: $650.00**

EMF/DAKOTA

SINGLE ACTION REVOLVERS

MODEL 1873 (With Extra Cylinder)
$580.00

SPECIFICATIONS
Calibers: 22 LR, 22 Mag., 357 Mag., 45 Long Colt, 30 M1 Carbine, 38-40 cal., 32-20 cal., 44-40 cal. **Barrel lengths:** 4³/₄″, 5¹/₂″, 7¹/₂″. **Finish:** Engraved models, blue or nickel. **Special feature:** Each gun is fitted with second caliber.

DAKOTA TARGET
$500.00

SPECIFICATIONS
Calibers: 45 Long Colt, 357 Magnum, 22 LR. **Barrel lengths:** 5¹/₂″ and 7¹/₂″. **Finish:** Polished blue. **Special features:** Case-hardened frame, one-piece walnut grips, brass back strap, ramp front blade target sight and adjustable rear sight.

MODEL 1875 "OUTLAW"
$485.00 ($520.00 Nickel)

SPECIFICATIONS
Calibers: 45 Long Colt, 357 Magnum, 44-40 cal. **Barrel length:** 7¹/₂″. **Finish:** Blue. **Special features:** Case-hardened frame, walnut grips; an exact replica of Remington #3 revolver produced from 1875 to 1889. Factory Engraved Model: **$600.00**

DAKOTA 1894 BISLEY
$540.00

SPECIFICATIONS
Calibers: 22, 44-40, 45 Long Colt, 357 Magnum. **Barrel lengths:** 4⁵/₈″, 5¹/₂″ and 7¹/₂″. Also available: **Dakota Bisley Engraved Model** with same barrel lengths and calibers **$700.00**. Nickel finish **$640.00** (add **$140** for engraving).

ERMA TARGET ARMS

MODEL 777

MODEL 777 SPORTING REVOLVER

SPECIFICATIONS
Caliber: 357 Magnum
Capacity: 6 cartridges
Barrel length: 5¹/₂″ and 4″
Overall length: 11.3″ and 9.7″
Weight: 43.7 oz.; 39.2 oz. w/4″ barrel
Sight radius: 8″ and 6.4″
Grip: Checkered walnut
Price: **$1093.00**

Also available:
MODEL 773 MATCH (32 S&W Wadcutter). Same specifications as Model 777 (5¹/₂″ barrel only), but with adjustable match grip and 6″ barrel. **Weight:** 45.8 oz. . . . **$1225.00**
MODEL 772 MATCH (22 LR). Same specifications as Model 773, except weight is 47¹/₄ oz. **$1225.00**

MODEL ESP 85

MODEL ESP 85 SPORTING PISTOL

SPECIFICATIONS
Caliber: 22 LR or 32 S&W Wadcutter
Action: Semiautomatic
Capacity: 5 cartridges (8 in 22 LR optional)
Barrel length: 6.″
Overall length: 10.2″
Weight: 40 oz.
Sight radius: 8″
Sights: Micrometer rear sight; fully adjustable interchangeable front and rear sight blade (3.5mm/4.0mm)
Grip: Checkered walnut grip with thumbrest
Price:
22 LR $1119.00
22 LR Match Pistol 1225.00
   Same as above in left-hand model 1253.00
32 S&W 1169.00
Chrome Sporting (22 LR only) 1200.00

FEDERAL ORDNANCE

PETERS STAHL PSP-07 COMBAT COMPENSATOR

SPECIFICATIONS
Caliber: 45 ACP or 10mm
Barrel length: 6″
Weight: 45 oz.
Capacity: 7+1 (45 ACP) or 8+1 (10mm)
Finish: Blued or Stainless
Grips: Pachmayr Presentation
Sights: Peters Stahl adj. rear; interchangeable front
Features: Semi-extended slide stop and thumb safety; adj. Videcki trigger; hammer-forged polygon rifled linkless barrel w/integral PS competition compensator; Stainless steel Wilson beavertail grip safety

Prices:
MODEL PSP-07 COMBAT (45 ACP) $2599.95
   Same as above in 10mm 2650.95

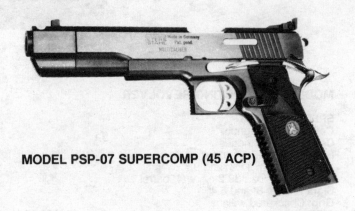

MODEL PSP-07 SUPERCOMP (45 ACP)

RANGER TEN

RANGER ALPHA

SPECIFICATIONS
Caliber: 45 ACP, 10mm, 38 Super
Barrel length: 5″ or 6″
Capacity: 7+1 (45 ACP); 8+1 (10mm); 9+1 (38 Super)
Weight: 42 oz.
Finish: Blued
Grips: Wraparound rubber
Sights: Peters Stahl adj. rear; interchangeable front
Features: Extended grip and thumb safeties; slide and magazine releases; Peters Stahl linkless barrel system; hammer-forged polygon rifling (porting optional)

Prices:
RANGER ALPHA (5″ 45 ACP and 38 Super) . . . . . $ 999.95
   5″ 45 ACP Ported, 6″ 45 ACP, 5″ 10mm, 5″ 38 Super ported, 6″ 38 Super 1015.95
   6″ 45 ACP ported, 5″ 10mm period, 6″ 10mm, 6″ 38 Super ported 1024.95

Also available:
RANGER SUPERCOMP (45 ACP and 10mm) $1389.95
RANGER LITE (32 oz., 45 ACP only) 464.95
RANGER TEN (10mm only, 5″ barrel, 40 oz.) 779.95

RANGER LITE

FEDERAL ORDNANCE PISTOLS

RANGER AMBO
$479.95

SPECIFICATIONS
Caliber: 45 ACP
Barrel length: 5″ (hammerforged rifling)
Capacity: 7+1
Weight: 40 oz.
Sights: Millett high profile, fixed
Grips: Checkered, walnut
Finish: Blued
Features: Ambidextrous slide release and safety

RANGER EXT
$459.95

Specifications same as **RANGER AMBO** but without ambidextrous slide release and safety.

G.I. RANGER
$439.95

Specifications same as **RANGER AMBO** and **EXT** (above) but has matte blue finish, G.I. sights, and plastic grips.

F.I.E. PISTOLS

MODEL TZ75 (Series '88)
$519.29 to $799.95

SPECIFICATIONS
Caliber: 9mm double action, 41 A.E.
Capacity: 16 + 1 (10 + 1 in 41 A.E.)
Barrel length: 4½″
Overall length: 8¼″
Height: 5½″
Weight: 35 oz.
Sights: D/T ramp front (white insert); rear (white outline) adjustable for windage
Grips: European walnut, black rubber (optional)

COWBOY
$94.95

SPECIFICATIONS
Calibers: 22 Short, Long, Long Rifle or 22 Magnum
Capacity: 6 rounds
Barrel length: 3¼″ or 6½″
Weight: 28 oz. (3¼″ bbl.); 32 oz. (6½″ bbl.)
Finish: Blue with ebony nylon grips
Sights: Blade front, fixed rear
Features: Floating firing pin, manual shell extraction
Also available: Convertible models supplied with 22 LR and 22 Magnum cylinders. **Price: $117.18.**

MODEL SSP

SPECIFICATIONS
Calibers: 22 LR, 32 ACP, 380 ACP
Barrel length: 3¼″
Overall length: 6½″
Weight: 25½ oz.
Capacity: 10 + 1 (6 in 32 ACP and 380 ACP)
Finish: Blue
Grip: European walnut
Sights: Integral tapered post front sight; windage adjustable rear sight

Models	Prices
22 LR Blue	$160.65
32 and 380 ACP Blue	145.53
32 and 380 ACP Chrome	164.43
Lady 32 or **Lady 380**	249.95

MODEL 722TP SILHOUETTE PISTOL (not shown)
$262.71

SPECIFICATIONS
Caliber: 22 LR
Capacity: 10 rounds
Action: Bolt action with adjustable trigger and bolt retainer
Barrel length: 10⅜″ (free floating)
Weight: 3.4 lbs.
Finish: Walnut
Sights: Globe front (insert-type with match post); square-notch rear, fully adjustable

F.I.E. HANDGUNS

DERRINGER D-86 SINGLE SHOT
$94.50 ($103.95 Dyna-Chrome)

SPECIFICATIONS
Caliber: 38 Special
Barrel length: 3″
Weight: 12 oz.
Sights: Fixed
Safety: Transfer bar
Finish: Dyna-chrome hard matte or bright blue
Grips: Black nylon (Standard) and walnut (Deluxe)

MODEL E28 SEMIAUTOMATIC
$58.95

SPECIFICATIONS
Caliber: 25 ACP
Barrel length: 2¹/₂″
Weight: 12 oz.
Sights: Ramp front, fixed rear
Hammer: Serrated external
Grips: European walnut
Trigger lock: Thumb operated
Also available: $ 64.26 Dyna-Chrome
153.09 Titan Tigress (Ladies' Pistol)

TITAN TIGER DOUBLE ACTION REVOLVER
$175.77

SPECIFICATIONS
Calliber: 38 Special
Barrel length: 2″ or 4″
Sights: Ramp front, fixed rear
Grips: Composite, checkered
Features: Swing-out cylinder with thumb latch release

ARMINIUS DOUBLE ACTION REVOLVERS

SPECIFICATIONS
Calibers: 22S/L/LR, 22 WMR, 2 Combo w/interchangeable
  cylinders, 32 S&W Long, 38 Special, 357 Magnum
Barrel lengths: 3″, 4″ and 6″
Sights: Fixed or micro-adjustable
Weight: 26 oz. - 30 oz.
Capacity: 8 rds. (22), 7 rds. (32 S&W), 6 rds. (all others)
Prices: $154.95 (22 LR 4″ and 6″)
         184.95 (38 Special 4″ and 6″)
         239.95 (357 Magnum 3″, 4″ and 6″)

FREEDOM ARMS

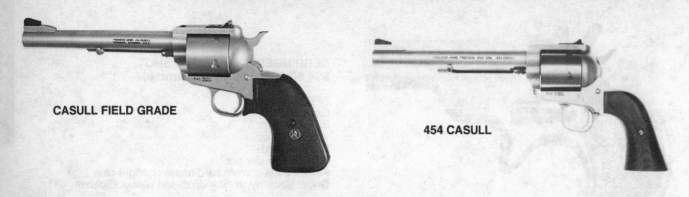

CASULL FIELD GRADE

454 CASULL

454 CASULL PREMIER & FIELD GRADES

SPECIFICATIONS
Calibers: 454 Casull, 45 Colt, 44 Rem. Mag.
Action: Single action
Capacity: 5 rounds
Barrel lengths: 4³/₄″, 6″, 7¹/₂″, 10″
Overall length: 14″ (w/7¹/₂″ barrel)
Weight: 3 lbs. 2 oz. (w/7¹/₂″ barrel)
Safety: Patented sliding bar
Sights: Notched rear; blade front (optional adjustable rear and replaceable front blade)
Grips: Impregnated hardwood
Finish: Brushed stainless
Features: Patented interchangeable forcing cone bushing (optional); Bo-Mar silhouette, Millett competition, and ex-press sights are optional; SSK T'SOB 3-ring scope mount optional

Prices:
MODEL FA-454AS (Premier Grade) w/adj.
sights **$1149.75**
Same as above w/fixed sights **1044.75**
MODEL FA-454FGAS (Field Grade) with stainless steel matte finish, adj. sight, Pachmayr presentation grips **929.00**
Same as above w/fixed sights (4³/₄″ bbl. only) **847.00**
MODEL FA-454ASM U.S. Deputy Marshall
With adj. sights (3″ barrel only) **1225.00**
Same as above w/fixed sights **1120.00**

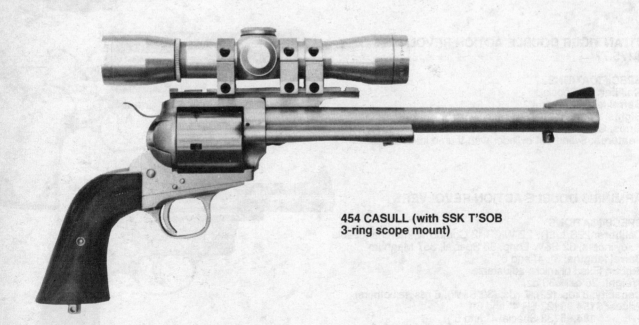

**454 CASULL (with SSK T'SOB
3-ring scope mount)**

GLOCK PISTOLS

MODEL 17
$511.60

First launched in 1983, the Glock handgun represents a trend-setting development. The company's trial weapons have now passed 300,000 rounds of testfiring without visible wear and with continuing accuracy. The guns' main features include a limited number of components, a new "safe-action" system, low weight with soft recoil, 17-round capacity, and use of space-age polymers that can withstand extreme cold and heat (up to 200°C.) without structural damage.

SPECIFICATIONS
Caliber: 9mm Parabellum
Magazine capacity: 17 rounds
Barrel length: 4¹/₂″ (hexagonal profile with right-hand twist
Overall length: 7¹/₂″
Weight: 22 oz. (without magazine)
Sights: Fixed or adjustable rear sights

MODEL 17

MODEL 17L COMPETITION
$773.53

SPECIFICATIONS
Caliber: 9mm Parabellum
Magazine capacity: 17 rounds
Barrel length: 6.02″
Overall length: 8.77″
Weight: 23.35 oz. (without magazine)
Sights: Fixed or adjustable rear sights

MODEL 17L COMPETITION

MODEL 19 COMPACT

MODEL 19 COMPACT
$511.60

SPECIFICATIONS
Caliber: 9mm Parabellum
Magazine capacity: 17 rounds
Barrel length: 4.02″
Overrall length: 6.74″
Weight: 21 oz. (without magazine)
Sights: Fixed or adjustable rear sights

GLOCK PISTOLS

MODEL 20

MODEL 20
$598.00

SPECIFICATIONS
Caliber: 10mm
Magazine capacity: 15 rounds
Action: Double action
Barrel length: 4.6″
Overall length: 8.27″
Height: 5.2″ (w/sights)
Weight: 27.55 oz. (empty)
Features: 3 safeties, "safe action" system, polymer frame

GRENDEL PISTOLS

MODEL P-10 (not shown)
$155.00 (Blue)
$170.00 (Nickel)

SPECIFICATIONS
Caliber: 380 ACP
Capacity: 11 rounds
Barrel length: 3″
Overall length: 5.3″
Weight: 15 oz. (loaded)
Sight radius: 4¹/₂″
Features: Integrated double column magazine; grip extension
and longer barrel; speed loader
Also available in Green **($155.00)** and Nickel Green **($175.00)**

MODEL P-30M

MODEL P-30
$255.00

SPECIFICATIONS
Caliber: 22 WRF Magnum
Capacity: 30 rounds
Barrel length: 5″
Overall length: 8¹/₂″
Weight: 21 oz. (empty)
Sight radius: 7.2″
Features: Fixed barrel, flat trajectory, low recoil, ambidextrous
safety levers, front sight adjustable for windage.
Also available: **Model P-30M** (w/removable muzzle brake):
$235.00

MODEL P-30

HECKLER & KOCH PISTOLS

MODEL P7M8

MODEL P7M8 SELF-LOADING PISTOL

Features the Continuous Motion Principle in the form of a unique cocking lever. The gun can be drawn, cocked and fired with single-action accuracy in one continuous motion with either hand. Also featured are a low-profile slide, polygonal rifling and rugged forged, machined steel construction.

SPECIFICATIONS
Caliber: 9mm × 19 (Luger)
Capacity: 8 rounds
Barrel length: 4.13"
Overall length: 6.73"
Weight: 1.75 lbs. (empty)
Sight radius: 5.83"
Sights: Adjustable rear
Price: with 2 magazines . . . . $ 908.00
Also available: **MODEL P7M13** with same barrel
    length, but slightly longer overall, heavier and
    13-round capacity 1132.00

MODEL P7K3

Model P7K3 uses a unique oil-filled buffer to decrease recoil and increase control. An easy-to-install conversion kit in 22 LR is available as an accessory.

SPECIFICATIONS
Calibers: 22 LR, 380
Capacity: 8 rounds
Barrel length: 3.8"
Overall length: 6.3"
Weight: 1.65 lbs. (empty)
Sight radius: 5.5"
Sights: Adjustable rear
MODEL P7K3 with 2 magazines $908.00
    22 LR Conversion Kit 474.00

MODEL P7K3

MODEL SP89

MODEL SP89

This multi-purpose sporting/security pistol features a rotary-aperture rear sight adjustable for windage and elevation; a hooded front sight; and a shape designed to accept H&K claw-lock mounts for adding a telescopic sight.

SPECIFICATIONS
Caliber: 9mm
Action: Semiautomatic, recoil-operated, delayed roller-locked
    bolt system
Capacity: 15 rounds
Barrel length: 4$^{1}/_{2}$"
Overall length: 13"
Weight: 4.4 lbs.
Price: $1193.00

IAI PISTOLS

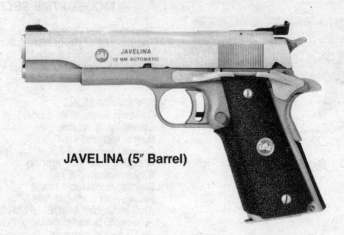

JAVELINA (5″ Barrel)

JAVELINA
$600.00

SPECIFICATIONS
Caliber: 10mm
Capacity: 8 shots
Barrel lengths: 5″ and 7″
Overall length: 8¹/₂″ (5″ barrel); 10¹/₂″ (7″ barrel)
Weight: 38 oz. (5″); 48 oz. (7″)
Sights: Millett adjustable
Features: Standard matte rib barrel (5″); long grip safety; wraparound Neoprene grips; beveled magazine; wide adjustable trigger

JAVELINA (7″ Barrel)

AUTOMAG III
$674.00

SPECIFICATIONS
Calibers: 30 M1 Carbine, 45 Win. Mag., 9mm Win. Mag.
Capacity: 8 shots
Barrel length: 6³/₈″
Overall length: 10¹/₂″
Weight: 43 oz.
Sights: Millett adjustable
Grips: Carbon fiber
Finish: Stainless steel

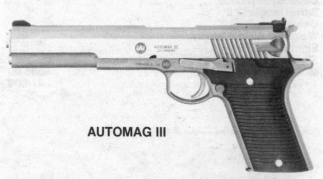

AUTOMAG III

AUTOMAG IV
$695.00

SPECIFICATIONS
Caliber: 45 Win. Mag.
Capacity: 7 shots
Barrel length: 6¹/₂″
Overall length: 10¹/₂″
Weight: 46 oz.
Sights: Millett adjustable
Grips: Carbon fiber
Finish: Stainless steel

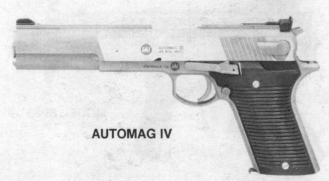

AUTOMAG IV

IVER JOHNSON PISTOLS

TRAILSMAN MODEL TM22
$230.00

SPECIFICATIONS
Caliber: 22 LR
Capacity: 10 rounds
Barrel lengths: 4³/₄" and 6"
Overall length: 9" (4³/₄" barrel); 10¹/₄" (6" barrel)
Height: 4¹/₂"
Weight: 30 oz. (4³/₄" barrel); 36 oz. (6" barrel)

TRAILSMAN MODEL TM22

TP-22 DOUBLE ACTION PISTOL
$165.00

This 22-caliber pocket pistol offers a maximum of convenience when carried. The 7-shot capacity, small size and light weight are enhanced by the hammer safety and fast-handling double-action design.

SPECIFICATIONS
Barrel length: 3"
Overall length: 5.5"
Weight: 12 oz. (empty)
Grips: Black plastic
Finish: Blue or matte
Also available: **Silver Hawk** in stainless steel $250.00

TP-22 POCKET PISTOL

PONY MODEL PO380B

PONY MODEL PO308B
$330.00

SPECIFICATIONS
Caliber: 380 ACP
Capacity: 6 rounds
Barrel length: 3"
Overall length: 6"
Weight: 20 oz.
Sights: Blade front, fixed rear
Grips: Hardwood (or checkered walnut)
Finish: Blue

KBI PISTOLS

MODEL PSP-25
$249.00

SPECIFICATIONS
Caliber: 25 ACP
Barrel length: 2¹/₈″
Overall length: 4¹/₈″
Weight: 9.5 oz. (empty)
Height: 2⁷/₈″
Features: Dual safety system; all-steel construction; honed, polished and blued.
Also available:
MODEL PSP-25 in hard chrome **$310.70**
SIGNATURE EDITION signed by Michael Kassnar . **430.00**

MODEL PSP-25

MODEL 941 JERICHO
$882.70

This multi-caliber semiautomatic pistol features interchangeable barrels and a conversion kit, plus all-steel construction, precision machined with a deep-blue satin matte finish.

SPECIFICATIONS
Calibers: 9mm/41 AE
Barrel length: 4.4″
Overall length: 8.8″
Height: 5.5″
Magazine capacity: 11 shots (41AE); 16 shots (9mm)
Rifling: 1 turn in 10″ (9mm); 1 turn in 18.5″ (41 AE)
Weight: 33 oz.
Features: 3-dot tritium sight system; custom loaded carrying case; custom RIG cleaning kit; 2 boxes of ammo; polygonal rifling; double action; easy-operating slide-mounted thumb safety; deep-groove serrated slide grip for positive operation; manual safety/decocking lever; non-slip modified combat hammer; impact-resistant Polymer grips.

MODEL 941 JERICHO

L.A.R. GRIZZLY

MARK I
GRIZZLY WIN MAG
$775.00

This semiautomatic pistol is a direct descendant of the tried and trusted 1911-type .45 automatic, but with the added advantage of increased caliber capacity.

SPECIFICATIONS
Calibers: 45 Win. Mag., 45 ACP, 357 Mag., 10mm
Barrel length: 6½″
Overall length: 10½″
Weight (empty): 48 oz.
Height: 5¾″
Sights: Fixed, ramped blade (front); fully adjustable for elevation and windage (rear)

Magazine capacity: 7 rounds
Grips: Checkered rubber, nonslip, combat-type
Safeties: Grip depressor, manual thumb, slide-out-of-battery disconnect
Materials: Mil spec 4140 steel slide and receiver with noncorrosive, heat-treated, special alloy steels for other parts
Same model in 357 Magnum $800.00

Also available:
Win Mag Compensator 87.00
Win Mag Scope Mount 104.00

GRIZZLY WIN MAG
6½″ BARREL

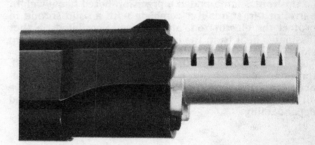

45 WIN. MAG.
COMPENSATOR

Also available:
Grizzly Win Mag with 8″ and 10″ barrels in 45 Win Mag, 357 Magnum, 45 ACP and 357/45 Grizzly Win Mag.

Model G-WM8 (8″ barrel in 45 Win Mag, 45 ACP, or 357/45 Grizzly Win Mag $1250.00
Model G357M8 (8″ barrel in 357 Magnum) 1275.00
Model G-WM10 (10″ barrel in 45 Win Mag, 45 ACP, or 357/45 Grizzly Win Mag 1313.00
Model G357M10 (10″ barrel in 357 Magnum) . . . 1337.50

8″ BARREL

10″ BARREL

LLAMA REVOLVERS

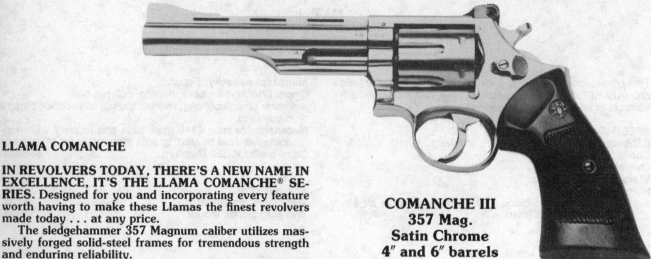

LLAMA COMANCHE

IN REVOLVERS TODAY, THERE'S A NEW NAME IN EXCELLENCE, IT'S THE LLAMA COMANCHE® SERIES. Designed for you and incorporating every feature worth having to make these Llamas the finest revolvers made today . . . at any price.

The sledgehammer 357 Magnum caliber utilizes massively forged solid-steel frames for tremendous strength and enduring reliability.

Up front, Llama added a precision-bored heavyweight barrel of target quality, complete with a solid shroud to protect the ejector rod, and a raised ventilated-rib that dissipates heat from the barrel to give you a clear, sharp sight image even when the action gets hot.

On the inside, everything is finely fitted and polished, for a double action that's slick and smooth, and a single-action trigger pull that's light, crisp and clean. Llama gave all Comanches a floating firing pin for greater safety and dependability.

COMANCHE III
357 Mag.
Satin Chrome
4″ and 6″ barrels

357 Mag. Standard Blue 4″, 6″ **$339.00**
357 Mag. Satin Chrome 4″, 6″ **395.00**

SPECIFICATIONS COMANCHE III

CALIBERS:	357 Magnum
BARREL LENGTH:	4 and 6-inch
NUMBER OF SHOTS:	6 shots
FRAME:	Forged high hensile strength steel. Serrated front and back strap.
ACTION:	Double-action.
TRIGGER:	Wide grooved target trigger
HAMMER:	Wide spur target hammer with serrated gripping surface.
SIGHTS:	Square notch rear sight with windage and elevation adjustments; serrated quick-draw front sight on ramp.
SIGHT RADIUS:	With 4-inch barrel—5³/₄″; with 6-inch barrel—7³/₄″.
GRIPS:	Oversized target, walnut. Checkered.
WEIGHT:	w/4″ bbl.—2 lbs., 4ozs. w/6″ bbl.—2 lbs., 7 ozs.
OVER-ALL LENGTH:	With 4-inch barrel—9¹/₄″; with 6-inch barrel—11″.
FINISH:	High-polished, deep blue. Deluxe models; satin chrome (.357 w/4″ & 6″ bbl.)
SAFETY FEATURE:	The hammer is mounted on an eccentric cam, the position of which is controlled by the trigger. Only when the latter is fully depressed can the firing pin contact the primer.

LLAMA REVOLVERS

SUPER COMANCHE IV
44 Magnum $440.00
Available in 6″ and 8½″ barrels

LLAMA SUPER COMANCHE
44 MAGNUM

If ever a handgun was conceived, designed and built to fit the requirements of big bore handgunners, this one is it. The frame, for example, is massive. The weight and balance are such that the heavy recoil generated by the powerful .44 Magnum cartridge is easily and comfortably controlled.

Instead of a single cylinder latch, the Llama has two. In addition to the conventional center pin at the rear of the ratchet, there's a second latch up front that locks the crane to the frame, resulting in a safer, more secure lockup. The hammer is mounted on an eccentric cam, the position of which is controlled by the trigger. Only when the trigger is fully depressed can the firing pin contact the primer.

To minimize leading and to enhance accuracy, Llama has perfected a new honing process that imparts a mirror-smooth finish to the bore.

Additional features include a precision-lapped, heavy-weight bull barrel with target accuracy. A matte finish, ventilated rib for more efficient heat dissipation, less glare and less target mirage. Oversized grips that soak up recoil for better control and a faster recovery for a second shot. A super-wide trigger for a more comfortable, controlled pull.

A three-point crane/cylinder provides support for a stronger, more rigid lockup.

The finish is highly polished and deeply blued with genuine walnut grips.

SPECIFICATIONS

	Super Comanche .44 Mag.	
Type:	Double action	
Calibers:	.44 Magnum	
Barrel Length:	6″	8½″
Number of Shots:	6	
Frame:	Forged high tensile strength steel.	
Trigger:	Smooth extra wide	
Hammer:	Wide spur, deep positive serrations.	
Sights:	Rear-click adjustable for windage and elevation, leaf serrated to cut down on glare. Front-ramped blade.	
Sight Radius:	8″	10³⁄₈″
Grips:	Oversized target, walnut. Checkered.	
Weight:	3 lbs., 2 ozs.	3 lbs., 8 ozs.
Overall Length:	11³⁄₄″	14½″
Finish:	High polished, deep blue	

LLAMA AUTOMATIC PISTOLS

Llama's newest 9mm single action is a compact version of its 9mm semi-auto, a gun which over the years has earned the kind of trust that has made it the issue side arm of countless military and law enforcement agencies throughout the world. It is also available in 45 caliber automatic and 38 Super.

The small-frame Llama models, available in 22 LR and 380 Auto., are impressively compact handguns. All frames are precision machined of high strength steel, yet weigh a featherlight 23 ounces. A full complement of safeties . . . side lever, half-cock and grip . . . is incorporated.

Every small-frame Llama offers a wide-spur serrated target-type hammer and adjustable rear sight.

The large-frame Llama models, available in potent 45 ACP, are completely crafted of high strength steel.

**9mm PARABELLUM
STANDARD BLUE
$385.00**

**LLAMA COMPACT 45 & 38 SUPER
$385.00**

**LLAMA SMALL-FRAME
AUTOMATIC WITH
DEEP BLUE FINISH
22, 32 and 380 Caliber
$325.00**

LLAMA AUTOMATIC PISTOLS

**LLAMA SMALL-FRAME
AUTOMATIC PISTOL IN
SATIN CHROME FINISH
22 and 380 Caliber
$399.00**

LLAMA AUTOMATIC PISTOL SPECIFICATIONS

TYPE:	SMALL FRAME AUTO PISTOLS			COMPACT FRAME AUTO PISTOLS			LARGE FRAME AUTO PISTOLS
CALIBERS:	22 LR	32	380 Auto	9mm Parabellum	38 Super	45 Auto	45 Auto
FRAME:	Precision machined from high-strength steel. Serrated front strap, checkered (curved) backstrap.			Precision machined from high-strength steel. Serrated front strap, checkered (curved) backstrap.			Precision machined from high-strength steel. Plain front strap, checkered (curved) backstrap.
TRIGGER:	Serrated			Serrated			Serrated
HAMMER:	External. Wide spur, serrated.			External. Wide spur, serrated.			External. Wide spur, serrated.
OPERATION:	Straight blow-back.			Locked breech.			Locked breech.
LOADED CHAMBER INDICATOR:	No	Yes	Yes	No	No	No	Yes
SAFETIES:	Side lever thumb safety, grip safety.			Side lever thumb safety, grip safety.			Side lever thumb safety, grip safety.
GRIPS:	Modified thumbrest black plastic grips.			Matte black polymer.			Matte black polymer.
SIGHTS:	Square notch rear, and Patridge-type front, adjustable rear sight for windage			Square notch rear, and Patridge-type front, adjustable rear sight for windage.			Square notch rear, and Patridge-type front, adjustable rear sight for windage.
SIGHT RADIUS:	$4^1/_4''$			$6^1/_4''$			$6^1/_4''$
MAGAZINE CAPACITY:	8-shot	7-shot	7-shot	9-shot	8-shot	7-shot	7-shot
WEIGHT:	23 ounces			34 ounces			36 ounces
BARREL LENGTH:	$3^{11}/_{16}''$			$5''$			$5''$
OVERALL LENGTH:	$6^1/_2''$			$7^7/_8''$			$8^1/_2''$
HEIGHT:	$4^3/_8''$			$5^7/_{16}''$			$5^1/_3''$
FINISH:	Std. models; High-polished, deep blue. Deluxe models; satin chrome (22 & 380)			Std. models; High-polished, deep blue. Deluxe models; satin chrome (9 mm & 45)			Std. models; High-polished, deep blue. Deluxe models; satin chrome (45)

LLAMA AUTOMATIC PISTOLS

Machined and polished to perfection. These truly magnificent firearms offer a wide-spur checkered target-type hammer, windage adjustable rear sight and black polymer grips.

In addition to High Polished Deep Blue, the following superb handguns are available in handsome Satin Chrome 22 LR, 380 Auto, 9mm and 45 ACP.

**LLAMA LARGE-FRAME
AUTOMATIC PISTOL IN
SATIN CHROME FINISH**
45 Auto Caliber
$499.00

**LLAMA LARGE-FRAME
AUTOMATIC WITH
DEEP BLUE FINISH**
45 Auto Caliber
38 Super
$385.00

LLAMA PISTOLS

MODEL M-82 (9mm) DOUBLE ACTION
$975.00

SPECIFICATIONS

Caliber: 9mm Parabellum
Magazine: 15 cartridges (15 + 1 shot)
Barrel length: $4^{1}/_4''$
No. of barreling grooves: 6
Overall length: $8''$
Height: $5^{5}/_{16}''$
Maximum width: $1^{3}/_8''$
Weight: 39 oz. (empty)
Sights: High visibility, 3-dot sights; rear sight drift adj.
Sight radius: $6''$
Grips: Matte black polymer
Stocks: Plastic
Finish: Blued satin

After nearly a decade of research, development and testing, the new Llama M-82 is being offered to the gun buying public. Representing the state-of-the-art in double action, semiauto pistol design, this handgun offers a unique blend of highly innovative technical features, combined with the kind of ergonomic design and practical performance that are so important in day-to-day use. It's the kind demanded by military and law enforcement personnel, as well as by competitive combat shooters and otherwise knowledgeable handgunners.

Whatever criteria are used in judging a DA semiauto—whether accuracy, reliability, simplicity of design, looks, compactness, quality of fit, or finish—all are effectively combined in the M-82. The following features indicate why pistol experts are already hailing this new Llama as the world's finest production combat handgun.

1. MINIMAL BARREL/SLIDE DISPLACEMENT: As the slide moves rearward during the firing cycle, the lineal displacement required to unlock the action is but a fraction of that in other double action designs. This translates into less wear and tear on the mechanism, as well as allowing tighter tolerances. That, in turn, means greater accuracy, greater durability.

2. POSITIVE SAFETY MECHANISM: Even when at rest and with the safety disengaged, the hammer does not contact the firing pin, making this gun one of the safest handguns available today.

3. TWIN LUG LOCK-UP: Unlike other DA's, which rely on a single locking lug engagement in the ceiling of the slide, the M-82 has two lugs in the "three and nine o'clock" position. This unique system provides greater strength, greater rigidity. . . . and greater accuracy.

4. FULL-LENGTH GUIDE RAILS: For more positive, accurate alignment of barrel, slide and frame, the Llama's slide is engaged by guide rails the entire length of its movement (some autos allow as much as two inches of unsupported slide movement).

5. MAXIMUM FIREPOWER: The M-82's staggered magazine holds 15 rounds, plus one in the chamber. This potent firepower is made possible by an overall grip dimension small enough to fit comfortably in the average hand.

6. RECESSED BREECH FACE: Unlike other guns featuring flat breech faces, the Llama's is recessed, much like most modern high-powered rifles. This additional support in the critical case head area means greater safety.

7. AMBIDEXTROUS SAFETY: Allows the M-82 to be used with equal speed and convenience by both right- and left-handed shooters.

8. CHANGEABLE MAGAZINE RELEASE: Normally positioned on the left side of the grip for right-handed shooters, the clip release button on the M-82 can be changed easily to the other side for southpaw use.

9. ARTICULATED FIRING PIN: Another excellent Llama feature is its virtually unbreakable firing pin. In fact, it's guaranteed not to break—for life.

10. COMPACT SIZE: Despite its 16-shot capability, the M-82 is neither heavy nor bulky. Its overall dimensions are short—$8^{1}/_4''$ in length, $5^{5}/_6''$ in height, and $1^{3}/_8''$ in extreme width. Empty weight is 39 ounces.

11. ENLARGED EJECTION PORT: To preclude any sort of ejection problems brought about by variation in loads or in slide velocity, the ejection port is slightly oversize.

12. MODULAR GRIP DESIGN: The hammer strut and main spring are housed in a separate sub-assembly which easily detaches from the frame for routine cleaning and maintenance.

13. INSTANT DISASSEMBLY: The M-82 can be field stripped in less than five seconds—without tools.

LLAMA PISTOLS

LLAMA M-87 COMP PISTOL (9mm)
$1450.00

Llama, located in the heart of the Basque region of Spain, has been manufacturing high-grade quality handguns since 1903 and has recently made a substantial investment in high tech computer-controlled machining centers. This 21st-century hi-tech machinery has enabled the factory to produce the "match ready" LLAMA M-87 Comp pistol designed specifically for the professional shooter. All of the features demanded by the serious competitive shooter are already built into the M-87 so that it is virtually "out-of-the-box" ready for the range.

COMPENSATOR: Full profile • reduces muzzle lift • increased speed to get back "on target" • dual port internal expansion chamber • reduces recoil.
TRIGGER: Clean • crisp • smooth • positive • creep-free • concave, checkered and extended trigger guard.
SAFETIES: Manual thumb safety allows for quick release • oversized and extended lever for speed • conventional hammer block safety with ambidextrous (dual) levers.
MAGAZINE: 15 rounds • ambidextrous magazine release button is oversized and extended • tapered top allows for quick insertion • bumper pad ensures positive seating • pad also minimizes damage from dropping while rapid firing.

FRAME: Investment casting from Llama's state-of-the-art investment casting factory • beavertail extension for greater hand control and comfort • magazine well flared and beveled, providing for rapid magazine insertion.
SIGHTS: Low-profile combat sights • rapid target acquisition.
TILTING-BLOCK LOCK-UP MECHANISM: Operates "in line" with the barrel • eliminates downward drop to unlock • no separate barrel bushing, which in turn provides a more solid and stable enclosure at the muzzle for greater accuracy.

SPECIFICATIONS
Caliber: 9mm double action
Capacity: 15 round magazine plus 1 in the chamber
Finish: Satin-nickel finish frame: matte black grip panels, operating levers, slide and compensator
Front sights: Low-profile combat; micrometer click; adjustable for windage
Grips: 2-piece polymer
Barrel length: 5¼"
Overall length: 9½"
Weight: 40 oz.

MAGNUM RESEARCH
DESERT EAGLE PISTOLS

SPECIFICATIONS	357 MAGNUM	41/44 MAGNUM
Length, with 6-inch barrel	10.6 inches	10.6 inches
Height	5.6 inches	5.7 inches
Width	1.25 inches	1.25 inches
Trigger reach	2.75 inches	2.75 inches
Sight radius (wh 6-inch barrel)	8.5 inches	8.5 inches
Additional available barrels	14 inch	14 inch & 10 inch
Weight	See below	See below
Bore rifling — Six rib	Polygonal: 1 turn in 14 inches	Polygonal: 1 turn in 18 inches
Method of operation	Gas operated	Gas operated
Method of locking	Rotating bolt	Rotating bolt
Magazine capacity	9 rounds (plus one in chamber)	8 rounds (plus one in chamber)

**DESERT EAGLE MARK I
(10" Barrel)**

DESERT EAGLE — WEIGHT TABLES
357 Magnum

Frame	Without Magazine		With Empty Magazine	
	6" Barrel	14" Barrel	6" Barrel	14" Barrel
	ounces	ounces	ounces	ounces
Aluminum	47.8	55.0	51.9	59.1
Steel	58.3	65.5	62.4	96.6
Stainless	58.3	65.5	62.4	69.6

41/44 Magnum

Frame	Without Magazine		With Empty Magazine	
	6" Barrel	14" Barrel	6" Barrel	14" Barrel
	ounces	ounces	ounces	ounces
Aluminum	52.3	61.0	56.4	65.1
Steel	62.8	71.5	66.9	75.6
Stainless	62.8	71.5	66.9	75.6

**357 MAGNUM
$789.00 w/6" Barrel
629.00 w/Alloy Frame
839.00 w/Stainless Steel
949.00 w/Stainless (10" barrel)
999.00 w/Stainless (14" barrel)**

**DESERT EAGLE SEMIAUTO PISTOLS
41 MAGNUM (6" & 14" Barrels)
$799.00 w/Standard Parkerized Finish
849.00 w/Stainless Steel
739.00 w/Alloy Frame**

**44 MAGNUM (6", 10", 14" Barrels)
$ 839.00 w/Standard Parkerized Finish
889.00 w/Stainless Steel (6" Barrel)
979.00 w/10" Barrel
1019.00 w/Stainless (10" Barrel)
989.00 w/14" Barrel
1029.00 w/Stainless (14" Barrel)
749.00 w/Alloy Frame**

**DESERT EAGLE
44 MAGNUM (6" Barrel)**

MITCHELL ARMS

SINGLE ACTION ARMY REVOLVERS

The Mitchell Arms Single Action Army Model Revolver is a modern version of the original "gun that won the West," adopted by the U.S. Army in 1873. Faithful to the original design, these revolvers are made of modern materials and use up-to-date technology; for example, a special safety device is built into the hammer assembly as a backstop to the traditional safety.

SPECIFICATIONS
Calibers: 357 Mag., 44 Mag., 45 Colt
Barrel lengths: 4³/₄", 5¹/₂" and 6"
Frame: Forged steel, fully machined with traditional color casehardening. Two-piece style backstrap made of solid brass.
Action: Traditional single action with safety position and half-cock position for loading and unloading.
Sights: Rear sight is fully adjustable for windage and elevation. Front sight is two-step ramp style with non-glare serrations. Fixed sight models feature deep notch with fixed-blade front sight.
Grip: One-piece solid walnut grip built in the style of the old black powder revolvers.
Accuracy: High-grade steel barrel honed for accuracy with smooth lands and grooves; precise alignment between cylinder and barrel. Fully qualified for big-game hunting or silhouette shooting.
Prices:
Fixed Sight Models $309.95–379.95
Also available:
SPECIAL SILHOUETTE MODELS 44 Magnum only in 12" and 18" barrel lengths. **$395.95. ($419.95 w/10" barrel).**

**SINGLE ACTION ARMY MODEL
(44 MAGNUM)
$328.00 (w/Adjustable Sights)**

1875 REMINGTON REVOLVER

1875 REMINGTON REVOLVER
$350.00

SPECIFICATIONS
Calibers: 44-40, 45 Colt, 357 Magnum
Barrel lengths: 5" (44-40 and 45 Colt only); 7¹/₂"
Grips: Walnut
Finish: Blue with color case
Features: Hardened frame; solid brass trigger guard

MOA MAXIMUM PISTOL

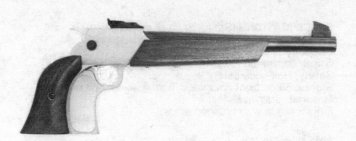

MAXIMUM

This single-shot pistol with its unique falling block action performs like a finely tuned rifle. The single piece receiver of chromoly steel is mated to a Douglas barrel for optimum accuracy and strength.

SPECIFICATIONS
Calibers: 22 Hornet to 358 Win.
Barrel lengths: 8¾″, 10½″ and 14″
Weight: 3 lbs. 8 oz. (8¾″ bbl.); 3 lbs. 13 oz. (10½″ bbl.); 4 lbs. 3 oz. (14″ bbl.)
Price: $499.00

NEW ENGLAND FIREARMS

STANDARD MODEL NICKEL
(32 H&R Mag., 4″ Barrel)
$114.75

STANDARD MODEL
(22 LR, 2½″ Barrel)

ULTRA MODEL (6″ Barrel)

STANDARD REVOLVER
$105.00

SPECIFICATIONS
Caliber: 22 LR
Capacity: 9 shots
Barrel lengths: 2½″ and 4″
Overall length: 7″ (2½″ barrel) and 8½″ (4″ barrel)
Weight: 25 oz. (2½″ bbl.) and 28 oz. (4″ bbl.)
Sights: Blade front; fixed rear
Grips: American hardwood, walnut finish
Finish: Blue or nickel
Also available in 22 Win. Mag. (6-shot) and 32 H&R Mag. (5-shot)

ULTRA REVOLVER
$114.13

SPECIFICATIONS
Calibers: 22 LR, 22 Win. Mag. and 32 H&R Mag.
Capacity: 9 shots (22 LR); 6 shots (22 Win. Mag.,); 5 shots (32 H&R Mag.)
Barrel lengths: 3″ and 6″
Overall length: 7⅝″ (3″ barrel) and 10⅝″ (6″ barrel)
Weight: 31 oz. (3″ bbl.); 36 oz. (6″ bbl.)
Sights: Blade on rib front; fully adjustable rear
Grips: American hardwood, walnut finish

NORTH AMERICAN ARMS REVOLVERS

22 MAGNUM

22 LR STAINLESS STEEL

MINI-REVOLVERS

SPECIFICATIONS (Standard on all models)
Caliber: 22 Short, LR or Magnum
Capacity: 5-shot cylinder
Grips: Laminated rosewood
Safety: Half-cock safety
Sights: Blade front (integral w/barrel); fixed, notched rear
Material: Stainless steel
Finish: Matte with brushed sides

Also available:
Collector Set—three-gun set with matching serial numbers, walnut display case, high-polish finish with matte contours $669.00
Deluxe Collector 3-Gun Set includes high-polish finish over entire gun 722.00
Mini-Master 22 LR or Mag. with 4″ heavy vent barrel 265.00

SPECIFICATIONS: NORTH AMERICAN ARMS

Model No.	Weight	Barrel Length	Overall Length	Overall Height	Overall Width	Prices
NAA-22S	4 oz.	1⅛″	4″	2⅜″	¾″	$148.00
NAA-22SL	4.2 oz.	1⅝″	4⅜″	2⅜″	¾″	148.00
NAA-22SE	4.5 oz.	2½″	5⅜″	2⅜″	¾″	164.00
NAA-22LR	4.5 oz.	1⅛″	4¼″	2⅜″	¹³/₁₆″	149.00
NAA-22LLR	4.6 oz.	1⅝″	4¾″	2⅜″	¹³/₁₆″	149.00
NAA-22ELR	5.1 oz.	2½″	5¾″	2⅜″	¹³/₁₆″	165.00
*NAA-22MS	5.9 oz.	1⅛″	5″	2⅞″	⅞″	170.00
*NAA-22M	6.2 oz.	1⅝″	5⅜″	2⅞″	⅞″	170.00
*NAA-22ML	6.6 oz.	2½″	6⅜″	2⅞″	⅞″	188.00

* Available with Conversion Cylinder chambered for 22 Long Rifle (**$203.00**).

RAVEN ARMS

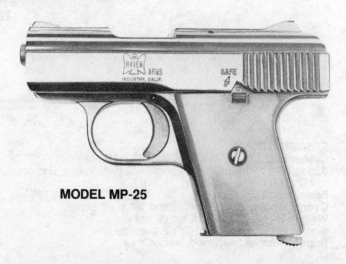

MODEL MP-25
$79.95

SPECIFICATIONS
Caliber: 25 Auto
Capacity: 6 rounds
Barrel length: 2⁷/₁₆″
Overall length: 4³/₄″
Height: 3⁷/₁₆″
Weight: 15 oz. (empty)
Features: Rotary thumb safety; hand-polished and made in the U.S.A.; choice of chrome, nickel or blued finish; walnut, simulated ivory or slotted grips

MODEL MP-25

REMINGTON LONG-RANGE PISTOLS

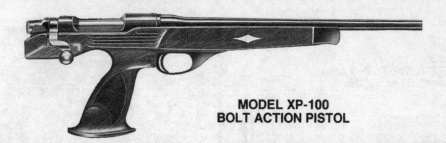

**MODEL XP-100
BOLT ACTION PISTOL**

"XP-100" LONG-RANGE CUSTOM PISTOLS

Remington's Model XP-100 Custom pistol is chambered for the 6mm BR Rem., 223 Rem., 250 Savage, 7mm BR, 7mm-08 Rem. and 35 Rem. All XP-100 Custom pistols are hand-crafted from select English walnut in right- and left-hand versions. All chamberings except the 35 Rem. (standard barrel only) are offered in a choice of standard 14½" barrels with adjustable rear leaf and front bead sights or 15½" barrels without sights. Receivers are drilled and tapped for scope mounts. **Weight** averages 4½ lbs. for standard models and 5½ lbs. for heavy barrel models. **Price: $943.00**

MODEL XP-100 SILHOUETTE TARGET AND "VARMINT SPECIAL" PISTOLS

These unique single-shot centerfire, bolt-action pistols have become legends for their strength, precision, balance and accuracy. Chambered for the 35 Rem. and 223 Rem. with a 14½" barrel, they are also available in 7mm BR, which many feel is the ideal factory-made metallic silhouette handgun for "unlimited" events. All XP-100 handguns have one-piece Du Pont "Zytel" nylon stocks with universal grips, two-position thumb safety switches, receivers drilled and tapped for scope mounts or receiver sights, and match-type grooved triggers.

Calibers: 35 Rem., 7mm BR Rem., 223 Rem. **Barrel length:** 14½". **Overall length:** 21¼". **Weight:** 4⅛ lbs. **Prices: $406.00** (7mm BR Rem.); **$419.00** (35. Rem.); **$398.00** (223 Rem.).

**MODEL XP-100 CUSTOM HEAVY BARREL
LONG-RANGE SINGLE-SHOT PISTOL**

**MODEL XP-100R CUSTOM REPEATER
BOLT ACTION CENTERFIRE (14½" Barrel)
Calibers: 223 Rem., 7mm-08 Rem., 35 Rem.
$798.00**

ROSSI REVOLVERS

MODEL 68

SPECIFICATIONS
Caliber: 38 Special
Barrel length: 2″ and 3″
Overall length: 6½″ (2″ barrel); 7½″ (3″ barrel)
Weight: 21 oz. (2″ barrel); 23 oz. (3″ barrel)
Capacity: 5 rounds
Finish: Blue or nickel
Price: w/3″ barrel **$180.00**
       w/2″ barrel **190.00**
       w/3″ barrel (nickel) **195.00**

MODEL M951 (not shown)
$233.00

SPECIFICATIONS
Caliber: 38 Special
Capacity: 6 rounds
Barrel length: 3″ and 4″
Overall length: 8″ and 9″
Weight: 27½ oz. and 30 oz.
Also available:
Model 971 (4″ barrel) 357 Magnum **$250.00**
  In stainless steel (4″ and 6″ barrels) **280.00**

MODEL 511 SPORTSMAN'S 22
$235.00

SPECIFICATIONS
Caliber: 22 LR
Barrel length: 4″
Overall length: 9″
Weight: 30 oz.
Capacity: 6 rounds
Finish: Stainless steel
Also available:
Model 89 (3″ barrel) 32 S&W **$215.00**

MODEL 68

**MODEL 511
SPORTSMAN'S 22**

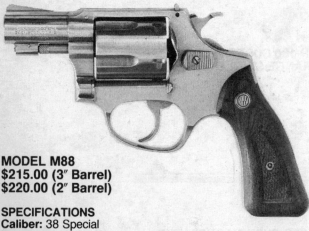

MODEL M88
$215.00 (3″ Barrel)
$220.00 (2″ Barrel)

SPECIFICATIONS
Caliber: 38 Special
Barrel length: 2″, 3″
Capacity: 5 rounds, swing-out cylinder
Weight: 21 oz.
Sights: Ramp front, square notch rear adjustable for windage
Finish: Stainless steel

MODEL 851
$253.00

SPECIFICATIONS
Capacity: 6 rounds
Barrel length: 3″ and 4″
Overall length: 8″ and 9″
Weight: 27½ oz. and 30 oz.
Frame: Medium

RUGER REVOLVERS

ALLOY STEEL REDHAWK

The popular Ruger Redhawk® double-action revolver is now available in an alloy steel model with blued finish in .41 Magnum and .44 Magnum calibers. The newest Redhawk, like the stainless steel model, is constructed of hardened chrome-moly and other alloy steels. The revolver is satin polished to a high lustre and finished in a rich blue.

Catalog Number	Caliber	Barrel Length	Overall Length	Approx. Weight (Ounces)	Price
RUGER REDHAWK REVOLVER					
RH-415	41 Mag.	5½"	11"	52	$436.75
RH-41	41 Mag.	7½"	13"	52	436.75
RH-41R*	41 Mag.	7½"	13"	52	473.00
RH-445	44 Mag.	5½"	11"	52	436.75
RH-44	44 Mag.	7½"	13"	52	436.75
RH-44R*	44 Mag.	7½"	13"	52	473.00

*Scope model, with Integral Scope Mounts, 1" Ruger Scope rings.

The **Super Redhawk** double-action revolver in stainless steel features a heavy extended frame with 7½" and 9½" barrels. Cushioned grip panels contain Goncalo Alves wood grip panel inserts to provide comfortable, nonslip hold.

REDHAWK DOUBLE-ACTION REVOLVER

There is no other revolver like the Ruger Redhawk. Knowledgeable sportsmen reaching for perfection in a big bore revolver will find that the Redhawk demonstrates its superiority at the target, whether silhouette shooting or hunting. Scope sight model shown above incorporates the patented Ruger integral Scope Mounting System with 1" stainless steel Ruger scope rings.

Catalog Number	Caliber	Barrel Length	Overall Length	Approx. Weight (Ounces)	Price
RUGER REDHAWK REVOLVER					
KRH-415	41 Mag.	5½"	11"	52	$492.25
KRH-41	41 Mag.	7½"	13"	52	492.25
KRH-41R*	41 Mag.	7½"	13"	52	530.75
KRH-445	44 Mag.	5½"	11"	52	492.25
KRH-44	44 Mag.	7½"	13"	52	492.25
KRH-44R*	44 Mag.	7½"	13"	52	530.75

*Scope model, with Integral Scope Mounts, 1" Stainless Steel Ruger Scope rings.

SUPER REDHAWK
DOUBLE-ACTION REVOLVER

SPECIFICATIONS
Caliber: 44 Magnum
Barrel length: 7½" and 9½"
Overall length: 13" w/7½" bbl.; 15" w/9½" bbl.
Weight (empty): 3 lbs. 5 oz. (7½" bbl.); 3 lbs. 10 oz. (9½" bbl.)
Sight radius: 9½" (7½" bbl.); 11¼" (9½" bbl.)
Finish: Stainless steel; satin polished

KSRH-7 (7½" barrel) $561.00
KSRH-9 (9½" barrel) 561.00

RUGER REVOLVERS

**BLACKHAWK SINGLE-ACTION
REVOLVER**

SPECIFICATIONS
Caliber: 357 Magnum (interchangeable with 38 Special); 41 Magnum
Barrel lengths: 4⁵/₈″ and 6¹/₂″
Frame: Chrome molybdenum steel with bridge reinforcement and rear-sight guard
Springs: Music wire springs throughout
Weight: 40 oz. with 4⁵/₈″ barrel and 42 oz. with 6¹/₂″ barrel (in 357 Mag.); 38 oz. with 4⁵/₈″ barrel and 40 oz. with 6¹/₂″ barrel (41 Mag.)
Sights: Patridge style, ramp front matted blade ¹/₈″ wide; rear sight click adjustable for windage and elevation
Grips: Genuine walnut
Finish: Polished and blued or stainless steel (357 Mag. only)

Catalog No./Specifications	Prices
BN-34 357 Mag.; 38 Special interchangeably; 4⁵/₈″ barrel	$312.25
KBN-34 Same as BN-34 in stainless steel	384.75
BN-36 357 Mag.; 38 Special interchangeably; 6¹/₂″ barrel	312.25
KBN-36 Same as BN-36 in stainless steel	384.75
BN-34X/36X Same as BN-34/BN-36 fitted with 9mm Parabellum extra cylinder (not available in stainless steel)	327.25
BN-41 41 Magnum; 4⁵/₈″ barrel	312.25
BN-42 41 Magnum; 6¹/₂″ barrel	312.25
BN-44 45 Long Colt; 4⁵/₈″ barrel	312.25
BN-45 45 Long Colt; 7¹/₂″ barrel	312.25
S-45N 44 Magnum; 5¹/₂″ barrel	360.50
KS-45N 44 Mag.; 5¹/₂″ barrel, stainless steel	394.00

**SUPER BLACKHAWK
SINGLE-ACTION REVOLVER**

SPECIFICATIONS
Caliber: 44 Magnum; interchangeable with 44 Special
Barrel: 7¹/₂″, 10¹/₂″
Frame: Chrome molybdenum steel with bridge reinforcement and rear sight guard
Springs: Music wire springs throughout
Weight: 48 oz. (7¹/₂″ bbl.) and 51 oz. (10¹/₂″ bbl.)
Sights: Patridge style, ramp front matted blade ¹/₈″ wide; rear sight click and adjustable for windage and elevation
Grip frame: Chrome molybdenum steel enlarged and contoured to minimize recoil effect

Trigger: Wide spur, low contour, sharply serrated for convenient cocking with minimum disturbance of grip
Overall length: 13³/₈″
Finish: Stainless steel

KS47N 7¹/₂″ barrel with steel grip frame		$394.00
KS411N 10¹/₂″ barrel with steel grip frame		394.00
S47N 7¹/₂″ barrel, with steel grip frame		360.50
S411N 10¹/₂″ barrel, with steel grip frame		360.50

RUGER REVOLVERS

NEW MODEL SUPER SINGLE-SIX REVOLVER

Caliber: 22 LR (fitted with WMR cylinder). **Barrel lengths:** 4⁵/₈″, 5¹/₂″, 6¹/₂″, 9¹/₂″ (stainless steel model in 5¹/₂″ and 6¹/₂″ lengths only). **Weight** (approx.): 33 oz. (with 5¹/₂″ barrel). **Sights:** Patridge-type ramp front sight; rear sight click adjustable for elevation and windage; protected by integral frame ribs. **Finish:** Blue or stainless steel. **Price: $267.75.** In stainless steel: **$337.00.**

NEW MODEL SINGLE-SIX SSM™ REVOLVER
$257.00

Caliber: 32 H&R Magnum; also handles 32 S&W and 32 S&W Long. **Barrel lengths:** 4⁵/₈″, 5¹/₂″, 6¹/₂″, 9¹/₂″. **Weight** (approx.): 34 oz. with 6¹/₂″ barrel.

NEW MODEL BISLEY REVOLVER
$372.25 (not shown)

Calibers: 357 Mag., 41 Mag., 44 Mag., 45 Long Colt. **Barrel length:** 7¹/₂″. **Weight** (approx.): 48 oz. **Sights:** Adjustable rear sight, ramp-style front sight. **Special features:** Unfluted cylinder rollmarked with classic foliate engraving pattern (or fluted cylinder without engraving); hammer is low with smoothly curved, deeply checkered wide spur positioned for easy cocking.

Also available in 22LR and 32 Mag. **Weight:** 41 oz. **Barrel length:** 6¹/₂″. **Sights:** Adjustable or fixed. **Price: $313.00.**

MODEL BN-31
BLACKHAWK SINGLE-ACTION REVOLVER
(In 30 Carbine Caliber) $300.25

Caliber: 30 Carbine. **Barrel length:** 7¹/₂″; 6-groove rifling; 20-inch twist. **Overall length:** 13¹/₈″. **Weight:** 44 oz. **Springs:** Unbreakable music wire springs used throughout; no leaf springs. **Screws:** For security, Nylok® screws are used at all five locations that might be affected by recoil. **Sights:** Patridge-style, ramp front sight with ¹/₈″ wide blade, matted to eliminate glare; rear sight adjustable for windage and elevation. **Ignition system:** Independent alloy steel firing pin, mounted in frame, transfer bar. **Frame:** Same cylinder frame as 44 Mag. Super Blackhawk. **Grips:** Genuine walnut. **Finish:** Polished, blued and anodized.

RUGER REVOLVERS/PISTOLS

MODEL P-85 AUTO PISTOL

MARK II GOVERNMENT
TARGET MODEL (not shown)

SPECIFICATIONS
Caliber: 22 Rimfire. **Capacity:** 10-shot magazine. **Barrel length:** 6⅞″ bull barrel. **Overall length:** 11⅛″. **Weight:** 47½ oz. (loaded). **Sight radius:** 9¼″; laser sighting device.

MODEL MK678G $300.25

GP-100 357 MAGNUM
Cat. No. KGP-161, Stainless
6″ Heavy Barrel

MODEL SP101
5-SHOT REVOLVER

SPECIFICATIONS
Calibers: 22 LR, 38 Special and 38 Special + P. **Barrel lengths:** 2¼″, 3″ and 4″. **Weight:** 1 lb. 9 oz. (2¼″ barrel); 1 lb. 11 oz. (3″ barrel). **Capacity:** 5 rounds (6 rounds in 22 LR). **Features:** One-piece Monsanto Santoprene grips and Xenoy resin inserts provide a secure hold and help reduce recoil. When cylinder is in firing position, it is securely locked to frame in two places, assuring proper cylinder/barrel alignment. Hammer locking mechanism is contained within trigger guard and inserted into frame as a single unit. Can be field-stripped in seconds without special tools. Stainless steel finish.

KSP-221 22 LR (2¼″ barrel) $388.50
KSP-240 22 LR (4″ barrel) 388.50
KSP-241 22 LR (4″ heavy barrel) 388.50
KSP-821 38 Special (2¼″ barrel) 388.50
KSP-830 38 Special (3″ barrel) 388.50

MODEL P-85 AUTO PISTOL

SPECIFICATIONS
Caliber: 9mm. **Action:** Double action. **Capacity:** 15 rounds. **Weight:** 2.38 lbs. (loaded). **Barrel length:** 4½″. **Overall length:** 7.84″. **Sight radius:** 6.12″. **Mechanism type:** Recoil-operated, semiautomatic. **Breech locking mode:** Tilting barrel, link actuated.

P-85, P-85D, P-85DA $357.50
P-85C, P-85DC, P-85DAC with plastic case,
   decocker and/or extra magazine 390.50
Stainless Steel (all models) add: 40.00

RUGER SP101
Cat. No. KSP-821, 38 Special

GP-100 357 MAGNUM

The GP-100 is designed for the unlimited use of 357 Magnum ammunition in all factory loadings; it combines strength and reliability with accuracy and shooting comfort. (Revolvers chambered for the 357 Magnum cartridge also accept the 38 Special cartridge.)

SPECIFICATIONS

Catalog Number	Finish*	Sights†	Shroud††	Barrel Length	Wt. (oz.)	Prices
GP-141	B	A	F	4″	41	$393.75
GP-160	B	A	S	6″	43	393.75
GP-161	B	A	F	6″	46	393.75
GPF-330	B	F	S	3″	35	378.00
GPF-331	B	F	F	3″	36	378.00
GPF-340	B	F	S	4″	37	378.00
GPF-341	B	F	F	4″	38	378.00
KGP-141	S	A	F	4″	41	425.25
KGP-160	S	A	S	6″	43	425.25
KGP-161	S	A	F	6″	46	425.25
KGPF-330	S	F	S	3″	35	409.50
KGPF-331	S	F	F	3″	36	409.50
KGPF-340	S	F	S	4″	37	409.50
KGPF-341	S	F	F	4″	38	409.50

* B = blued; S = stainless. † A = adjustable; F = fixed. †† F = full; S = short.

RUGER 22 AUTOMATIC PISTOLS

RUGER MARK II STANDARD MODEL

SPECIFICATIONS

Caliber: 22 Long Rifle only, standard or high velocity. **Barrel:** 4³/₄" or 6" length; medium weight; 6-groove rifling; 14" twist. **Weight:** 2¹/₄ lbs. with 4³/₄" barrel. **Overall length:** 8⁵/₁₆" with 4³/₄" barrel; 10⁵/₁₆" with 6" barrel. **Sights:** Front sight is fixed, .093" wide blade Patridge-type; square notch rear sight is dovetail mounted and can be adjusted for windage. **Sight radius:** 7¹/₂" with 4³/₄" barrel. Catalog No. MK-4 (4³/₄" barrel) blued finish; MK-6 (6" barrel) blued finish; KMK-4 (4³/₄" barrel) stainless steel; KMK-6 (6" barrel) stainless steel.

MK-4, MK-6	**$224.75**
KMK-4, KMK-6	299.25

RUGER MARK II TARGET MODEL

SPECIFICATIONS

Same as for Mark II Model with the following exceptions. **Barrel:** 6⁷/₈" tapered, button rifled. **Weight:** Approx. 2⁵/₈ lbs. **Overall length:** 11¹/₈". **Sights:** Patridge-type front blade, .125" wide, undercut to prevent glare; rear sight with click adjustments for windage and elevation. **Sight radius:** 9¹/₄" for 6⁷/₈" barrel.

MK-678 Blued	**$280.50**
KMK-678 Stainless steel	355.25
MK678G Bull barrel, Govt. Model	324.25

The Mark II Bull barrel pistol is identical to the Mark II Target Model except that it is equipped with a heavier Bull barrel offered in two lengths, 5¹/₂ inches/10 inches. The Bull barrel configuration was developed to meet the needs of those shooters who prefer a greater concentration of weight at the muzzle. The longer barrel model meets all IHMSA regulations.

SPECIFICATIONS

Same as for Mark II model with the following exceptions: **Barrel:** 5¹/₂" or 10"; button rifled; shorter barrel untapered, longer barrel has slight taper. **Weight:** Approx. 2⁵/₇ lbs. with 5¹/₂" barrel; 3¹/₄ lbs. with 10" barrel. **Sights:** Patridge-type front sight. Rear sight with click adjustments for windage and elevation. **Sight radius:** 7⁷/₈" for 5¹/₂" barrel, 12³/₈" for 10" barrel; blued finish. Catalog No. MK-512 5¹/₂" barrel and MK-10 10" barrel.

RUGER MARK II BULL BARREL MODEL

MK-512 and MK-10 Blued	**$280.50**
KMK-512 and KMK-10 Stainless steel	355.25

SIG SAUER DOUBLE ACTION PISTOLS

MODEL 220 "EUROPEAN"

MODEL 220 "EUROPEAN"

SPECIFICATIONS
Caliber: 38 Super, 9mm Parabellum, 45 ACP
Capacity: 9 rounds; 7 rounds in 45 ACP
Barrel length: 4.4″
Overall length: 7.79″
Weight (empty): 26½ oz.; 25.7 oz. in 45 ACP
Finish: Blue
Prices:
In 9mm Para. & 38 Super $695.00
In 45 ACP 720.00
    Electroless nickel w/"Siglite" night sights 890.00
    Blue w/"Siglite" night sights 820.00

MODEL 225 (not shown)

SPECIFICATIONS
Caliber: 9mm Parabellum
Capacity: 8 rounds
Barrel length: 3.85″
Overall length: 7″
Weight (empty): 26.1 oz.
Finish: Blue
Price: $750.00
    850.00 with "Siglite" night sights

MODEL 226

SPECIFICATIONS
Caliber: 9mm Parabellum
Capacity: 15 rounds
Barrel length: 4.4″
Overall length: 7¾″
Weight (empty): 26.5 oz.
Finish: Blue
Price: $780.00
    880.00 with "Siglite" night sights
    815.00 with K-Kote
    915.00 with K-Kote & "Siglite" night sights
Also available:
MODEL 228. Slightly smaller (7.08″) than Model 226, fires 13 rounds. **Price: $780.00** (add **$100.00** for "Siglite" night sights).

MODEL 226

MODEL 230

MODEL 230

SPECIFICATIONS
Caliber: 380ACP
Capacity: 7 rounds
Barrel length: 3.6″
Overall length: 6.6″
Weight (empty): 16¼ oz.; 20.8 oz. in stainless steel
Finish: Blue and stainless steel
Price: $495.00 in blue
    575.00 in stainless steel

SMITH & WESSON AUTO PISTOLS

MODEL 422
22 SINGLE ACTION
$206.00 (Fixed Sight)
$257.00 (Adjustable Sight)

Caliber: 22 LR
Capacity: 10 round (magazine furnished)
Barrel lengths: 4¹/₂″ and 6″
Overall length: 7¹/₂″ (4¹/₂″ barrel) and 9″ (6″ barrel)
Weight: 22 oz. (4¹/₂″ barrel) and 23 oz. (6″ barrel)
Stock: Plastic (field version) and checkered walnut w/S&W monogram (target version)
Front sight: Serrated ramp w/.125″ blade (field version); Patridge w/.125″ blade (target version)
Rear sight: Fixed sight w/.125″ blade (field version): adjustable sight w/.125″ blade (target version)
Hammer: .250″ internal
Trigger: .312″ serrated
Also available:
MODEL 622. Same specifications as Model 422 in stainless steel. **Price: $266.00.** (Add $50 for adj. sights).

22 CAL. AUTOMATIC PISTOL
MODEL NO. 41
$657.50 Blue Only

Caliber: 22 Long Rifle
Magazine capacity: 10 rounds
Barrel lengths: 5¹/₂″ and 7″
Overall length: 12″ with 7³/₈″ barrel
Sight radius: 9⁵/₁₆″ with 7³/₈″ barrel
Weight: 43¹/₂ oz. with 7³/₈″ barrel
Sights: Front, ¹/₈″ Patridge undercut; rear, S&W micrometer click sight adjustable for windage and elevation
Stocks: Checkered walnut with modified thumb rest, equally adaptable to right- or left-handed shooters
Finish: S&W Bright Blue
Trigger: ³/₈″ width, with S&W grooving and an adjustable trigger stop

38 MASTER MODEL NO. 52
SINGLE ACTION CENTERFIRE PISTOL
$834.00 Bright Blue Only

Caliber: 38 S&W Special (for Mid-Range Wad Cutter only)
Magazine capacity: 5 rounds (2 five-round magazines furnished)
Barrel length: 5″
Overall length: 8⁵/₈″
Sight radius: 6¹⁵/₁₆″
Weight: 41 oz. with empty magazine
Sights: Front, ¹/₈″ Patridge on ramp base; rear, new S&W micrometer click sight with wide ⁷/₈″ sight slide
Stocks: Checkered walnut with S&W monograms
Finish: S&W Bright Blue with sandblast stippling around sighting area to break up light reflection
Trigger: ³/₈″ width with S&W grooving and an adjustable trigger stop

SMITH & WESSON PISTOLS
THIRD GENERATION DOUBLE ACTION PISTOLS

Smith & Wesson's double-action semiautomatic line includes 12 custom-built pistols combining the following features: fixed barrel bushing for greater accuracy; smoother trigger pull plus a slimmer, contoured grip and lateral relief cut where trigger guard meets frame; three-dot sights; wraparound grips; beveled magazine well for easier reloading; ambidextrous safety lever secured by spring-loaded plunger; low-glare bead-blasted finish.

MODEL 3900 SERIES
$545.00 (Model 3904)
$596.00 (Model 3906)

Caliber: 9mm Auto-Loading DA Luger (Parabellum)
Capacity: 8 rounds
Barrel length: 4″
Overall length: 7¹/₂″
Weight (empty): 25¹/₂ oz. (Model 3904); 34 oz. (Model 3906)
Sights: Post w/white dot front; fixed rear adj. for windage only w/2 white dots. Adjustable sight models include micrometer click, adj. for windage and elevation w/2 white dots. Deduct **$25** for fixed sights.
Finish: Blue (Model 3904); satin stainless (Model 3906)

Also available:
MODEL 3913 w/3¹/₂″ barrel (6.8″ overall). Stainless finish. **Price: $541.00.**
MODEL 3914. w/same specifications as Model 3913, in blue finish. **Price: $493.00.**
MODEL 3913 LADYSMITH and **MODEL 3914 LADYSMITH** also available (w/same prices and specifications).

MODEL 3904
FIXED SIGHT

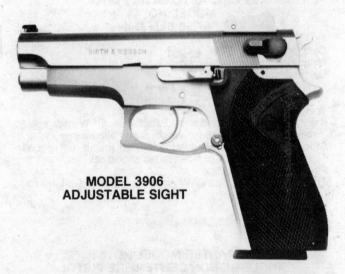

MODEL 3906
ADJUSTABLE SIGHT

MODEL 4506
FIXED SIGHT

MODEL 4500 SERIES
$674.00 (Models 4506 and 4516)

Caliber: 45 ACP Auto-Loading DA
Capacity: 8 rounds (Model 4506); 7 rounds (Model 4516)
Barrel length: 5″ (Model 4506); 3³/₄″ (Model 4516)
Overall length: 8¹/₂″
Weight (empty): 36 oz. (Model 4506); 34 oz. (Model 4516)
Sights: Post w/white dot front; fixed rear, adj. for windage only. Adj. sight incl. micrometer click, adj. for windage and elevation w/2 white dots. Add **$27.00** for adj. sights.
Stocks: Delrin one-piece wraparound, arched backstrap, textured surface
Finish: Satin stainless

SMITH & WESSON PISTOLS
THIRD GENERATION DOUBLE ACTION PISTOLS

MODEL 5900 SERIES
$570.00 (Model 5904)
$621.00 (Model 5906)

Caliber: 9mm Auto-Loading DA Luger (Parabellum)
Capacity: 14 rounds
Barrel length: 4"
Overall length: 7$\frac{1}{2}$"
Weight (empty): 26 oz. (Model 5904); 34$\frac{1}{2}$ oz. (Model 5906)
Sights: Post w/white dot front; fixed rear, adj. for windage only w/2 white dots. Adjustable sight models include micrometer click, adj. for windage and elevation w/2 white dots. Add **$27** for adj. sights.
Finish: Blue (Model 5904); satin stainless (Model 5906)

Also available:
MODEL 5903. Same as Model 5906, except with aluminum alloy frame. **Price: $600.00.** (Add **$28** for adjustable sight).

MODEL 5904
FIXED SIGHT

MODEL 5906
ADJUSTABLE SIGHT

MODEL 6904
FIXED SIGHT

MODEL 6900 SERIES
$539.00 (Model 6904)
$589.00 (Model 6906)

Caliber: 9mm Auto-Loading DA Luger (Parabellum)
Capacity: 12 rounds
Barrel length: 3$\frac{1}{2}$"
Overall length: 6$\frac{7}{8}$"
Weight (empty): 23$\frac{1}{2}$ oz.
Sights: Post w/white dot front; fixed rear, adj. for windage only w/2 white dots
Stocks: Delrin one-piece wraparound, arched backstrap, textured surface
Finish: Blue (Model 6904); clear anodized/satin stainless (Model 6906)

SMITH & WESSON REVOLVERS
SMALL FRAME

32 REGULATION POLICE
MODEL NO. 31
$365.00

Caliber: 32 S&W Long
Number of shots: 6
Barrel length: 2″, 3″
Overall length: 8 1/2″ with 4″ barrel
Weight: 18 3/4 oz. with 4″ barrel
Sights: Front, fixed, 1/10″ serrated ramp; rear square notch
Stocks: Checked walnut Service with S&W monograms
Finish: S&W blue

MODEL NO. 34
1953 22/32 KIT GUN
$366.00 Blue

Caliber: 22 Long Rifle
Number of shots: 6
Barrel length: 2″, 4″
Overall length: 8″ with 4″ barrel and round butt
Weight: 22 1/4 oz. with 4″ barrel and round butt
Sights: Front, 1/10″ serrated ramp; rear, S&W micrometer click
sight adjustable for windage and elevation
Stocks: Checked walnut Service with S&W monograms, round
or square butt
Finish: S&W blue

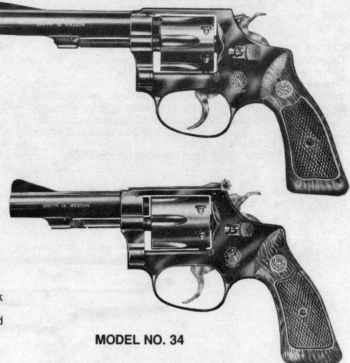

MODEL NO. 34

MODELS 36-LS & 60-LS
LADYSMITH HANDGUNS
$352.00
$379.00 w/carrying case

Caliber: 38
Capacity: 5 shots
Barrel length: 2″ or 3″
Sights: Serrated ramp front; fixed notch rear
Grips: Contoured rosewood (2″ barrel); Goncalo Alves finger-
grooved stocks w/Carnauba wax finish (3″ barrel)
Finish: Glossy deep blue
Features: Model 36-LS is made of carbon steel
MODEL 60-LS has the same specifications as Model 36-LS,
but is made of stainless steel with a frosted finish. **Price:**
$400.00. (Add **$27** for carrying case).

MODEL 36 LADYSMITH

MODEL 60 LADYSMITH

SMITH & WESSON REVOLVERS
SMALL FRAME

38 CHIEFS SPECIAL MODEL 36
$338.00 Blue
$349.00 Nickel

Caliber: 38 S&W Special
Number of shots: 5
Barrel length: 2″ or 3″
Overall length: 6¹/₂″ with 2″ barrel and round butt
Weight: 19 oz. with 2″ barrel and round butt
Sights: Front, fixed, ¹/₁₀″ serrated ramp; rear square notch
Stocks: Checked walnut Service with S&W monograms, round or square butt
Finish: S&W blue or nickel
MODEL 37: Same as Model 36 except weight 14 oz. **$331.00;** with nickel finish **$344.00.**

38 BODYGUARD "AIRWEIGHT"
MODEL NO. 38
$379.00 Blue
$392.00 Nickel

Caliber: 38 S&W Special
Number of shots: 5
Barrel length: 2″
Overall length: 6³/₈″
Weight: 14¹/₂ oz.
Sights: Front, fixed ¹/₁₀″ serrated ramp; rear square notch
Stocks: Checked walnut Service with S&W monograms
Finish: S&W blue or nickel

38 BODYGUARD MODEL 49
$359.00

Caliber: 38 S&W Special
Capacity: 5-shot cylinder
Barrel length: 2″
Overall length: 6¹/₄″
Weight (empty): 20 oz.
Sights: Serrated ramp (front); fixed square notch (rear)
Finish: S&W blue

SMITH & WESSON REVOLVERS
SMALL FRAME

38 CHIEFS SPECIAL STAINLESS
MODEL NO. 60
$386.00

Caliber: 38 S&W Special
Number of shots: 5
Barrel length: 2″
Overall length: 6¹/₂″
Weight: 19 oz.
Sights: Front fixed, ¹/₁₀″ serrated ramp; rear square notch
Stocks: Checked walnut Service with S&W monograms
Finish: Satin

MODEL NO. 63
1977 22/32 KIT GUN
$402.00

Caliber: 22 Long Rifle
Number of shots: 6
Barrel length: 4″
Weight: 24¹/₂ oz. (empty)
Sights: ¹/₈″ red ramp front sight; rear sight is black stainless steel S&W micrometer click square-notch, adjustable for windage and elevation
Stocks: Square butt
Finish: Satin stainless

MODEL NO. 63

MODEL 649 BODYGUARD
$408.00

Caliber: 38 Special
Capacity: 5 shots
Barrel length: 2″
Overall length: 6¹/₄″
Sights: Serrated ramp front, fixed square notch rear
Weight: 20 oz.
Grips: Round butt; checkered walnut service
Finish: Stainless steel

SMITH & WESSON REVOLVERS

MEDIUM FRAME

38 MILITARY & POLICE
MODEL NO. 10
$333.00 Blue
$345.00 Nickel (4″ barrel only)

Caliber: 38 S&W Special
Capacity: 6 shots
Barrel length: 2″, 4″ (also 4″ heavy barrel)
Weight: 30½ oz. with 4″ barrel
Sights: Front, fixed ⅛″ serrated ramp; rear square notch
Stocks: Checkered walnut Service with S&W monograms, round or square butt
Finish: S&W blue or nickel

357 MILITARY & POLICE (HEAVY BARREL)
MODEL NO. 13
$339.00

Caliber: 357 Magnum and 38 S&W Special
Rounds: 6-shot cylinder capacity
Barrel length: 3″ and 4″
Overall length: 9¼″
Weight: 34 oz.
Sights: Front, ⅛″ serrated ramp; rear square notch
Stocks: Checkered walnut Service with S&W monograms, square butt (3″ barrel has round butt)
Finish: S&W blue

38 COMBAT MASTERPIECE
MODEL NO. 15
$361.00

Caliber: 38 S&W Special
Number of shots: 6
Barrel lengths: 2″, 4″, 6″
Overall length: 7¼″ (2″ barrel); 9⁵⁄₁₆″ (4″ barrel); 11⅛″ (6″ barrel)
Weight (loaded): 34 oz. with 4″ barrel
Sights: Front, ⅛″ Baughman Quick Draw on plain ramp; rear, S&W micrometer click sight adjustable for windage and elevation
Stocks: Checkered walnut Service with S&W monograms
Finish: S&W blue or nickel

SMITH & WESSON REVOLVERS

MEDIUM FRAME

K-22 MASTERPIECE
MODEL NO. 17
$379.00 (4″ or 6″ barrel)
$427.00 (8³⁄₈″ barrel)

Caliber: 22 Long Rifle
Number of shots: 6
Barrel length: 4″, 6″, 8³⁄₈″
Overall length: 9⁵⁄₁₆″ (4″ barrel); 11¹⁄₈″ (6″ barrel); 13¹⁄₂″ (8³⁄₈″ barrel)
Weight (loaded): 38¹⁄₂ oz. with 6″ barrel; 42¹⁄₂ oz. with 8³⁄₈″ barrel
Sights: Front, ¹⁄₈″ plain Patridge; rear, S&W micrometer click sight adjustable for windage and elevation
Stocks: Checkered walnut Service with S&W monograms
Finish: S&W blue

357 COMBAT MAGNUM
MODEL NO. 19
$355.00—$421.00 Bright Blue or Nickel

Caliber: 357 Magnum (actual bullet dia. 38 S&W Spec.)
Number of shots: 6
Barrel length: 2¹⁄₂″, 4″ and 6″
Overall length: 9¹⁄₂″ with 4″ barrel; 7¹⁄₂″ with 2¹⁄₂″ barrel; 11¹⁄₂″ with 6″ barrel
Weight: 35 oz. (2¹⁄₂″ model weighs 31 oz.)
Sights: Front, ¹⁄₈″ Baughman Quick Draw on 2¹⁄₂″ or 4″ barrel, ¹⁄₈″ Patridge on 6″ barrel; rear, S&W micrometer click sight adjustable for windage and elevation
Stocks: Checkered Goncalo Alves Target with S&W monograms
Finish: S&W bright blue or nickel

38 MILITARY & POLICE STAINLESS
MODEL NO. 64
$417.00

Caliber: 38 S&W Special
Capacity: 6 shots
Barrel length: 4″ heavy barrel, square butt; 3″ heavy barrel, round butt; 2″ regular barrel, round butt
Overall length: 9¹⁄₄″ w/4″ barrel; 7⁷⁄₈″ w/3″ barrel; 6⁷⁄₈″ w/2″ barrel
Weight: With 4″ barrel, 34 oz.; with 3″ barrel, 30¹⁄₂ oz.; with 2″ barrel, 28 oz.
Sights: Fixed, ¹⁄₈″ serrated ramp front; square notch rear
Stocks: Checked walnut Service with S&W monograms
Finish: Satin
Ammunition: 38 S&W Special, 38 S&W Special Mid Range

SMITH & WESSON REVOLVERS

MEDIUM FRAME

357 MILITARY & POLICE STAINLESS HEAVY BARREL MODEL NO. 65
$368.00

Caliber: 357 Magnum and 38 S&W Special
Rounds: 6-shot cylinder capacity
Barrel length: 4″ heavy barrel, square butt; 3″ heavy barrel, round butt
Length overall: With 4″ barrel, 9¼″; with 3″ barrel, 7⁵/₁₆″
Weight: With 4″ barrel, 34 oz.; with 3″ barrel, 31 oz.
Sights: Fixed, ⅛″ serrated ramp front; square notch rear
Stocks: Checked walnut Service with S&W monograms, square butt
Finish: Satin

357 COMBAT MAGNUM
MODEL NO. 66
$404.00—$450.00 Stainless Steel

Caliber: 357 Magnum (actual bullet dia. 38 S&W Spec.)
Number of shots: 6
Barrel length: 6″ or 4″ with square butt; 2½″ with round butt
Length overall: 9½″ with 4″ barrel; 7½″ with 2½″ barrel; 11³/₈″ with 6″ barrel
Weight: 35 oz. with 4″ barrel; 30½ oz. with 2½″ barrel; 39 oz. with 6″ barrel
Sights: Front: ⅛″. Rear: S&W Red Ramp on ramp base, S&W Micrometer Click Sight, adjustable for windage and elevation
Stocks: Checked Goncalo Alves target with square butt with S&W monograms
Finish: Satin
Trigger: S&W grooving with an adjustable trigger stop
Ammunition: 357 S&W Magnum, 38 S&W Special Hi-Speed, 38 S&W Special, 38 S&W Special Mid Range

DISTINGUISHED COMBAT MAGNUM
MODEL 586
$401.00—$436.00 (Blue or Nickel)

Caliber: 357 Magnum
Capacity: 6 shots
Barrel length: 4″, 6″, 8³/₈″
Overall length: 9³/₄″ with 4″ barrel; 11½″ with 6″ barrel; 13¹³/₁₆″ with 8³/₈″ barrel
Weight: 42 oz. with 4″ barrel; 46 oz. with 6″ barrel; 53 oz. with 8³/₈″ barrel
Sights: Front is S&W Red Ramp; rear is S&W Micrometer Click adjustable for windage and elevation; White outline notch. Option with 6″ barrel only—plain Patridge front with black outline notch
Stocks: Checkered Goncalo Alves with speedloader cutaway
Finish: S&W Blue or Nickel
MODEL 686: Same as Model 586 except finish is stainless steel, $422.00—$479.00.

SMITH & WESSON REVOLVERS

LARGE FRAME

MODEL NO. 25
$429.00 (4″ and 6″)
$437.00 (8³/₈″)

Caliber: 45 Colt
Capacity: 6 shots
Barrel lengths: 4″, 6″, 8³/₈″
Overall lengths: 9⁹/₁₆″ (4″ barrel); 11³/₈″ (6″ barrel); 13⁷/₈″ (8³/₈″ barrel)
Weight (empty): 44 oz. (4″ barrel); 46 oz. (6″ barrel); 50 oz. (8³/₈″ barrel)
Sights: S&W red ramp on ramp base (front); S&W micrometer click sight w/white outline notch (rear), adj. for windage and elevation
Finish: S&W Bright blue or nickel

357 MAGNUM MODEL NO. 27
$451.00 (4″) $423.00 (6″)
$431.00 (8³/₈″)

Caliber: 357 Magnum (actual bullet dia. 38 S&W Spec.)
Number of shots: 6
Barrel length: 4″, 6″ and 8³/₈″
Weight: 44 oz. with 4″ barrel; 45¹/₂ oz. with 6″; 49 oz. with 8³/₈″
Sights: Front, S&W Red Ramp (4″ barrel) and Patridge (6″ and 8³/₈″ barrels); rear, S&W micrometer click sight adjustable for windage and elevation
Stocks: Checkered walnut Service with S&W monograms
Frame: Finely checked top strap and barrel rib
Finish: S&W bright blue or nickel

44 MAGNUM MODEL NO. 29
$482.00 (4″ and 6″) $492.00 (8³/₈″)
$527.00 (8³/₈″, w/scope mount)
$536.00 (10⁵/₈″ Blue only)

Caliber: 44 Magnum
Number of shots: 6
Barrel lengths: 4″, 6″, 8³/₈″ and 10⁵/₈″ (blue only)
Overall length: 11⁷/₈″ with 6¹/₂″ barrel
Weight: 43 oz. with 4″ barrel; 47 oz. with 6″ barrel; 51¹/₂ oz. with 8³/₈″ barrel
Sights: Front, ¹/₈″ S&W Red Ramp; rear, S&W micrometer click sight adjustable for windage and elevation; white outline notch
Stocks: Special oversize target type of checked Goncalo Alves; with S&W monograms
Hammer: Checkered target type
Trigger: Grooved target type
Finish: S&W bright blue or nickel
Also available in nickel: **$492.50** (4″ and 6″) and **$503.00** (8³/₈″).

SMITH & WESSON REVOLVERS

LARGE FRAME

41 MAGNUM MODEL NO. 57
$427.00 (4″ and 6″)
$442.00 (8³/₈″)

Caliber: 41 Magnum
Number of shots: 6
Barrel length: 4″, 6″ and 8³/₈″
Overall length: 11³/₈″ with 6″ barrel
Weight: 48 oz. with 6″ barrel
Sights: Front, ¹/₈″ S&W Red Ramp; rear, S&W micrometer click sight adjustable for windage and elevation; white outline notch
Stocks: Special oversize Target type of checkered Goncalo Alves, with S&W monograms
Hammer: Checked target type
Trigger: Grooved target type
Finish: S&W bright blue

MODEL 625 (not shown)
$535.00

Caliber: 45 ACP
Capacity: 6 shots
Barrel lengths: 3″, 4″, 5″
Overall length: 8³/₈″, 9³/₈″, 10³/₈″
Weight (empty): 41 oz. (3″ barrel); 43 oz. (4″), 46 oz. (5″)
Sights: Serrated black ramp front; S&W micrometer click rear, adj. for windage and elevation
Stock: Packmayr SK/GR gripper, round butt

MODEL 629 (not shown)
$510.00

Calibers: 44 Magnum, 44 S&W Special
Capacity: 6 shots
Barrel lengths: 4″, 6″, 8³/₈″
Overall length: 9⁵/₈″, 11³/₈″, 13⁷/₈″
Weight (empty): 44 oz. (4″); 47 oz. (6″ barrel); 51¹/₂ oz. (8³/₈″)
Sights: S&W red ramp front; plain blade rear w/S&W micrometer click; adj. for windage and elevation; scope mount
Stock: Checkered Goncalo Alves target
Finish: Stainless steel

MODEL 657 STAINLESS
$471.00 (8³/₈″)
$455.00 (6″)

Caliber: 41 Magnum
Capacity: 6 shots
Barrel lengths: 6″, 8³/₈″
Overall length: 11³/₈″ (6″ barrel); 13¹⁵/₁₆″ (8³/₈″ barrel)
Weight (empty): 48 oz. (6″ barrel); 52¹/₂ oz. (8³/₈″ barrel)
Sights: Serrated black ramp on ramp base (front); Blue S&W micrometer click sight adj. for windage and elevation (rear)
Finish: Satin

SPRINGFIELD ARMORY

**MODEL 1911-A1
STANDARD**

**MODEL 1911-A1
COMMANDER**

MODEL 1911-A1 STANDARD

An exact duplicate of the M1911-A1 pistol that served the U.S. Armed Forces for more than 70 years, this model has been precision manufactured from forged parts, including a forged frame, then hand-assembled.

SPECIFICATIONS
Calibers: 9mm Parabellum, 10mm, 38 Super and 45 ACP
Capacity: 8 in mag. 1 in chamber (9mm); 7 in mag. 1 in chamber (45 ACP)
Barrel length: 5.04″
Overall length: 8.59″
Weight: 35.62 oz.
Trigger pull: 5 to 6.5 lbs.
Sight radius: 6.481″
Rifling: 1 turn in 16; left-hand, 4-groove (9mm); right-hand, 6-groove (45 ACP)

MODEL 1911-A1 (45 ACP or 9mm)
Blued **$487.00**
Same model with Parkerized finish **454.00**

1911-A1 DEFENDER w/fixed combat sights, bobbed hammer, walnut grips, beveled magazine well, extended thumb safety, 45 ACP, Parkerized finish **567.00**
Same as above w/blued finish **601.00**

1911-A1 COMMANDER with ½″ shortened slide and barrel, 45 ACP, Parkerized finish **514.00**
Same as above w/blued finish **545.00**

1911-A1 38 SUPER w/Parkerized finish **643.00**
Same as above w/blued finish **676.00**

1911-A1 COMPACT w/blued finish **545.00**
Same as above w/duotone finish **592.00**

**1911-A2 S.A.S.S.
SPRINGFIELD ARMORY SINGLE SHOT**

MODEL 1911-A2 S.A.S.S.
(Springfield Armory Single Shot)

SPECIFICATIONS
Calibers: 22 LR, 44 Mag., 357 Mag., 7mm BR (10.7″ barrel); 358 Win., 7mm × 308, 223 and 308 (14.9″ barrel)
Barrel length: 10.7″ or 14.9″ (interchangeable)
Prices:
1911-A2 S.A.S.S. 14.9″ barrel **$519.00**
10.7″ barrel **519.00**
Conversion Units 14.9″ barrel **259.00**
10.7″ barrel **259.00**
Interchangeable Barrels 14.9″ barrel **128.70**
10.7″ barrel **128.70**

SPRINGFIELD ARMORY

OMEGA

Springfield's Omega model includes a ported slide with adjustable rear sight and interchangeable front sights; a hammer forged polygon barrel (with or without stabilizing ports); special lockup system for greater safety with high velocity loads; and a dual extractor system for fast barrel changes.

SPECIFICATIONS
Calibers: 10mm, 38 Super, 45 ACP (interchangeable)
Barrel length: 5″ or 6″
Overall length: 8.53″ (5″ barrel); 9.53″ (6″ barrel)
Weight: 42.88 oz. (5″ barrel); 45.36 oz. (6″ barrel)
Rifling: 6 grooves, right-hand; 1 turn in 14 (38 Spec.); 1 turn in 16 (10mm); 1 turn in 18 (45 ACP)
Grips: Rubberized wraparound
Finish: Blue
Price: . . . . $ 849.00
Interchangeable barrels with hard chrome slide, blued frame, unported barrel (5″ and 6″) **1233.00**
Note: in 6″ model, 38 Special is available unported only; 5″ available ported or unported in all 3 calibers.

OMEGA

MODEL P9 DOUBLE ACTION

MODEL P9 DOUBLE ACTION

SPECIFICATIONS
Caliber: 9mm Parabellum
Capacity: 16 rounds; 10 rounds Compact Model
Barrel length: 4.72″; 3.66″ Compact Model
Overall length: 8.1″; 7.24″ Compact Model
Weight: 35.3 oz.; 32.1 oz. Compact Model
Rifling: Right-hand; 1 turn in 10″, 4-groove
Grips: Checkered walnut
Features: Serrated front and rear frame straps; frame-mounted thumb safety, Commander-style hammer
Prices:
P9 STANDARD (Parkerized finish) **$467.00**
P9C COMPACT MODEL **485.00**
P9 LSP (Long Slide Ported) **493.00**

MODEL P9C COMPACT

MODEL P9 LSP

STAR AUTOMATIC PISTOLS

STAR BKM & BM
9mm PARABELLUM

The Model BM offers all-steel construction, and the BKM offers a high strength, weight-saving duraluminum frame. An improved thumb safety locks both the slide and hammer with hammer cocked or uncocked; further, an automatic magazine safety llocks the sear when the magazine is removed.

Barrel length: 3.9″. **Overall length:** 7.17″. **Magazine capacity:** 8 rounds. **Weight:** 34.06 oz. (BM); 25.59 oz. (BKM)

Model BM Blue	**$375.00**
Model BM Starvel	425.00
Model BKM Blue	395.00

MODEL BM

STAR MODELS 31P & 31PK
9mm PARABELLUM

The Model 31 features a staggered 15-round button release magazine, square notch rear sight (click-adjustable for windage) and square front sight (notched to diffuse light). Removable backstrap houses complete firing mechanism. All-steel frame (Model 31PK has alloy frame).

Barrel length: 3.86″. **Overall length:** 7.06″. **Weight:** 39.4 oz.; 30 oz. (Model 31PK)

Model 31P Blue finish	**$535.00**
Starvel finish	570.00
Model 31PK Alloy frame	535.00
Model 30M Steel frame...................	535.00

MODEL 31PK

MODEL M43 FIRESTAR
9mm PARABELLUM

This pocket-sized pistol (one of the smallest 9mm's on the market) features all-steel construction, a triple-dot sight system (fully adjustable rear), and ambidextrous safety. The Acculine barrel design reseats and locks the barrel after each shot. Checkered rubber grips.

Barrel length: 3.39″. **Overall length:** 6½″. **Weight:** 30.65 oz. **Capacity:** 7 rounds.

Firestar Blue finish	**$405.00**
Firestar Starvel finish	435.00

MODEL M43 FIRESTAR

MODEL PD

STAR MODEL PD
45 ACP

Chambered for the sledgehammer 45 ACP, the PD is one of the smallest .45 caliber production pistols in the world.

Barrel length: 4″. **Overall length:** 7″. **Weight:** 25.5 oz. **Finish:** Blue. **Capacity:** 6 rounds.

Model PD Blue finish.....................	**$450.00**
Model PD w/Starvel finish................	495.00

TANARMI/TARGA

**TANARMI
MODEL BTA90C
$430.00 Blue
$450.00 Chrome**

SPECIFICATIONS
Caliber: 9mm Para.
Barrel length: 4″
Weight: 30 oz.
Capacity: 12 shots
Finish: Matte chrome
Frame: Steel
Grips: Neoprene

**TANARMI
MODEL TA90B
$415.00 Blue ($500 w/adj. sights)
$430.00 Chrome**

SPECIFICATIONS
Calibers: 9mm Para., 41 AE
Barrel length: 4³/₄″
Capacity: 15 shots
Finish: Matte blue or chrome
Grips: Black Neoprene
Sights: Available with adjustable
    sights; add **$85.00**

**TARGA
MODEL GT380XE
$235.00**

SPECIFICATIONS
Caliber: 380 ACP
Capacity: 11 shots
Barrel length: 3.88″
Weight: 26 oz.
Finish: Satin blue
Frame: Steel
Grips: Walnut

**TARGA
MODEL GT26S
$115.00**

SPECIFICATIONS
Caliber: 25 ACP
Capacity: 6 shots
Barrel length: 2¹/₄″
Weight: 15 oz.
Frame: Steel
Finish: Satin blue
Grips: Walnut

**TARGA
MODEL GT22T
$200.00**

SPECIFICATIONS
Caliber: 22 LR
Capacity: 12 shots
Barrel length: 6″
Weight: 28 oz.
Frame: Steel
Finish: Satin blue
Grips: Walnut

TAURUS PISTOLS

MODEL PT 92

Caliber: 9mm Parabellum
Action: Semiautomatic double action
Hammer: Exposed
Barrel length: 4.92″
Overall length: 8.54″
Height: 5.39″
Width: 1.45″
Weight: 34 oz. (empty)
Rifling: R.H., 6 grooves
Front sight: Blade integral with slide
Rear sight: Notched bar dovetailed to slide
Safeties: (a) Ambidextrous manual safety locking trigger mechanism and slide in locked position; (b) half-cock position; (c) inertia operated firing pin; (d) chamber loaded indicator
Magazine: Staggered 15-shot capacity
Slide: Hold open upon firing last cartridge
Finish: Blue or satin nickel
Grips: Smooth Brazilian walnut

MODEL PT 92
$446.00 (Blue)
$482.00 (Nickel)

MODEL PT 99

Caliber: 9mm Parabellum
Action: Semiautomatic double action
Hammer: Exposed
Barrel length: 4.92″
Overall length: 8.54″
Height: 5.39″
Width: 1.45″
Weight: 34 oz. (empty)
Rifling: R.H., 6 grooves
Front sight: Blade Integral with slide
Rear sight: Micrometer click adjustable for elevation and windage
Safeties: (a) Ambidextrous manual safety locking trigger mechanism and slide in locked position; (b) half-cock position; (c) inertia operated firing pin; (d) chamber loaded indicator. **Magazine:** Staggered, 15-shot capacity
Slide: Hold open upon firing last cartridge
Finish: Blue or satin nickel
Grips: Smooth Brazilian walnut

MODEL PT 99
$483.00 (Blue)
$523.00 (Nickel)

MODEL PT 58

SPECIFICATIONS
Caliber: 380 ACP
Action: Semiautomatic double action
Capacity: Staggered 13 shot
Barrel length: 4″
Overall length: 7.1″
Weight: 30 oz.
Hammer: Exposed
Sights: Front, blade integral w/slide; rear, notched bar dovetailed to slide
Finish: Blue or satin nickel
Grips: Smooth Brazilian walnut

MODEL PT 58
$399.00 (Blue)
$427.00 (Nickel)

TAURUS REVOLVERS

MODEL 73
$210.00 (Blue)
$230.00 (Nickel)

SPECIFICATIONS
Caliber: 32 Long
Capacity: 6 shot
Barrel length: 3″ heavy barrel
Weight: 20 oz.
Sights: Rear, square notch
Action: Double
Stock: Standard checkered
Finish: Blue or satin nickel

MODEL 83
$215.00 (Blue)
$228.00 (Nickel)

SPECIFICATIONS
Caliber: 38 Special
Action: Double
Number of shots: 6
Barrel length: 4″
Weight: 34½ oz.
Sights: Ramp, front; rear micrometer click adjustable for windage and elevation
Finish: Blue or satin nickel
Stocks: Checkered walnut target

MODEL 86 TARGET MASTER
$290.00

SPECIFICATIONS
Caliber: 38 Special
Capacity: 6 shot
Barrel length: 6″
Weight: 34 oz.
Sights: Patridge-type front; micrometer click adjustable rear for windage and elevation
Action: Double
Stock: Checkered walnut target
Finish: Bright royal blue

Model 96 Target Scout: Same as Model 86 Target Master except 22 LR caliber. Blue.

MODEL 669
$268.00 (Blue)
$337.00 (Stainless Steel)

SPECIFICATIONS
Calibers: 357 Magnum, 38 Special
Capacity: 6 shots
Barrel length: 4″ and 6″
Weight: 36 oz.
Action: Double
Sights: Serrated ramp front; rear micrometer click adjustable for windage and elevation
Finish: Royal blue or stainless
Stock: Checkered walnut target

TAURUS REVOLVERS

MODEL 94
$235.00 (Blue)
$280.00 (Stainless Steel)

SPECIFICATIONS
Caliber: 22 LR
Barrel length: 4″
Weight: 25 oz.
Number of shots: 9
Action: Double
Sights: Serrated ramp front; rear micrometer click adjustable for windage and elevation
Finish: Blue or stainless steel
Stock: Brazilian hardwood

MODEL 80
$204.00 (Blue)
$218.00 (Nickel)

SPECIFICATIONS
Caliber: 38 Special
Capacity: 6 shot
Barrel lengths: 3″, 4″
Weight: 33 oz.
Action: Double
Stock: Checkered walnut
Finish: Blue or satin nickel

MODEL 82
$204.00 (Blue)
$218.00 (Nickel)

SPECIFICATIONS
Caliber: 38 Special
Capacity: 6 shot
Barrel lengths: 3″, 4″
Weight: 34 oz.
Action: Double
Stock: Checkered walnut
Finish: Blue or satin nickel

TAURUS REVOLVERS

MODEL 65
$235.00 (Blue)
$249.00 (Nickel)

SPECIFICATIONS
Caliber: 357 Magnum
Capacity: 6 shot
Barrel length: 3″, 4″
Weight: 34 oz.
Sights: Rear square notch; front ramp
Action: Double
Stock: Checkered walnut target
Finish: Royal blue or satin nickel

MODEL 66
$258.00 (Blue) $272.00 (Nickel)
$328.00 (Stainless Steel)

SPECIFICATIONS
Caliber: 357 Magnum, 38 Special
Capacity: 6 shot
Barrel length: 3″, 4″, 6″
Weight: 35 oz.
Sights: Serrated ramp front; rear micrometer click adjustable
   for windage and elevation
Action: Double
Stock: Checkered walnut magna grips (3″); checkered walnut
   target grips (4″ & 6″)
Finish: Royal blue, satin nickel or stainless steel

MODEL 85
$223.00 (Blue) $272.00 (Nickel)
$280.00 (Stainless Steel)

SPECIFICATIONS
Caliber: 38 Special
Capacity: 5 shot
Barrel length: 2″ and 3″
Weight: 21 oz.
Sights: Notch rear sight, fixed sight
Action: Double
Stock: Brazilian checkered walnut
Finish: Blue, satin nickel or stainless steel

THOMPSON/CENTER

CONTENDER BULL BARREL

**CONTENDER
OCTAGON BARREL MODELS**

This standard barrel is interchangeable with any model listed here. Available in 10-inch length, it is supplied with iron sights. Octagon barrel is available in 22 LR. No external choke in this model **$345.00**

CONTENDER SUPER "14"

**CONTENDER
SUPER "14" MODELS**

Chambered in 11 calibers (22 LR, 222 Remington and 223 Remington, 7-30 Waters, 7mm T.C.U., 10mm Auto, 30/30 Winchester, 357 Rem. Max., 35 Remington and 44 Mag. and 445 Super Mag.), this gun is equipped with a 14-inch bull barrel, fully adjustable target rear sight and ramped front sight (Patridge-style). It offers a sight radius of 13½ inches. **Overall length:** 18¼". **Weight:** 3½ lbs. **$355.00**

CONTENDER BULL BARREL MODELS

This pistol with 10-inch barrel features fully adjustable Patridge-style iron sights.

Standard and Custom calibers available:
22 Long Rifle, 22 Hornet, 22 Win. Mag., 7-30 Waters, 223 Rem., 270 Rem., 10mm Auto, 32/20 Win., 7mm T.C.U., 30/30 Win., 357 Mag., 44 Mag., 44 Super, 357 Rem. Max., and 30 M1 Carbine.
Bull Barrel (less internal choke) **$345.00**
Standard calibers available w/internal choke:
45 Colt/.410 . . . . **350.00**

CONTENDER HUNTER

Chambered in 7-30 Waters, 223 Rem., 30/30 Win., 35 Rem., 45/70 Government, 357 Rem. Max., and. 44 Rem. Mag., the most popular commercially loaded cartridges available to handgunners. **Barrel length:** 12". **Overall length:** 16". **Weight:** 4 lbs. (approx.). **Features:** T/C Muzzle Tamer (to reduce recoil); a mounted T/C Recoil Proof 2.5X scope with lighted reticle, QD sling swivels and nylon sling, plus suede leather carrying case **$595.00**

CONTENDER SUPER "16"
VENTILATED RIB/INTERNAL CHOKE MODELS
(not shown)

Featuring a raised ventilated (7/16-inch wide) rib, this Contender model is available in 45 Colt/.410 caliber. Its rear leaf sight folds down to provide an unobstructed sighting plane when the pistol is used with .410 ga. shot shells. A patented detachable choke (1 7/8 inches long) screws into the muzzle internally. **Barrel length:** 10 inches **$385.00**

Also available:
10" Vent Rib Model w/internal choke **$365.00**

A. UBERTI REPLICAS

1871 ROLLING BLOCK TARGET PISTOL
$305.50

SPECIFICATIONS
Calibers: 22 LR, 22 Hornet, 22 Magnum, 357 Magnum
Capacity: Single shot
Barrel length: $9^7/_8''$ (half octagonal, half round)
Overall length: 14''
Weight: 2.75 lbs.
Sights: Fully adjustable rear; ramp front
Grip and forend: Walnut
Trigger guard: Brass
Frame: Color casehardened steel

1871 ROLLING BLOCK TARGET PISTOL

1873 CATTLEMAN QUICK DRAW
$309.00 (Brass)
$335.00 (Steel)

SPECIFICATIONS
Calibers: 22 LR, 22 Magnum, 357 Magnum, 38 Special, 38-40, 44 Special, 44-40, 45 L.C., 45 ACP
Barrel lengths: $4^3/_4''$, $5^1/_2''$, $7^1/_2''$; round tapered
Overall length: $10^3/_4''$ w/$5^1/_2''$ barrel
Weight: 2.42 lbs.
Capacity: 6 shots
Grip: One-piece walnut
Frame: Color casehardened steel

1873 CATTLEMAN QUICK DRAW

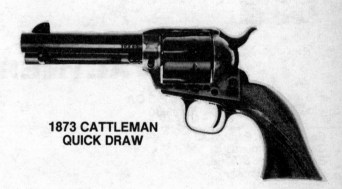

1875 REMINGTON ARMY S.A. "OUTLAW"
$318.50

SPECIFICATIONS
Calibers: 357 Magnum, 45 Long Colt, 44-40
Barrel length: $7^1/_2''$ round tapered
Overall length: $13^3/_4''$
Weight: 2.75 lbs.
Grips: Two-piece walnut
Frame: Color casehardened steel

Also available in nickel plate: **$350.00**

1875 REMINGTON ARMY S.A. "OUTLAW"

1890 REMINGTON OUTLAW

1890 REMINGTON OUTLAW
$331.50

SPECIFICATIONS
Calibers: 357 Magnum, 45 Long Colt, 44-40
Barrel length: $5^1/_2''$
Finish: Black

VICTORY ARMS

MODEL MC5

MODEL MC5
$499.00

SPECIFICATIONS
Calibers: 9mm Parabellum, 10mm, 38 Super, 41 Action Express, 45 ACP (interchangeable)
Capacity: 10 + 1 (45 ACP); 12 + 1 (41 AE); 17 + 1 (9mm Para, 38 Super)
Barrel lengths: 4³/₈″, 5⁷/₈″, 7¹/₂″
Overall length: 8¹/₂″
Weight: 45 oz. (empty)
Sight radius: 6¹/₂″ (w/standard 4³/₈″ barrel)
Automatic safeties: Firing pin lock; disconnector; hammer blocked unless slide is fully forward and locked
Finish: Service matte black; custom high-luster blue
Extra barrels **$100.00**
Magazines (each) **25.00**

WALTHER PISTOLS

MODEL P-5 DA
$895.00

Caliber: 9mm Parabellum
Capacity: 8 rounds
Barrel length: 3¹/₂″
Overall length: 7″
Weight: 28 oz.
Finish: Blue
Features: Four automatic built-in safety functions; lightweight alloy frame; supplied with two magazines
Also available:
MODEL PP in 32 ACP or 380 ACP calibers. **Barrel length:** 3.8″. **Overall length:** 6.7″. **Weight:** 23.5 oz. **Prices:**
   In 32 ACP .... $ 850.00
   In 380 ACP 875.00
MODEL P-5 COMPACT 1225.00

MODEL P-5 DA

MODEL FP (FREE PISTOL)
$1700.00

Caliber: 22 LR
Barrel length: 11.7″
Overall length: 17.2″
Weight: 48 oz.
Trigger: Electronic

MODEL FP

MODEL P-88 DA (not shown)
$1285.00

Caliber: 9mm Parabellum
Capacity: 15 rounds
Barrel length: 4″
Overall length: 7³/₈″
Weight: 31¹/₂ oz.
Finish: Blue
Sights: Rear adjustable for windage and elevation
Features: Internal safeties; ambidextrous de-cocking lever and magazine release button; lightweight alloy frame; loaded chamber indicator

U.I.T.-BV UNIVERSAL
(not shown)

Caliber: 22 LR
Barrel length: 25¹/₂″
Overall length: 44³/₄″
Weight: 9 lbs.
Bolt action: Single shot; falling block
Prices:
U.I.T.-BV $1700.00
U.I.T. Match 1300.00

WALTHER TARGET PISTOLS

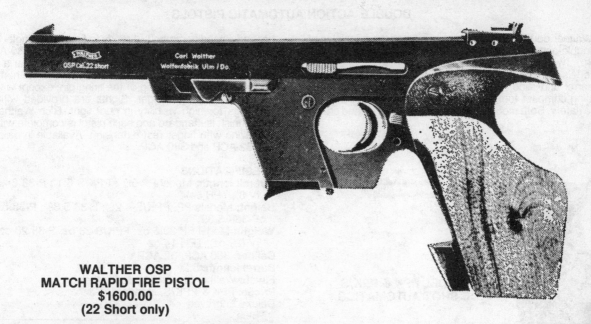

WALTHER OSP
MATCH RAPID FIRE PISTOL
$1600.00
(22 Short only)

Walther match pistols are built to conform to ISU and NRA match target pistol regulations. The model GSP, caliber 22 LR is available with either 2.2 lb. (1000 gm) or 3.0 lbs. (1360 gm) trigger, and comes with 4½-inch barrel and special hand-fitting designed walnut stock. Sights consist of fixed front and adjustable rear sight. The GSP-C 32 S&W wadcutter centerfire pistol is factory tested with a 3.0 lb. trigger. The 22 LR conversion unit for the model GSP-C consists of an interchangeable barrel, a slide assembly and two magazines. **Weight:** 44.8 oz. (22 caliber); 49.4 oz. (32 S&W). **Overall length:** 11.8″. **Magazine capacity:** 5 shots.

WALTHER GSP MATCH PISTOL
22 LR & 32 S&W Wadcutter

Prices:
GSP—22 Long Rifle w/carrying case $1450.00
GSP-C—32 S&W wadcutter w/carrying case 1700.00
22 LR conversion unit for GSP-C 750.00
22 Short conversion unit for GSP-C 925.00
32 S&W wadcutter conversion unit for GSP-C . . . 950.00

GSP JR. SEMIAUTOMATIC (not shown)
$1450.00 (w/Carrying Case)

Caliber: 22 LR
Capacity: 5 rounds
Barrel length: 4½″
Overall length: 11.8″
Weight: 40.1 oz.

WALTHER PISTOLS

DOUBLE-ACTION AUTOMATIC PISTOLS

The Walther double-action system combines the principles of the double-action revolver with the advantages of the modern pistol . . . without the disadvantages inherent in either design.

Models PP and PPK/S differ only in the overall length of the barrel and slide. Both models offer the same features, including compact form, light weight, easy handling and absolute safety. Both models can be carried with a loaded chamber and closed hammer, but ready to fire either single- or double-action. Both models in calibers 32 ACP and 380 ACP are provided with a live round indicator pin to signal a loaded chamber. An automatic internal safety blocks the hammer to prevent accidental striking of the firing pin, except with a deliberate pull of the trigger. Sights are provided with white markings for high visibility in poor light. Rich Walther blue/black finish is standard and each pistol is complete with extra magazine with finger rest extension. Available in calibers 22 LR, 32 ACP and 380 ACP.

MODEL PPK & PPK/S
6-SHOT AUTOMATICS

SPECIFICATIONS
Overall length: Model PP 6.7″; PPK/S 6.1″; P-38 8½″; P-38 IV 8″; TPH 5³/₈″
Height: Models PP, PPK/S 4.28″; P-38 5.39″; P-38 IV 5.39″; P-38K 5.39″
Weight: Model PP 23.5 oz; PPK/S 23 oz; P-38 28 oz.; P-38 IV (29 oz); TPH 14 oz.
Caliber: 380 ACP, 32 ACP
Barrel length: 3.2″
Finish: Walther blue or stainless steel
Prices: PPK & PPK/S, standard . . . . $ 549.00
Deluxe Engraved
    Blue 1550.00
    Chrome 1600.00

MODEL TPH DOUBLE ACTION

Walther's Model TPH is considered by government agents and professional lawmen to be one of the top undercover/back-up guns available. A scaled-down version of Walther's PP-PPK series chambered for 22 LR.

Barrel length: 2¹/₄″. **Overall length:** 5³/₈″. **Weight:** 14 oz. **Finish:** Stainless steel. **Price:** $419.00

MODEL P-38 DOUBLE ACTION

The Walther P-38 is a double-action, locked breech, semi-automatic pistol with an external hammer. Its compact form, light weight and easy handling are combined with the superb performance of the 9mm Luger Parabellum cartridge. The P-38 is equipped with both a manual and automatic safety, which allows it to be carried safely while the chamber is loaded. Available in calibers 9mm Luger Parabellum, 30 Luger and 22 LR with either a rugged non-reflective black finish or a polished blue finish.

Caliber: 9mm Parabellum, 30 Luger, 22 LR
Barrel length: 5″
Weight: 28 oz. (alloy); 34 oz. (steel)
Finish: Blue
Prices:
9mm Parabellum, standard . . . . $ 995.00
Deluxe Engraved
    Blue 1750.00
    Silver 1950.00
    Chrome 1850.00
Also available: custom **all steel** classic (34 oz.) . . 1400.00

MODEL TPH

MODEL P-38

DAN WESSON REVOLVERS

**357 MAGNUM
w/6″ Barrel**

357 MAGNUM REVOLVERS

Introduced in 1935, the 357 Magnum iis still the top selling handgun caliber. It makes an excellent hunting sidearm, and many law enforcement agencies have adopted it as a duty caliber. Take your pick of Dan Wesson 357s; then, add to its versatility with an additional barrel assemblyoption to alter it to your other needs.

SPECIFICATIONS
Action: Six-shot double and single action. **Ammunition:** 357 Magnum, 38 Special Hi-speed, 38 Special Mid-range. **Typical dimension:** 4″ barrel revolver, 9¼″×5¾″. **Trigger:** Smooth, wide tang (³/₈″) with overtravel adjustment. **Hammer:** Wide spur (³/₈″) with short double-action travel. **Sights: Models 14 and 714,** ¹/₈″ fixed serrated front; fixed rear integral with frame. **Models 15 and 715,** ¹/₈″ serrated interchangeable front blade; red insert standard, yellow and white available; rear notch (.125, .080, or white outline) adjustable for windage and elevation; graduated click. 10″, 12,″ 15″ barrel assemblies have special front sights and instructions. **Rifling:** Six lands and grooves, right-hand twist, 1 turn in 18.75 inches (2¹/₂″ thru 8″ lengths); six lands & grooves, right-hand twist, 1 turn in 14 inches (10″, 12″, 15″ lengths). **Note:** All 2¹/₂″ guns shipped with undercover grips. 4″ guns are shipped with service grips and the balance have oversized target grips.

38 SPECIAL REVOLVER

For decades a favorite of security and law enforcement agencies, the 38 special still maintains it's reputation as a fine caliber for sportsmen and target shooters. Dan Wesson offers a choice of many barrel lengths in either the service or target configuration.

SPECIFICATIONS
Action: Six-shot double and single action. **Ammunition:** 38 Special Hi-speed, 38 Special Mid-range. **Typical dimension:** 4″ barrel revolver, 9¼″×5¾″. **Trigger:** Smooth, wide tang (³/₈″) with overtravel adjustment. **Hammer:** Wide spur (³/₈″) with short double travel. **Sights:** Models 8 and 708, ¹/₈″ fixed serrated front; fixed rear integral with frame. Models 9 and 709, ¹/₈″ serrated interchangeable front blade; red insert standard, yellow and white available; rear, standard notch (.125, .080, or white outline) adjustable for windage and elevation; graduated click. **Rifling:** Six lands and grooves, right-hand twist, 1 turn in 18.75 inches. **Note:** All 2¹/₂″ guns shipped with undercover grips. 4″ guns are shipped with service grips and the balance have oversized target grips.

**Price:
Pistol Pac Models 14-2S thru 715-VH** . . . . **$455.80 to
$887.81**

MODEL	CALIBER	TYPE	BARREL LENGTHS & WEIGHT IN OUNCES							FINISH
			2½″	4″	6″	8″	10″	12″	15″	
14-2	.357 Magnum	Service	30	34	38	NA	NA	NA	NA	Satin Blue
14-2B	.357 Magnum	Service	30	34	38	NA	NA	NA	NA	Brite Blue
15-2	.357 Magnum	Target	32	36	40	44	50	54	59	Brite Blue
15-2V	.357 Magnum	Target	32	35	39	43	49	54	59	Brite Blue
15-2VH	.357 Magnum	Target	32	37	42	47	55	61	70	Brite Blue
714	.357 Magnum	Service	30	34	40	NA	NA	NA	NA	Satin Stainless Steel
715	.357 Magnum	Target	32	36	40	45	50	54	59	Satin Stainless Steel
715-V	.357 Magnum	Target	32	35	40	43	49	54	59	Satin Stainless Steel
715-VH	.357 Magnum	Target	32	37	42	49	55	61	70	Satin Stainless Steel

**Price:
38 Special Pistol Pacs** . . . . **$455.80—804.85**
Stainless Steel . . . . **516.68—887.81**

MODEL	CALIBER	TYPE	BARREL LENGTHS & WEIGHT IN OUNCES				FINISH
			2½″	4″	6″	8″	
8-2	.38 Special	Service	30	34	38	N/A	Satin Blue
8-2B	.38 Special	Service	30	34	38	N/A	Brite Blue
9-2	.38 Special	Target	32	36	40	44	Brite Blue
9-2V	.39 Special	Target	32	35	39	43	Brite Blue
9-2VH	.38 Special	Target	32	37	42	47	Brite Blue
708	.38 Special	Service	30	34	38	N/A	Satin Stainless Steel
709	.38 Special	Target	32	36	40	44	Satin Stainless Steel
709-V	.38 Special	Target	32	35	39	43	Satin Stainless Steel
709-VH	.38 Special	Target	32	37	42	47	Satin Stainless Steel

DAN WESSON REVOLVERS

357 SUPER MAG

SPECIFICATIONS

Action: Six-shot double and single action. **Ammunition:** 357 Maximum. **Overall length:** 14.375″ with 8″ barrel. **Height:** 6.5″. **Trigger:** Clean let-off, wide tang with overtravel adjustment. **Hammer:** Wide spur with short double-action travel. **Sights:** ¹/₈″ serrated interchangeable front blade; red insert standard, yellow and white available; rear, new interchangeable blade (.125 or optional .080); screwdriver adjustable for windage and elevation. **Rifling:** Six lands and grooves, right-hand twist, 1 in 18³/₄ inches.

SPECIFICATIONS

Model	Caliber	Type	Barrel lengths & Weight (oz.)			Finish	Price*
			6″	8″	10″		
740-V	357 Max	Target	59.5	65	62	Stainless	
740-VH	357 Max	Target	62	72	76	Stainless	$568.97—641.89
740-V8S	357 Max	Target		64		Stainless	

*Model 40 (Blue): $508.32–574.50

32 MAGNUM SIX SHOT

This target and small-game gun offers a high muzzle velocity and a flat trajectory for better accuracy. Available in blue and stainless steel.

SPECIFICATIONS

Model	Caliber	Type	Barrel lengths & Weight in ounces				Finish	Pistol Pac
			2½″	4″	6″	8″		
32	.32 Magnum	Target	35	39	43	48	Brite Blue	
32V	.32 Magnum	Target	35	39	43	48	Brite Blue	$614.73–$804.85
32VH	.32 Magnum	Target	35	40	46	53	Brite Blue	
732	.32 Magnum	Target	35	39	43	48	Satin Stainless Steel	
732V	.32 Magnum	Target	35	39	43	48	Satin Stainless Steel	$689.01–$887.81
732VH	.32 Magnum	Target	35	40	46	53	Satin Stainless Steel	

DAN WESSON REVOLVERS

41 AND 44 MAGNUM REVOLVERS

The Dan Wesson 41 and 44 Magnum revolvers are available with a patented "Power Control" to reduce muzzle flip. Both the 41 and the 44 have a one-piece frame and patented gain bolt for maximum strength.

SPECIFICATIONS
Action: Six-shot double- and single-action. **Ammunition:** Models 41 and 741, 41 Magnum; Models 44 and 744, 44 Magnum and 44 Special. **Typical dimension:** 6″ barrel revolver, 12″×6.″ **Trigger:** Smooth, wide tang (³/₈″) with overtravel adjustment. **Hammer:** Wide checkered spur with short double-action travel. **Sights:** Front, ¹/₈″ serrated interchangeable blade; red insert standard, yellow and white available; rear, standard notch (.125, .080, or white outline) adjustable for windage and elevation; click graduated. **Rifling:** Eight lands and grooves, right-hand twist, 1 turn in 18.75 inches. **Note:** 4″, 6″, and 8″ 44 Magnum guns will be shipped with unported and Power Control barrels. 10″ 44 Magnum guns available only without Power Control. Only jacketed bullets should be used with the 44 Mag. Power Control or excessive leading will result.

Price:
Pistol Pac Model 41	**$623.60—672.27**
Stainless Steel	690.40—739.20
Pistol Pac Model 44	707.52—757.80
Stainless Steel	814.38—867.03

Now available: 445 caliber double-action revolver. Specifications same as Supermag models, but gun is designed to handle the new heavier bullets in the 280 to 300 grain class (240 grain 44 Mag. bullets produce 1200-1600 feet per second without excessive pressures). **Prices: $561.20–$614.80** (Blue); **$608.98–$682.96** (Stainless)

MODEL	CALIBER	TYPE	BARREL LENGTHS & WEIGHT IN OUNCES				FINISH
			4″	6″	8″	10″*	
41-V	.41 Magnum	Target	48	53	58	64	Brite Blue
41-VH	.41 Magnum	Target	49	56	64	69	Brite Blue
44-V	.44 Magnum	Target	48	53	58	64	Brite Blue
44-VH	.44 Magnum	Target	49	56	64	69	Brite Blue
741-V	.41 Magnum	Target	48	53	58	64	Satin Stainless Steel
741-VH	.41 Magnum	Target	49	56	64	69	Satin Stainless Steel
744-V	.44 Magnum	Target	48	53	58	64	Satin Stainless Steel
744-VH	.44 Magnum	Target	49	56	64	69	Satin Stainless Steel

22 RIMFIRE and 22 WIN. MAGNUM REVOLVERS

Built on the same frames as the Dan Wesson 357 Magnum, these 22 rimfires offer the heft and balance of fine target revolvers. Affordable fun for the beginner or the expert.

SPECIFICATIONS
Action: Six-shot double and single action. **Ammunition:** Models 22 & 722, 22 Long Rifle; Models 22M & 722M, 22 Win. Mag. **Typical dimension:** 4″ barrel revolver, 9¹/₄″×5³/₄″. **Trigger:** Smooth, wide tang (³/₈″) with overtravel adjustment. **Hammer:** Wide spur (³/₈″) with short double-action travel. **Sights:** Front, ¹/₈″ serrated, interchangeable blade; red insert standard, yellow and white available; rear, standard wide notch (.125, .080, or white outline) adjustable for windage and elevation; graduated click. **Rifling:** Models 22 and 722, six lands and grooves, right-hand twist, 1 turn in 12 inches; Models 22M and 722M, six lands and grooves, right-hand twist, 1 turn in 16 inches. **Note:** All 2¹/₂″ guns are shipped with undercover grips. 4″ guns are shipped with service grips and the balance have oversized target grips.

Now available: 10″ barrel with combat-style grip, .080 narrow notch rear sight blade, and Patridge-style front sight blade. **Prices: $430.00** (Blue); **$458.43** (Stainless).

Price:
Pistol Pac Models 22 thru 722M . . . . . . **$614.73—$922.52**

MODEL	CALIBER	TYPE	BARREL LENGTHS & WEIGHT IN OUNCES				FINISH
			2¹/₄″	4″	6″	8″	
22	.22 L.R.	Target	36	40	44	49	Brite Blue
22-V	.22 L.R.	Target	36	40	44	49	Brite Blue
22-VH	.22 L.R.	Target	36	41	47	54	Brite Blue
22-M	.22 Win Mag	Target	36	40	44	49	Brite Blue
22M-V	.22 Win Mag	Target	36	40	44	49	Brite Blue
22M-VH	.22 Win Mag	Target	36	41	47	54	Brite Blue
722	.22 L.R.	Target	36	40	44	49	Satin Stainless Steel
722-V	.22 L.R.	Target	36	40	44	49	Satin Stainless Steel
722-VH	.22 L.R.	Target	36	41	47	54	Satin Stainless Steel
722M	.22 Win Mag	Target	36	40	44	49	Satin Stainless Steel
722M-V	.22 Win Mag	Target	36	40	44	49	Satin Stainless Steel
722M-VH	.22 Win Mag	Target	36	41	47	54	Satin Stainless Steel

HUNTER PACS

Offered in all magnum calibers with the following:
1. Complete gun in choice of caliber (22, 32, 357, 41, 44, 357 Supermag and 375 Supermag) with 8″ vent-heavy shroud.
2. 8″ vent shroud only, equipped with Burris scope mounts and scope (1¹/₂X-4X variable or fixed 2X).
3. Barrel changing tool and Dan Wesson emblem packed in attractive case.

Prices: $723.49 (32 Magnum w/2X) to **$1077.01** (357 Supermag Stainless w/1¹/₂X-4X)

WILDEY PISTOLS

These new gas-operated pistols are designed to meet the needs of hunters who want to use handguns for big game. The Wildey pistol includes such features as: • Ventilated rib • Reduced recoil • Double-action trigger mechanism • Patented hammer and trigger blocks and rebounding fire pin • Sights adjustable for windage and elevation • Stainless construction • Fixed barred for increased accuracy • Increased action strength (with 3-lug and exposed face rotary bolt) • Selective single or autoloading capability • Ability to handle high-pressure loads.

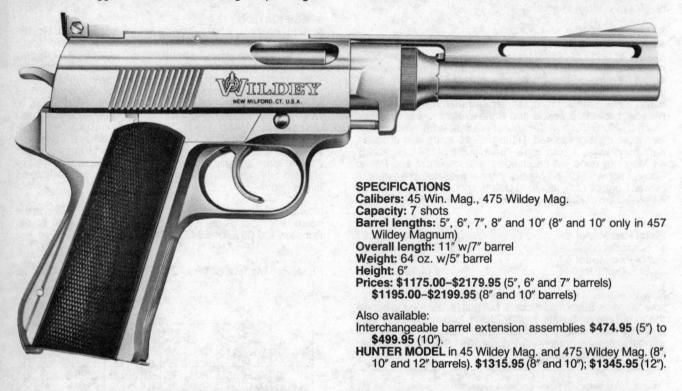

SPECIFICATIONS
Calibers: 45 Win. Mag., 475 Wildey Mag.
Capacity: 7 shots
Barrel lengths: 5″, 6″, 7″, 8″ and 10″ (8″ and 10″ only in 457 Wildey Magnum)
Overall length: 11″ w/7″ barrel
Weight: 64 oz. w/5″ barrel
Height: 6″
Prices: $1175.00–$2179.95 (5″, 6″ and 7″ barrels)
$1195.00–$2199.95 (8″ and 10″ barrels)

Also available:
Interchangeable barrel extension assemblies $474.95 (5″) to $499.95 (10″).
HUNTER MODEL in 45 Wildey Mag. and 475 Wildey Mag. (8″, 10″ and 12″ barrels). **$1315.95** (8″ and 10″); **$1345.95** (12″).

WILKINSON ARMS PISTOLS

MODEL "LINDA" PISTOL
$682.36

SPECIFICATIONS
Caliber: 9mm Luger
Barrel length: 8$^{15}/_{16}$″
Overall length: 12$^{1}/_{4}$″
Weight: 4 lbs. 13 oz.
Height: 10″ with magazine
Sights: Wilkinson adjustable peep (fixed)
Foregrip: Maple wood
Features: Full blowback semiauto (fires from a closed breech); bolt-type safety and magazine catch; timed barrel; ejection port equipped with automatic trap door; receiver equipped with dovetail for scope mount.

Rifles

FOR ADDRESSES AND PHONE
NUMBERS OF MANUFACTURERS AND
DISTRIBUTORS INCLUDED IN THIS
SECTION, SEE *DIRECTORY OF
MANUFACTURERS AND SUPPLIERS*

ACTION ARMS

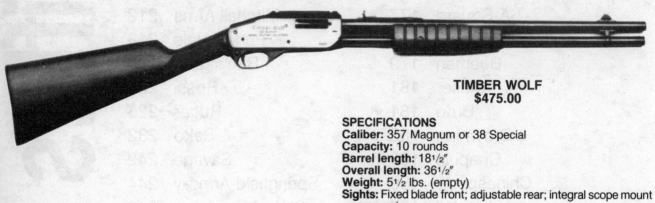

TIMBER WOLF
$475.00

SPECIFICATIONS
Caliber: 357 Magnum or 38 Special
Capacity: 10 rounds
Barrel length: 18½"
Overall length: 36½"
Weight: 5½ lbs. (empty)
Sights: Fixed blade front; adjustable rear; integral scope mount on receiver
Stock: Walnut
Operation: Locked breech
Safety system: Push button on trigger guard

AMERICAN ARMS

MODEL EXP-64
$169.00

SPECIFICATIONS
Caliber: 22 LR
Capacity: 10 rounds
Action: Semiautomatic; straight blowback design
Barrel length: 21"
Rate of twist: 1 in 16" (R.H.)
Overall length: 40"
Safety: Lever safety (located on trigger guard) blocks trigger
Sights: Ramp and post fixed front; adjustable rear

Receiver & frame: Lightweight alloy receiver w/black matte finish; barrel take-down screw located on front bottom of receiver; grooved for scope mounting
Stock: Synthetic black stock with storage compartments

Also available:
MODEL SM-64. Same as EXP-64, but with hardwood stock.
  Price: $149.00

SM-64

ANSCHUTZ SPORTER RIFLES
MATCH 54 SPORTER MODELS

MODEL 1700D CUSTOM
$999.50 (22 LR) $1029.00 (22 Magnum)
$1130.00 (22 Hornet & 222 Rem.)
$995.00 (Featherweight)
$1195.00 (Featherweight Deluxe)

BAVARIAN 1700
$999.50 (22 LR) $1029.00 (22 Magnum)
$1130.00 (22 Hornet & 222 Rem.)

MODEL 1700D CLASSIC
$988.50 (22 LR) $1015.00 (22 Magnum)
$1100.00 (22 Hornet & 222 Rem.)

SPECIFICATIONS

	Custom	Bavarian	Classic	1700 FWT
	22 Long Rifle, 22 Magnum, 22 Hornet, 222 Remington			22 LR
Length—Overall	43″	43″	43″	43″
Barrel	24″	24″	24″	24″
Pull	14″	14″	14″	14″
Drop at—Comb	1¼″	1¼″	1¼″	1¼″
Monte Carlo	1″	—		1″
Heel	1½″	1½″	1½″	1½″
Average Weight	7½ lbs.	7½ lbs.	6¾ lbs.	6¼ lbs.
Trigger—Single Stage 5096 (.222 Rem., 5095)	•	•	•	•
Rate of Twist	Right Hand—one turn in 16.5″ for .22 LR; 1-16″ for .22 Mag & .22 Hornet; 1-14″ for .222 Rem.			
Take Down Bolt Action With Removable Firing Pin	•	•	•	•
Swivel Studs	•	•	•	•
Grooved for Scope	•	•	•	•
Tapped for Scope Blocks	•	•	•	•
Sights—Front-Hooded Ramp Rear-Folding Leaf	•	•	•	
Trigger Single Stage 5096 5095 .222 Rem.	5096 •	5096 •	5096 •	5096
*Adjustable for Creep, Pull, Overtravel	•	•	•	•
Factory Set for 2.6 lbs. Adjustable for Overtravel	•	•	•	•
Clip Magazine Safety—Wing	•	•	•	•
Stock—Monte Carlo	•			
Cheek Piece		•		
Roll Over Cheek Piece	•			

ANSCHUTZ SPORTER RIFLES

MATCH 64 SPORTER MODELS

MODEL 1416D CLASSIC
$589.00

MODEL 1416D CUSTOM

MODEL 1416D CLASSIC/CUSTOM
$552.00   ($589.00 22 Magnum)
$630.00 (Left Hand)

1418D MANNLICHER
$830.00   ($847.00 22 Magnum)

MODEL 525 SPORTER
$435.00

SPECIFICATIONS

	Classic 1416D** 1516D	Custom 1416D 1516D	Mannlicher 1418D 1518D	Model 525 Sporter
Length—Overall	41″	41″	38″	43″
Barrel	22½″	22½″	19¾″	24″
Pull	14″	14″	14″	14″
Drop at—Comb	1¼″	1¼″	1¼″	1⅛″
Monte Carlo	1½″	1½″	1½″	1¾″
Heel	1½″	2½″	2½″	2⅝″
Average Weight	5½ lbs.	6 lbs.	5½ lbs.	6½ lbs.
Rate of Twist Right Hand—one turn in 16.5″ for .22 LR; 1–16″ for .22 Mag				
Take Down Bolt Action With Removable Firing Pin	•	•	•	
¾″ Swivel				
Swivel Studs	•		•	•

ANSCHUTZ MATCH RIFLES

MODEL 1403D

INTERMEDIATE MATCH RIFLES
$699.50 (1403D)
$806.00 (1803D)

SPECIFICATIONS

	1403D*	1803D*
Barrel Length	Precision rifled .22 long rifle only 25" medium heavy $^{11}/_{16}$" dia.	25½"¾" dia.
Action	Match 64	Match 64
Trigger	1.1 lbs. Single stage, adjustable* for weight of pull, take-up over travel. #5093	#5091 2 stage adjustable* from 9.2 to 10.6 oz.
Safety	Slide safety locks sear and bolt.	Slide safety locks sear and bolt.
Stock	Walnut finished hardwood. Cheekpiece/Swivel Rail. Stippling.	Blonde finish, adjustable cheekpiece. Stippled pistol grip and fore stock. Swivel rail.
Sights	Takes Anschutz 6723 Sight Set (available separately.)	Takes Anschutz 6723 Sight Set (available separately.)
Overall Length	43¼"	43¼"
Weight (avg.)	8.6 lbs. with sights	8.6 lbs.
Left Hand		1803D Left

RIFLES

METALLIC SILHOUETTE RIFLES

MODEL 64MS

MODEL 54.18MS

64MS	$ 717.00
Left Hand	793.00
1700 FWT	995.00
54.18MS	1212.00
Left Hand	1273.00
54.18MS-REP	1395.00
54.18MS-REP DELUXE	1755.00

SPECIFICATIONS AND FEATURES

	64MS	54.18MS	54.18MS-REP*	1700 FWT
Grooved for scope	•	•	•	•
Tapped for scope mount	•	•	•	•
Overall length	39.5"	41"	41–49"	43"
Barrel length	21½"	22"	22–30"	34"
Length of pull	13½"	13¾"	13¾"	14"
High cheekpiece with Monte Carlo effect	•	•	•	•
Drop at Comb	1½"	1½"	1½"	1¼"
Average weight	8 lbs.	8 lbs. 6 oz.	7 lbs. 12 oz.	6¼ lbs.
Trigger:	#5091	#5018	#5018	#5096
Stage	Two	Two	Two	Single
Factory adjusted weight	5.3 oz.	3.9 oz.	3.9 oz.	2.6 lbs.
Adjustable weight	4.9–7 oz.	2.1–8.6 oz.	2.1–8.6 oz.	2.6–4.4 lbs.
Safety	Slide	Slide	Slide	Slide
True Left-hand Model	•	•	•	

* **Deluxe** model features Fibergraine stock

ANSCHUTZ INTERNATIONAL TARGET RIFLES

**MODEL 1913
SUPER MATCH**
$2255.00 ($2440.00 Left Hand)

**MODEL 1910 (not shown)
SUPER MATCH II**
$2013.00 ($2183.00 Left Hand)

**MODEL 1911
PRONE MATCH**
$1576.00 ($1714.00 Left Hand)

**MODEL 1808ED
SUPER RUNNING**
$1290.00 ($1400.00 Left Hand)

MODEL 1903D (not shown)
Features adj. cheekpiece of walnut-finished European hardwood, full-length stippled checkering on forend. **$831.00** ($873.00 Left)

**MODEL 1907
ISU STANDARD**
$1344.00 ($1462.00 Left Hand)

INTERNATIONAL MATCH RIFLES: SPECIFICATIONS AND FEATURES

	1913	1911	1910	1907	1808ED-Super
Barrel Length O/D	27¼" ⅞" (23.4 mm)	27¼" ⅞" (23.4 mm)	27¼" ⅞" (23.4 mm)	26" ⅞" (22 mm)	32½" ⅞" (22 mm)
Stock	Int'l.- Thumb Hole Adj. Palm Rest Adj. Hand Rest	Prone	Int'l.- Thumb Hole	Standard	Thumb Hole
Cheek Piece **Butt Plate**	Adj. Adj. Hook 10 Way Hook	Adj. Adj. 4 Way	Adj. Adj. Hook 10 Way Hook	Removable Adj. 4 Way	Adj. Adj. 4 Way
Recommended **Sights**	6820, 6823 *6820 Left	6820, 6823 *6820 Left	6820, 6823 *6820 Left	6820, 6823 *6820 Left	Grooved for Scope Mounts
Overall Length	45"-46"	45"-46"	45"-46"	43¾"-44½"	50½"
Overall Length **to Hook**	49.6"-51.2"		49.6"-51.2"		
Weight (approx) **without sights**	15.2 lbs.	11.7 lbs.	13.7 lbs.	11.2 lbs.	9.4 lbs.
True Left- **Hand Version**	1913 Left	1911 Left	1910 Left	1907 Left	1808 Left

Trigger
    Stage
    Factory Set Wt.
    Adjust. Wt.
	#5018
	Two
	3.9 oz.
	2.1-8.6 oz.
		#5018
		Two
		3.9 oz.
		2.1-8.6 oz.
			#5018
			Two
			3.9 oz.
			2.1-8.6 oz.
				#5018
				Two
				3.9 oz.
				2.1-8.6 oz.
					5020D
					Single
					1.2 lbs.
					14 oz.-2.4 lbs.

ANSCHUTZ RIFLES

THE ACHIEVER
$319.50

This new rifle has been designed especially for young shooters and is equally at home on range or field. It meets all NRA recommendations as an ideal training rifle.

SPECIFICATIONS
Caliber: 22 LR
Capacity: 5- or 10-shot clips available
Action: Mark 2000-type repeating

Barrel length: 19 1/2″
Overall length: 36 1/4″
Weight: 5 lbs.
Trigger: #5066-two stage (2.6 lbs.)
Safety: Slide
Sights: Hooded ramp front; marble folding-leaf rear, adjustable for windage and elevation
Stock pull: 12″
Stock: European hardwood

MODEL 1449
$229.90

SPECIFICATIONS
Caliber: 22 LR
Capacity: 5-shot clip magazine
Action: Mark 2000
Barrel length: 16 1/4″
Overall length: 32 1/2″
Weight: 3 1/2 lbs.
Trigger: 3 lbs.
Sights: Hooded ramp front; adjustable open rear
Pull: 12 1/4″
Stock: Walnut-finished European hardwood

A-SQUARE RIFLES

HANNIBAL MODEL
$1700.00

HANNIBAL MODEL (416 Rigby)
w/2xLER Scope and 3-Leaf
Express Sights

SPECIFICATIONS
Calibers:
Group I: 30-06
Group II: 7mm Rem. Mag., 300 Win. Mag., 416 Taylor, 425 Express, 458 Win. Mag.
Group III: 300 H&H, 300 Weatherby, 8mm Rem. Mag., 340 Weatherby, 375 H&H, 375 Weatherby, 404 Jeffrey, 416 Hoffman, 416 Rem. Mag., 450 Ackley, 458 Lott
Group IV: 338 A-Square Mag., 375 A-Square Mag., 378 Weatherby, 416 Rigby, 416 Weatherby, 460 Short A-Square Mag., 460 Weatherby, 495 A-Square Mag., 500 A-Square Mag.
Barrel lengths: 20″ to 26″
Length of pull: 12″ to 15 1/4″
Finish: Deluxe walnut stock; oil finish; matte blue
Features: Flush detachable swivels, leather sling, ammo carrier, dual recoil lugs, coil spring ejector, ventilated recoil pad, premium honed barrels, contoured ejection port, adjustable target-style trigger, Mauser-style claw extractor and controlled feed, positive safety

A-SQUARE RIFLES

CAESAR MODEL (Left Hand)
$1750.00

CAESAR MODEL (416 Hoffman)
w/2x7 Variable Scope and
3-Leaf Express Sights

SPECIFICATIONS
Calibers: Groups I, II and III only (see Hannibal Model)
Features: Selected Claro walnut stock with oil finish; three-position safety; three-way adjustable target trigger

Also available:
HANNIBAL SYNTHETIC STOCK MODEL
Calibers: 7mm Rem., 375, 416, 458 & 500 Mag. **Capacity:** 4 to 7 rounds (depending on sights and caliber). **Features:** Syn-thetic stock; full glass bedding with steel bedding inserts; flush detachable swivels with sling. **Price: $1900.00**

AUTO-ORDNANCE

THOMPSON MODEL M1
$761.85

SPECIFICATIONS
Caliber: 45 ACP
Barrel length: 16½"
Overall length: 38"
Weight: 11½ lbs.

Sights: Blade front; fixed rear
Stock: Walnut stock and forend
Finish: Military black
Features: Side cocking lever; frame and receiver milled from solid steel

THOMPSON MODEL 1927 A1
$735.00

SPECIFICATIONS
Caliber: 45 ACP
Barrel length: 16"
Overall length: 42"
Weight: 11½ lbs.
Sights: Blade front; open rear adjustable
Stock: Walnut stock; vertical forend

Also available:
THOMPSON 1927A-1C LIGHTWEIGHT. Same as the 1927A1 model, but 20% lighter. **Price: $668.95**
THOMPSON MODEL 1927A3. Same as above, but in caliber 22 LR. **Weight:** 7 lbs. **Price: $487.50**

BEEMAN RIFLES

BEEMAN/WEIHRAUCH HW 60 SMALLBORE RIFLE
$698.00 (Right) $739.95 (Left)

Caliber: 22 LR, single shot. Improved bolt action. Adjustable match trigger with push button safety. Precision rifled barrel. Stippled forearm and pistol grip. Precision aperture sights, hooded front sight ramp. **Barrel length:** 26.8″. **Overall length:** 45.7″. **Weight:** 10.8 lbs.

BEEMAN/WEIHRAUCH HW 60J-ST
BOLT-ACTION RIFLE
$688.00 (60J) $488.00 (60J-ST)

Calibers: 222 Rem. (60J); 22 LR (60J-ST). Features include: walnut stock with cheekpiece; cut-checkered pistol grip and forend; polished blue finish; oil-finished wood. **Sights:** Hooded blade on ramp front; open rear adjustable. **Barrel length:** 22.8″. **Overall length:** 41.7″. **Weight:** 6½ lbs. Imported from West Germany by Beeman.

BEEMAN/WEIHRAUCH HW 660 MATCH RIFLE
$725.00 (Right Hand)

Caliber: 22 LR. Match-type walnut stock with adjustable cheekpiece and buttplate. Adjustable match trigger; stippled pistol grip and forend; forend accessory rail. **Sights:** Globe front; match aperture rear. **Barrel length:** 26″. **Overall length:** 45.3″. **Weight:** 10.7 lbs. Imported from West Germany by Beeman.

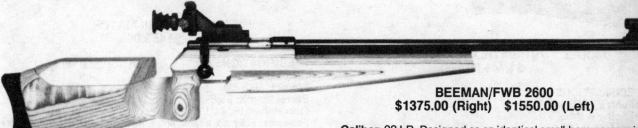

BEEMAN/FWB 2600
$1375.00 (Right) $1550.00 (Left)

Caliber: 22 LR. Designed as an identical small-bore companion to the Beeman/FWB 600 Match air rifle. Super rigid stock made of laminated hardwood. Bull barrel free floats. Stock is cut low to permit complete ventilation around barrel. Match trigger has fingertip weight adjustment dial. Adjustable comb; match sights; single shot.

BEEMAN RIFLES

BEEMAN/KRICO

Beeman/Krico rifles bring West German tradition to the world of varmint and big game hunting and target shooting in North America. Noted worldwide for their superb balance and handling, these rifles feature hammer forged, precision rifled barrels, exceptionally fine triggers, smoothly operating bolt actions, and interchangeable trigger modules. All models have cheek-pieces and fine handcut checkering on the grips and forearms (except target models, which are stippled). All Beeman/Krico rifles are proofed at the factory for accuracy (at 100 meters, hunting rifles must group shots under 1.2 inches; target rifles are under .75 inches).

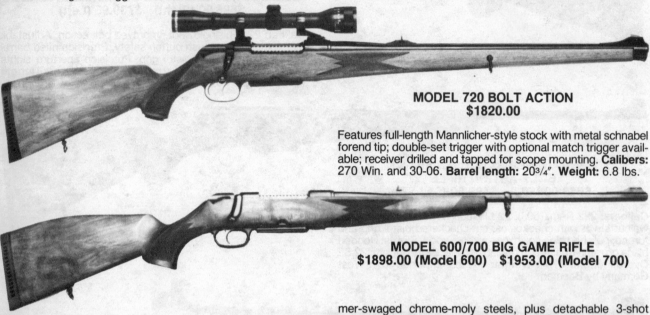

MODEL 720 BOLT ACTION
$1820.00

Features full-length Mannlicher-style stock with metal schnabel forend tip; double-set trigger with optional match trigger available; receiver drilled and tapped for scope mounting. **Calibers:** 270 Win. and 30-06. **Barrel length:** 20¾″. **Weight:** 6.8 lbs.

MODEL 600/700 BIG GAME RIFLE
$1898.00 (Model 600) $1953.00 (Model 700)

Features classic-style European walnut stock with Wundhammer palm swell, rosewood schnabel forend, checkering and rubber butt pad. Also a silent safety and barrel made of hammer-swaged chrome-moly steels, plus detachable 3-shot magazine. **Calibers:** 243 Win. (Model 600) and 270 or 30-06 (Model 700). **Barrel length:** 23½″. **Overall length:** 43½″. **Weight:** 7 lbs. **Sights:** Open rear adjustable for windage; hooded front ramp. Imported from West Germany by Beeman.

BEEMAN/UNIQUE

MODEL T.66 MATCH
$1458.00

SPECIFICATIONS
Caliber: 22 LR
Weight: 10.8 lbs.
Barrel length: 25.6″
Overall length: 44.1″
Features: Fully adjustable firing; movable trigger; Micro-Match target sight; French walnut stock; adjustable butt plate and cheek rest; left hand model available.

MODEL T.791 BIATHLON (not shown)
$1,748.00

SPECIFICATIONS
Caliber: 22 LR
Capacity: 5 shots
Barrel length: 22.6″
Overall length: 40.2″
Weight: 10.1 lbs.
Features: French walnut stock; movable trigger; fully adjustable firing; micro-metric target sight with snow shield; left hand model available.

BLASER RIFLES

MODEL R 84 BOLT ACTION

SPECIFICATIONS
Calibers: (interchangeable)
    Standard: 22-250, 243 Win., 6mm Rem., 25-06, 270 Win., 280 Rem., 30-06

Magnum: 257 Weatherby Mag., 264 Win. Mag., 7mm Rem. Mag., 300 Win. Mag., 300 Weatherby Mag., 338 Win. Mag., 375 H&H
Barrel lengths: 23″ (Standard) and 24″ (Magnum)
Overall length: 41″ (Standard) and 42″ (Magnum)
Weight: (w/scope mounts) 7 lbs. (Standard) and 7¼ lbs. (Magnum)
Safety: Locks firing pin and bolt handle
Stock: Two-piece Turkish walnut stock and forend; solid black recoil pad, handcut checkering (18 lines/inch, borderless)
Length of pull: 13¾″
Prices:
Standard calibers w/scope mounts **$1595.00**
Magnum calibers w/scope mounts **1595.00**
Left-Hand Standard w/scope mounts **1645.00**
Left-Hand Magnum w/scope mounts **1645.00**
Interchangeable barrels **545.00**

BRNO RIFLES

MODEL ZKK 600

MODEL ZKK 602

MODEL ZKK SPECIFICATIONS

Model	Action Type	Cal.	Barrel Specifications			Overall Length	Weight	Magazine Capacity	Sighted In
			Length	Rifling Twist	#Lands				
ZKK 600	bolt	270 Win	23.5 in	1 in 10″	4	44.0 in.	7 lbs. 2 oz.	5	110 yd.
		7×57		1 in 9″	4				
		7×64		1 in 9″	4				
		30.06 Spring			4				
ZKK 601	bolt	223 Rem	23.5 in.	1 in 12″	4	43.0 in.	6 lbs. 3 oz.	5	110 yd.
		243 Win		1 in 10″	4				
ZKK 602	bolt	300 Win mag	25.0 in.	1 in 10″	4	45.5 in.	9 lbs. 4 oz.	5	110 yd.
		8×68		1 in 11″	4				
		375 H&H		1 in 12″	4				

Model ZKK 600 Standard **$780.00**
Model ZKK 601 Monte Carlo Stock **845.00**

Model ZKK 602 Standard **895.00**
Monte Carlo Stock **975.00**

RIFLES

BROWNING LEVER ACTION RIFLES

MODEL 53 LIMITED EDITION LEVER ACTION RIFLE
$675.00

Caliber: 32-20 (round nose and hollow-point bullets only). **Capacity:** 7 rounds (magazine is tubular, half-style loaded through side port). **Action:** Lever action with twin vertical locks. **Hammer:** Exposed, three-position. **Barrel length:** 22″, round, tapered. **Overall length:** 39½″. **Weight:** 6 lbs. 8 oz. **Sights:** Open; post bead-style front and blade-style adjustable rear. **Sight radius:** 19″. **Stock:** Select walnut with high-gloss finish; cut checkering on stock and forearm; metal grip cap; full pistol grip with semi-beavertail forearm. **Finish:** Deeply blued on all metal surfaces.

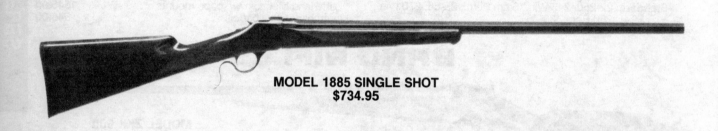

MODEL 1885 SINGLE SHOT
$734.95

Calibers: 22-250; 223, 30-06, 270, 7mm Rem. Mag., 45-70 Govt. **Bolt system:** Falling block. **Barrel length:** 28″ (recessed muzzle). **Overall length:** 43½″. **Weight:** 8 lbs. 12 oz. **Action:** High wall type, single shot, lever action. **Sights:** Drilled and tapped for scope mounts; two-piece scope base available. **Hammer:** Exposed, serrated, three-position with inertia sear. **Stock and Forearm:** Select Walnut, straight grip stock and Schnabel forearm with cut checkering. Recoil pad standard.

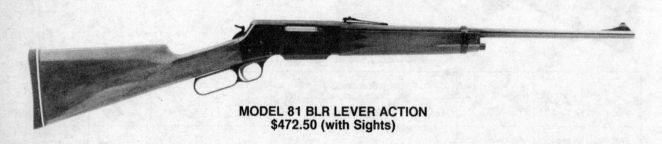

MODEL 81 BLR LEVER ACTION
$472.50 (with Sights)

Calibers: 223 Rem., 22-250 Rem., 243 Win., 257 Roberts, 7mm-08 Rem., 284 Win., 308 Win. and 358 Win. **Action:** Lever action with rotating head, multiple lug breech bolt with recessed bolt face. Side ejection. **Barrel length:** 20″. Individually machined from forged, heat treated chrome-moly steel; crowned muzzle. **Rifling:** 243 Win., one turn in 10″; 308 and 358 Win., one turn in 12″. **Magazine:** Detachable, 4-round capacity. **Overall length:** 39¾″. **Approximate Weight:** 6 lbs. 15 oz. **Trigger:** Wide, grooved finger piece. Short crisp pull of 4½ pounds. Travels with lever. **Receiver:** Non-glare top. Drilled and tapped to accept most top scope mounts. Forged and milled steel. All parts are machine-finished and hand-fitted. Surface deeply polished. **Sights:** Low profile, square notch, screw adjustable rear sight. Gold bead on a hooded raised ramp front sight. Sight radius: 17¾″. **Safety:** Exposed, 3-position hammer. Trigger disconnect system. Inertia firing pin. **Stock and forearm:** Select walnut with tough oil finish and sure-grip checkering, contoured for use with either open sights or scope. Straight grip stock. Deluxe recoil pad installed.

Length of pull . . . . 13¾″
Drop at comb . . . . 1¾″
Drop at heel . . . . 2⅜″

BROWNING RIFLES

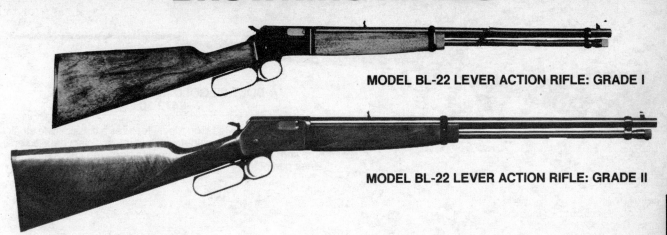

MODEL BL-22 LEVER ACTION RIFLE: GRADE I

MODEL BL-22 LEVER ACTION RIFLE: GRADE II

MODEL BL-22 SPECIFICATIONS

Action: Short throw lever action. Lever travels through an arc of only 33 degrees and carries the trigger with it, preventing finger pinch between lever and trigger on the upward swing. The lever cycle ejects the fired shell, cocks the hammer and feeds a fresh round into the chamber. **Magazine:** Rifle is designed to handle 22 caliber ammunition *in any combination* from tubular magazine. Magazine capacity is 15 Long Rifles, 17 Longs and 22 Shorts. The positive magazine latch opens and closes easily from any position. **Safety:** A unique disconnect system prevents firing until the lever and breech are fully closed and pressure is released from and reapplied to the trigger. An inertia firing pin and an exposed hammer with a half-cock position are other safety features. **Receiver:** Forged and milled steel. Grooved. All parts are machine-finished and hand-fitted. **Trigger:** Clean and crisp without creep. Average pull 5 pounds. Trigger gold-plated on Grade II model. **Stock and forearm:** Forearm and straight grip butt stock are shaped from select, polished walnut. Hand checkered on Grade II model. Stock dimensions:

Length of Pull . . . . $13\frac{1}{2}$"
Drop at Comb . . . . $1\frac{5}{8}$"
Drop at Heel . . . . $2\frac{1}{4}$"

Sights: Precision, adjustable folding leaf rear sight. Raised bead front sight. **Scopes:** Grooved receiver will accept the Browning 22 riflescope (Model 1217) and two-piece ring mount (Model 9417) as well as most other groove or tip-off type mounts or receiver sights. **Engraving:** Grade II receiver and trigger guard are engraved with tasteful scroll designs. **Barrel length:** 20"; recessed muzzle. **Overall length:** $36\frac{3}{4}$". **Weight:** 5 pounds.

Price: Grade I **$301.50**
       Grade II 343.50

MODEL A-BOLT 22 BOLT ACTION
$356.50   ($367.50 w/Sights)

Caliber: 22 LR. **Barrel length:** 22". **Overall length:** $40\frac{1}{4}$". **Average weight:** 5 lbs. 9 oz. **Action:** Short throw bolt. Bolt cycles a round with 60° of bolt rotation. Firing pin acts as secondary extractor and ejector, snapping out fired rounds at prescribed speed. **Magazine:** Five and 15-shot magazine standard. Magazine/clip ejects with a push on magazine latch button. **Trigger:** Gold colored, screw adjustable. Pre-set at approx. 4 lbs. **Stock:** Laminated walnut, classic style with pistol grip. **Length of pull:** $13\frac{3}{4}$". **Drop at comb:** $\frac{3}{4}$". **Drop at heel:** $1\frac{1}{2}$". **Sights:** Available with or without sights (add $10 for sights). Ramp front and adjustable folding leaf rear on open sight model. **Scopes:** Grooved receiver for 22 mount. Drilled and tapped for full-size scope mounts.

Available in 22 Magnum (with open sights) **$419.50**
Without sights 409.50

SPECIFICATIONS RIMFIRE RIFLES

Model	Caliber	Barrel Length	Sight Radius	Overall Length	Average Weight
A-Bolt 22	22 Long Rifle	22"	$17\frac{5}{8}$"	$40\frac{1}{4}$"	5 lbs. 9 oz.
22 Semi-Auto	22 Long Rifle	$19\frac{1}{4}$"	$16\frac{1}{4}$"	37"	4 lbs. 4 oz.
BL-22	22 Long Rifle, Longs, Shorts	20"	$15\frac{3}{8}$"		5 lbs.

BROWNING RIFLES

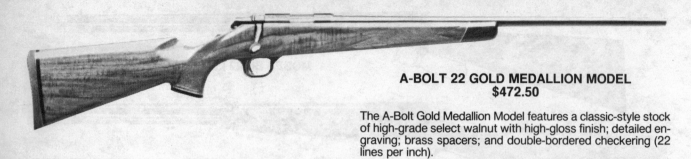

A-BOLT 22 GOLD MEDALLION MODEL
$472.50

The A-Bolt Gold Medallion Model features a classic-style stock of high-grade select walnut with high-gloss finish; detailed engraving; brass spacers; and double-bordered checkering (22 lines per inch).

A-BOLT COMPOSITE STALKER
$477.95

Browning's new graphite-fiberglass composite stock resists the nicks and scrapes of hard hunting and is resistant to weather and humidity. Its recoil-absorbing properties also make shooting a more pleasant experience. This series is available in three models: Stainless Stalker, Composite Stalker and Camo Stalker. The newest of these—the A-Bolt Composite Stalker—has the same features as Browning's A-Bolt Hunter plus the graphite-fiberglass composite stock, which helps ensure accuracy as well as durability. The stock is checkered for a good grip and has a nonglare textured finish. All exposed metal surfaces have a nonglare matte blued finish.

22 SEMIAUTOMATIC RIMFIRE RIFLES
GRADES I AND VI

SPECIFICATIONS
Caliber: 22 LR. **Overall length:** 37". **Barrel length:** 19¼".
Weight: 4 lbs. 4 oz. **Safety:** Cross-bolt type. **Capacity:** 11 cartridges in magazine, 1 in chamber. **Trigger:** Grade I is blued; Grade VI is gold colored. **Sights:** Gold bead front, adjustable folding leaf rear; drilled and tapped for Browning scope mounts. **Length of pull:** 13¾". **Drop at comb:** 1³⁄₁₆". **Drop at heel:** 2⅝". **Stock & Forearm:** Grade I, select walnut with checkering (18 lines/inch); Grade VI, high-grade walnut with checkering (22 lines/inch).
Grade I $344.95
Grade VI 708.95

GRADE VI

BROWNING RIFLES

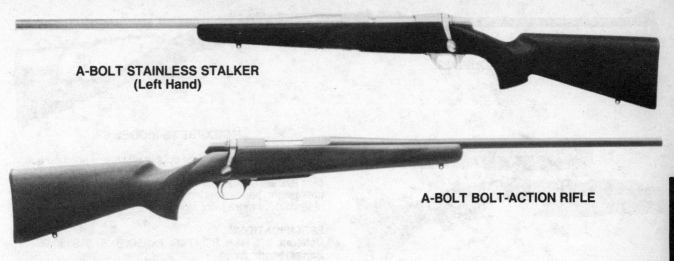

A-BOLT STAINLESS STALKER
(Left Hand)

A-BOLT BOLT-ACTION RIFLE

A-BOLT BOLT-ACTION RIFLES

Calibers: 25-06 Rem., 270 Win., 280 Rem., 30-06 Sprg., 375 H&H, 7mm Rem. Mag., 300 Win. Mag., 338 Win. Mag. **Action:** Short throw bolt of 60 degrees. Plunger-type ejector. **Magazine:** Detachable. Depress the magazine latch and the hinged floorplate swings down. The magazine can be removed from the floorplate for reloading or safety reasons. **Trigger:** Adjustable within the average range of 3 to 6 pounds. Also grooved to provide sure finger control. **Stock and forearm:** Stock is select grade American walnut cut to the lines of a classic sporter with a full pistol grip.

Scopes: Closed. Clean tapered barrel. Receiver is drilled and tapped for a scope mount; or select **Hunter** model w/open sights. **Barrel length:** 24". Hammer forged rifling where a precision machined mandrel is inserted into the bore. The mandrel is a reproduction of the rifling in reverse. As hammer forces are applied to the exterior of the barrel, the barrel is actually molded around the mandrel to produce flawless rifling and to guarantee a straight bore. Free floated. **Overall length:** 44¼".

Weight: 7 lbs. 8 oz. in Magnum; 6 lbs. 8 oz. in Short Action; 7 lbs. in Standard (Long Action).

    Short Action A-Bolt available in 22 Hornet (Micro Medallion), 223 Rem., 22-250 Rem., 243 Win., 257 Roberts, 7mm-08 Rem., and 308 Win.

Prices:

Hunter	**$477.95**
Hunter w/open sights	538.95
Medallion (no sights)	554.95
Medallion Left-Hand Model	578.95
Medallion 375 H&H (open sights)	648.95
Micro Medallion (no sights)	554.95
Gold Medallion	724.95
Stainless Stalker (no sights)	608.95
Stainless Stalker Left Hand Model	627.95
Stainless Stalker 375 H&H (open sights)	721.95

BAR SEMIAUTOMATIC RIFLES
(Grade I with Sights)

Standard Calibers	**$608.50**
Magnum Calibers	658.50

Model	Calibers	Barrel Length	Sight Radius*	Overall Length	Average Weight	Rate of Twist (Right Hand)
Magnum	338 Win. Mag.	24"	19 1/2"	45"	8 lbs. 6 oz.	1 in 12"
Magnum	300 Win Mag.	24"	19 1/2"	45"	8 lbs. 6 oz.	1 in 10"
Magnum	7mm Rem Mag.	24"	19 1/2"	45"	8 lbs. 6 oz.	1 in 9 1/2"
Standard	30-06 Sprg.	22"	17 1/2"	43"	7 lbs. 6 oz.	1 in 10"
Standard	280 Rem.	22"	17 1/2"	43"	7 lbs. 9 oz.	1 in 10"
Standard	270 Win.	22"	17 1/2"	43"	7 lbs. 9 oz.	1 in 10"
Standard	308 Win.	22"	17 1/2"	43"	7 lbs. 9 oz.	1 in 12"
Standard	243 Win.	22"	17 1/2"	43"	7 lbs. 10 oz.	1 in 10"

*All models are available with or without open sights. All models drilled and tapped for scope mounts.

CHAPUIS RIFLES

RGEXPRESS MODEL 89

**RGEXPRESS MODEL 89
w/Claw Mounted Scope**

RGEXPRESS MODEL 89

This big game, side-by-side double rifle has a notched action zone, long trigger guard, coin metal finish, automatic ejectors, Blitz system center side lock, quarter rib, adjustable rear express sight, hand-cut checkering, oil finish, and grip cap (with reservoir) for extra front sight.

SPECIFICATIONS
Calibers: 375 H&H, 9.3×74R, 7×65R, 8×57JRS, 30-06
Barrel length: 23.6″
Weight: 8 lbs. 6 oz.
Stock: French walnut with pistol grip Monte Carlo cheekpiece
Price: $7000.00

CHINASPORTS

**MODEL 64/70
$489.00**

SPECIFICATIONS
Calibers: 243 Win., 308 Win., 270 Win., 30-06, 7mm Rem. Mag., 300 Win. Mag.
Capacity: 5 rounds (standard); 3 rounds (Magnum)
Barrel length: 22″ (standard); 24″ (Magnum)
Weight: 8½ lbs.
Safety: 3-position
Sights: Drilled and tapped for scope mount
Stock: American walnut
Finish: Blued

**NORINCO TYPE EM-332
BOLT ACTION REPEATER
$239.00**

SPECIFICATIONS
Caliber: 22 LR
Capacity: 5 rounds
Barrel length: 18½″
Overall length: 41½″
Weight: 4½ lbs.
Feature: Double magazine holder (underside of stock)

CHURCHILL RIFLES

REGENT RIFLE/SHOTGUN COMBO
$926.95

Churchill's rifle/shotgun combination features a stock made of extra select European walnut with hand-checkering and natural oil finish. The integral dovetail mount, integral iron sights and engraved antique silver-finish receiver are standard features. The 12-gauge improved modified choke is available with the following calibers: 222 Rem., 223 Rem., 270 Win., 308 Win., 30-06 Springfield. **Barrel length:** 25″. **Chamber:** 3″. **Weight:** 8 lbs.

HIGHLANDER BOLT-ACTION RIFLE
$439.95   ($459.95 in 25-06 & 243 Win.)

This repeating bolt-action rifle comes with an oil-finished walnut stock with classic design. Other features include twin locking lugs, gas relief port, swivel posts, positive non-slip thumb-operated safety (allows bolt to be opened for chamber inspection and unloading). **Calibers:** 243, 25-06, 270 Win., 30-06 Springfield, 7mm Rem. Mag., 300 Win Mag., and 308 Win. **Barrel length:** 22″. **Capacity:** 4 rounds (3 in Magnum calibers). **Weight:** 7½ to 8 lbs.

COLT RIFLES

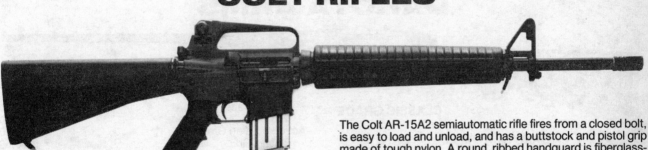

MODEL AR-15A2 GOVERNMENT MODEL

The Colt AR-15A2 semiautomatic rifle fires from a closed bolt, is easy to load and unload, and has a buttstock and pistol grip made of tough nylon. A round, ribbed handguard is fiberglass-reinforced to ensure better grip control. **For law enforcement sales only.**
Also available: **MODEL AR-15A2 GOVERNMENT CARBINE. Barrel length:** 16″. **Weight:** 5 lbs. 13 oz. **Price:** $879.95.

SPECIFICATIONS

MODEL NO.	MODEL	CALIBER	BBL LENGTH (inches)	FINISH	APPROX. WEIGHT (lbs.)	O/A LENGTH (inches)	SIGHT RADIUS (inches)	ROUNDS	PRICES
R6600DH	Colt Match Delta H-BAR w/scope and access.	223 Rem.	20	M	10	39	19.75	5	**$1424.95**
R6600	Colt Match H-BAR	223 Rem	20	M	8.0	39	19.75	5	899.95
R6550	Colt Target Government Model	223 Rem	20	M	7.5	39	19.75	5	859.95

COLT RIFLES

MODEL AR-15 22 LR CONVERSION KIT

The new Colt 22 LR Conversion Kit makes it possible to chamber the 223 caliber Colt semiautomatic Sporter Rifle so that it will accommodate the economical 22LR rimfire cartridge. Lightweight and compact, the conversion kit takes only seconds to install on the range or in the field. It allows the sportsman or law enforcement officer the option of shooting two of the most popular cartridges in the world from the same rifle. **Price: $167.95.**

DAKOTA ARMS

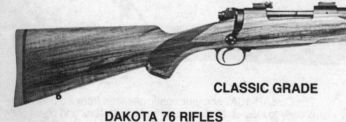

CLASSIC GRADE

DAKOTA 76 RIFLES

SPECIFICATIONS
Calibers:
    Safari Grade: 338 Win. Mag., 300 Win. Mag., 375 H&H Mag., 458 Win. Mag.
    Classic Grade: 257 Roberts, 270 Win., 280 Rem., 30-06, 7mm Rem. Mag., 338 Win. Mag., 300 Win. Mag., 375 H&H Mag., 458 Win. Mag.
Barrel length: 23″
Weight: 7½ lbs. (Classic); 8½ lbs. (Safari)
Safety: Three-position striker-blocking safety allows bolt operation with safety on
Sights: Ramp front sight; standing leaf rear sight
Stock: Medium fancy walnut stock fitted with recoil pad (Classic); fancy walnut with ebony forend tip and recoil pad (Safari)
Prices:
Safari Grade $2850.00
Classic Grade 1950.00

Barreled actions: Safari Grade 1800.00
    Classic Grade 1450.00
    Alpine Grade 1350.00
    416 Rigby African Grade 2500.00
Actions: Safari Grade 1400.00
    Classic Grade 1200.00
    Alpine Grade 1100.00

Note: Numerous options are available, including choice of wood (English, Black/Claro, Bastogne), quarter rib, ebony forend tip, wraparound checkering, etc.

DAKOTA 76 Alpine Short Action, a scaled-down version of Dakota's standard length action designed specifically for shorter cartridges (standard chamberings include 22-250, 243, 6mm Rem., 250-3000, 7mm-08, 308 and 358). Available in right- and left-hand versions in two grades—Classic and Alpine. **Barrel length:** 21″. The Alpine Grade is a lighter weight rifle featuring a blind magazine, slimmer stock and barrel, with a 4-round capacity. **Weight:** approx. 6½ lbs. **Price: $1850.00.**
416 RIGBY African Grade Rifle is designed specifically for the 416 Rigby cartridge. Features include a special magazine (4-round capacity), select wood, cross bolts in the stock, and all other features found in Safari Grade rifles. **Price: $3500.00.**

FRANCOTTE RIFLES

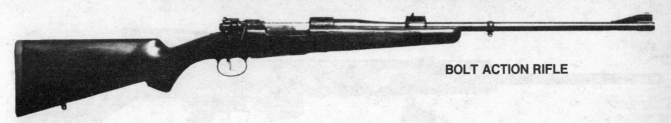

BOLT ACTION RIFLE

SPECIFICATIONS

Calibers: 243, 270, 7×64, 30-06, 308, 300 Win. Mag., 338, 7mm Rem. Mag., 375 H&H, 458
Barrel length: 23¹/₂″ to 26″
Weight: 8 to 10 lbs.
Stock: Deluxe walnut blank
Engraving: English or Nimsky scroll
Sights: Front and rear sights ring mounted; fixed leaf rear sight
Features: Ejection by bolt action; 98 Mauser commercial mechanism; standard checkering; oil finish; recoil pad; steel grip cap
Options: Scope mounts; quarter rib; fold-down front sight tunnel; left-hand mechanism
Prices:
Calibers 7×64, 30-06, 270, etc. . . . . $ 6,789.00
Calibers 243, 308, etc. (short action) 8,434.00
Calibers 375 H&H, etc. (Rimag) 13,229.00
(*Note:* All prices are based on current estimates and are subject to change without notice.)

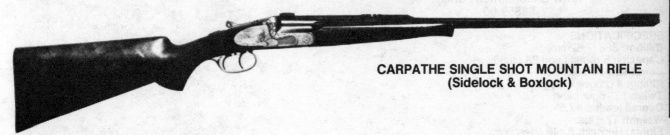

CARPATHE SINGLE SHOT MOUNTAIN RIFLE
(Sidelock & Boxlock)

SPECIFICATIONS

Calibers: 243 Win., 270 Win., 30-06, 308 Win., 300 Win. Mag., 7mm Rem. Mag.
Barrel length: 23¹/₂″ to 26″, round
Forend length: 8¹/₂″
Stock: Deluxe walnut; oil finish; fine checkering
Action: Left sidelock with rear mainspring; manual safety; sensitive trigger; special steel reinforced receiver
Engraving: Light English scrolls
Features: Extractor; scope mounts; choice of barrel rib; splinter forend; oil finish; central locking mechanism
Prices:
Boxlock $10,457.00
Sidelock 21,771.00

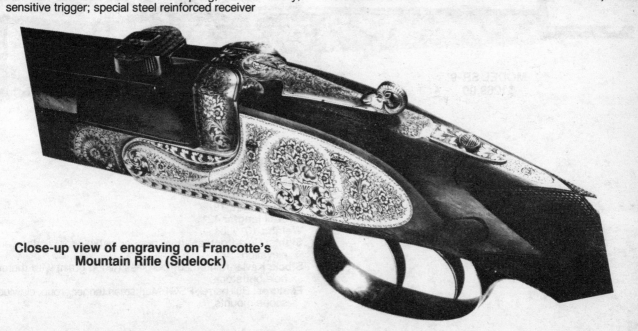

Close-up view of engraving on Francotte's Mountain Rifle (Sidelock)

HECKLER & KOCH RIFLES

**MODEL HK PSG-1 HIGH PRECISION
MARKSMAN'S RIFLE
(Law Encorcement Only)
$8859.00**

SPECIFICATIONS
Caliber: 308 (7.62mm)
Capacity: 5 rounds and 20 rounds
Barrel length: 25.6″
Rifling: 4 groove, polygonal
Twist: 12″, right hand
Overall length: 47.5″
Weight: 17.8 lbs.
Sights: Hensoldt 6×42 telescopic
Stock: Matte black, high-impact plastic
Finish; Matte black, phosphated

**MODEL SR-9
$1269.00**

SPECIFICATIONS
Caliber: 308 Win.
Capacity: 5 rounds
Barrel length: 19½‴
Overall length: 42⅜″
Weight: 10½ lbs.
Sights: Post front; aperture rear, adjustable for windage and
elevation
Stock: Kevlar-reinforced fiberglass (wood grain) with thumb-
hole buttstock
Features: Bull barrel; PSG1 Marksman trigger group; clawlock
scope mounts

HEYM RIFLES

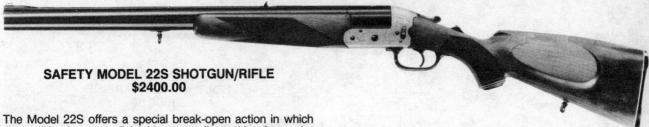

SAFETY MODEL 22S SHOTGUN/RIFLE
$2400.00

The Model 22S offers a special break-open action in which the cocking is accomplished by manually pushing forward a cocking slide located on the tang. For ultimate safety, the gun will automatically uncock by means of a built-in rocker weight if it is dropped or jostled about. The Model 22S comes with single-set trigger, left-side barrel selector, arabesque engraving, walnut stock and an integral dovetail base for scope mounting.

SPECIFICATIONS
Shotgun barrels: 12 ga., 2³/₄″; 16 ga., 2³/₄″; 20 ga., 2³/₄″ and 3″. **Rifle barrels:** 22 Hornet; 222 Rem.; 222 Rem. Mag.; 5.6 × 52 R Mag.; 6.5 × 57 R; 7 × 57 R; 243 Win. **Barrel length:** 24″. **Length of pull:** 14¹/₂″. **Overall length:** 40″.

MAGNUM

STANDARD

MODEL SR20

Features two rugged Mauser-type locking lugs. A special guide rail allows the bolt to operate smoothly through the full length of travel. All parts are interchangeable. The magazine holds five regular or three Magnum cartridges. A hinged floorplate with convenient latch makes unloading easy.

SPECIFICATIONS
Calibers: (Standard) 243 Win., 270 Win., 308 Win., 30-06; (Magnum) 7mm Rem. Mag., 300 Win. Mag., 338 Win. Mag., 375 H&H Mag., plus metric calibers. **Barrel length:** 22″ and

24″ (Standard); 23″ (Magnum) **Length of pull:** 14″ **Weight:** 7 lb. 10 oz. (Standard); 8 lbs. (Magnum) **Stock:** French walnut, hand checkering, Pachmayr Old English pad, oil finish, steel grip cap
Prices:
Model SR20 (Standard) $1500.00
Model SR20 (Magnum) 1600.00
Left-hand action and stock 350.00

MODEL SR20 CLASSIC SPORTER SERIES
$1850.00

SPECIFICATIONS
Calibers: 22-250, 243 Win., 270 Win., 308 Win., 30-06, 7mm Rem. Mag., 300 Win. Mag., 338 Win. Mag., 375 H&H
Capacity: 5 rounds (standard); 3 rounds (Magnum)
Barrel length: 22″ (standard); 24″ (Magnum)
Overall length: 43¹/₂″ (standard); 45¹/₂″ (Magnum)

Weight: 7¹/₂ lbs.
Safety: 3-position style
Trigger: Single adjustable style
Sights: Open or express optional; adj. rear and front
Stock: AAA grade European walnut; oil-finished and hand rubbed

HEYM RIFLES

MODEL SR20 ALPINE SERIES
BOLT ACTION CARBINE
$1900.00

SPECIFICATIONS
Calibers: 243 Win., 270 Win., 308 Win., 30-06
Capacity: 5 rounds
Barrel length: 20″
Overall length: 41″
Weight: 7¹/₂″ lbs.
Safety: 3-position style
Trigger: Single adjustable
Sights: Adj. front and rear (open or express)
Features: AAA grade European walnut stock w/sculptured cheekpiece; "Old English" recoil pad; quick detachable swivel studs

MODEL SR20 MAGNUM EXPRESS

MODEL SR20 CLASSIC SAFARI SERIES
BIG GAME RIFLE
$2250.00

SPECIFICATIONS
Calibers: 404 Rim. Jeffrey, 425 Express, 458 Win. Mag.
Capacity: 3 rounds
Barrel length: 24″
Overall length: 43¹/₂″
Weight: 8¹/₄ lbs.
Sights: 3-leaf express (regulated for 50, 100 & 200 meters)
Features: Barrel-mounted, ring-type front Q.D. swivel and stock-mounted rear Q.D. swivel: AAA grade European walnut stock w/sculptured cheekpiece; double recoil lug bolts.
Also available:
MAGNUM EXPRESS SERIES BIG GAME RIFLE. Calibers: 375 H&H, 404 Rim. Jeffrey, 416 Rigby, 450 Ackley, 460 Win. Mag., 500 NE. **Overall length:** 45¹/₄″. **Weight:** 10 lbs. **Price: $3700.00.**

MODEL SR20 TROPHY SERIES
$2450.00

SPECIFICATIONS
Calibers: 243 Win., 270 Win., 308 Win., 30-06, 7mm Rem. Mag., 300 Win. Mag., 338 Win. Mag., 375 H&H. Other specifications same as Classic Sporter-Series but includes Krupp-Special steel shaped in tapered octagon form with classic quarter rib, rear open sight and raised front sight rib.

HEYM RIFLES

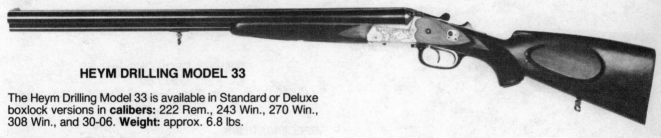

HEYM DRILLING MODEL 33

The Heym Drilling Model 33 is available in Standard or Deluxe boxlock versions in **calibers:** 222 Rem., 243 Win., 270 Win., 308 Win., and 30-06. **Weight:** approx. 6.8 lbs.

Prices:
Standard with arabesque engraving $6000.00
Deluxe with hunting scene engraving 6400.00

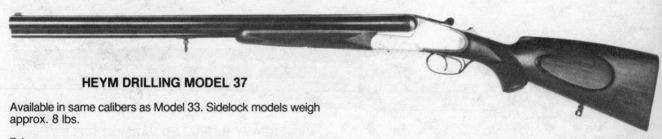

HEYM DRILLING MODEL 37

Available in same calibers as Model 33. Sidelock models weigh approx. 8 lbs.

Prices:
Standard with border engraving . . . . $ 9,400.00
Deluxe with hunting scene engraving 11,000.00

MODEL 88B SAFARI DOUBLE RIFLE

This German-built boxlock model has a modified Anson & Deeley action with standing sears, plus Purdey-type double underlocking lugs and Greener extension with crossbolt. Actions are furnished with sliding safeties and cocking indicators on the top tang, nonbreakable coil springs, front single set triggers and steel trigger guards.

SPECIFICATIONS
Calibers: 375 H&H, 458 Winchester, 470 & 500 Nitro Express
Barrel length: 25″
Overall length: 42″
Weight: 10 lbs. (approx.)
Sights: Three-leaf express sight with standing, shallow V-sight; large gold bead front sight

Price:
Model 88 B Safari in 375 H&H and 458 Win. . . .$13,000.00

HOWA RIFLES

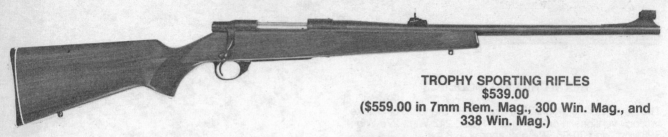

TROPHY SPORTING RIFLES
$539.00
($559.00 in 7mm Rem. Mag., 300 Win. Mag., and 338 Win. Mag.)

SPECIFICATIONS
Calibers: 22-250, 223, 243 Win., 270 Win., 308 Win., 30-06, 7mm Rem. Mag., 300 Win. Mag., 338 Win. Mag.
Capacity: 5 rounds
Barrel length: 22"
Overall length: 42½"
Weight: 7½ lbs.

HEAVY-BARRELED VARMINT RIFLES
$579.00

SPECIFICATIONS
Calibers: 223, 22-250 and 308
Barrel length: 24"
Overall length: 44½"
Weight: 9¼ lbs.

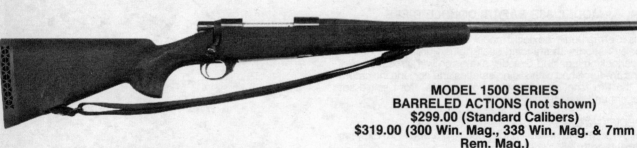

HOWA LIGHTNING SPORTING RIFLES
$539.00
($559.00 in 7mm Rem. Mag. and 300 Win. Mag.)

SPECIFICATIONS
Calibers: 270, 30-06, 7mm Rem. Mag., 300 Win. Mag.
Barrel length: 22"
Overall length: 42½"
Weight: 7 lbs.
Stock: Lightweight Carbolite

MODEL 1500 SERIES
BARRELED ACTIONS (not shown)
$299.00 (Standard Calibers)
$319.00 (300 Win. Mag., 338 Win. Mag. & 7mm Rem. Mag.)

SPECIFICATIONS
Calibers: 243 Win., 270 Win., 30-06, 308 Win. (standard); 223 Rem., 22-250 Rem. (heavy barreled varmint); 7mm Rem. Mag., 300 Win. Mag. (Magnum), 338 Win. Mag.
Capacity: 5 rounds (3 rounds in Magnum)
Barrel lengths: 22" (standard); 24" (heavy barreled varmint and Magnum)
Overall lengths: 27¾" (standard); 29¾" (heavy barreled and Magnum)
Weight: 5 lbs. 5 oz. (standard); 7 lbs. 1 oz. (heavy barreled varmint); 7 lbs. 9 oz. (Magnum)

IVER JOHNSON RIFLES

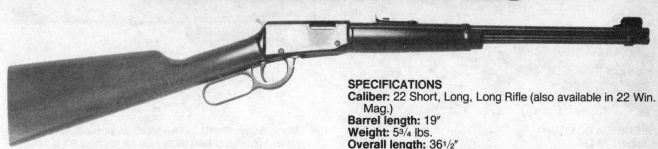

WAGONMASTER LEVER ACTION
$199.87 (22 S, L, LR)
$230.00 (22 Win. Mag.)

SPECIFICATIONS
Caliber: 22 Short, Long, Long Rifle (also available in 22 Win. Mag.)
Barrel length: 19"
Weight: 5³/₄ lbs.
Overall length: 36¹/₂"
Sights: Hooded ram front; adjustable rear
Capacity: 21 Short, 17 Long, or 15 Long Rifle; can be mixed and loaded simultaneously; Magnum has 12-shot capacity
Finish: Blue
Stock: Hardwood

TARGETMASTER
$199.87

SPECIFICATIONS
Caliber: 22 Short, Long, or Long Rifle
Magazine capacity: 19 Short, 15 Long, or 12 Long Rifle (can be mixed and loaded simultaneously
Barrel length: 18"
Overall length: 36¹/₂"
Weight: 5³/₄ lbs.
Sights: Hooded ramp front; adjustable rear

KDF RIFLES

MODEL K15 AMERICAN
$1510.00 ($1565.00 in Magnum)

SPECIFICATIONS
Calibers: 25-06, 257 Wby. Mag., 270 Win., 270 Wby. Mag., 7mm Rem. Mag., 30-06, 300 Win. Mag., 300 Wby. Mag., 338 Win. Mag., 340 Wby. Mag., 375 H&H Mag., 411 KDF Mag., 416 Rem. Mag., 458 Win. Mag.
Capacity: 4 rounds (3 rounds in Magnum)
Barrel length: 22" (24" in Magnum)
Overall length: 44" (46" in Magnum)
Weight: 8 lbs. (approx.)
Receiver: Drilled and tapped for scope mounts (KDF bases available to take 1" or 30mm rings)
Trigger: Competition-quality single stage; adjustable for travel, pull and sear engagement

Safety: Located on right-hand side
Stocks: Kevlar composite or laminate stock; Pachmayr decelerator pad; quick detachable swivels; AAA grade walnut stocks with 22-line hand-checkering; ebony forend; pistol grip cap and crossbolts (walnut stocks may be ordered in classic, schnabel or thumbhole style)
Features and options: Iron sights; recoil arrestor; choice of metal finishes; 3 locking lugs w/large contact area; 60-degree lift for fast loading; box-style magazine system; easily accessible bolt release catch; fully machined, hinged bottom metal

KIMBER RIFLES

MODEL 82 RIMFIRE SPORTING RIFLE

SPECIFICATIONS
Caliber: 22 LR
Capacity: 5 or 10-shot detachable magazine
Barrel length: 22″ (6 grooves, 1 in 16″ twist)
Overall length: 40¹/₂″
Weight: 6¹/₂lbs.
Stock: Deluxe grade is AA Claro walnut with ebony tip and Niedner-style checkered steel buttplate (no cheekpiece). Also includes hand-checkering and fully inletted swivel studs. **Super Grade** is AAA Claro walnut with ebony forend tip and beaded cheekpiece. Also hand-checkering, Niedner-style buttplate and fully inletted swivel studs. Both grades have round top receivers with screw-on two-piece scope mount bases.

Prices:
DELUXE GRADE (no sights, Sporterweight)	**$1195.00**
SUPER AMERICA (no sights, Sporterweight)	1295.00
HUNTER GRADE (laminate stock)	895.00

MODEL 82 RIMFIRE GOVERNMENT TARGET

SPECIFICATIONS
Caliber: 22 LR (rear-locking, bolt-action, single-shot target rifle)
Barrel length: 25″ (6 grooves, 1 turn in 16″)
Overall length: 43¹/₂
Weight: 10 to 10³/₄ lbs.
Stock: Claro walnut
Features: Single stage trigger fully adjustable for overtravel, sear engagement and pressure. Match-grade barrel is precision-rifled, step-crowned and air-gauge inspected. Grooved receiver accepts Kimber scope mounts. Barrel has 2 rear bases for barrel-mounted scopes.

Price:
MODEL 82 GOVT. TARGET (without sights)	**$595.00**
Also available:	
ALL-AMERICAN MATCH (Medium Target)	895.00

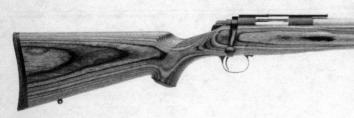

MODEL 84 MINI-MAUSER CENTERFIRE SPORTER

SPECIFICATIONS
Calibers: 17 Rem., 222 Rem., 223
Magazine capacity: 5 shots
Barrel length: 24″ varminter
Overall length: 40¹/₂″ (Sporter); 42¹/₂″ (Varminter)
Weight: 6¹/₂ lbs. (Sporter); 7¹/₄ lbs. (Super Varminter)
Stocks: Deluxe Grade—AA Claro walnut w/ebony forend tip (no cheekpiece); hand-checkering; Niedner-style buttplate; fully inletted swivel studs and steel grip cap. **Super Grade**—AAA Claro walnut w/ebony forend tip; beaded cheekpiece; hand-checkering; Niedner-style buttplate; fully inletted swivel studs and steel grip cap. **Ultra Varminter** stock is made of laminated birch (no cheekpiece), plus curved rubber butt pad and conventional swivel studs. **Super Varminter** stock is AAA Claro walnut w/ebony forend tip, beaded cheekpiece, hand-checkering, curved rubber butt pad and fully inletted swivel studs.
Features: Mauser-type head locking repeater; steel trigger guard and hinged floorplate; fully adjustable trigger; positive rotating disc-type safety; round top receivers with two-piece screw-on scope mount bases.

Prices:
DELUXE GRADE (no sights, Sporterweight)	**$1295.00**
SUPER AMERICA (no sights; Sporterweight)	1495.00
HUNTER GRADE (laminate stock)	995.00
ULTRA VARMINT (no sights; medium-heavy stainless barrel and laminated stock)	1295.00
SUPER VARMINT (no sights, medium-heavy barrel)	1495.00

KIMBER RIFLES

MODEL 89 BIG GAME RIFLE

SPECIFICATIONS

Calibers: *Featherweight*—257 Roberts, 25-06, 7x57, 270 Win., 280 Win., 30-06; *Medium*—7mm Rem. Mag., 300 Win. Mag., 300 H&H, 338 Win. Mag, 35 Whelen

Barrel length: 22″ (24″ for magnums)

Weight: 7½ lbs. (8½ lbs. in 300, 338 and 375 calibers)

Stocks: Deluxe Grades—AA Claro walnut w/ebony forend tip (270, 280, 30-06 calibers); "A" English walnut (magnum calibers). Plain buttstock (no cheekpiece). Rubber recoil pad and fully inletted swivel studs. **Super Grades**—AAA Claro walnut w/ebony forend tip (AA English walnut in magnum calibers). Beaded cheekpiece, rubber recoil pad and fully inletted swivel studs.

Features: Model 70-type override trigger design and Presentation Model 70-type ejector. Mauser-type head locking bolt action w/steel trigger guard and floorplate. Fully adjustable trigger; Mauser-type extractor. Chrome Moly barrel and 3-position Winchester-style safety.

Prices:

DELUXE GRADE (no sights, round top receiver)

Featherweight	**$1795.00**
Medium	**1995.00**
In 375 H&H	**1995.00**

SUPER AMERICA (no sights, square bridge, dovetail receiver) Featherweight **1995.00**

Medium	**2095.00**
In 375 H&H	**2195.00**

HUNTER GRADE

In 270 and 30-06	**1595.00**
In 375 H&H (laminate stock)	**1695.00**

MODEL 89 AFRICAN

SPECIFICATIONS

Calibers: 375 H&H, 404 Jeffrey, 416 Rigby, 460 Weatherby, 505 Gibbs

Barrel length: 24″ (6 grooves, 1 turn in 10″)

Overall length: 47″

Weight: 10 to 10½ lbs.

Stock: AA grade English walnut w/ebony forend tip; beaded English-style cheekpiece

Features: Controlled feed head-locking Kimber magnum-sized action; Mauser-style extractor and bolt stop; express sights on contoured quarter rib; banded front sight. Also, barrel-mounted recoil lug and integral receiver lug, plus twin recoil cross pins in stock.

Price:

MODEL 89 AFRICAN **$3595.00**

KRIEGHOFF DOUBLE RIFLES

MODEL TECK O/U

MODEL TECK OVER/UNDER

SPECIFICATIONS
Calibers: 308, 30-06, 300 Win. Mag., 9.3x74R, 458 Win. Mag.
Barrel length: 25″
Action: Boxlock; double greener-type crossbolt and double barrel lug locking, steel receiver
Weight: 7½ lbs.
Triggers: Double triggers; single trigger optional
Safety: Located on top tang
Sights: Open sight with right angle front sight
Stock: German-styled with pistol grip and cheekpiece; oil-finished
Length of stock: 14³/₈″
Finish: Nickel-plated steel receiver with satin grey finish
Prices:
Model Teck (Boxlock) **$7400.00**
   In 9.3x74R and 458 Win. Mag. **8500.00**
Teck-Handspanner (16 ga. receiver only;
   7x65R, 30-06, 308 Win.) **8750.00**
Also available:
TRUMPF SBS (Side-by-side boxlock) **9500.00**

MODEL ULM OVER/UNDER

SPECIFICATIONS
Calibers: 308 Win., 30-06, 300 Win. Mag., 9.3x74R, 458 Win. Mag.
Barrel length: 25″
Weight: 7.8 lbs.
Triggers: Double triggers (front trigger=bottom; rear trigger=upper
Safety: Located on top tang
Sights: Open sight w/right angle front sight
Stock: German-styled with pistol grip and cheekpiece; oil-finished
Length of stock: 14³/₈″
Forearm: Semi-beavertail
Prices:
Model ULM (Sidelock) **$12,500.00**
Primus (Deluxe Sidelock) **15,500.00**
Dekor (Light scroll engraving) **11,500.00**
Also available:
NEPTUN SBS (Side-by-side sidelock) **14,500.00**

MARK X RIFLES
ACTIONS & BARRELED ACTIONS

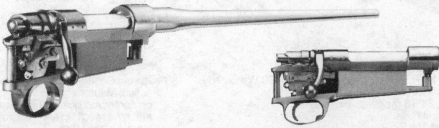

BARRELED ACTIONS
$300.00 (223)
$310.00 (Standard Calibers)
$330.00 (7mm Rem. Mag., 300 Win. Mag.)
$385.00 (375 H&H, 458 Win. Mag.)

Hand-fitted with premium hammer-forged barrels created from corrosion resistant chrome vanadium steel. Each barreled action is carefully proofed and marked under close government control, ready to drop into the stock of your choice.

Calibers: 223, 22-250, 243, 25-06, 270, 7×57, 7mm Rem. Mag., 300 Win. Mag., 308, 30-06. **Barrel length:** 24″. **Weight:** 5½ lbs. (5¾ lbs. in 22-250, 243, and 25-06). **Rifling twist:** 10 (14 in 22-250 and 9.5 in 7×57).

   Also available in 375 H&H Mag. and 458 Win. Mag. Same barrel length but different weights: 6 lbs. (375 H&H Mag.) and 5.75 lbs. (458 Win. Mag.). **Rifling twist:** 12 (375 H&H Mag.) and 14 (458 Win. Mag.).

MAUSER SYSTEM ACTIONS
$220.00 (Single Shot)

Type A: 7×57mm to 30-06. Standard magazine
   (3³/₈″) and bolt face (.470″) **$255.00**
Type B: 22-250 to 308. Short magazine (2⁷/₈″);
   standard bolt face **255.00**
Type C: 7mm Rem. Mag. to 458 Win. Mag. Standard
   magazine and Magnum bolt face (.532″) **260.00**
Type D: 300 Win. Mag. to 375 H&H. Magnum
   magazine (3¹¹/₁₆″) and Magnum bolt face **285.00**
Mini-Mark X (.17 to .223) **245.00**

MARK X RIFLES

MINI-MARK X
$429.00 (with sights)

SPECIFICATIONS
Caliber: 223
Capacity: 5 rounds
Barrel length: 20″
Twist: I turn in 10″
Overall length: 39³/4″
Weight: 6.35 lbs.
Trigger: Adjustable

MARK X LTW SPORTER
$519.00 (270 and 30-06)
$539.00 (7mm Rem. Mag. and 300 Win. Mag.)

SPECIFICATIONS
Calibers: 270, 30-06, 7mm Rem. Mag.
Capacity: 5 rounds; 3 in 7mm Rem. Mag.
Barrel length: 20″
Twist: 1 turn in 10″
Weight: 7 lbs.
Stock: Carbolite

AMERICAN FIELD MAUSER SYSTEM
SPORTING RIFLES $619.00
$639.00 (7mm Rem. Mag. and 300 Win. Mag.)

Features forged and machined Mauser System actions . . . Hammer-forged, chrome, vanadium steel barrels . . . Drilled and tapped for scope mounts and receiver sights . . . Hooded ramp front and fully adjustable rear sight . . . All-steel button release magazine floor plate . . . Detachable sling swivels . . . Silent sliding thumb safety . . . Prime European walnut stocks . . . Sculpted, low-profile cheekpiece . . . Rubber recoil butt plate . . . Steel grip cap.

Calibers: 22-250, 243 Win., 25-06, 270 Win., 7 × 57, 308 Win., 30-06, 7mm Rem. Mag., 300 Win. Mag. **Barrel length:** 24″. **Overall length:** 44″. **Weight:** 7 lbs. **Capacity:** 5 rounds.

Also available: **VISCOUNT MAUSER SYSTEM SPORTING RIFLES.** Same as American Field, but without European walnut stock: **$499.00.** In 7mm Rem. Mag. or 300 Win. Mag.: **$519.00**

MARLIN 22 RIFLES

MODEL 70HC
$147.95

SPECIFICATIONS
Caliber: 22 LR
Capacity: 15-shot clip magazine
Barrel length: 18″
Overall length: 36½″

Weight: 5½ lbs.
Action: Semiautomatic; side ejection; manual bolt hold-open; receiver top has serrated, non-glare finish; cross-bolt safety

Sights: Adjustable open rear, ramp front; receiver grooved for tip-off scope mount
Stock: Monte Carlo walnut-finished hardwood with full pistol grip

MODEL 70P "PAPOOSE"
$165.95

SPECIFICATIONS
Caliber: 22 LR
Capacity: 7-shot clip
Barrel length: 16¼″
Overall length: 35¼″

Weight: 3¾ lbs.
Action: Semiautomatic; side ejection; manual and "last-shot" bolt hold-open
Sights: Adjustable open rear; ramp front

Stock: Walnut-finished hardwood with full pistol grip
Features: Zippered carrying case included

MODEL 75C
$131.95

SPECIFICATIONS
Caliber: 22 LR
Capacity: 13-shot tubular magazine
Barrel length: 18″
Overall length: 36½″

Weight: 5 lbs.
Stock: Monte Carlo walnut finish hardwood
Action: Semiautomatic; side ejection;

manual and "last-shot" automatic bolt hold-opens
Sights: Adjustable open rear; ramp front sight

MARLIN 22 RIFLES

MARLIN 995
$175.95

SPECIFICATIONS

Caliber: 22 Long Rifle
Action: Semiautomatic
Capacity: 7-shot clip magazine
Barrel: 18″ with Micro-Groove® rifling (16 grooves)

Stock: Monte Carlo genuine American black walnut with full pistol grip; checkering on pistol grip and forend
Sights: Adjustable folding semi-buckhorn rear; ramp front sight with brass bead, Wide-Scan™ hood

Overall length: 36³/₄″
Weight: About 5¹/₂ lbs.
Features: Receiver grooved for tip-off scope mount; bolt hold-open device; cross-bolt safety

MARLIN 15YN "LITTLE BUCKAROO™"
Single Shot 22 Beginner's Rifle
$134.95

SPECIFICATIONS

Caliber: 22 Short, Long or Long Rifle
Capacity: Single shot
Action: Bolt action; easy-load feed throat; thumb safety; red cocking indicator

Barrel length: 16¹/₄″ (16 grooves)
Overall length: 33¹/₄″
Weight: 4¹/₄ lbs.

Sights: Adjustable open rear; ramp front sight
Stock: One-piece walnut finish hardwood Monte Carlo with full pistol grip; tough Mar-Shield® finish

MARLIN RIFLES

MODEL 30AS
$304.95

SPECIFICATIONS
Caliber : 30-30
Capacity: 6-shot tubular magazine
Action: Lever action w/hammer block safety; solid top receiver w/side ejection; hammer block safety

Stock: Walnut-finish hardwood stock w/ pistol grip; Mar-Shield® finish
Sights: Tapped for scope mount and receiver sight; also available in combination w/4x, 32mm, 1″ scope

Barrel: 20″ Micro-Groove® barrel
Overall length: 38¼″
Weight: Approx. 7 lbs.

MODEL 25MN
$159.95 with scope

SPECIFICATIONS
Caliber: 22 Win. Mag Rimfire (not interchangeable with any other 22 cartridge)

Stock: One-piece walnut-finished hardwood Monte Carlo with full pistol grip
Barrel length: 22″ with Micro-Groove® rifling
Overall length: 41″

Weight: 6 lbs.
Sights: Adjustable open rear, ramp front sight; receiver grooved for tip-off scope mount

MODEL 25N
$139.95

Same specifications as Model 25MN, except **caliber** 22 LR and **weight** 5½ pounds.

MARLIN RIFLES

MODEL 9 CAMP CARBINE
$330.95

SPECIFICATIONS
Caliber: 9mm
Capacity: 14-shot clip (20-shot magazine available)
Action: Semi-automatic. Manual bolt hold-open. Garand-type safety, magazine safety, loaded chamber indicator. Solid-top, machined steel receiver is sandblasted to prevent glare, and is drilled and tapped for scope mounting.
Stock: Walnut finished hardwood with pistol grip; tough Mar-Shield® finish; rubber rifle butt pad; swivel studs
Barrel length: 16½″ with Micro-Groove® rifling
Sights: Adjustable rear, ramp front sight with brass bead; Wide-Scan™ hood. Receiver drilled and tapped for scope mount.
Overall length: 35½″
Weight: 6¾ lbs.

MODEL 45
$330.95

SPECIFICATIONS
Caliber: 45 Auto
Capacity: 7-shot clip
Barrel length: 16½″
Overall length: 35½″
Weight (approx.): 6.75 lbs.
Stock: Walnut finished hardwood with pistol grip; rubber rifle butt pad; swivel studs
Sights: Adjustable open rear; ramp front sight with brass bead; Wide-Scan™ hood

MARLIN 60
$131.95

SPECIFICATIONS
Caliber: 22 Long Rifle
Capacity: 17-shot tubular magazine with patented closure system
Barrel length: 22″
Weight: 5½ lbs.
Overall length: 40½″
Sights: Ramp front sight; adjustable open rear, receiver grooved for tip-off scope mount
Action: Semiautomatic; side ejection; manual and automatic "last-shot" hold-open devices; receiver top has serrated, non-glare finish; cross-bolt safety
Stock: One-piece walnut-finished hardwood Monte Carlo stock with full pistol grip; Mar-Shield® finish

MARLIN BOLT ACTION RIFLES

MARLIN 880
$192.95

MARLIN 881
$200.95

SPECIFICATIONS (MODEL 880)
Caliber: 22 Long Rifle
Capacity: Clip magazine holds 7 cartridges
Action: Bolt action; serrated, anti-glare receiver top; positive thumb safety; red cocking indicator

Stock: Monte Carlo genuine American black walnut with full pistol grip; checkering on pistol grip and forend; tough Mar-Shield® finish; rubber butt pad; swivel studs
Barrel: 22″ with Micro-Groove® rifling (16 grooves)
Sights: Adjustable folding semi-buckhorn rear; ramp front with Wide-

Scan™ with hood; receiver grooved for tip-off scope mount
Overall length: 41″
Weight: About 5½ lbs.

MARLIN 881: Specifications same as Marlin 880, except with tubular magazine that holds 17 Long Rifle cartridges. **Weight:** About 6 lbs.

MARLIN 883 MAGNUM
$219.95

SPECIFICATIONS
Caliber: 22 Win. Magnum Rimfire (not interchangeable with any other 22 cartridge)
Capacity: 12-shot tubular magazine with patented closure system
Action: Bolt action; serrated, anti-glare receiver top; positive thumb safety; red cocking indicator

Stock: Monte Carlo genuine American black walnut with full pistol grip; checkering on pistol grip and underside of forend; rubber butt pad; swivel studs; tough Mar-Shield® finish
Barrel: 22″ with Micro-Groove® rifling (20 grooves)

Sights: Adjustable folding semi-buckhorn rear; ramp front with Wide-Scan™ hood; receiver grooved for tip-off scope mount
Overall length: 41″
Weight: About 6 lbs.

MARLIN 882 MAGNUM
$212.95

Specifications same as Model 883 Magnum, except with 7-shot clip magazine.

MARLIN LEVER ACTION CARBINES

MARLIN 1895SS
$433.95

SPECIFICATIONS
Caliber: 45/70 Government
Capacity: 4-shot tubular magazine
Action: Lever action w/square finger lever; hammer block safety; receiver top sandblasted to prevent glare

Stock: American black walnut pistol grip stock w/rubber rifle butt pad and Mar-Shield® finish; white pistol grip and butt spacers
Barrel: 22″ Micro-Groove® barrel
Sights: Ramp front sight w/brass bead

and Wide-Scan™ hood; receiver tapped for scope mount or receiver sight
Overall length: 40½″
Weight: 7½ lbs.

MARLIN 1894S
$401.95

SPECIFICATIONS
Calibers: 44 Rem. Mag./44 Special, 45 Colt
Capacity: 10-shot tubular magazine
Action: Lever action w/square finger lever; hammer block safety

Stock: American black walnut stock w/ Mar-Shield™ finish; blued steel forend cap
Barrel: 20″ Micro-Groove® barrel
Sights: Ramp front sight w/brass bead

and Wide-Scan™ hood; solid top receiver tapped for scope mount or receiver sight
Overall length: 37½″
Weight: 6 lbs.

MARLIN 1894CS 357 MAGNUM
$401.95

SPECIFICATIONS
Calibers: 357 Magnum, 38 Special
Capacity: 9-shot tubular magazine
Action: Lever action w/square finger lever; hammer block safety; side ejection; solid top receiver; deeply blued metal surfaces; receiver top sandblasted to prevent glare

Stock: Straight-grip two-piece genuine American black walnut with white butt plate spacer; tough Mar-Shield® finish.
Barrel: 18½″ long with modified Micro-Groove® rifling (12 grooves)
Sights: Adjustable semi-buckhorn folding rear, bead front; solid top receiver

tapped for scope mount or receiver sight; offset hammer spur for scope use—adjustable for right- or left-hand use
Overall length: 36″
Weight: 6 lbs.

MARLIN LEVER ACTION CARBINES

MODEL 444SS
$433.95

Caliber: 444 Marlin
Capacity: 5-shot tubular magazine
Barrel: 22″ Micro-Groove®
Overall length: 40½″
Stock: American black walnut pistol grip stock with rubber rifle butt pad; swivel studs

Sights: Ramp front sight with brass bead and Wide-Scan® hood; receiver tipped for scope mount or receiver sight
Weight: 7½ lbs.

MARLIN GOLDEN 39AS
$358.95

The Marlin lever-action 22 is the oldest (since 1891) shoulder gun still being manufactured.

Solid Receiver Top. You can easily mount a scope on your Marlin 39 by screwing on the machined scope adapter base provided. The screw-on base is a neater, more versatile method of mounting a scope on a 22 sporting rifle. The solid top receiver and scope adapter base provide a maximum in eye relief adjustment. If you prefer iron sights, you'll find the 39 receiver clean, flat and sandblasted to prevent glare. Exclusive brass magazine tube.

Micro-Groove® Barrel. Marlin's famous rifling system of multi-grooving has consistently produced fine accuracy because the system grips the bullet more securely, minimizes distortion, and provides a better gas seal.

And the Model 39 maximizes accuracy with the heaviest barrels available on any lever-action 22.

SPECIFICATIONS
Caliber: 22 Short, Long and Long Rifle
Capacity: Tubular magazine holds 26 Short, 21 Long and 19 Long Rifle Cartridges
Action: Lever action; solid top receiver; side ejection; one-step takedown; deeply blued metal surfaces; receiver top sandblasted to prevent glare;

hammer block safety; rebounding hammer
Stock: Two-piece genuine American black walnut with fluted comb; full pistol grip and forend; blued-steel forend cap; swivel studs; grip cap; white butt and pistol-grip spacers; tough Mar-Shield® finish; rubber rifle butt pad
Barrel: 24″ with Micro-Groove® rifling (16 grooves)
Sights: Adjustable folding semi-buckhorn rear, ramp front sight with new Wide-Scan™ hood; solid top receiver tapped for scope mount or receiver sight; scope adapter base; offset hammer spur for scope use—works right or left
Overall length: 40″
Weight: About 6¾ lbs.

MODEL 39 TAKE-DOWN
$399.95 (incl. carrying case)

SPECIFICATIONS
Caliber: 22 Short, Long or Long Rifle
Capacity: Tubular magazine holds 16 Short, 12 Long, or 10 Long Rifle cartridges
Barrel length: 16½″ lightweight barrel (16 grooves)
Overall length: 32⅝″

Weight: 5¼ lbs.
Safety: Hammer block safety
Sights: Adjustable semi-buckhorn rear, ramp front with brass bead and Wide-Scan™ hood; top receiver tapped for scope mount and receiver sight; scope adapter base; offset hammer spur (right or left hand) for scope use

Stock: Two-piece straight-grip American black walnut with scaled-down fore-arm and blued steel forend cap; Mar-Shield® finish
Action: Lever action; solid top receiver; side ejection; rebounding hammer; one-step take-down; deep blued metal surfaces; gold-plated trigger

MARLIN LEVER ACTION CARBINES

MODEL 1894 CLASSIC
$431.95

SPECIFICATIONS
Calibers: 218 Bee, 25-20 Win. and 32-20 Win.
Capacity: 6-shot tubular magazine
Barrel length: 22″ (6-groove rifling)
Overall length: 38³/₄″
Weight: 6¹/₄ lbs.

Action: Lever action with squared finger lever; side ejection; solid receiver top sandblasted to prevent glare; hammer block safety
Sights: Adjustable semi-buckhorn folding rear, brass bead front; solid top

receiver tapped for scope mount and receiver sight; offset hammer spur
Stock: Straight-grip American black walnut with Mar-Shield® finish; blued steel forearm cap

MARLIN 336CS
$357.95 (without scope)

SPECIFICATIONS
Calibers: 30-30 Win., 35 Rem., 375 Win.
Capacity: 6-shot tubular magazine
Action: Lever action w/hammer block safety; deeply blued metal surfaces; receiver top sandblasted to prevent glare

Stock: American black walnut pistol-grip stock w/fluted comb and Mar-Shield® finish; rubber rifle butt pad
Barrel: 20″ Micro-Groove® barrel
Sights: Adjustable folding semi-buckhorn rear; ramp front sight w/brass bead and removable Wide-Scan™

hood; tapped for receiver sight and scope mount; offset hammer spur for scope use (works right or left)
Overall length: 38¹/₂″
Weight: 7 lbs.

MAUSER RIFLES

MODEL 66 SAFARI
$2200.00
Calibers 375 H&H and 458 Win.

MAUSER RIFLES

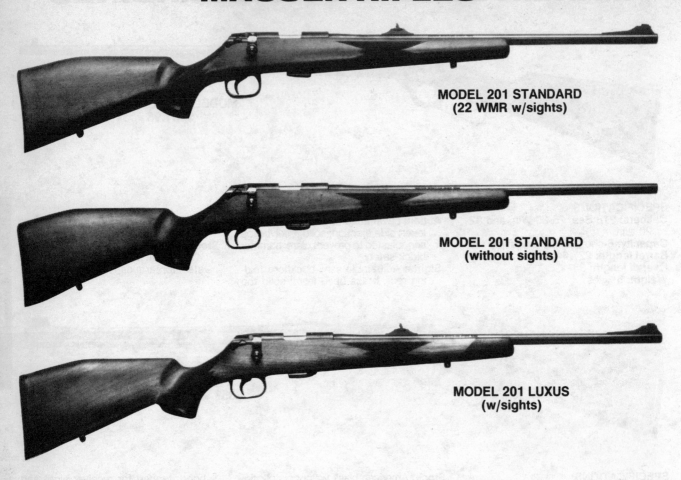

MODEL 201 STANDARD
(22 WMR w/sights)

MODEL 201 STANDARD
(without sights)

MODEL 201 LUXUS
(w/sights)

MODEL 201 RIMFIRE

SPECIFICATIONS
Calibers: 22 LR or 22 WMR
Capacity: 5 shots (optional 8-shot available)
Barrel length: 21″
Overall length: 40″
Weight: 6¹/₂ lbs.
Sights: Metallic (optional)
Features: Receiver drilled and tapped for scope mounts; single-stage trigger (adj. from 1¹/₂ to 7 lbs.); positive silent tang safety locks bolt, sear and trigger; dual extractors for positive extraction of empty cases; hammer-forged steel barrels w/6 lands and grooves

Also available:
LUXUS MODELS with European walnut stocks, hand-checkered rosewood forends, rubber butt pad and 1″ quick disconnect sling swivels
Prices:
Standard 22 LR **$445.00**
Standard 22 WMR **490.00**
Luxus 22 LR **595.00**
Luxux 22 WMR **640.00**
(Deduct **$25.00** from above prices for models without sights)

MODEL 86 SPECIALTY RIFLE
(not shown)

SPECIFICATIONS
Caliber: 308 Win. (7.62×51)
Capacity: 9 shots (+ 1 in chamber)
Barrel length: 28.8″
Overall length: 47.7″
Weight: 10.8 lbs.
Features: Match trigger adjustable for two-stage or single stage; trigger slack, pull and position adjustable externally; scope mount; detachable receiver sight; receiver of chrome/moly steel
Prices:
Model 86 w/laminated wood stock **$3875.00**
Model 86 w/Fiberglass stock **3990.00**
Model 86 w/Match Thumbhole wood stock **4900.00**

MAUSER RIFLES

MODEL 66 STUTZEN

MODEL 66

These bolt-action centerfire repeating rifles feature a telescopic short-stroke action that allows the receiver to be two inches shorter than in most standard bolt-action rifles. Model 66 also provides interchangeability of barrels.

SPECIFICATIONS
Calibers: Standard—243 Win., 270 Win., 30-06, 308 Win.
Magnum—7mm Rem., 300 Win., 300 Wby.
Safari—375 H&H, 458 Win.
Capacity: 3-shot internal magazine
Barrel lengths: 21″ (Stutzen); 24″ (Standard); 26″ (Magnum & Safari)
Overall lengths: 39″ (Stutzen); 42″ (Standard); 44″ (Magnum & Safari)

Weight: 7½ lbs. (Stutzen & Standard); 7.9 lbs. (Magnum); 9.3 lbs. (Safari)
Sights: Rectangular front blade and cover; open rear adjustable for windage and elevation
Features: Silent safety catch; barrel band front sling swivel; two large front bolt-locking lugs; mini-claw extractor for positive extraction of spent cases; single-stage adjustable trigger
Prices:
Standard calibers $1885.00
Magnum calibers 1985.00
Safari calibers 2200.00
Stutzen full stock models 1985.00

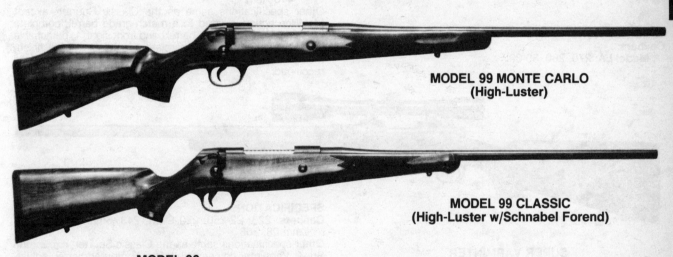

MODEL 99 MONTE CARLO
(High-Luster)

MODEL 99 CLASSIC
(High-Luster w/Schnabel Forend)

MODEL 99

SPECIFICATIONS
Calibers: Standard—243 Win., 25-06 Win., 270 Win., 30-06, 308 Win.
Magnum—7mm Rem., 257 Wby., 270 Wby., 300 Wby., 300 Win., 338 Win., 375 H&H
Capacity: 4 shots (Standard); 3 shots (Magnum)
Barrel lengths: 24″ (Standard); 26″ (Magnum)
Overall lengths: 44″ (Standard); 46″ (Magnum)
Weight: 8 lbs.
Sights: None
Features: Chrome/Moly hammer-forged steel barrels; 60° bolt throw; 3 front bolt-locking lugs; stellite insert for strong lockup between receiver and barrel; jeweled bolt; dual cocking cam and patented two-stage floating firing pin for

fast lock time (1.6 milli-seconds); mini-claw extractor for positive extraction of spent cases; single-stage trigger (adj. from 1½ to 7 lbs.); steel floor plate and trigger guard
Prices:
MODEL 99 CLASSIC
Standard calibers (w/oil finish) $1345.00
Magnum calibers (w/oil finish) 1245.00
Same as above w/High-Luster finish 1395.00
MODEL 99 MONTE CARLO STOCK
Standard calibers (w/oil finish) 1195.00
With High-Luster finish 1345.00
Magnum calibers (w/oil finish) 1245.00
With High-Luster finish 1395.00

McMILLAN SIGNATURE RIFLES

CLASSIC SPORTER
$1795.00   ($1950.00 Stainless)

SPECIFICATIONS
Calibers:
  Model SA: 22-250, 243, 6mm Rem., 7mm-08, 284, 308
  Model LA: 25-06, 270, 280 Rem., 30-06

Model MA: 7mm Rem. Mag., 300 Win. Mag., 300 Weatherby, 338 Win. Mag., 340 Weatherby, 375 H&H, 416 Rem.
Capacity: 4 rounds; 3 rounds in magnum calibers
Weight: 7 lbs; 7 lbs. 9 oz. in long action
Barrel lengths: 22″, 24″, 26″
Options: Fibergrain; wooden stock, optics, 30mm rings, muzzle brakes, steel floor plates, iron sights

ALASKAN
$2495.00

Model MA: 7mm Rem. Mag., 300 Win. Mag., 300 H&H, 300 Weatherby, 358 Win., 340 Weatherby, 375 H&H, 416 Rem.
Other specifications same as the Classic Sporter, except McMillan action is fitted to a match-grade barrel, complete with single-leaf rear sight, barrel band front sight, 1″ detachable rings and mounts, steel floorplate, electroless nickel finish. Monte Carlo stock features cheekpiece, palm swell and special recoil pad.

SPECIFICATIONS
Calibers:
  Model LA: 270, 280, 30-06

SUPER VARMINTER
$1850.00

SPECIFICATIONS
Calibers: 223, 22-250, 220 Swift, 243, 6mm Rem., 25-06, 7mm-08, 308
Other specifications same as the Classic Sporter, except the Super Varminter comes with heavy contoured barrel, adjustable trigger, field bipod and hand-bedded fiberglass stock.

TITANIUM MOUNTAIN RIFLE
$2495.00

SPECIFICATIONS
Calibers:
  Model LA: 270, 280 Rem., 30-06
  Model MA: 7mm Rem. Mag., 300 Win. Mag.
Weight: 5½ lbs.
Other specifications same as the Classic Sporter, except barrel is made of chrome-moly (titanium alloy light contour match-grade barrel is available at additional cost of **$500.00**).

McMILLAN SIGNATURE RIFLES

SAFARI
$3195.00

SPECIFICATIONS
Calibers: 300 Win. Mag., 300 Weatherby, 300 H&H, 338 Win. Mag., 340 Weatherby, 375 H&H, 378 Weatherby, 416 Rem., 416 Rigby, 416 Wby., 458 Win.
Other specifications same as the Classic Sporter, except for match-grade barrel, positive extraction McMillan Safari action, quick detachable 1" scope mounts, positive locking steel floorplate, multi-leaf express sights, barrel band ramp front sight, barrel band swivels, and McMillan's Safari stock.

NATIONAL MATCH RIFLE
$2045.00

SPECIFICATIONS
Caliber: 308
Mag. Capacity: 5 rounds
Weight: Approx. 11 lbs. (12½ lbs. with heavy contour barrel. Available for right-hand shooters only. Features modified ISU fiberglass stock with adjustable butt plate, stainless steel match barrel with barrel band and Tompkins front sight; McMillan repeating bolt action with clip shot and Canjar trigger. Barrel twist is 1:12".

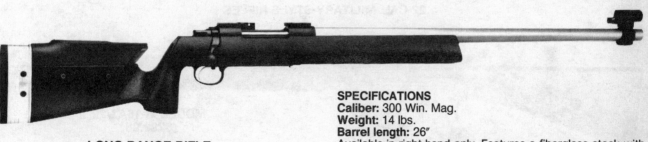

LONG RANGE RIFLE
$2045.00

SPECIFICATIONS
Caliber: 300 Win. Mag.
Weight: 14 lbs.
Barrel length: 26"
Available in right-hand only. Features a fiberglass stock with adjustable butt plate and cheekpiece. Stainless steel match barrel comes with barrel band and Tompkins front sight. McMillan solid bottom single-shot action and Canjar trigger. Barrel twist is 1:12".

McMILLAN BENCHREST RIFLE
$2200.00 (not shown)

SPECIFICATIONS
Calibers: 6mm PPC, 243, 6mm BR, 6mm Rem., 308
Built to individual specifications to be competitive in hunter, light varmint and heavy varmint classes. Features solid bottom or repeating bolt action, Canjar trigger, fiberglass stock with recoil pad, stainless steel match-grade barrel and reloading dies. Right- or left-hand models.

MITCHELL ARMS

REPRODUCTIONS

1858 HENRY RIFLE
$829.00

This classic reproduction features an octagonal barrel, solid brass frame, shiny brass receiver, original loading system and solid European walnut stock. **Caliber:** 44-40 or 22 Long Rifle.

1866 WINCHESTER RIFLE
$654.00

This lever-action Winchester with octagonal barrel has a solid brass frame, original loading system and solid European walnut stock. **Calibers:** 44-40, 38 Special and 22 Long Rifle.

1873 WINCHESTER RIFLE
$795.00

Features steel side plates, color casehardened frame and side plates, octagonal barrel, solid walnut buttstock and forend. Lever action. Uses centerfire ammo. **Calibers:** 22 Long Rifle, 38 Special and 45 Colt.

22 CAL. MILITARY STYLE RIFLES

MODEL M-16A1/22
$299.95

MODEL CAR-15/22
$329.95

These full-size, full-weight 22 caliber versions of the U.S. Army M-16 and CAR-15 models feature the new round hand guards and basket flash hiders. A 15-round magazine is concealed within each full-size magazine well.

PARKER-HALE RIFLES

MODEL M81 CLASSIC
$879.95

SPECIFICATIONS
Calibers: 22/250, 243 Win., 6mm Rem., 270 Win., 308 Win., 30-06, 300 Win. Mag., 7mm Rem. Mag.
Barrel length: 24″
Overall length: 44 1/2″
Capacity: 4 rounds
Weight: 7.75 lbs.
Length of pull: 13 1/2″

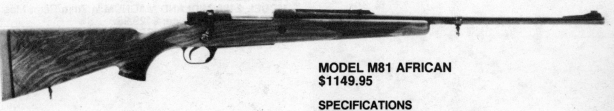

MODEL M81 AFRICAN
$1149.95

SPECIFICATIONS
Calibers: 375 H&H, 9.3 × 62mm
Barrel length: 24″
Overall length: 44 1/2″
Weight: 7.75 lbs.
Stock: Hand-checkered walnut
Features: All-steel trigger guard, adjustable trigger, barrel band front swivel, African express rear sight, hand-engraved receiver

MODEL 1100 LIGHTWEIGHT
$599.95

SPECIFICATIONS
Calibers: 22-250, 243 Win., 6mm Rem., 270 Win., 308 Win., 30-06
Barrel length: 22″
Overall length: 43″
Weight: 6 1/2 lbs.
Capacity: 4 rounds
Length of pull: 13 1/2″

MODEL 1100M AFRICAN MAGNUM (404 Jeffrey and 458 Win. Mag. only). **Barrel length:** 24″. **Overall length:** 46″. **Weight:** 9 1/2 lbs. **Price:** $999.95.

PARKER-HALE RIFLES

MODEL 2100 MIDLAND
$399.95

SPECIFICATIONS
Calibers: 22/250, 243 Win., 6mm Rem., 270 Win., 308 Win., 30-06
Barrel length: 22″ (24″ in cal. 22/250)
Overall length: 43″
Weight: 7 lbs.
Capacity: 4 rounds
Length of pull: 13½″
Also available:
MODEL 2100 MIDLAND MAGNUM in 7mm Rem. Mag. and 300 Win. Mag. **Price: $429.95.**
MODEL 2600 MIDLAND SPECIAL in 30-06, 308, 270 and 243. **Price: $329.95.**

MODEL 1200 SUPER
$699.95

SPECIFICATIONS
Calibers: 22/250, 243 WWin., 6mm Rem., 270 Win., 308 Win., 30-06
Barrel length: 24″
Overall length: 44½″
Weight: 7½ lbs.
Capacity: 4 rounds
Length of pull: 13½″
Also available:
MODEL 1200M SUPER MAGNUM (300 Win. Mag. and 7mm Rem. Mag. only): Same specifications as Model 1200 Super but capacity is 3 rounds. **Price: $699.95.**
MODEL 1200C SUPER CLIP (243 Win., 6mm Rem., 270 Win., 30-06 and 308 Win. only). Same specifications as Model 1200 Super but weighs 7¾ lbs. **Price: $759.95.** Also available in 300 Win. Mag. and 7mm Rem. Mag. (3 rounds only).

REMINGTON BOLT ACTION RIFLES

MODEL 700 LS
$469.00   ($491.00 in 7mm Rem. Mag.)

The Model 700 LS features a traditional wood stock made by laminating alternate strips of light and dark wood with waterproof adhesive and impregnating it with a phenolic resin for greater stability. Other features include low-gloss satin finish, cut checkering, sling swivel studs and open factory sights. **Calibers:** 243 Win., 270 Win., 30-06 and 7mm Rem. Mag. **Capacity:** 5 (4 in 7mm Rem. Mag.). **Barrel length:** 22″ (24″ in 7mm Rem. Mag.). **Weight:** 7¼ lbs. **Stock dimensions:** drop at heel 1⁵⁄₁₆″; drop at comb ¹¹⁄₁₆″; length of pull 13³⁄₈″.

MODEL 700 MOUNTAIN RIFLE
$503.00

A special lightweight version of the Remington Model 700 bolt action centerfire rifle. **Calibers:** 243 Win., 270 Win., 7mm-08 Rem., 7mm Mauser, 280 Rem., 30-06 and 308 Win. **Weight:** 6³⁄₄ lbs. **Barrel length:** 22″. **Overall length:** 41⁵⁄₈″. **Stock:** Straight-line comb with cheekpiece; satin stock finish.

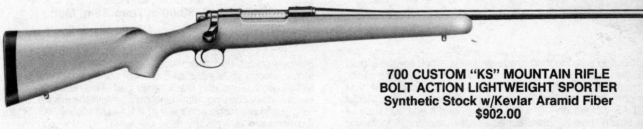

700 CUSTOM "KS" MOUNTAIN RIFLE
BOLT ACTION LIGHTWEIGHT SPORTER
Synthetic Stock w/Kevlar Aramid Fiber
$902.00

Calibers: 270 Win., 280 Rem., 30-06, 7mm Rem. Mag., 300 Win. Mag., 300 Weatherby Mag., 35 Whelen, 338 Win. Mag., 8mm Rem. Mag., and 375 H&H Mag.

MODEL 700 CUSTOM GRADE RIFLES
(not shown)

Grade I	$1314.00
Grade II	2335.00
Grade III	3650.00
Grade IV	5695.00

REMINGTON BOLT ACTION RIFLES

MODEL 700 CLASSIC LIMITED EDITION
$579.00

Caliber: 25-06 Remington
Capacity: 3 shots (1 in chamber)
Barrel length: 24″
Overall length: 44¹/₂″
Weight: 7³/₄ lbs.
Bolt: Jeweled with shrouded firing pin

Receiver: Drilled and tapped for scope mounts; fixed magazine with or without hinged floor plate
Stock: Cut-checkered select American walnut with quick detachable sling swivels installed; recoil pad standard equipment on Magnum rifles; installed at extra charge on others

MODEL 700 ADL DELUXE
$392.00   ($415.00 in 7mm Rem. Mag.)

Calibers: 22-250, 243 Win., 270 Win., 30-06, 308 Win., 7mm Rem. Mag.
Also available: **Laminated Stock Model** in calibers 7mm Rem. Mag., 243 Win., 270 Win., and 30-06: **$469.00.** In 7mm Rem. Mag.: **$491.00.**

MODEL 700 AS
$512.00   ($533.00 in 7mm Rem. Mag.)

Remington's production-grade synthetic stock for the Model 700 bolt action rifle is called Model 700 AS. The rifle's stock is made of a fiberglass-reinforced thermoplastic resin that matches other similar materials in strength and weight. Model 700 AS weighs only 6¹/₂ lbs. All exposed metal surfaces of the action have a nonreflective, black matte finish, including the bolt body. Also nonreflective is the dull, flat finish of the stock, whose style includes a straight comb with cheekpiece, sling swivel studs and black recoil pad. The result is a lightweight, easy carrying, fast-handling rifle with the rigidity, barrel length and repetitive accuracy of a full-size Model 700. Specifications are listed in the table below.

	Calibers	Mag. Capacity	Barrel Length	Overall Length	Twist R-H 1 turn in	Avg. Wt. (lbs.)
Model 700™ AS Synthetic Stock BDL (black)	22.250 Rem.	4	24″	43⁵/₈″	14″	6¹/₂
	243 Win.	4	22″	41⁵/₈″	9¹/₈″	6¹/₂
	270 Win.	4	22″	42¹/₂″	10″	6¹/₂
	280 Rem.	4	22″	42¹/₂″	9¹/₄″	6¹/₂
	30-06	4	22″	42¹/₂″	10″	6¹/₂
	308 Win.	4	22″	41⁵/₈″	10″	7
	7mm Rem. Mag.	3	24″	44¹/₂″	9¹/₄″	6³/₄
	300 Weatherby Mag.	3	24″	44¹/₂″	12″	7

REMINGTON BOLT ACTION RIFLES

The Model 700 BDL heavy barrel "Varmint Special" comes equipped with a 24-inch heavy target-type barrel. The "Varmint Special" is available in a wide range of popular high-velocity, varmint **calibers:** 222 Rem., 223 Rem., 22-250 Rem., 308 Win., 6mm Rem., 243 Win., and 7mm-08 Rem. The "Varmint Special" was designed for maximum-range precision shooting, suitable for chucks, foxes and other varmints.

Features: hinged floor plate; quick release, swivels and strap; crisp trigger pull; American walnut stock, Monte Carlo style with cheekpiece; positive cut skip-line checkering on grip and all three sides of forend, grip cap with white line spacer and butt plate; DuPont developed RK-W wood finish. **Stock dimensions:** 13 3/8-inch length of pull; 1 3/8 inch drop at heel; 1/2-inch drop at comb (from open sight line). The safety is a thumb-lever type and is serrated. The bolt knob is oval shaped, serrated top and bottom. As in the Model 700 BDL, the cartridge head is completely encased by the bolt face and is supported by three rings of steel when the action is closed. The model is a very popular choice for metallic silhouette shooting.

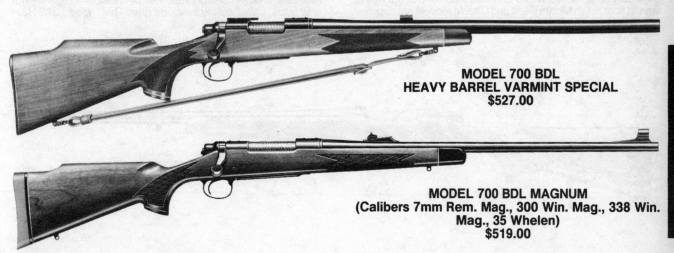

**MODEL 700 BDL
HEAVY BARREL VARMINT SPECIAL
$527.00**

**MODEL 700 BDL MAGNUM
(Calibers 7mm Rem. Mag., 300 Win. Mag., 338 Win. Mag., 35 Whelen)
$519.00**

RIFLES

MODEL 700 SPECIFICATIONS

Calibers	Mag. Cap.	Barrel Length[1]	Overall Length/Avg. Wt. (lb.)				Twist R-H 1 turn in
			"Mountain Rifle"*	"Limited Classic"	Varmint Special	ADL, BDL & "Custom"	
17 Rem.	5	24"	—	—	—	43 1/2"/7 1/4	9"
222 Rem.	5	24"	—	—	43 1/2"/9	43 1/2"/7 1/4	14"
22-250 Rem.	4	24"	—	—	43 1/2"/9	43 1/2"/7 1/2	14"
223 Rem.	5	24"	—	—	43 1/2"/9	43 1/2"/7 1/4	12"
6mm Rem.*	4	22"	—	—	43 1/2"/9	41 1/2"/7 1/4	9 1/8"
243 Win.	4	22"	—	—	43 1/2"/9	41 1/2"/7 1/4	9 1/8"
25-06 Rem.	4	24"	—	—	—	41 1/2"/7 1/4	10"
270 Win.	4	22"	42 1/2"/6 3/4	—	—	41 1/2"/7 1/4	10"
280 Rem.	4	22"	42 1/2"/6 3/4	—	—	—	—
7mm-08 Rem.	4	22"	—	—	43 1/2"/9	41 1/2"/7 1/4	9 1/4"
7mm Mauser	4	22"	41 5/8"/6 3/4	—	—	—	9 1/4"
30-06	4	22"	42 1/2"/6 3/4	—	—	41 1/2"/7 1/4	10"
308 Win.	4	22"	41 5/8"/6 3/4	—	—	41 1/2"/7 1/4	10"
	4	24"	—	—	43 1/2"/9	—	12"
	3	22"	—	—	—	41 5/8"/7 1/4	10"
300 Win. Mag.	3	24"	—	44 1/2"/7 3/4	—	—	—
7mm Rem. Mag.[2]	3	24"	—	—	—	44 1/2"/7 3/4	9 1/4"
300 Win. Mag.[2]	3	24"	—	—	—	44 1/2"/7 3/4	10"
35 Whelen[2]	4	22"	—	—	—	44 1/2"/7 1/4	16"
338 Win. Mag.[2]	4	24"	—	44 1/2"/7 1/4	—	—	10"
SAFARI GRADE (Custom Shop Only)							
8mm Rem. Mag.	3	24"	—	—	—	44 1/2"/9	10"
375 H&H Mag.[2]	3	24"	—	—	—	44 1/2"/9	12"
416 Rem. Mag.[2]	—	24"	—	—	—	44 1/2"/9	14"
458 Win. Mag.[2]	3	24"	—	—	—	44 1/2"/9	14"

[1] "Varmint Special" equipped only with a 24" barrel.   [2] Recoil pad included.

REMINGTON RIFLES
SAFARI GRADE BOLT ACTION RIFLES

Three versions of Model 700 Safari grade bolt action rifles are now chambered for the new .416 Remington Magnum cartridge, providing big-game hunters with a choice of three different stock styles and two stock materials. Model 700 Safari Monte Carlo (with Monte Carlo comb and cheekpiece) and Model 700 Safari Classic (with straight-line classic comb and no cheekpiece) are the wood-stocked models. Also available is Model 700 Safari KS with a synthetic stock of DuPont Kevlar aramid fiber. Both Monte Carlo and Classic models are supplied with a satin wood finish decorated with hand-cut checkering

18 lines to the inch and fitted with two reinforcing cross bolts covered with rosewood plugs. The Monte Carlo model also has a rosewood pistol grip cap and forend tip. Safari KS is completely impervious to temperature changes and moisture, making it ideal for hunting in the African jungle or the Alaskan peninsula. All three models are fitted with sling swivel studs. A barrel band replaces the front swivel on the Safari KS model. All three have 24″ barrels with 1 in 14″ twist. Average weight is 9½ lbs. Other calibers include 8mm Rem. Mag., 375 H&H Magnum, and .458 Win. Mag.

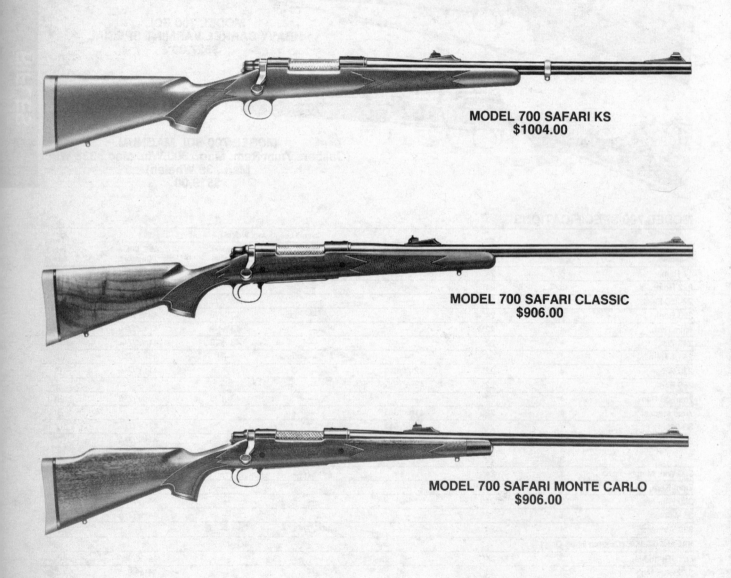

MODEL 700 SAFARI KS
$1004.00

MODEL 700 SAFARI CLASSIC
$906.00

MODEL 700 SAFARI MONTE CARLO
$906.00

REMINGTON BOLT ACTION RIFLES

Every Model Seven is built to the accuracy standards of our famous Model 700 and is individually test fired to prove it. Its 18½" Remington special steel barrel is free-floating out to a single pressure point at the forend tip. And there is ordnance-quality steel in everything from its fully enclosed bolt and extractor system to its steel trigger guard and floor plate. Ramp front and fully adjustable rear sights, sling swivel studs are standard.

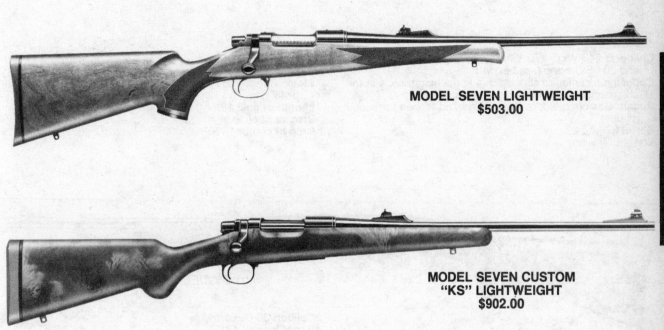

MODEL SEVEN LIGHTWEIGHT
$503.00

MODEL SEVEN CUSTOM
"KS" LIGHTWEIGHT
$902.00

Models	Calibers	Clip Mag. Capacity	Barrel Length	Overall Length	Twist R-H 1 turn in	Avg. Wt. (lbs.)
MODEL SEVEN™	223 Rem.	5	18½"	37¾"	12"	6¼
	243 Win.	4	18½"	37¾"	9⅛"	6¼
	6mm Rem.	4	18½"	37¾"	9⅛"	6¼
	77mm-08 Rem.	4	18½"	37¾"	9¼"	6¼
	308 Win.	4	18½"	37¾"	10"	6¼
MODEL 7400™ AND MODEL 7600™	243 Win.		22"	42⅝"	9⅛"	7½
	270 Win.		22"	42⅝"	10"	7½
	280 Rem.		22"	42⅝"	9¼"	7½
	30-60 Carbine		18½"	38⅛"	10"	7¼
	30-06		22"	42⅝"	10"	7½
	308 Win.		22"	42⅝"	10"	7½
	35 Whelen		22"	42⅝"	16"	7

STOCK DIMENSIONS: 13³⁄₁₆" length of pull, ⁵⁄₁₆" drop at heel, ⁹⁄₁₆" drop at comb. Model 7600 also accepts 30-06 and 308 Accelerator® cartridges. Each has a positive cross-bolt safety switch.

REMINGTON RIFLES

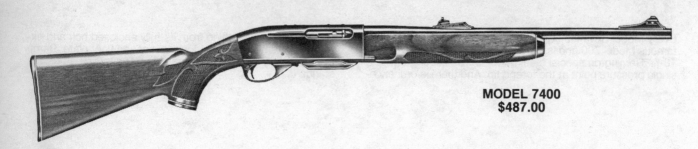

MODEL 7400
$487.00

Calibers: 243 Win., 270 Win., 280 Rem., 30-06, 308 Win., and 30-06 Carbine (see below)
Capacity: 5 centerfire cartridges (4 in the magazine, 1 in the chamber); extra 4-shot magazine available
Action: Gas-operated; receiver drilled and tapped for scope mounts
Barrel length: 22″
Weight: 7¹/₂ lbs.

Overall length: 42″
Sights: Standard blade ramp front; sliding ramp rear
Stock: Checkered American walnut stock and forend; curved pistol grip
Length of pull: 13³/₈″
Drop at heel: 2¹/₄″
Drop at comb: 1¹³/₁₆″

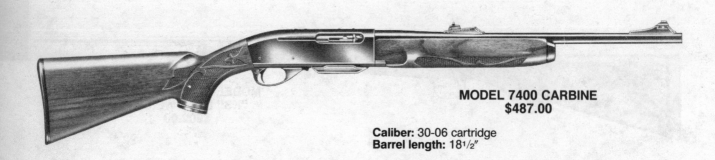

MODEL 7400 CARBINE
$487.00

Caliber: 30-06 cartridge
Barrel length: 18¹/₂″

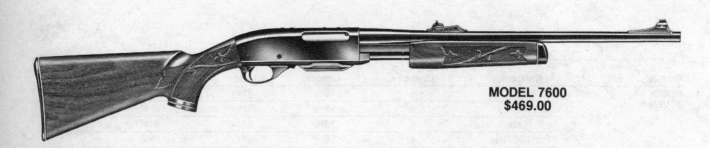

MODEL 7600
$469.00

Calibers: 243 Win., 270 Win., 280 Rem., 30-06, 308 Win., 35 Whelen, and 30-06 Carbine (see below)
Capacity: 5-shot capacity in all six calibers (4 in the removable magazine, 1 in the chamber)
Action: Pump action
Barrel length: 22″ (18¹/₂″ in 30-06 Carbine)
Overall length: 42″
Weight: 8 lbs.
Sights: Standard blade ramp front sight; sliding ramp rear, both removable

Stock: Checkered American walnut
Length of pull: 13³/₈″
Drop at heel: ¹⁵/₁₆″
Drop at comb: ⁹/₁₆″

Also available:
MODEL 7600 CARBINE with 18¹/₂″ barrel; chambered for 30-06 cartridge

REMINGTON RIMFIRE RIFLES

MODEL 541-T BOLT ACTION
$355.00

RIMFIRE RIFLE SPECIFICATIONS

Model	Action	Barrel Length	Overall Length	Average Wt. (lbs.)	Magazine Capacity
541-T	Bolt	24″	42½″	5⅞	5-Shot Clip
581-S	Bolt	24″	42½″	5⅞	5-Shot Clip
552 BDL Deluxe Speedmaster	Auto	21″	40″	5¾	15 Long Rifle
572 BDL Deluxe Fieldmaster	Pump	21″	40″	5½	15 Long Rifle

MODEL 572 BDL DELUXE FIELDMASTER
$223.00

MODEL 572 DELUXE

Features of this rifle with big-game feel and appearance are: DuPont's beautiful, tough RK-W finish; centerfire-rifle-type rear sight fully adjustable for both vertical and horizontal sight alignment; big-game style ramp front sight; handsome Remington impressed checkering on both stock and forend.

Action: Pump repeater
Caliber: 22 Short, Long and Long Rifle rimfire
Capacity: Tubular magazine holds 20 Short, 17 Long, 15 Long Rifle cartridges

Stock and forend: Model A, walnut finished hardwood; Model BDL, American walnut with tough DuPont RK-W lustrous finish and fine-line custom checkering
Sights: Model A, adjustable rear, bead front; Model BDL, fully adjustable rear, ramp front; screw removable
Safety: Positive cross bolt
Receiver: Grooved for "tip-off" scope mounts
Overall length: 40″
Barrel length: 21″
Average weight: 5½ lbs.

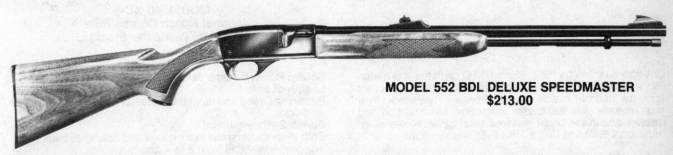

MODEL 552 BDL DELUXE SPEEDMASTER
$213.00

A deluxe model with all the tried and proven dependable mechanical features on the inside, plus special design and appearance extras on the outside. The 552 BDL sports tasteful Remington custom-impressed checkering on both stock and forend. Tough DuPont RK-W lifetime finish brings out the lustrous beauty of the walnut while protecting it. Sights are ramp-style in front and rugged big-game type fully adjustable in rear.

REMINGTON TARGET RIFLES

MODEL 40-XR
Rimfire Position Rifle
$1168.00 (w/Kevlar Stock)

Stock designed with deep forend for more comfortable shooting in all positions. Butt plate vertically adjustable. Exclusive loading platform provides straight line feeding with no shaved bullets. Crisp, wide, adjustable match trigger. Meets all International Shooting Union standard rifle specifications.

Action: Bolt action, single shot
Caliber: 22 Long Rifle rimfire
Capacity: Single loading
Sights: Optional at extra cost. Williams Receiver No. FPTK and Redfield Globe front match sight
Safety: Positive serrated thumb safety
Receiver: Drilled and tapped for receiver sight
Barrel: 24″ medium weight target barrel countersunk at muzzle. Drilled and tapped for target scope blocks. Fitted with front sight base

Bolt: Artillery style with lock-up at rear. 6 locking lugs, double extractors
Trigger: Adjustable from 2 to 4 lbs.
Stock: Position style with Monte Carlo, cheekpiece and thumb groove; 5-way adjustable butt plate and full length guide rail
Overall length: 42½″
Average weight: 9¼ lbs.

Also available:
MODEL 40-XR CUSTOM SPORTER (22 caliber)

Grade I	$1314.00
Grade II	2335.00
Grade III	3650.00
Grade IV	5695.00

MODEL 40-XC
National Match Course Rifle
$1241.00 (w/Kevlar Stock)

Chambered solely for the 7.62mm NATO cartridge, this match rifle was designed to meet the needs of competitive shooters firing the national match courses. Position-style stock, five-shot repeater with top-loading magazine, anti-bind bolt and receiver and in the bright stainless steel barrel. Meets all International Shooting Union Army Rifle specifications.

Action: Bolt action, single shot
Caliber: 22 Long Rifle rimfire
Capacity: Single loading
Sights: Optional at extra cost. Williams Receiver No. FPTK and Redfield Globe front match sight

Safety: Positive thumb safety
Length of pull: 13½″
Receiver: Drilled and tapped for receiver sight or target scope blocks
Barrel: 24″ heavy barrel
Bolt: Heavy, oversized locking lugs and double extractors
Trigger: Adjustable from 2 to 4 lbs.
Stock: Position style with front swivel block on forend guide rail
Overall length: 43½″
Average weight: 11 lbs.

REMINGTON TARGET RIFLES

MODEL 40-XB "RANGEMASTER"
Centerfire Rifle
$1023.00

Barrels, in either standard or heavy weight, are unblued steel. Comb-grooved for easy bolt removal. Mershon White Line non-slip rubber butt plate supplied.

Action: Bolt—single shot in either standard or heavy barrel versions; repeater in heavy barrel only; receiver bedded to stock; barrel is free floating
Calibers: Single-shot, 222 Rem., 22-250 Rem., 6mm Rem., 243 Win., 7.62mm NATO (308 Win.), 30-06, 30-338 (30-7mm Mag.), 300 Win. Mag., 25-06 Rem., 7mm Rem. Mag.
Sights: No sights supplied; target scope blocks installed
Safety: Positive thumb operated

Receiver: Drilled and tapped for scope block and receiver sights
Barrel: Drilled and tapped for scope block and front target iron sight; muzzle diameter S2—approx. 3/4", H2—approx. 7/8"; unblued stainless steel only, 27 1/4" long
Trigger: Adjustable from 2 to 4 lbs. pull; special 2-oz. trigger available at extra cost; single shot models only
Stock: American walnut; adjustable front swivel block on rail; rubber non-slip butt plate
Overall length: Approx. 45 3/4"
Average weight: S2—9 1/4 lbs.; H2—11 1/4 lbs.

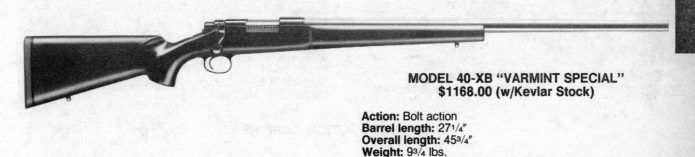

MODEL 40-XB "VARMINT SPECIAL"
$1168.00 (w/Kevlar Stock)

Action: Bolt action
Barrel length: 27 1/4"
Overall length: 45 3/4"
Weight: 9 3/4 lbs.

BENCH REST CENTERFIRE RIFLE
$1052.00

Built with all the features of the extremely accurate Model 40-XB-CF but modified to give the competitive bench rest shooter a standardized rifle that provides the inherent accuracy advantages of a short, heavy, extremely stiff barrel. Wider, squared off forend gives a more stable rest on sandbags or other supports and meets weight limitations for the sporter and light-varmint classes of National Bench Rest Shooters Association competition.

Action: Bolt, single shot only
Calibers: 222 Rem., 22 Bench Rest Rem., 7.62 NATO (308 Win.), 6mm Bench Rest Rem., 223 Rem., 6x47
Sights: Supplied with target scope blocks

Safety: Positive thumb operated
Receiver: Drilled and tapped for target scope blocks
Barrel: Unblued stainless steel only; 20" barrel for Light Varmint Class; 24" barrel for Heavy Varmint Class.
Trigger: Adjustable from 1 1/2 to 3 1/2 lbs.; special 2-oz. trigger available at extra cost
Stock: Kevlar; 12" length of pull
Overall length: 38" with 20" barrel; 44" with 24" barrel
Average weight: Light Varmint Class (20" barrel) 9 1/4 lbs.; Heavy Varmint Class (24" barrel) 11 lbs.

Also available: **MODEL 40XB-BR KEVLAR. $1241.00**

ROSSI RIFLES

PUMP-ACTION GALLERY GUNS

MODEL M62 SAC
$195.00   ($210.00 Nickel)

SPECIFICATIONS
Caliber: 22 LR
Capacity: 12 rounds
Barrel length: 16¹/₂″
Overall length: 32³/₄″
Weight: 4¹/₄″
Finish: Blue

MODEL M62 SA
$195.00   ($210.00 Nickel)

SPECIFICATIONS
Caliber: 22 LR
Capacity: 13 rounds
Barrel length: 23″
Overall length: 39¹/₄″
Weight: 5¹/₂″ lbs.
Finish: Blue
Model M62 SA w/Octagonal barrel $220.00
Model 59 22 Magnum 240.00

PUMA LEVER-ACTION CARBINES

MODEL M92 SRC

MODEL M92 SRC
$305.00

SPECIFICATIONS
Caliber: 38 Special or 357 Magnum
Capacity: 10 rounds
Barrel length: 20″
Overall length: 37″
Weight: 5³/₄″
Also available:
Model M65SRC in 44 Magnum $325.00

MODEL M92 SRS
$305.00 (not shown)

SPECIFICATIONS
Caliber: 38 Special or 357 Magnum
Capacity: 7 rounds
Barrel length: 16″
Overall length: 33″
Weight: 5 lbs.
Finish: Blue

RUGER CARBINES

RUGER MINI-14

Materials: Heat-treated chrome molybdenum and other alloy steels as well as music wire coil springs are used throughout the mechanism to ensure reliability under field-operating conditions. **Safety:** The safety blocks both the hammer and sear. The slide can be cycled when the safety is on. The safety is mounted in the front of the trigger guard so that it may be set to Fire position without removing finger from trigger guard. **Firing pin:** The firing pin is retracted mechanically during the first part of the unlocking of the bolt. The rifle can only be fired when the bolt is safely locked. **Stock:** One-piece American hardwood reinforced with steel liner at stressed areas. Handguard and forearm separated by air space from barrel to promote cooling under rapid-fire conditions. **Field stripping:** The Carbine can be field stripped to its eight (8) basic sub-assemblies in a matter of seconds and without use of special tools.

MINI-14 SPECIFICATIONS
Caliber: 223 (5.56mm). **Length:** 37¼″. **Weight:** 6 lbs. 4 oz. **Magazine:** 5-round, detachable box magazine. 20-shot and 30-shot magazines available. **Barrel length:** 18½″.

Mini-14/5 Blued **$468.75**
K-Mini-14/5 Stainless Steel **516.00**
(Scopes not included)

MINI-14 RANCH RIFLE

Caliber: 223 (5.56mm) or 7.62×39. **Length:** 37¼″. **Weight:** 6 lbs. 8 oz. **Magazine:** 10-shot and 20-shot magazines available. **Barrel length:** 18¼″.

Mini-14/5R Blued **$504.50**
K-Mini-14/5R Stainless Steel **552.50**

RUGER CARBINES

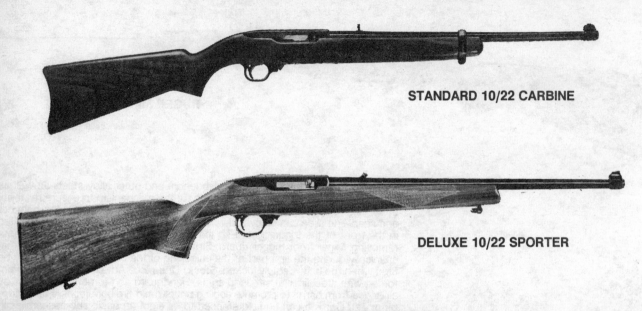

STANDARD 10/22 CARBINE

DELUXE 10/22 SPORTER

MODEL 10/22 CARBINE
22 LONG RIFLE CALIBER

Identical in size, balance and style to the Ruger 44 Magnum Carbine and nearly the same in weight, the 10/22 is a companion to its high-power counterpart. Construction of the 10/22 Carbine is rugged and follows the Ruger design practice of building a firearm from integrated sub-assemblies. For example, the trigger housing assembly contains the entire ignition system, which employs a high-speed, swinging hammer to ensure the shortest possible lock time. The barrel is assembled to the receiver by a unique dual-screw dovetail system that provides unusual rigidity and strength—and accounts, in part, for the exceptional accuracy of the 10/22.

SPECIFICATIONS
Caliber: 22 Long Rifle, high-speed or standard-velocity loads.
Barrel: 18½" long; barrel is assembled to the receiver by unique dual-screw dovetail mounting for added strength and rigidity.
Weight: 5 lbs. **Overall length:** 37". **Sights:** 1/16" gold bead front sight; single folding leaf rear sight, adjustable for elevation; receiver drilled and tapped for scope blocks or tip-off mount adapter. **Magazine:** 10-shot capacity, exclusive Ruger rotary design; fits flush into stock. **Trigger:** Curved finger surface, 3/8" wide. **Safety:** Sliding cross-button type; safety locks both sear and hammer and cannot be put in safe position unless gun is cocked. **Stocks:** 10/22 R Standard Carbine is walnut; 10/22 RB is birch; 10/22 SP Deluxe Sporter is American walnut. **Finish:** Polished all over and blued or anodized.

Model 10/22-RB Standard (birch stock) **$192.00**
Model 10/22-DSP Deluxe **242.50**

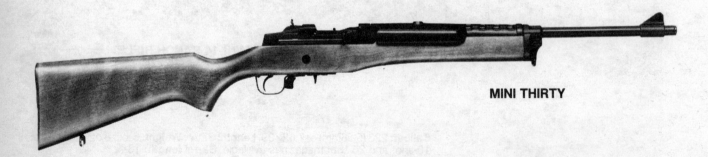

MINI THIRTY

This modified version of the Ruger Ranch rifle is chambered for the 7.62 × 39mm Russian service cartridge (used in the SKS carbine and AKM rifle). Designed for use with telescopic sights, it features a low, compact scope mounting for greater accuracy and carrying ease. **Barrel length:** 18½". **Overall**

length: 37¼". **Weight:** 7 lbs. 3 oz. (empty). **Magazine capacity:** 5 shots. **Rifling:** 6 grooves, right-hand twist, one turn in 10". **Finish:** polished and blued overall.

Price **$504.50**

RUGER SINGLE-SHOT RIFLES

The following illustrations show the variations currently offered in the Ruger No. 1 Single-Shot Rifle Series. Ruger No. 1 rifles come fitted with selected American walnut stocks. Pistol grip and forearm are hand-checkered to a borderless design. Price for any listed model is **$603.75** (except the No. 1 RSI International Model: **$624.75**).

NO. 1A LIGHT SPORTER

Calibers: 243 Win.; 30/06; 270 Win., 7×57mm. **Barrel length:** 22″. **Sight:** Adjustable folding-leaf rear sight mounted on quarter rib with ramp front sight base and dovetail-type gold bead front sight; open. **Weight:** 7¼ lbs.

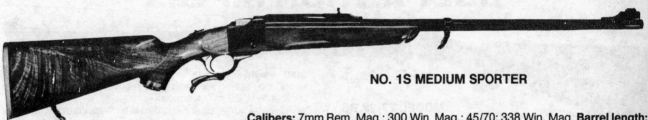

NO. 1S MEDIUM SPORTER

Calibers: 7mm Rem. Mag.; 300 Win. Mag.; 45/70; 338 Win. Mag. **Barrel length:** 26″ (22″ in 45/70). **Sights:** (same as above). **Weight:** 8 lbs. (7¼ lbs. in 45/70).

NO. 1B STANDARD RIFLE

Calibers: 22/250; 243 Win.; 6mm Rem.; 25/06; 270 Win.; 30/06; 7mm Rem. Mag.; 220 Swift; 338 Mag.; 280; 223; 257 Roberts, 270 Weatherby, 300 Mag., 300 Weatherby. **Barrel:** 26″. **Sights:** Ruger steel tip-off scope rings, 1″. **Weight:** 8 lbs.

NO. 1V SPECIAL VARMINTER

Calibers: 22/250; 25/06; 220 Swift; 223; 6mm. **Barrel length;** 24″. **Sights:** Ruger steel blocks and tip-off scope rings, 1″. **Weight:** 9 lbs.

RUGER RIFLES

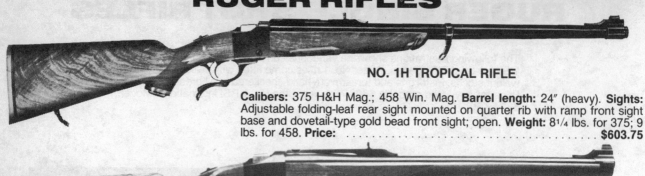

NO. 1H TROPICAL RIFLE

Calibers: 375 H&H Mag.; 458 Win. Mag. **Barrel length:** 24″ (heavy). **Sights:** Adjustable folding-leaf rear sight mounted on quarter rib with ramp front sight base and dovetail-type gold bead front sight; open. **Weight:** 8¼ lbs. for 375; 9 lbs. for 458. **Price:** **$603.75**

NO. 1RSI INTERNATIONAL
With Mannlicher Style Forearm

SPECIFICATIONS
Caliber: 243 Win., 30-06, 270 Win., and 7×57mm. **Barrel length:** 20″ (lightweight). **Overall length:** 36½″. **Weight:** 7¼ lbs. **Sights:** Adjustable folding leaf rear sight mounted on quarter rib with ramp front sight base and dovetail-type gold bead front sight. **Price:** **$624.75**

BOLT ACTION RIFLES

MODEL 77/22 RS

MODEL 77/22 BOLT-ACTION RIMFIRE RIFLE

The Ruger 22-caliber rimfire 77/22 bolt-action rifle offers the sportsman quality and value. It represents a blend of characteristics long associated with the famous Ruger M-77 rifle and the internationally popular Ruger 10/22 semiautomatic rimfire rifle. It has been built especially to function with the patented Ruger 10-Shot Rotary Magazine concept. The magazine throat, retaining lips, and ramps that guide the cartridge into the chamber are solid alloy steel that resists bending or deforming.

The bolt assembly is built to military rifle standards of quality, but it has been modified to function with the 22 rimfire cartridge. Accordingly, the front part of the bolt is nonrotating and the locking lugs have been moved back to the middle of the action. The rear part of the bolt rotates and cams like that of the Ruger M-77 rifle, and it is connected to the nonrotating forward part of the bolt by a sturdy joint.

The 77/22 weighs just under six pounds and provides the smallbore shooter with a compact, featherweight arm that delivers performance and reliability. The heavy-duty receiver incorporates the integral scope bases of the patented Ruger Scope Mounting System, with 1-inch Ruger scope rings. A new 3-position safety offers a new dimension in security. With safety in its "lock" position, a dead bolt is cammed forward, locking the bolt handle down. In this position the action is locked closed and the handle cannot be raised.

A simplified bolt stop fits flush with the left side of the receiver and permits the bolt to be withdrawn from receiver merely by pressing down tightly. The bolt locking system ensures positive lock-up by two large locking lugs on rotating part of bolt. A nonadjustable trigger mechanism is set for me-dium weight trigger pull. This mechanism includes a single strong coil spring for both sear recovery and trigger return. Lock time is 2.7 milliseconds.

All metal surfaces are finished in a deep, lustrous blue with nonglare surfaces on top of receiver. Stock is selected straight-grain American walnut, hand checkered with an attractive and durable polyurethane finish.

An All-Weather, all-stainless steel **MODEL K77/22RS** features a stock made of 6/6 glass-fiber reinforced nylon. **Weight:** approx. 6 lbs.

SPECIFICATIONS
Caliber: 22 LR. **Barrel length:** 20″. **Overall length:** 39¼″. **Weight:** 5¾ lbs. (w/o scope, magazine empty). **Feed:** Detachable 10-Shot Ruger Rotary Magazine.
Prices:

77/22R plain barrel w/o sights, 1″ Ruger rings	**$382.75**
77/22S gold bead front sight, folding leaf rear sight	**382.75**
77/22RM walnut stock, plain barrel, no sights, 1″ Ruger rings, 22 Mag.	**382.75**
77/22RS sights included, 1″ Ruger rings	**403.75**
77/22-RP Synthetic stock, plain barrel with 1″ Ruger rings	**315.00**
77/22-SP Synthetic stock, gold bead front sight, folding-leaf rear sight	**315.00**
77/22-RSP Synthetic stock, gold bead front sight, folding-leaf rear sight and Ruger 1″ rings	**336.00**
K77/22-RP Synthetic stock, stainless steel, plain barrel with 1″ Ruger rings	**378.00**
K77/22-SP Synthetic stock, stainless steel, gold bead front sight, folding-leaf rear sight	**378.00**
K77/22-RMP Synthetic stock, stainless steel, plain barrel, 1″ Ruger rings	**399.00**
K77/22-RSP Synthetic stock, stainless steel, gold bead front sight, folding-leaf rear, Ruger 1″ rings	**399.00**

RUGER BOLT ACTION RIFLES

MODEL M-77RS

Integral Base Receiver, Ruger steel 1″ rings, open sights. **Calibers:** (Magnum action) 270, 7 × 57mm, 30-06 (with 22″ barrels), 25-06, 7mm Rem. Mag., 300 Win. Mag., 338 Win. Mag. (with 24″ barrels); and (Short Stroke action) 243, 308 (with 22″ barrels). **Weight:** Approx. 7 lbs.

Price **$587.00**
Also available in 458 Win. Mag. with steel trigger guard and floor plate 679.75

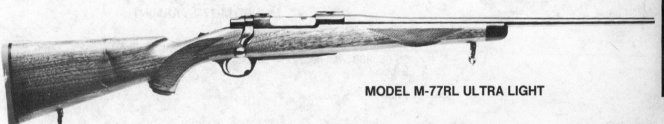

MODEL M-77RL ULTRA LIGHT

New 6-pound big game rifle in both long- and short-action versions, with Integral Base Receiver and 1″ Ruger scope rings. Luxury detailing throughout. **Calibers:** (Magnum action) 270, 30-06, 257 (all with 20″ barrels); and (Short Stroke action) 22-250, 243, .250-3000, 308 (with 22″ barrels). **Weight:** Approx. 6 lbs.

Price **$564.25**

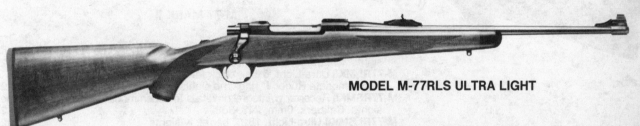

MODEL M-77RLS ULTRA LIGHT

This big game bolt-action rifle encompasses the traditional features that have made the Ruger M-77 one of the most popular centerfire rifles in the world. It includes a sliding top tang safety, a one-piece bolt with Mauser-type extractor and diagonal front mounting system. American walnut stock is hand-checkered in a sharp diamond pattern. A rubber recoil pad, pistol grip cap and studs for mounting quick detachable sling swivels are standard. **Calibers:** 270, 30-06 (Magnum action); 243 and 308 (short stroke action). **Barrel length:** 18½″. **Overall length:** 38⅞″. **Weight:** 6 lbs. (empty). **Sights:** Open.

Price **$564.25**

RUGER BOLT ACTION RIFLES

MODEL M-77RSI INTERNATIONAL

Mannlicher-type stock, Integral Base Receiver, open sights, Ruger 1″ steel rings. **Calibers:** (Short Stroke action) 22-250, 250-3000, 243, 270, 30-06, and 308 (all with 18¹/₂″ barrels). **Weight:** Approx. 7 lbs.

Price **$593.75**

MODEL M-77V VARMINT

Integral Base Receiver, 1″ scope rings. No sights. **Calibers:** 22-250, 6mm, 243, 25-06, 308 (with heavy 24″ barrels); 220 Swift (with 26″ barrel). **Weight:** Approx. 9 lbs.

Price **$546.25**

M-77 MARK II

M-77RMKII Receiver w/integral dovetails to accommodate Ruger 1″ rings, no sights. **Calibers:** 223, 6mm, 243, 308 . . . . **$531.25**
M-77RLMKII Ultra-Light, 6 lbs., black forend tip, receiver w/integral dovetails to accommodate Ruger 1″ rings, no sights. **Calibers:** 223, 243, 308 . . **564.25**
M-77RSMKII Receiver w/integral dovetails to accommodate Ruger 1″ rings, open sights. **Calibers:** 6mm, 243, 308 . . . . **564.25**
M-77RLSMKII Ultra-Light, 18¹/₂″ barrel, w/sights **564.25**
KM-77RPMKII Receiver w/integral dovetails to accommodate Ruger 1″ rings, no sights, stainless steel, synthetic stock. **Calibers:** 223, 243, 308 . . **531.25**

MODEL M-77R (not shown)

Integral Base Receiver, 1″ scope rings. No sights. **Calibers:** (Magnum action) 270, 7×57mm, 257 Roberts, 280 Rem., 30-06 (all with 22″ barrels); 25-06, 7mm Rem. Mag., 300 Win. Mag., 338 Win. Mag. (all with 24″ barrels); and (Short Stroke action) 22-250, 6mm, 243, 308 (all with 22″ barrels); 220 Swift (with 24″ barrel). **Weight:** Approx. 7 lbs.

Price **$531.25**

RUGER BOLT ACTION RIFLES

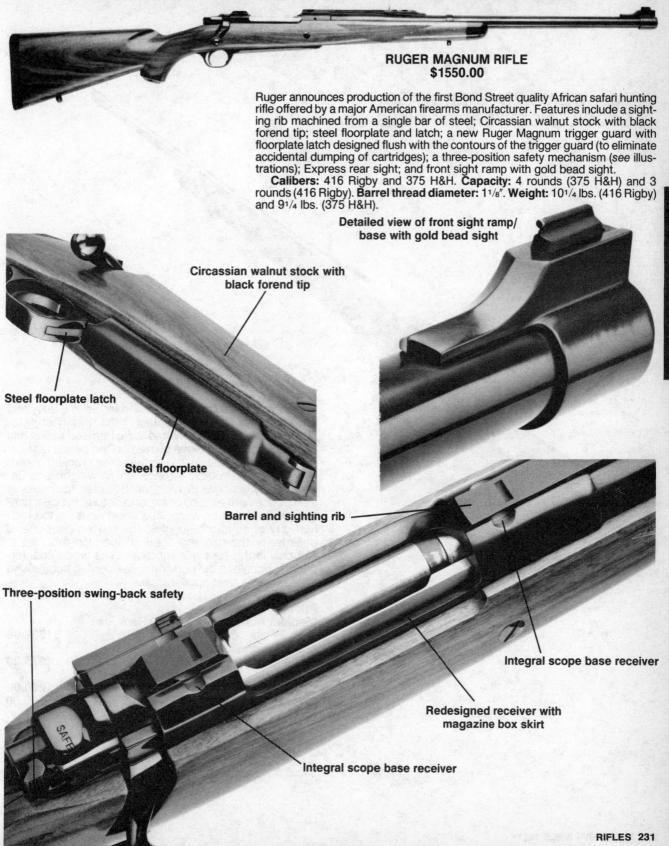

RUGER MAGNUM RIFLE
$1550.00

Ruger announces production of the first Bond Street quality African safari hunting rifle offered by a major American firearms manufacturer. Features include a sighting rib machined from a single bar of steel; Circassian walnut stock with black forend tip; steel floorplate and latch; a new Ruger Magnum trigger guard with floorplate latch designed flush with the contours of the trigger guard (to eliminate accidental dumping of cartridges); a three-position safety mechanism (*see* illustrations); Express rear sight; and front sight ramp with gold bead sight.

Calibers: 416 Rigby and 375 H&H. **Capacity:** 4 rounds (375 H&H) and 3 rounds (416 Rigby). **Barrel thread diameter:** 1 1/8″. **Weight:** 10 1/4 lbs. (416 Rigby) and 9 1/4 lbs. (375 H&H).

Detailed view of front sight ramp/ base with gold bead sight

Circassian walnut stock with black forend tip

Steel floorplate latch

Steel floorplate

Barrel and sighting rib

Three-position swing-back safety

SAFE

Integral scope base receiver

Redesigned receiver with magazine box skirt

Integral scope base receiver

SAKO FIBERCLASS RIFLES

ALL-WEATHER FIBERGLASS-STOCKED CENTERFIRE RIFLE

FIBERCLASS

In answer to the increased demand for Sako quality and accuracy in a true "all-weather" rifle, this fiberglass-stock version of the renowned Sako barreled action has been created. Long since proven on the bench rest circuit to be the most stable material for cradling a rifle, fiberglass is extremely strong, light in weight, and unaffected by changes in weather. Because fiberglass is inert, it does not absorb or expel moisture, hence it cannot swell, shrink or warp. It is impervious to the high humidity of equatorial jungles, the searing heat of arid deserts, or the rain and snow of the high mountains. Not only is this new rifle lighter than its wood counterpart, it appeals to the performance-oriented hunter who seeks results over appearance.

Prices:
Medium Action (All): 22-250 Rem.,
243 Rem., 308 Win. & 7mm-08 . . . . **$1239.00**
Long Action (AV):
25-06 Rem., 270 Win., 280 Rem., 30-06 . . . **1275.00**
7mm Rem. Mag., 300 Win. Mag.,
338 Win. Mag. **1290.00**
375 H&H Mag. **1299.00**

SAKO RIFLES

HUNTER RIFLE

HUNTER LIGHTWEIGHT

Here's one case of less being more. Sako has taken its famed bolt-action, centerfire rifle, redesigned the stock and trimmed the barrel contour. In fact, in any of the short action (A1) calibers—17 Rem., 222 or 223 Rem.—the Hunter weighs in at less than 7 pounds, making it one of the lightest wood stock production rifles in the world.

The same cosmetic upgrading and weight reduction have been applied to the entire Hunter line in all calibers and action lengths, standard and magnum. All the precision, quality and accuracy for which this Finnish rifle has been so justly famous are still here. Now it just weighs less.

The Sako trigger is a rifleman's delight—smooth, crisp and fully adjustable. If these were the only Sako features, it would still be the best rifle available. But the real quality that sets Sako apart from all others is its truly outstanding accuracy.

While many factors can affect a rifle's accuracy, 90 percent of any rifle's accuracy potential lies in its barrel. And the creation of superbly accurate barrels is where Sako excels.

The care that Sako takes in the cold-hammering processing of each barrel is unparalleled in the industry. As an example, after each barrel blank is drilled, it is diamond-lapped and then optically checked for microscopic flaws. This extra care affords the Sako owner lasting accuracy and a finish that will stay "new" season after season.

You can't buy an unfired Sako. Every gun is test fired using special overloaded proof cartridges. This ensures the Sako owner total safety and uncompromising accuracy. Every barrel must group within Sako specifications or it's scrapped. Not recycled. Not adjusted. Scrapped. Either a Sako barrel delivers Sako accuracy, or it never leaves the factory.

And hand-in-hand with Sako accuracy is Sako beauty. Genuine European walnut stocks, flawlessly finished and checkered by hand.

Available with either a matte lacquer or oil finish.

Prices:
Short Action (AI)
In 17 Rem.	**$948.00**
In 222 Rem. & 223 Rem.	**899.00**

Medium Action (AII)
In 22-250 Rem., 7mm-08, 243 Win. & 308 Win.	**899.00**

Long Action (AV)
In 25-06 Rem., 270 Win., 280 Rem. and 30-06	**931.00**
In 7mm Rem. Mag., 300 Win. Mag., 338 Win. Mag.	**948.00**
In 375 H&H Mag.	**963.00**
In 300 Weatherby Mag.	**979.00**

SAKO CARBINES

SAKO CARBINE

Sako's Carbines combine the handiness and carrying qualities of the traditional, lever-action "deer rifle" with the power of modern, high-performance cartridges. An abbreviated 18½-inch barrel trims the overall length of the Carbine to just over 40 inches in the long (or AV) action calibers, and 39½" in the medium (or All) action calibers. Weight is a highly portable 7 and 6½ pounds, respectively (except in the 338 and 375 H&H calibers, which tip the scale at 7½ pounds).

As is appropriate for a rifle of this type, the Carbine is furnished with an excellent set of open sights; the rear is fully adjustable for windage and elevation, while the front is a nonglare serrated ramp with protective hood.

The Carbine is available in the traditional wood stock of European walnut done in a contemporary Monte Carlo style with hand-rubbed oil or matte lacquer finish. Hand-finished checkering is standard. The Mannlicher-style full stock Carbine wears Sako's exclusive two-piece forearm, which joins beneath the barrel band and also features an oil finish. This independent forward section of the forearm eliminates the bedding problems normally associated with the full forestock. A blued steel muzzle cap puts the finishing touches on this European-styled Carbine.

For the hunter whose primary concerns are ruggedness and practicality, there's the Fiberclass Carbine.

Stocked in the same distinctive black fiberglass stock as Sako's famed Fiberclass Rifle model, the Carbine offers the same advantages but in a shorter, lighter configuration. The fiberglass Carbines in 338 and 375 H&H have become favorites with Alaskan guides, bush pilots, and all those who work or travel regularly in big bear country.

Prices:
Sako Carbine

In 22-250 Rem. (Med. Action)	$ 899.00
In 25-06 Rem. (Long Action)	931.00
In 7mm Rem. Mag. and 338 Win. Mag. (Long Action)	948.00

Sako Fiberclass Carbine

In 25-06 Rem., 270 Win., & 30-06 (Long Action)	$1275.00
In 7mm Rem. Mag., 300 Win. Mag. and 338 Win. Mag. (Long Action)	1290.00

Sako Mannlicher-Style Carbine

In 243 Win. & 308 Win. (Medium Action)	$1045.00
In 25-06 Rem., 270 Win., & 30-06 (Long Action)	1075.00
In 7mm Rem. Mag., 300 Win. Mag. and 338 Win. Mag. (Long Action)	1095.00
In 375 H&H Mag.	1099.00

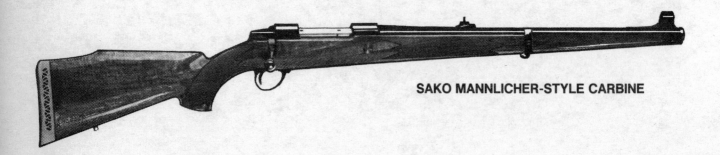

SAKO MANNLICHER-STYLE CARBINE

SAKO RIFLES

LAMINATED STOCK MODELS

In response to the growing number of hunters and shooters who seek the strength and stability that a fiberglass stock provides, coupled with the warmth and feel of real wood, Sako features its Laminated Stock models.

Machined from blanks comprised of 36 individual layers of 1/16-inch hardwood veneers that are resin-bonded under extreme pressure, these stocks are virtually inert. Each layer of hardwood has been vacuum-impregnated with a permanent brown dye. The bisecting of various layers of veneers in the shaping of the stock results in a contour-line appearance similar to a piece of slab-sawed walnut. Because all Sako Laminated Stocks are of real wood, each one is unique, with its own shading, color and grain.

These stocks satisfy those whose sensibilities demand a rifle of wood and steel, but who also want state-of-the-art performance and practicality. Sako's Laminated Stock provides both, further establishing it among the most progressive manufacturers of sporting rifles—and the *only* one to offer hunters and shooters their choice of walnut, fiberglass or laminated stocks in a wide range of calibers and left-handed models.

Prices:

Laminated Stock Models

In 22-250, 243 Rem., 308 Win. and 7mm-08
(Medium Action) **$1030.00**
In 25-06 Rem., 270 Win., 280 Rem. & 30-06
(Long Action) **1069.00**
In 7mm Rem. Mag., 300 Win. Mag. & 338 Win. Mag.
(Long Action) **1083.00**
In 375 H&H Mag. (Long Action) **1099.00**

SAKO RIFLES

LEFT-HANDED MODELS

Sako's Left-Handed models are based on mirror images of the right-handed models enjoyed by Sako owners for many years, with handle, extractor and ejection port all located on the port side. Naturally, the stock is also reversed, with the cheekpiece on the opposite side and the palm swell on the port side of the grip.

Otherwise, these guns are identical to the right-hand models. That means hammer-forged barrels, one-piece bolts with integral locking lugs and handles, integral scope mount rails, three-way adjustable triggers and Mauser-type inertia ejectors.

Sako's Left-Handed rifles are available in all Long Action models. The Hunter Grade carries a durable matte lacquer finish with generous-size panels of hand-cut checkering, a presentation-style recoil pad and sling swivel studs installed. The Deluxe model is distinguished by its rosewood forend tip and grip cap, its skip-line checkering and gloss lacquer finish atop a select-grade

of highly figured European walnut. The metal work carries a deep, mirro-like blue that looks more like black chrome.

Prices:

Hunter Lightweight

In 25-06, 270 Win., 280 Rem. & 30-06	**$ 999.00**
In 7mm Rem. Mag., 300 Win. Mag. and 338 Win. Mag.	**1033.00**
In 375 H&H Mag.	**1048.00**

Deluxe (All Long Action)

In 25-06, 270 Win. Mag., 280 Rem. & 30-06	**$1335.00**
In 7mm Rem. Mag, 300 Win. Mag. and 338 Win. Mag.	**1350.00**
In 375 H&H Mag.	**1365.00**

SAKO RIFLES

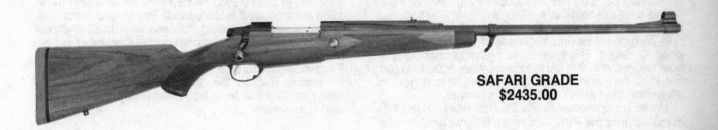

**SAFARI GRADE
$2435.00**

Crafted in the tradition of the classic British express rifles, Safari Grade is truly a professional's rifle. Every feature has been carefully thought out and executed with one goal in mind: performance. The magazine is extended, allowing four belted magnums to be stored inside (instead of the usual three). The steel floorplate straddles the front of the trigger guard bow for added strength and security.

An express-style quarter rib provides a rigid, non-glare base for the rear sight, which consists of a fixed blade and one auxiliary fold-down. The front swivel is carried by a contoured barrel band to keep the stud away from the off-hand under the recoil of big calibers. The front sight assembly is also a barrel-band type for maximum strength. The blade sits on a non-glare ramp and is protected by a steel hood.

The Safari's barreled action carries a subtle semi-matte blue, which lends an understated elegance to this eminently practical rifle. The functional, classic-style stock is of European walnut selected especially for its strength with respect to grain orientation as well as for color and figure. A rosewood forend tip, rosewood pistol grip cap with metal insert suitable for engraving, an elegant, beaded cheekpiece and presentation—style recoil pad complete the stock embellishments.

Calibers: 338 Win. Mag. & 375 H&H Mag. See also **Specifications Table.**

**VARMINT
$1030.00**

The Sako Varmint is specifically designed with a prone-type stock for shooting from the ground or bench. The forend is extra wide to provide added steadiness when rested on sandbags or makeshift field rests.

Calibers: 17 Rem., 222 Rem. & 223 Rem. (Short Action); 22-250, 243 Rem., 7mm-08 & 308 Win. (Medium Action). Also available in 6mm PPC and 22 PPC (single shot). **Price: $1199.00.**

SAKO RIFLES

Ever since Dr. Lou Palmisano and Farris Pindel introduced their custom-made PPC ammo in 1975, it has become widely recognized as the "world's most accurate cartridge," having broken well over 200 records since its debut. The impossible dream of making one-hole targets with five cartridges may never be realized, but PPC cartridges have come closer to that goal of perfection than anything in today's market.

Under an agreement with Dr. Palmisano, Sako has manufactured the PPC benchrest, heavy barrel, single-shot rifle in both 6 PPC and 22 PPC since late 1987; in 1988 it introduced factory-made ammo and brass. Because of its outstanding success with the benchrest model, Sako now makes both calibers available in a repeater version of its new Hunter and Deluxe models. Each model features a soft, luxurious matte lacquer finish and is built to the demanding specifications and workmanship that have become synonymous with Finnish gunmakers.

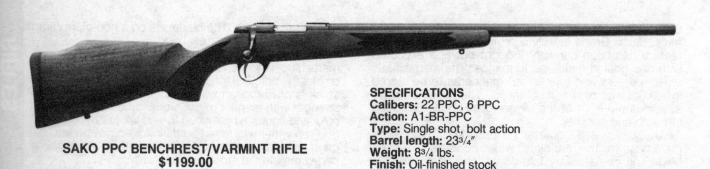

SAKO PPC BENCHREST/VARMINT RIFLE
$1199.00

SPECIFICATIONS
Calibers: 22 PPC, 6 PPC
Action: A1-BR-PPC
Type: Single shot, bolt action
Barrel length: 23¾"
Weight: 8¾ lbs.
Finish: Oil-finished stock

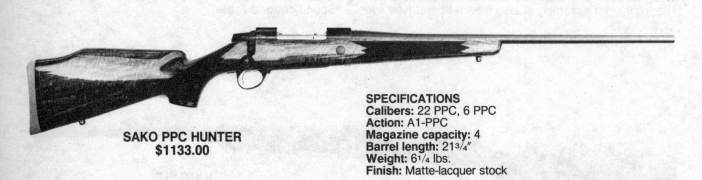

SAKO PPC HUNTER
$1133.00

SPECIFICATIONS
Calibers: 22 PPC, 6 PPC
Action: A1-PPC
Magazine capacity: 4
Barrel length: 21¾"
Weight: 6¼ lbs.
Finish: Matte-lacquer stock

SAKO PPC DELUXE
$1420.00

SPECIFICATIONS
Calibers: 22 PPC, 6 PPC
Action: A1-PPC
Capacity: 4
Barrel length: 21¾"
Weight: 6¼ lbs.
Finish: Matte-lacquer stock
Features: Deep-cut checkering; rosewood pistol-grip and forend caps; engraved floorplate; high-luster blue on barreled action

SAKO RIFLES

DELUXE

All the fine-touch features you expect of the deluxe grade Sako are here—beautifully grained French walnut, superbly done high-gloss finish, hand-cut checkering, deep rich bluing and rosewood forend tip and grip cap. And of course the accuracy, reliability and superior field performance for which Sako is so justly famous are still here too. It's all here—it just weighs less than it used to. Think of it as more for less.

In addition, the scope mounting system on these Sakos is among the strongest in the world. Instead of using separate bases, a tapered dovetail is milled right into the receiver, to which the scope rings are mounted. A beautiful system that's been proven by over 20 years of use. Sako scope rings are available in *low, medium,* and *high* in one-inch only.

Prices:
Short Action (AI)

In 17 Rem.	**$1275.00**
In 222 Rem. & 223 Rem.	**1225.00**

Medium Action (AII)

In 22-250 Rem., 243 Rem., 7mm-08 & 308 Win.	**1225.00**

Long Action (AV)

In 25-06 Rem., 270 Win., 280 Rem., 30-06	**1265.00**
In 7mm Rem. Mag., 300 Win. Mag. & 338 Win. Mag.	**1275.00**
In 375 H&H Mag.	**1290.00**
In 300 Weatherby Mag.	**1299.00**

SAKO SUPER DELUXE $2580.00

Sako offers the Super Deluxe to the most discriminating gun buyer. This one-of-a-kind beauty is available on special order.

Sidebar (vertical text, left margin): **BRASS AND AMMO ARE AVAILABLE FOR BOTH 6 PPC AND 22 PPC. BALLISTIC INFORMATION ON THESE TWO CALIBERS AVAILABLE UPON REQUEST FROM STOEGER INDUSTRIES.**

Note (under CUSTOM VARMINT column): *For varmint shooting, benchrest competition, target or hunting*

STOEGER

	PPC DELUXE	PPC HUNTER	BENCHREST VARMINT	CUSTOM VARMINT	CUSTOM SAFARI	CARBINE FIBERCLASS	CARBINE HANDY	CARBINE MANNLICHER STYLE	LAMINATED	FIBERCLASS	SUPERDELUXE	RIFLE DELUXE	RIFLE HUNTER
Action*	AI	AI	AI	AII / AI / All	AV	AV / AV / AV	All / AV / AV	All / AV / AV	AI / AV	AII / AV	AI / AII / AV	AI / AII / AV	AI / AII / AV
Left-handed											• • •		• • •
Total length (inches)	41½	41½	43¾	43¾ / 42½ / 43¼	43	39½ / 40½ / 40½ / 40½	40½	40½	41½ / 42½ / 44 / 46	41½ / 42½ / 43½ / 45½	41½ / 42½ / 43½ / 45½	41½ / 42½ / 44 / 46	41½ / 42½ / 44 / 46
Barrel length (inches)	21½	21½	23½	23¾ / 22¾ / 22¾	24	18½ / 18½ / 18½ / 18½	18½	18½	18¼ / 18½ / 24 / 24	21¼ / 21¾ / 22 / 24	21¼ / 21¾ / 22 / 24	21¼ / 21¼ / 22 / 24	21¼ / 21¼ / 22 / 24
Weight (lbs)	6½	6½	8¾	8¾ / 8½ / 8½	8½	7 / 7½ / 7½ / 7¾	7½ / 7½ / 7¾	8	7 / 7 / 8¼ / 8¾	5¾ / 6½ / 7¾ / 8¼	5¾ / 6½ / 7¾ / 8¼	5¾ / 6½ / 7¾ / 8¼	5¾ / 6½ / 7¾ / 8¼
17 Rem / 10"				•								•	•
222 Rem / 14"				•								•	•
223 Rem / 12"				•								•	•
22 PPC / 14"	PPC	PPC	PPC	•									
6mm PPC / 14"	PPC	PPC	PPC	•									
22-250 Rem / 14"				•			•		•	•	•	•	•
243 Win / 10"				•			•		•	•	•	•	•
7mm-08 / 9½"				•					•	•	•	•	•
308 Win / 12"				•			•		•	•	•	•	•
25-06 Rem / 10"									•	•	•	•	•
270 Win / 10"									•	•	•	•	•
30-06 / 10"									•	•	•	•	•
7mm / Rem Mag / 9½"						•	•		•	•	•	•	•
300 Win Mag / 10"						•			•	•	•	•	•
300 Wby Mag / 10"											•	•	•
338 Win Mag / 10"					•		•	•	•	•	•	•	•
375 H&H Mag / 12"					•				•		•	•	•
Lacquered											•	•	•
Matte Lacquered									•	•			•
Oiled				•	•		•	•			•	•	•
Without sights *				•	•				•	•			
Open sights *					•	•	•	•	•	•	•	•	•
Base for telescopic sight mounts				•	•	•	•	•	•	•	•	•	•
Magazine capacity	5	6	5		4	5 / 3 / 3	5 / 3	5	6 / 3	5 / 3	6 / 5 / 3	6 / 5 / 3	6 / 5 / 3
Rubber				•	•	•	•	•	•	•	•		•

Right-margin grouping labels: **Model · Dimensions · Caliber/Rate of Twist · Stock Finish · Sights · Mag. · Buttplate**

SAKO ACTIONS

Only by building a rifle around a Sako action do shooters enjoy the choice of three different lengths, each scaled to a specific family of cartridges. The AI (Short) action is miniaturized in every respect to match the 222 family, which includes everything from 17 Remington to 222 Remington Magnum. The AII (Medium) action is scaled down to the medium-length cartridges of standard bolt face—22-250, 243, 308 or similar length cartridges. The AV (Long) action is offered in either standard or Magnum bolt face and accommodates cartridges of up to 3.65 inches in overall length, including rounds like the 300 Weatherby and 375 H&H Magnum. **For left-handers, only the Long Action is offered in either standard or Magnum bolt face.** All actions are furnished in-the-white only.

AI-1 (SHORT ACTION)
CALIBERS:
17 Rem., 222 Rem.
222 Rem. Mag.
223 Rem.
$458.00

AI PPC (Short Action) Hunter and
Single Shot 22 PPC and 6 PPC
$499.00

AI PPC (Short Action)
Single Shot 22 PPC and 6 PPC
$554.00

AII-1 (MEDIUM ACTION)
CALIBERS:
22-250 Rem. (AII-3)
243 Win.
308 Win.
$458.00

AV-4 (LONG ACTION)
CALIBERS:
25-06 Rem. (AV-1)
270 Win. (AV-1)
280 Rem. (AV-1)
30-06 (AV-1)
7mm Rem. Mag.
300 Win. Mag.
300 Wby. Mag.
338 Win. Mag.
375 H&H Mag.
$458.00

Also available:
LEFT-HANDED ACTIONS
Long Action only: $488.00

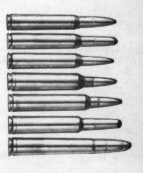

SAVAGE CENTERFIRE RIFLES

MODEL 110-E

MODEL 110 BOLT-ACTION CENTERFIRE RIFLES
Standard and Magnum Calibers

The Savage 100 Series features solid lockup, positive gas protection, precise head space, precision-rifled barrels, and select walnut Monte Carlo stocks. See specifications tables below for full details.

Prices:

Model	Price
Model 110G	$400.00
Model 110GX	392.16
Model 110GL (Left Hand)	465.88
Model 110GXL	458.04
Model 110GV	443.92
Model 110F	489.41
Model 110FX	481.57
Model 110B	476.87
Model 110FP (Heavy Barrel)	564.71

SPECIFICATIONS

Rifle	Calibers	Capacity**	Barrel Length	O.A. Length	Avg. Wt. Lbs.	Twist R.H.	Stock	Sights
110G*							Cut Checkered Walnut Finished Hardwood with Recoil Pad	110G Adj.
110GX*	.22/250	5	22″	43 1/2″	7 1/2	1 in 14″		110 GX Integral Scope Mount
	.223	5	22″	43 1/2″	7 1/2	1 in 14″		
110F	.243	5	22″	43 1/2″	7 1/2	1 in 10″	Black Rynite®	110F Adj.
	.308	5	22″	43 1/2″	7 1/2	1 in 12″		
110FX	30/06	5	22″	43 1/2″	7 1/2	1 in 10″		110FX Integral Scope Mount
	.270	5	22″	43 1/2″	7 1/2	1 in 10″		
110B	7mm Rem. Mag.	4	24″	45 1/2″	7 1/2	1 in 9 1/2″	Brown Laminate Wood with Recoil Pad	Adj.
	300 Win. Mag.	4	24″	45 1/2″	7 1/2	1 in 10″		
110GV	.22/250	5	24″	45 1/2″	7 3/4	1 in 14″	Cut Checkered Walnut Finished Hardwood with Recoil Pad	Receiver Drilled & Tapped
	.223	5	24″	45 1/2″		1 in 14″		

Features: 3 Position safety, twin gas ports and double front locking lugs; 13 1/2″ pull on all models.
 * Left hand models available in 270, 30-06, 7mm Rem. Mag.
**Includes one (1) in chamber.

SAVAGE CENTERFIRE RIFLES

MODEL 99C LEVER ACTION
$616.47

Clip magazine allows for the chambering of pointed, high-velocity big-bore cartridges. **Calibers:** 243 Win., 308 Win. **Action:** Hammerless, lever action, cocking indicator, top tang safety.

Magazine: Detachable clip; holds 4 rounds plus one in the chamber. **Stock:** Select walnut with high Monte Carlo and deep fluted comb. Cut checkered stock and forend with swivel studs. Recoil pad and pistol grip cap. **Sights:** Detachable hooded ramp front sight, bead front sight on removable ramp adjustable rear sight. Tapped for top mount scopes. **Barrel length:** 22″. **Overall length:** 42³/₄″. **Weight:** 7³/₄ lbs.

SAVAGE MODEL 24F COMBINATION RIFLE/SHOTGUN

Match a 12- or 20-gauge shotgun with any of three popular centerfire calibers. Frame is color casehardened and barrel is a deep, lustrous blue and tapped, ready for scope mounting. Two-way top opening lever. All models are stocked with tough Du Pont Rynite™, plus hammerblock safeties that limit hammer

SAVAGE MODEL 24F-12T TURKEY
with Camo Rynite Stock

travel in the safe position. Other features include interchangeable chokes (extra full tube supplied), and factory swivel studs.
Prices:
Model 24F-20 . . . . $431.37
Model 24F-12 . . . . 450.20
Model 24F-12T (Full Choke) 467.45

MODEL 389 (not shown)

Features a select hand-checkered walnut stock, folding rear sight, twin trigger for instant barrel selection, and interchangeable choke tubes. **Weight:** About 8 lbs. Additional specifications are listed in the accompanying table. **Price:** $919.21

O/U Comb. Model	Gauge Caliber	Choke	Chamber	Barrel Length	O.A. Length	Twist R.H.	Stock
24F-20	20 ga./22 Hor.	Mod Barrel	2³/₄ & 3″	24″	40¹/₂″	1 in 14″	Black Rynite®
	20 ga./223					1 in 14″	
	20 ga./30/30					1 in 12″	
24F-12	12 ga./22 Hor.	Mod Choke Tube	2³/₄ & 3″	24″	40¹/₂″	1 in 14″	Black Rynite®
	12 ga./223					1 in 14″	
	12 ga./30/30					1 in 12″	
24F-12T Turkey	12 ga./22 Hor. 12 ga./223	Full Choke Tube	2³/₄ & 3″	24″	40¹/₂″	1 in 14″	Camo Rynite®
						1 in 14″	

Features: Hammer block safety, Tough Dupont Rynite® stocks and positive extraction.

389	12 ga./222	Full Mod IC Choke Tubes	2³/₄ & 3″	25³/₄″	43″	1 in 14″	Cut checkered Walnut with Recoil Pad
	12 ga./308					1 in 12″	

Features: Folding rear sight, twin triggers for instant barrel selection, and interchangeable choke tubes. All models have 14″ pull and weigh about 8 lbs.

SPRINGFIELD ARMORY RIFLES

SPRINGFIELD M1A STANDARD

SPECIFICATIONS
Caliber: 308 Win./7.62mm NATO
Capacity: 5, 10 or 20-round box magazine
Barrel length: 22″
Overall length: 44¹/₂″
Weight: 8 lbs. 15 oz.
Sights: Military square post front; military aperture rear, adjustable for windage and elevation

Sight radius: 26³/₄″
Rifling: 6 groove, RH twist, 1 turn in 11″
Prices:
M1A Standard	$ 970.00
W/Walnut stock	1045.00
W/Shaw IPSC walnut stock	1086.00
W/Heavy Comp stock	1119.00

SPRINGFIELD M1A MATCH RIFLE

MIA MATCH

Specifications are the same as Standard M1A, except trigger pull is 4¹/₂ lbs. (vs. 7¹/₂ lbs. max.). Comes with National Match barrel, flash suppressor, gas cylinder, special glass-bedded walnut stock and match-tuned trigger assembly.

Prices:
W/Walnut stock	$1269.00
W/Heavy Comp stock	1424.00
W/Competition Fiberglass stock	1583.00

Also available:
M1A SUPER MATCH. Features heavy match barrel and permanently attached figure-8-style operating rod guide, plus special heavy walnut match stock, longer pistol grip and contoured area behind rear sight for better grip. **Price: $1525.00**

SPRINGFIELD M1A-A1 BUSH RIFLE

SPECIFICATIONS
Caliber: 308 Win./7.62mm
Barrel length: 18¹/₄″
Overall length: 40¹/₂″
Weight: 8 lbs. 12 oz.

Prices: M1A BUSH RIFLE
W/Camo GI Fiberglass stock	$1000.00
W/Walnut stock	1066.00
W/Heavy Comp stock	1143.00
W/Shaw IPSC walnut stock	1106.00

SPRINGFIELD ARMORY RIFLES

MODEL SAR-4800 STANDARD RIFLE
(w/Thumbhole Sporter Stock)

MODEL SAR-4800 BUSH RIFLE
(w/Compact Accurizing Package)

MODEL SAR-4800 SPORTER

This new production semiautomatic rifle includes a forged receiver and bolt and a hammer-forged chrome-lined barrel. It comes equipped with a traditional thumbhole sporter stock and an unsuppressed muzzle with thread protector as standard equipment. An optional accurizing package is available, including an accuracy-enhancing flash suppressor and black pistol grip and stock.

SPECIFICATIONS
Caliber: 308 Win./7.62mm
Barrel length: 21″; 18″ Bush and Compact Models
Overall length: 43.3″
Weight: 9½ lbs.; 8.6 lbs. Bush Rifle
Sights: Rear adjustable; protected front post
Rifling: Four groove; RH twist; 1 turn in 12″
Prices:
Model SAR-4800 Sporter $1229.00
Model SAR-4800 Bush Rifle 1229.00
Model SAR-4800 Compact 1233.00

MODEL SAR-8 STANDARD RIFLE
(w/Thumbhole Sporter Stock)

MODEL SAR-8 STANDARD RIFLE
(w/Compact Accurizing Package)

MODEL SAR-8 SPORTER

This new sporter rifle (formerly the SAR-3) comes equipped with a traditional thumbhole sporter stock and an unsuppressed muzzle with thread protector. An optional accurizing package is available. Other features include roller-lock action, fluted chamber, and distinctive front and rear sights (same as the HK-91).

SPECIFICATIONS
Caliber: 308 Win./7.62mm
Magazine capacity: 20 rounds
Barrel length: 18″
Overall length: 40.38″
Weight: 8.7 lbs.
Sights: Rotary-style adjustable rear aperture; protected front post
Rifling: Four groove; RH twist; 1 turn in 12″
Price: $1164.00

STEYR-MANNLICHER RIFLES

MODEL SSG MARKSMAN
(Shown with synthetic stock and optional Kahles ZF69 scope)

SPECIFICATIONS
Calibers: 243 Win., 308 Win. (7.62mm NATO)
Barrel length: 26″
Weight: 8.6 lbs. (9.9 lbs. with Kahles scope)
Overall length: 44.5″
Stock: Choice of synthetic half stock of ABS "Cycolac" or walnut; removable spacers in butt section adjusts length of pull from 12¾″ to 14″
Sights: Hooded blade front; folding rear leaf sight

Features: Parkerized finish; choice of interchangeable single- or double-set triggers; detachable 5-shot rotary straight-line feed magazine of "Makrolon"; 10-shot magazine optional; heavy-duty receiver drilled and tapped for scope mounting.

Prices:
Cycolac half stock	$1665.00
Walnut half stock	2083.00
SSG Scope Mount	194.00
Model SSG P-11 Sniper (308 Win.)	1784.00

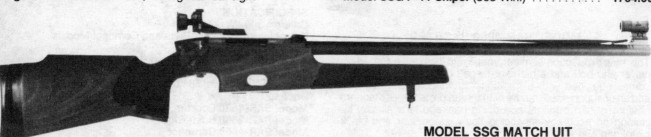

Features 26″ heavy barrel, 10-shot box magazine, match bolt, Walther target peep sights, mirage cover, and adjustable rail in forend to adjust sling travel. **Weight:** 11 lbs. **Caliber:** 308 Win.

MODEL SSG MATCH UIT

Price:
With walnut half stock $2836.00
Also available:
SSG MATCH RIFLE w/26″ heavy barrel, 308 caliber, synthetic stock. **Price: $1875.00.** With walnut stock: **$2125.00.**

LUXUS MODELS L, M & S
(L=Light M=Medium S=Magnum)

SPECIFICATIONS
Calibers:
  Model L (standard calibers) 22-250 Rem., 6mm Rem., 243 Win., 308 Win.
  Model L (optional metric calibers) 5.6×57
  Model M (standard calibers) 25-06 Rem., 270 Win., 7×57, 7×64, 30-06
  Model M (optional metric calibers) 6.5×55, 6.5×57, 7.5 Swiss, 9.3×62

Model S 300 Win. Mag., 7mm Rem. Mag., 6.5×68, 8×68S
Barrel lengths: 20″ (full stock); 23.6″ (half stock); 26″ (Model S)
Weight: 6.8 lbs. (full stock); 6.9 lbs. (half stock)
Overall length: 39″ (full stock); 43″ (half stock)
Stock: Hand-checkered walnut with Monte Carlo cheekpiece; either full Mannlicher or half stock; European hand-rubbed oil finish or high-gloss lacquer finish
Sights: Ramp front adjustable for elevation; open U-notch rear adjustable for windage
Features: Single combination trigger (becomes hair trigger when moved forward before firing); detachable 3-shot steel straight-line feed magazine (6-shot optional). 6 rear locking lugs; drilled and tapped for scope mounts

Prices:
Full stock (in **Model L & M** calibers)	$2495.00
Half stock (in **Model L & M** calibers)	2364.00
Half stock (in **Model S** calibers)	2567.00

STEYR-MANNLICHER RIFLES

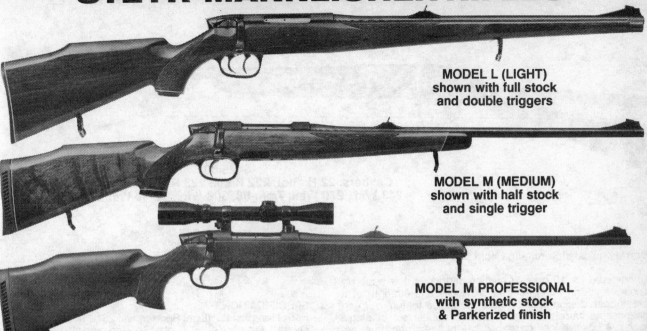

MODEL L (LIGHT)
shown with full stock
and double triggers

MODEL M (MEDIUM)
shown with half stock
and single trigger

MODEL M PROFESSIONAL
with synthetic stock
& Parkerized finish

SPECIFICATIONS
Calibers:
  Model SL (Super Light, standard calibers only) 222 Rem., 222 Rem. Mag., 223 Rem.
  Model L (standard calibers) 22-250 Rem., 6mm Rem., 243 Win., 308 Win.
  Model L (optional metric caliber) 5.6×57
  Model M (standard calibers) 25-06 Rem., 270 Win., 7×57, 7×64, 30-06 Spr.
  Model M (optional metric calibers) 6.5×57, 7.5 Swiss, 8×57JS, 9.3×62
Barrel length: 20″ (full stock); 23.6″ (half stock)
Weight: 6.8 lbs. (full stock); 6.9 lbs. (half stock); 7.5 lbs. (Professional)
Overall length: 39″ (full stock); 43″ (half stock)
Stock: Full Mannlicher or standard half stock with Monte Carlo cheekpiece and rubber recoil pad; hand-checkered walnut in skip-line pattern; Model M with half stock is available in a "Professional" version with a parkerized finish and synthetic stock made of ABS "Cycolac" (made with right-handed action only); left-handed action available in full stock and half stock.
Features: Choice of fine-crafted single- or double-set triggers. Detachable 5-shot rotary magazine of "Makrolon"; 6 rear locking lugs; drilled and tapped for scope mounting.
Prices:
Models SL, L, M Full stock $1939.00
Models SL, L, M Half stock 1812.00
Full stock, with left-handed action 2212.00
Half stock, with left-handed action 2083.00
Professional, with iron sights 1532.00
Model SL, L Varmint (270 Win., 30-06) 1939.00

MODEL S AND S/T MAGNUM

SPECIFICATIONS
Calibers:
  Model S 257 Weatherby Mag., 264 Win. Mag., 300 Win. Mag., 7mm Rem. Mag., 300 H&H Mag., 375 H&H Mag.
  Model S (Optional calibers) 6.5×68
  Model S/T (Heavy barrel) 375 H&H Mag., 458 Win. Mag.
  Model S/T (Optional caliber) 9.3×64
Barrel length: 26″ Model S/T (with 26″ heavy barrel)

Weight: 8.4 lbs. (Model S); 9.02 lbs. (Model S/T); add .66 lbs. for butt mag. opt.
Overall length: 45″
Stock: Half stock with Monte Carlo cheekpiece and rubber recoil pad; hand-checkered walnut in skip-line pattern; available with optional spare magazine inletted in butt stock.
Features: Choice of fine-crafted single- or double-set triggers; detachable 4-shot rotary magazine of "Makrolon"; 6 rear locking lugs; drilled and tapped for scope mounting.
Prices:
Model S $1952.00
Model S/T with opt. butt magazine 2176.00

THOMPSON/CENTER RIFLES

TCR '87 HUNTER SINGLE SHOT RIFLE
$425.00
Calibers: 22 Hornet, 222 Rem., 223 Rem., 22/250 Rem.,
243 Win., 270 Win., 7mm-08, 308 Win., 32-40 Win. or 30-06

Barrels quickly interchange from one caliber to the next

Chambered for 10 popular hunting cartridges, this superbly accurate sports rifle offers the simplicity and strength of a break-open design coupled with the unique feature of interchangeable barrels. Triggers function double set or single stage. A positive lock cross-bolt safety offers maximum security. Wood is hand-selected American black walnut from the Thompson/Center mill. All barrels are equipped with iron sights, removable for scope mounting.

SPECIFICATIONS
Barrel lengths: 23" (Light Sporter) and 25⁷/₈" (Medium Sporter)
Overall length: 39¹/₂" (Light Sporter) and 43³/₈" (Medium Sporter)
Weight: 6 lbs. 14 oz. (Light Sporter) and 7 lbs. 8 oz. (Medium Sporter)

THE CONTENDER CARBINE
$385.00

Available in 11 **calibers:** 22 LR, 22 Hornet, 22 WMR, 223 Rem., 7mm T.C.U., 7×30 Waters, 30-30 Win., 35 Rem., 44 Mag., 45-70 and 357 Rem. Max. **Barrels** are 21 inches long and are interchangeable, with adjustable iron sights and tapped and drilled for scope mounts. **Weight:** Only 5 lbs. 3 oz.
Also available:
Contender Vent Rib Carbine
  With 21" .410 barrel $405.00
Contender Youth Model Carbine w/16¹/₂" bbl. . . . 355.00
  With 16¹/₂" 45 Colt/.410 barrel 380.00
Contender Carbine w/Rynite Stock
  (Not available in 22 WMR or 45-70) 355.00
  Same as above in .410 gauge 375.00

TIKKA RIFLES

NEW GENERATION RIFLE

With the consolidation of three renowned Finnish firearms manufacturers—Tikka, Sako and Valmet—a "new generation" of Tikka rifles becomes a reality. These new rifles feature a "smooth as silk" bolt action made possible by a sleeve constructed of a space-age synthetic Polyarylamide material reinforced with fiberglass. The overall look of the rifle is enhanced by a walnut stock with matte lacquer finish and diamond point checkering. A short bolt throw allows for rapid firing, and a free-floating barrel increases accuracy. Barrel quality itself is ensured through Tikka's cold-hammered forging process. The trigger guard, made of synthetic materials for added strength,

is oversized for ease of shooting while wearing gloves. The recessed magazine release is located conveniently for quick and safe release. Tikka's wood-to-metal fit reflects the high standards of Finnish craftsmanship throughout. **Calibers:** 223 Rem., 22-250 Rem., 243 Win., 308 Win., 270 Win., 30-06, 7mm Rem. Mag., 300 Win. Mag., and 338 Win. Mag. **Barrel length:** 22". **Weight:** 7 1/8 lbs.

Prices NEW GENERATION:
Calibers 223 Rem., 22-250 Rem., 243 Win., 308 Win., 270 Win. and 30-06	**$765.00**
Calibers 7mm Rem. Mag., 300 Win. Mag., 338 Win. Mag.	795.00
Magazines (5 rounds)	66.50
(3 rounds)	55.00

The TIKKA Premium Grade rifle is designed and crafted by Sako of Finland for the discriminating shooter. This superb firearm features a detachable magazine, along with a "smooth as silk" bolt that is encased in a polymer sleeve. The luxurious matte lacquer stock incorporates a roll-over cheek-piece, rosewood pistol grip cap and forend tip and hand-checkered throughout. The cold-hammered barrel is deeply blued and free floated for maximum accuracy. The two action lengths

PREMIUM GRADE RIFLE

eliminate unnecessary weight and each trigger is designed and built to be crisp, clean and travel-free. For those who demand the very finest, the TIKKA Premium is a must. Available in a wide assortment of calibers.

Prices PREMIUM GRADE:
Calibers 223 Rem., 22-250 Rem., 243 Win., 308 Win., 270 Win., 30-06	**$930.00**
Calibers 7mm Rem. Mag., 300 Win. Mag., 338 Win. Mag.	965.00
Magazines (5 rounds)	66.50
(3 rounds)	55.00

The renowned Valmet 412S line of fine firearms is now being produced under the Tikka brand name and is being manufactured to the same specifications as the former Valmet. As a result of a joint venture entered into by Sako Ltd., the production facilities for these firearms are now located in Italy. The manufacture of the 412S series is controlled under the rigid quality standards of Sako Ltd., with complete interchangeability of parts between firearms produced in Italy and

MODEL 412S DOUBLE RIFLE
$1275.00

Finland. Tikka's double rifle offers features and qualities no other action can match: rapid handling and pointing qualities and the silent, immediate availability of a second shot. As such, this model overcomes the two major drawbacks usually associated with this type of firearm: price and accuracy.
SPECIFICATIONS
Calibers: 9.3×74R
Barrel length: 24"
Overall length: 40"
Weight: 8 1/2 lbs.
Stock: American walnut
Other: Extractors, automatic ejectors

A. UBERTI REPLICA RIFLES & CARBINES

MODEL 1866 SPORTING RIFLE
$663.00

SPECIFICATIONS
Calibers: 22 LR, 22 Magnum, 38 Special, 44-40
Barrel length: 24¼", octagonal, tapered
Overall length: 43¼"
Weight: 8.16 lbs.
Frame: Elevator and buttplate in brass
Stock: Walnut
Sights: Vertically adjustable rear; horizontally adjustable front

MODEL 1871 ROLLING BLOCK
BABY CARBINE
$357.50

SPECIFICATIONS
Calibers: 22 LR, 22 Hornet, 22 Magnum, 357 Magnum
Barrel length: 22"
Overall length: 35½"
Weight: 4.85 lbs.
Stock & forend: Walnut
Trigger guard: Brass
Sights: Fully adjustable rear; ramp front
Frame: Color casehardened steel

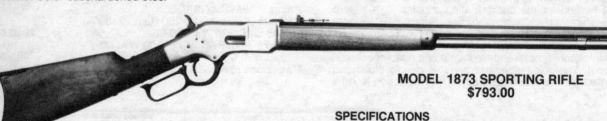

MODEL 1873 SPORTING RIFLE
$793.00

SPECIFICATIONS
Calibers: 22 LR, 22 Magnum, 357 Magnum, 38 Special, 45 and 44-40. Other specifications same as Model 1866.

1873 CARBINE
$747.50

SPECIFICATIONS
Calibers: 22 LR, 22 Magnum, 38 Special, 44-40, 357 Mag.
Barrel length: 19" round, tapered
Overall length: 38¼"
Weight: 7.38 lbs.
Sights: Fixed front; vertically adjustable rear
Also available:
1873 RIFLE w/24¼" barrel (43¼" overall) **$700.00.**

ULTRA LIGHT ARMS

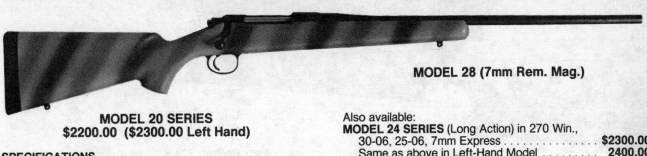

MODEL 28 (7mm Rem. Mag.)

MODEL 20 SERIES
$2200.00 ($2300.00 Left Hand)

SPECIFICATIONS
Calibers: 6mm Rem., 17 Rem., 22 Hornet, 222 Rem., 222 Rem. Mag., 223 Rem., 22-250 Rem., 243 Win., 250-3000 Savage, 257 Roberts, 257 Ackley, 7mm Mauser, 7mm Ack., 7mm-08 Rem., 284 Win., 300 Savage, 308 Win., 358 Win.
Barrel length: 22″
Weight: 4.75 lbs.
Safety: Two-position safety allows bolt to open or lock with sear blocked
Stock: Kevlar/Graphite composite; choice of 7 or more colors

Also available:
MODEL 24 SERIES (Long Action) in 270 Win.,
   30-06, 25-06, 7mm Express $2300.00
   Same as above in Left-Hand Model 2400.00
MODEL 28 SERIES (Magnum Action) in 264 Win.,
   7mm Rem., 300 Win., 338 . . . . 2700.00
   Same as above in Left-Hand Model 2800.00

MODEL 20 REB
$1300.00

SPECIFICATIONS
Calibers: 22-250 thru 308 standard (most silhouette calibers and other calibers on request)
Capacity: 5 shots
Barrel length: 14″ (Douglas No. 3)
Weight: 4 lbs.
Stock: Composite Kevlar, graphite reinforced; DuPont Imron paint (green, brown, black and camo)
Features: Timney adjustable trigger; 2-position, 3-function safety; benchrest-quality action; matte or bright stock and metal finish; left- or right-hand models

VARNER SPORTING ARMS

FAVORITE HUNTER MODEL
(Single Shot) $369.00

SPECIFICATIONS (FIELD GRADE)
Caliber: 22 LR
Barrel length: 21½″; 12-groove, match grade; half-round, half-octagonal
Weight: 5 lbs.
Sights: Peep and open rear sights adjustable for windage and elevation
Stock: Straight-grain American walnut
Finish: Blued steel
Features: All models are color hardened (frame and lever)

Also available:
HUNTER DELUXE (Hand-checkered AAA Fancy Walnut) $499.00.
PRESENTATION GRADE (w/AAA Fancy American walnut stock; hand-checkered grip and forearm) $569.00.

WALTHER TARGET RIFLES

U.I.T. MATCH
$1300.00

Caliber: 22 LR
Action: Bolt action, single shot
Barrel length: 25 1/2"
Overall length: 44 3/4"
Weight: 13 lbs.
Also available:
U.I.T. BV UNIVERSAL: $1700.00

MODEL GX-1
$2200.00

Caliber: 22 LR
Action: Bolt action, single shot
Barrel length: 25 1/2"
Overall length: 46"
Weight: 16 1/2"

KK/MS SILHOUETTE
$1100.00

Caliber: 22 LR
Action: Bolt action, single shot
Barrel length: 25 1/2"
Overall length: 44 3/4"
Weight: 8 3/4 lbs

RUNNING BOAR (not shown)
$1300.00

Caliber: 22 LR
Action: Bolt action, single shot
Barrel length: 23 1/2"
Overall length: 42"
Weight: 10 1/4 lbs.

WEATHERBY RIFLES

MARK V FIBERMARK

The Fibermark's hand-molded fiberglass stock is impervious to climatic changes. It shoots with constant accuracy no matter what the weather—from desert heat to mountain snow. The stock is finished with a non-glare black wrinkle finish for a positive grip, even in wet, humid weather. Available in right-hand only, 24″ or 26″ barrels. **Weight:** 7¼ lbs. (24″) and 8 lbs. (26″).

Additional specifications are listed on the following page.

Calibers	Prices
240, 257, 270, 7mm & 300 Wby.Mag. and 30-06	$1180.00
(24″ barrel; add $25 for 26″ barrel)	
340 Wby. Mag. (26″ barrel)	1205.00

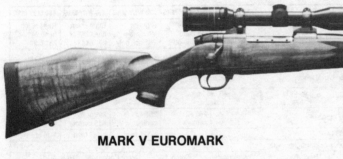

MARK V EUROMARK

The principal features of this Mark V model include a hand-rubbed, satin oil finish Claro walnut stock and non-glare special process blue matte barreled action. Specifications are listed on the following page. All calibers are available in right- or left-hand models, unless stated otherwise.

Calibers	Prices
240, 257, 270, 7mm, 30-06	
24″ barrel	$1095.00
26″ barrel	1120.00
300 Wby. Mag., L.H., 26″ bbl. only	1120.00
340 Wby. Mag., 26″ barrel	1120.00
416 Weatherby Mag.	
24″ barrel	1335.00
26″ barrel	1360.00
460 Weatherby Mag.	
24″ barrel	1460.00
26″ barrel	1485.00

MARK V ULTRAMARK

Features a hand-honed action with a damascened bolt and follower, checkered bolt knob and floorplate. Also, an extra-fancy American Claro Walnut stock with hand-checkering. **Calibers:** 240, 257, 270, 7mm, 300 Wby. Mag., 30-06, and 340 Wby. Mag.

Price:	
With 24″ barrel	$1315.00
With 26″ barrel	1340.00

WEATHERBY RIFLES

MARK V DELUXE RIFLE

Calibers

	Prices
224 Weatherby Mag. or 22-250 Varmintmaster	
Right-hand only, 24″ barrel	$1020.00
Right-hand only, 26″ barrel	1045.00
240, 257, 270, 7mm, 30-06	
24″ barrel	1040.00
26″ barrel	1065.00
300 Wby. Mag., L.H., 26″ bbl. only	1065.00

340 Weatherby Mag., 26″ barrel	1065.00
378 Weatherby Mag., 26″ barrel	1225.00
416 Weatherby Mag.	
24″ barrel	1335.00
26″ barrel	1360.00
460 Weatherby Mag.	
24″ barrel	1400.00
26″ barrel	1425.00

All calibers are available in right- or left-hand models, unless stated otherwise.

MARK V SPECIFICATIONS

CALIBER	.224 WBY MAG	.22/250	.240 WBY MAG	.257 WBY MAG	.270 WBY MAG	7mm WBY MAG	.30–06	.300 WB MAG	.340 WBY MAG	.378 WBY MAG	.416 WBY MAG	.460 WBY MAG
Model	Right hand 24″ or 26″ bbl. Left hand model not available		Right or left hand hand 24″ bbl. Right hand 26″ bbl. Left hand 26″ bbl. **available in** .300 cal. only						Right or left hand 26″bbl. only.	Right or left hand 26″ bbl. only.	Right or left hand 24″ or 26″ bbl.	Right or left hand 24″ or 26″ bbl.*
**Weight w/o sights	6½ lbs.		7¼ lbs.						8½ lbs.		9½ lbs.	10½ lbs.
Overall length	43⅜″ or 45⅜″ dependent on barrel length		44⅝″ or 46⅝″ dependent on barrel length						46⅝″		44¾″ or 46¾″	
Magazine Capacity	4, +1 in chamber	3, +1 in chamber	4, +1 in chamber		3, +1 in chamber		4, +1 in chamber		3, +1 in chamber		2, +1 in chamber	
Barrel	24″ standard or 26″ semi-target		24″ standard or 26″ #2 contour						26″ #2 contour	26″ #3 contour	24″ or 26″ #3.5 contour	24″ or 26″ #4 contour*
Rifling	1–14″ twist		1–10″ twist								1–12″ twist	1–14″ twist	1–16″ twist
Sights	Scopes or iron sights extra											
Stocks	Drop dimensions from bore centerline: **Mark V—** Comb: ¾″ Monte Carlo: ½″ Heel: 1½″ **Varmintmaster—** Comb: 9/16″ Monte Carlo: ¼″ Heel: 1⅛″											
Ultramark	Not available		Full fancy American walnut, individually hand-bedded to assure precision accuracy. High lustre, durable stock finish, quick detachable sling swivels, basket weave checkering with extension of checkering on pistol grip. Customized action.								Not available	
Deluxe	American walnut, individually hand-bedded to assure precision accuracy. High lustre, durable stock finish. Quick detachable sling swivels. Basket weave checkering. Monte Carlo style with cheek piece, especially designed for both scope and iron sighted rifles. Length of pull 13⅝″.										European Walnut Pull: 14″	
Euromark	American walnut, individually hand-bedded to assure precision accuracy. Satin finish. Ebony pistol grip cap and fore end tip. Custom fine line hand checkering with extension on pistol grip. Solid black recoil pad. Quick detachable sling swivels. Monte Carlo style with cheek piece, especially designed for both scope and iron sighted rifles. Length of pull 13⅝″.										European Walnut Pull: 14″	
Lazermark	American walnut, individually hand-bedded to assure precision accuracy. High lustre, durable stock finish. Quick detachable sling swivels. Laser carving on forearm, pistol grip and under cheek piece, Monte Carlo style with cheek piece, especially designed for both scope and iron sighted rifles. Length of pull 13⅝″.										European Walnut Pull: 14″	
Fibermark	Not available		Molded fiberglass, individually hand-bedded to assure precision accuracy. Non-glare, black, wrinkle finish. Quick detachable sling swivels. Monte Carlo style with cheek piece, especially designed for both scope and iron sighted rifles. Length of pull 13⅝″.								Not available	
Safari Grade Custom	Not available		European walnut with satin oil finish. Ebony tip and cap. Black presentation recoil pad. Fine line checkering with Fleur de Lis. Matte finish bluing with customized action. Floorplate is engraved "Weatherby Safari Grade." Standard rear stock swivel and barrel band front swivel. Sight is ¼″ rib rear with stationary leaf and one folding shallow. "V" leaf hooded ramp front with brass bead. Available left or right hand. 13⅞″ pull.										
Crown Custom	Not available		Fully checkered bolt knob. Damascened bolt and follower. Hand-honed action. Engraved floor plate. "Weatherby Custom." Super fancy walnut stock with pattern #7 butt stock and forearm inlays and pattern #16 stock carving. Gold monogram with name or initials. 13⅝″ pull. Available in right hand only.									Not available	
Action	A scaled-down version of the popular Mark V action, with 6 precision locking lugs in place of 9.		Featuring the Mark V, world's strongest and safest action. The nine locking lugs have almost double the shear area of the lugs found on conventional bolt rifles. The cartridge case head is completely enclosed in the bolt and barrel. .460: action includes hand honing, bolt knob fully checkered, bolt and follower damascened, custom engraved floor plate.										
Safety	Forward moving release, accessible and positive.											

BARRELED ACTION SPECIFICATIONS

CALIBER	.224 WBY MAG	.22/250	.240 WBY MAG	.257 WBY MAG	.270 WBY MAG	7mm WBY MAG	.30–06	.300 WB MAG	.340 WBY MAG	.378 WBY MAG	.416 WBY MAG	.460 WBY MAG
Model	Right hand 24″ or 26″ bbl. Left hand model not available		Right or left hand 24″ bbl. Right hand 26″ bbl. Left hand 26″ bbl. **available in** .300 cal. only						Right or left hand 26″bbl. only.	Right or left hand 26″ bbl. only.	Right or left hand 24″ or 26″ bbl. only.	Right or left hand 24″ or 26″ bbl. only.

*Available only with KDF.   **Weight varies due to wood density.

WEATHERBY RIFLES

MARK V LAZERMARK

With its intricately carved stock pattern, this Mark V model captures the beauty of Old World craftsmanship using today's most modern technology—laser. (Prices do not include scope; all calibers are available in right- or left-hand models, unless stated otherwise.)

Calibers	Prices
224 Weatherby Mag. or 22-250 Varminter	
Right-hand only, 24" barrel	$1140.00
Right-hand only, 26" barrel	1140.00
240, 257, 270, 7mm, 300 Wby. Mag. & 30-06	
24" barrel	1160.00
26" barrel	1185.00

340 Wby. Mag., 26" barrel	$1185.00
378 Wby. Mag., 26" barrel	1345.00
416 Weatherby Mag.	
24" barrel	1460.00
26" barrel	1485.00
460 Weatherby Mag.	
24" barrel	1525.00
26" barrel	1550.00

ACCUMARK CLASSIC 22

This new Weatherby rifle features a high-gloss finish, rosewood tip and cap, Monte Carlo forend, all-steel receiver, fluted bolt body, Mark V-type bolt sleeve, hand-checkering, rubber butt pad, and 60-degree bolt lift. **Caliber:** 22 LR. **Capacity:** 5 shots (8-shot optional). **Barrel length:** 24". **Weight:** 7 lbs.

Price: $635.00

WEATHERBY RIFLES

VANGUARD CLASSIC I
$490.00

Available in 223 Rem., 243 Rem., 270 Win., 7mm-08, 7mm Rem. Mag., 30-06 and 308 Win. Features include black recoil pad (on magnum calibers) and solid black butt pad on regular calibers. See table for additional information and specifications.

VANGUARD CLASSIC II
$635.00

Utilizing the classic styling of an American walnut stock with oil finish, the Classic II stock design features a 90-degree black forend tip (rather than Weatherby's original 45-degree models). The black pistol grip cap with a walnut diamond inlay and a solid black recoil pad make this a distinctive stock. All **barrels** are 24″ with matte finish bluing. Available in **calibers:** 22-250, 243 Win., 270 Win., 7mm Rem. Mag., 30-06, 270 Wby. Mag., 300 Win. Mag., 300 Wby. Mag., and 338 Win. Mag. For additional information and specifications, see the Vanguard table.

VANGUARD WEATHERGUARD
$435.00

Weatherby's new Weatherguard features a 24″ barrel and a synthetic injection molded stock designed to resist weather and humidity. Normal scratches from wear and tear are not visible because the black finish penetrates the entire stock. Stock comes complete with basket-weave checkering, solid black recoil pad, and front and rear swivel studs. **Calibers:** 223 Rem., 243 Rem., 270 Win., 7mm-08, 7mm Rem. Mag., 30-06 and 308 Win. For additional information and specifications, see the Vanguard table that follows.

WEATHERBY RIFLES

VANGUARD VGX DELUXE
Shown with Weatherby Supreme 3-9/XX44S
Variable Scope on Buehler mount
$635.00 (without sights)

VANGUARD VGX SPECIFICATIONS

VGX DELUXE AND CLASSIC II									
CALIBER	.22/250 Rem.	.243 Rem.	.270 WBY. MAG.	.270 Win.	7mm Rem. Mag.	.30-06	.300 Win. Mag.	.300 WBY. MAG.	.338 Win. Mag.
Barrel Length	24"	24"	24"	24"	24"	24"	24"	24"	24"
Barrel Contour	No. 3	No. 2	No. 2	No. 2	No. 2	No. 2	No. 2	No. 2	No. 2
**Approx. Weight	8 lb. 8 oz.	7 lb. 12 oz.	7 lb. 14 oz.	7 lb. 14 oz.	7 lb. 14 oz.	7 lb. 14 oz.	7 lb. 14 oz.	7 lb. 14 oz.	7 lb. 14 oz.
Overall Length	*44"	*44"	44½"	44½"	44½"	44½"	44½"	44½"	44½"
Magazine Capacity	5 rnds.	5 rnds.	3 rnds.	5 rnds.	3 rnds.	5 rnds.	3 rnds.	3 rnds.	3 rnds.
Rifling	1-14"	1-10"	1-10"	1-10"	1-10"	1-10"	1-10"	1-10"	1-10"

CLASSIC I AND WEATHERGUARD							
CALIBER	.223 Rem.	.243 Win.	.270 Win.	7mm/08 Rem.	7mm Rem. Mag.	.30-06	.308 Win.
Barrel Length	24"	24"	24"	24"	24"	24"	24"
Barrel Contour	No. 1	No. 1	No. 1	No. 1	No. 1	No. 1	No. 1
**Weight—Classic I	7 lb. 5 oz.	7 lb. 5 oz.	7 lb. 7 oz.	7 lb. 5 oz.	7 lb. 7 oz.	7 lb. 7 oz.	7 lb. 5 oz.
Weight—Weatherguard	7 lb. 14 oz.	7 lb. 14 oz.	8 lbs.	7 lb. 14 oz.	8 lbs.	8 lbs.	7 lb. 14 oz.
Overall Length	*44"	*44"	44½"	*44"	44½"	44½"	*44"
Magazine Capacity	5 rnds.	5 rnds.	5 rnds.	5 rnds.	3 rnds.	5 rnds.	5 rnds.
Rifling	1-12"	1-10"	1-10"	1-9.5"	1-10"	1-10"	1-10"

ALL MODELS	
Sights	Scope or iron sights available at extra cost.
Stocks: Classic II	American walnut, 13⅝" pull, custom hand checkered, satin finish, 90 degree black tip and pistol grip cap, solid black recoil pad.
VGX Deluxe	American walnut, 13⅝" pull, custom checkering, recoil pad, high lustre finish; 45 degree rosewood fore end tip and pistol grip cap.
Classic I	American walnut, 13⅝" pull, hand checkered, satin finish, black butt pad. (Recoil pad on 7mm Rem. Mag.)
Weatherguard	Synthetic checkered stock, wrinkle finish, 13⅞" pull, black butt pad. (Recoil pad on 7mm Rem. Mag.)
Action	Vanguard action of the improved Mauser type. *Action is ½" shorter than the standard action.
Safety	Side operated, forward moving release, accessible and positive.
Mounts	Vanguard action accepts same bases as Mark V action.

**Weight Approximate—varies due to stock density.

WHITWORTH SPORTING RIFLES

SAFARI GRADE EXPRESS RIFLE
$789.00

Features three safety-lug bolt design for added strength and security . . . Hand-rubbed European walnut stocks with sculpted continental-style cheekpiece . . . Custom three-leaf Express sight . . . Ramp mounted front sight with detachable hood . . . Three-point adjustable trigger . . . Premium hammer-forged chrome-vanadium steel barrels . . . Premium milled-steel Mauser System Action.

SPECIFICATIONS
Calibers: 375 H&H Magnum and 458 Win. Mag. **Barrel length:** 24″. **Overall length:** 44.75″. **Weight:** 7¹/₂ lbs. **Capacity:** 3 rounds.

WINCHESTER BOLT ACTION RIFLES

MODEL 70 FEATHERWEIGHT
$495.00

Model 70 Featherweight hunting rifles minimize weight for easy handling and carrying. Barrel and receiver have integral recoil lug machined from chrome molybdenum steel. Bolt body and locking lugs are machined from a single steel bar. Thermoplastic bedding mates the receiver recoil lug and the stock for maximum strength and accuracy. Bolt features a jeweled finish and knurled bolt handle. Three-position safety. Receivers drilled and tapped for scope mounting. One-piece walnut stocks are hand-worked and finished with genuine cut checkering.

SPECIFICATIONS: MODEL 70 FEATHERWEIGHT (WALNUT)

Caliber	Magazine Capacity (A)	Barrel Length	Overall Length	Nominal Length Of Pull	Nominal Drop At			Nominal Weight (Lbs.)	Rate of Twist 1 Turn In	Bases & Rings or Sights
					Comb	Heel	MC			
22-250 Rem.	5	22″	42″	13½″	⁹/₁₆″	⁷/₈″	—	6½	14″	B + R
223 Rem.	6	22	42	13½	⁹/₁₆	⁷/₈	—	6½	12	B + R
243 Win.	5	22	42	13½	⁹/₁₆	⁷/₈	—	6½	10	B + R
270 Win.	5	22	42½	13½	⁹/₁₆	⁷/₈	—	6¾	10	B + R
280 Rem.	4	22	42½	13½	⁹/₁₆	⁷/₈	—	6¾	10	B + R
30-06 Spgfld.	5	22	42½	13½	⁹/₁₆	⁷/₈	—	6¾	10	B + R
308 Win.	5	22	42	13½	⁹/₁₆	⁷/₈	—	6½	12	B + R

(A) For additional capacity, add one round in chamber when ready to fire. Drops are measured from center line of bore. B + R—Bases and Rings included. Rate of twist is right-hand.

WINCHESTER BOLT ACTION RIFLES

MODEL 70 LIGHTWEIGHT RIFLE

**MODEL 70 LIGHTWEIGHT WIN-TUFF
LAMINATED STOCK**

MODEL 70 LIGHTWEIGHT WALNUT

MODEL 70 LIGHTWEIGHT RIFLE

Model 70 Lightweight Walnut **$447.00**
Model 70 Win-Tuff Lightweight **447.00**
Model 70 Win-Cam Lightweight **447.00**

SPECIFICATIONS: MODEL 70 LIGHTWEIGHT

Model	Caliber	Magazine Capacity (A)	Barrel Length	Overall Length	Nominal Length Of Pull	Nominal Drop At Comb	Heel	MC	Nominal Weight (Lbs.)	Rate of Twist 1 Turn In
70 WALNUT Checkered, No Sights	22-250 Rem.	5	22"	42"	13½"	$^9/_{16}$"	$^7/_8$"	—	6¼	14"
	223 Rem.	6	22	42	13½	$^9/_{16}$	$^7/_8$	—	6¼	12
	243 Win.	5	22	42	13½	$^9/_{16}$	$^7/_8$	—	6¼	10
	270 Win.	5	22	42½	13½	$^9/_{16}$	$^7/_8$	—	6½	10
	280 Rem.	4	22	42½	13½	$^9/_{16}$	$^7/_8$	—	6½	10
	30-06 Spgfld.	5	22	42½	13½	$^9/_{16}$	$^7/_8$	—	6½	10
	308 Win.	5	22	42	13½	$^9/_{16}$	$^7/_8$	—	6¼	12
70 WIN-TUFF *Warm Brown Laminate,* Checkered, No Sights	223 Rem.	4	22	42	13½	$^9/_{16}$	$^7/_8$	—	6¾	12
	243 Win.	5	22	42	13½	$^9/_{16}$	$^7/_8$	—	6¾	10
	270 Win.	5	22	42½	13½	$^9/_{16}$	$^7/_8$	—	7	10
	30-06 Spgfld.	5	22	42½	13½	$^9/_{16}$	$^7/_8$	—	7	10
	308 Win.	5	22	42	13½	$^9/_{16}$	$^7/_8$	—	6¾	12
70 WIN-CAM *Camo Green Laminate*	270 Win.	5	22	42½	13½	$^9/_{16}$	$^7/_8$	—	7	10
	30-06 Spgfld.	5	22	42½	13½	$^9/_{16}$	$^7/_8$	—	7	10

(A) For additional capacity, add one round in chamber when ready to fire. Drops are measured from center line of bore. Rate of twist is right-hand. No sights.

WINCHESTER BOLT ACTION RIFLES

MODEL 70 WINLITE
$637.00

The fiberglass stock on this model sets high standards for lightness, strength, and accuracy. Receiver bedding stability is assured with the use of thermoplastic and by fitting the barreled action individually to the stock. Critical inletted areas are molded into the stock, and the action bed and forend are reinforced Kevlar/Graphite for strength and rigidity. Special bedding pads are easily removed for "free-floating" the barrel if desired. Despite a dramatic weight reduction, there is no increase in the recoil sensation since the fiberglass material compresses during recoil, becoming a total recoil absorption device. Hinged magazine floorplate, sling swivel studs, contoured rubber butt pad are standard. High-quality adjustable steel bases and rings are also included.

SPECIFICATIONS: MODEL 70 WINLITE

Caliber:	270 Win.	30-06 Spfd.	7mm Rem. Mag.	338 Win. Mag.	280 Rem.	300 Win. Mag.	300 Weath. Mag.
Mag. Cap.:	4*	4*	3*	3*	4	3	3
Barrel Length:	22″	22″	24″	24″	22″	24″	24″
Overall Length:	42 1/2″	42 1/2″	44 1/2″	44 1/2″	42 1/2″	44 1/2″	44 1/2″
Length of Pull:	13 1/2″	13 1/2″	13 1/2″	13 1/2″	13 1/2″	13 1/2″	13 1/2″
**Drop at Comb:	9/16″	9/16″	9/16″	9/16″	9/16″	9/16″	9/16″
**Drop at Heel:	1/2″	1/2″	1/2″	1/2″	1/2″	1/2″	1/2″
Weight (lbs.)	6 1/4″	6 1/4″	7 1/2″	7 1/2″	6 1/4–6 1/2	6 1/4–7	6 1/4–7
Rate of Twist:	10″	10″	9 1/2″	10″	10″	10″	10″

*For additional capacity, add one round in chamber when ready to fire.
**Drops are measured from centerline of bore.

MODEL 70 SUPER GRADE
$997.00 (not shown)

The new Winchester Model 70 Super Grade features a bolt with true claw-controlled feeding of belted magnums. The stainless steel claw extractor on the bolt grasps the round from the magazine and delivers it to the chamber and later extracts the spent cartridge. A newly developed gas block doubles as bolt stop and the bolt guard rail assures smooth action. Winchester's 3-position safety and field-strippable firing pin are standard equipment. Other features include a satin finish select walnut stock with sculptured cheekpiece designed to direct recoil forces rearward and away from the shooter's cheek; an extra-thick honeycomb recoil; all-steel bottom metal; and chrome molybdenum barrel with cold hammer-forged rifling for optimum accuracy. Specifications are listed in the table below.

WINCHESTER NEW MODEL 70 SUPER GRADE RIFLE

Model		New Symbol Number	Caliber	Magazine Capacity*	Barrel Length	Overall Length	Nominal Length of Pull	Nominal Drop at			Nominal Weight (Lbs.)	Rate of Twist 1 Turn in	Bases & Rings or Sights
								Comb	Heel	MC			
70 SUPER GRADE	*New*	3862	7mm Rem. Mag.	3	24″	44 1/2″	13 1/2″	9/16″	13/16″	—	7 3/4	9 1/2	B + R
	New	3888	300 Win. Mag.	3	24	44 1/2	13 1/2	9/16	13/16	—	7 3/4	10	B + R
	New	3904	338 Win. Mag.	3	24	44 1/2	13 1/2	9/16	13/16	—	7 3/4	10	B + R

* For additional capacity, add one round in chamber when ready to fire. Drops are measured from center line of bore. Rate of twist is right-hand.

WINCHESTER BOLT ACTION RIFLES

MODEL 70 SPORTER & SUPER EXPRESS RIFLES
$495.00

Featuring six standard calibers and nine magnum calibers (see table below), Winchester's Sporter and Super Express rifles feature one-piece Monte Carlo stocks with sculptured undercut cheekpieces, satin finish, deep-cut wraparound checkering, tapered forends and contoured rubber butt pads. Each rifle has a 24" cold-formed chrome molybdenum steel barrel, a field-strippable jeweled bolt, and 3-position safety.

MODEL 70 SUPER EXPRESS™
WALNUT MAGNUM
(375 H&H Magnum/458 Win. Mag.)
$792.00

This big game pair of rifles boasts all the Sporter Magnum features in 375 H&H and 458 Winchester Magnum calibers. The Sporter stock design has the same innovative cheekpiece, but is reinforced with two steel crossbolts for added strength. The forward sling swivel is mounted directly on the rifle barrel for improved carrying balance and strength. Magazine capacity is three Magnum cartridges. The Monte Carlo stock with sculpted cheekpiece on Model 70 XTR Sporter Magnum and Super Express Magnum rifles is shown in the photo above.

SPECIFICATIONS: MODEL 70 SPORTER & SUPER EXPRESS

Model	Caliber	Magazine Capacity (A)	Barrel Length	Overall Length	Nominal Length Of Pull	Nominal Drop At Comb	Heel	MC	Nominal Weight (Lbs.)	Rate of Twist 1 Turn In	Bases & Rings or Sights
70 SPORTER WALNUT	22-250 Rem.	5	24"	44"	13½"	$^9/_{16}$"	1$^5/_{16}$"	¾"	7¾"	14"	Sights
	22-250 Rem.	5	24	44	13½	$^9/_{16}$	1$^5/_{16}$	¾	7¾	14	B + R
	223 Rem.	6	24	44	13½	$^9/_{16}$	1$^5/_{16}$	¾	7¾	12	Sights
	223 Rem.	6	24	44	13½	$^9/_{16}$	1$^5/_{16}$	¾	7¾	12	B + R
	243 Win.	5	24	44	13½	$^9/_{16}$	1$^5/_{16}$	¾	7¾	10	Sights
	243 Win.	5	24	44	13½	$^9/_{16}$	1$^5/_{16}$	¾	7¾	10	B + R
	25-06 Rem.	5	24	44	13½	$^9/_{16}$	1$^5/_{16}$	¾	7¾	16	Sights
New	25-06 Rem.	5	24	44	13½	$^9/_{16}$	1$^5/_{16}$	¾	7¾	16	B + R
	264 Win. Mag.	3	24	44½	13½	$^9/_{16}$	1$^5/_{16}$	¾	7¾	9	Sight
	264 Win. Mag.	3	24	44½	13½	$^9/_{16}$	1$^5/_{16}$	¾	7¾	9	B + R
	270 Win.	5	24	44½	13½	$^9/_{16}$	1$^5/_{16}$	¾	7¾	10	Sights
	270 Win.	5	24	44½	13½	$^9/_{16}$	1$^5/_{16}$	¾	7¾	10	B + R
	270 Weath. Mag.	5	24	44½	13½	$^9/_{16}$	1$^5/_{16}$	¾	7¾	10	Sights
	270 Weath. Mag.	5	24	44½	13½	$^9/_{16}$	1$^5/_{16}$	¾	7¾	10	B + R
	7mm Rem. Mag.	3	24	44½	13½	$^9/_{16}$	1$^5/_{16}$	¾	7¾	9½	Sights
	7mm Rem. Mag.	3	24	44½	13½	$^9/_{16}$	1$^5/_{16}$	¾	7¾	9½	B + R
	30-06 Spgfld.	5	24	44½	13½	$^9/_{16}$	1$^5/_{16}$	¾	7¾	10	Sights
	30-06 Spgfld.	5	24	44½	13½	$^9/_{16}$	1$^5/_{16}$	¾	7¾	10	B + R
	300 H&H Mag.	3	24	44½	13½	$^9/_{16}$	1$^5/_{16}$	¾	7¾	10	Sights
	300 H&H Mag.	3	24	44½	13½	$^9/_{16}$	1$^5/_{16}$	¾	7¾	10	B + R
	300 Win. Mag.	3	24	44½	13½	$^9/_{16}$	1$^5/_{16}$	¾	7¾	10	Sights
	300 Win. Mag.	3	24	44½	13½	$^9/_{16}$	1$^5/_{16}$	¾	7¾	10	B + R
	300 Weath. Mag.	3	24	44½	13½	$^9/_{16}$	1$^5/_{16}$	¾	7¾	10	Sights
	300 Weath. Mag.	3	24	44½	13½	$^9/_{16}$	1$^5/_{16}$	¾	7¾	10	B + R
	338 Win. Mag.	3	24	44½	13½	$^9/_{16}$	1$^5/_{16}$	¾	7¾	10	Sights
	338 Win. Mag.	3	24	44½	13½	$^9/_{16}$	1$^5/_{16}$	¾	7¾	10	B + R
70 SUPER EXPRESS	375 H&H Mag.	3	24	44½	13½	$^9/_{16}$	1$^5/_{16}$	¾	8½	12	Sights
WALNUT MAGNUM	458 Win. Mag.	3	22	42½	13½	$^9/_{16}$	1$^5/_{16}$	¾	8½	14	Sights

(A) For additional capacity, add one round in chamber when ready to fire. Drops are measured from center line of bore. B + R—Bases and Rings included. Rate of twist is right-hand.

WINCHESTER BOLT ACTION RIFLES

MODEL 70 HEAVY BARREL VARMINT RIFLE
$511.00

Winchester's Varmint Rifle features a Sporter stock with undercut cheekpiece and 26″ counter-bored barrel. Rubber butt pad, swivel studs and receiver drilled and tapped for scope are standard, as is Winchester's 3-position safety.

MODEL 70 HEAVY BARREL VARMINT RIFLE SPECIFICATIONS

Model	Caliber	Magazine Capacity (A)	Barrel Length	Overall Length	Nominal Length Of Pull	Nominal Drop At			Nominal Weight (Lbs.)	Rate of Twist 1 Turn In	Sights
						Comb	Heel	MC			
70 VARMINT	22-250 Rem.	5	26″	46″	13½″	$^9/_{16}$″	$1^5/_{16}$″	¾″	9	14″	—
	223 Rem.	6	26	46	13½	$^9/_{16}$	$1^5/_{16}$	¾	9	12	—
	243 Win.	5	26	46	13½	$^9/_{16}$	$1^5/_{16}$	¾	9	10	—
New	308 Win.	5	26	46	13½	$^9/_{16}$	$1^5/_{16}$	¾	9	12	—

(A) For additional capacity, add one round in chamber when ready to fire. Drops are measured from center line of bore. Rate of twist is right-hand.

WINCHESTER RANGER®
BOLT ACTION CENTERFIRE RIFLE
$406.00

The Ranger Bolt Action Rifle comes with an American hardwood stock, a wear-resistant satin walnut finish, ramp beadpost front sight, steel barrel, three-position safety and engine-turned, anti-bind bolt. The receiver is drilled and tapped for scope mounting; accuracy is enhanced by thermoplastic bedding of the receiver. Barrel and receiver are brushed and blued.

WINCHESTER RANGER®
YOUTH BOLT ACTION CARBINE
$414.00

This carbine offers dependable bolt action performance combined with a scaled-down design to fit the younger, smaller shooter. It features anti-bind bolt design, jeweled bolt, three-position safety, contoured recoil pad, ramped bead front sight, semi-buckhorn folding leaf rear sight, and sling swivels. Receiver is drilled and tapped for scope mounting. Stock is of American hardwood with protective satin walnut finish. Pistol grip, length of pull, overall length, and comb are all tailored to youth dimensions (see table).

RANGER & YOUTH RIFLE SPECIFICATIONS

Model	Caliber	Magazine Capacity (A)	Barrel Length	Overall Length	Nominal Length Of Pull	Nominal Drop At			Nominal Weight (Lbs.)	Rate of Twist 1 Turn In	Bases & Rings Sights
						Comb	Heel	MC			
RANGER BOLT ACTION	270 Win.	5	22″	42¾″	13½″	$^9/_{16}$″	⅞″	—	6	10″	Sights
	30-06 Spgfld.	5	22	42¾	13½	$^9/_{16}$	⅞	—	6	10	Sights
RANGER YOUTH/LADIES BOLT ACTION	243 Win.	5	22″	41¼	12½″	¾″	1″	—	5¾	10″	Sights

(A) For additional capacity, add one round in chamber when ready to fire. Drops are measured from center line of bore. Rate of twist is right-hand.

WINCHESTER LEVER ACTION
CARBINES & RIFLES

Model 94 Side Eject™ Lever Action Centerfire carbines have been developed and refined through almost a century of sporting use and technological advancement. The new angled ejection system throws the spent cartridge away from the shooter's line of vision and does not interfere with top-mounted scopes. It features an improved, stabilized trigger mechanism with controlled pre-travel and short, crisp let-off.

Receivers are of forged steel. Chromium molybdenum barrels assure long-lasting strength. Chamber and rifling are cold-forged in a single operation for precise alignment and accuracy. The receiver is ported for angled ejection and scopes can be top-mounted.

MODEL 94 STANDARD WALNUT RIFLE

The top choice for lever-action styling and craftsmanship. Metal surfaces are highly polished and blued. American walnut stock and forearm have a protective stain finish with precise-cut wraparound checkering. It has a 20-inch barrel with hooded blade front sight and semi-buckhorn rear sight. **Calibers:** 30-30 Win., 307 Win., 356 Win. and 7-30 Waters.

Prices:
30-30 Win., checkered, 307 Win., 356 Win. **$319.00**
30-30 Win., 7-30 Waters **297.00**
30-30 Win. with scope **371.00**

MODEL 94 WALNUT TRAPPER CARBINE

With 16-inch short-barrel lever action and straight forward styling. Compact and fast-handling in dense cover, it has a magazine capacity of five shots (9 in 45 Colt or 44 Rem. Mag./44 S&W Special). **Calibers:** 30-30 Winchester, 45 Colt, and 44 Rem. Mag./44 S&W Special.

Prices:
30-30 Winchester **$297.00**
45 Colt, 44 Rem. Mag./44 S&W Special **313.00**

MODEL 94 SPECIFICATIONS

Model	Caliber	Magazine Capacity (A)	Barrel Length	Overall Length	Nominal Length Of Pull	Nominal Drop At Comb	Nominal Drop At Heel	Nominal Weight (Lbs.)	Rate of Twist 1 Turn In	Rings Sights
94 CHECKERED WALNUT	30-30 Win.	6	20″	37¾″	13″	1⅛″	1⅞″	6½	12″	Rifle
With 1.5-4.5 scope	30-30 Win.	6	20	37¾	13	1⅛	1⅞	6⅞	12	R/S
94 STANDARD WALNUT	30-30 Win.	6	20	37¾	13	1⅛	1⅞	6½	12	Rifle
	7-30 Waters	6	20	37¾	13	1⅛	1⅞	6½	9.9	Rifle
94 TRAPPER CARBINE WALNUT	30-30 Win.	5	16	33¾	13	1⅛	1⅞	6⅛	12	Rifle
	44 Rem. Mag. 44 S&W Spec.	9	16	33¾	13	1⅛	1⅞	6	38	Rifle
	45 Colt	9	16	33¾	13	1⅛	1⅞	6	38	Rifle

(A) For additional capacity, add one round in chamber when ready to fire. Drops are measured from center line of bore. Rate of twist is right-hand.

WINCHESTER LEVER ACTION RIFLES

MODEL 94 RANGER
$264.00 ($310.00 with Scope)

Model 94 Ranger is an economical version of the Model 94. Lever action is smooth and reliable. In 30-30 Winchester, the rapid-firing six-shot magazine capacity provides two more shots than most centerfire hunting rifles.

MODEL 94 BIG BORE WALNUT
$319.00

Winchester's powerful 307 and 356 hunting calibers combined with maximum lever-action power and angled ejection provide hunters with improved performance and economy.

MODEL 94 WIN-TUFF RIFLE
$319.00 (20″ Barrel)

Includes all features and specifications of standard Model 94 plus tough laminated hardwood styled for the brush-gunning hunter who wants good concealment and a carbine that can stand up to all kinds of weather.

MODEL 94 SPECIFICATIONS

Model	Caliber	Magazine Capacity (A)	Barrel Length	Overall Length	Nominal Length Of Pull	Nominal Drop At Comb	Nominal Drop At Heel	Nominal Weight (Lbs.)	Rate of Twist 1 Turn In	Sights
94 WIN-TUFF	30-30 Win.	6	20″	37¾″	13″	1⅛″	1⅞″	6½	12″	Rifle
94 BIG BORE WALNUT	307 Win.	6	20	37¾	13	1⅛	1⅞	6½	12	Rifle
	356 Win.	6	20	37¾	13	1⅛	1⅞	6½	12	Rifle
RANGER	30-30 Win.	6	20	37¾	13	1⅛	1⅞	6½	12	Rifle
Scope 4 × 32 see-through mounts	30-30 Win.	6	20	37¾	13	1⅛	1⅞	6⅞	12	R/S

(A) For additional capacity, add one round in chamber when ready to fire. Drops are measured from center line of bore. R/S-Rifle sights and Bushnell® Sportview™ scope with mounts. Rate of twist is right-hand.

WINCHESTER LEVER ACTION RIFLES

MODEL 9422 LEVER-ACTION RIMFIRE RIFLES

These Model 9422 rimfire rifles combine classic 94 styling and handling in ultra-modern lever action 22s of superb craftsmanship. Handling and shooting characteristics are superior because of their carbine-like size.

Positive lever action and bolt design ensure feeding and chambering from any shooting position. The bolt face is T-slotted to guide the cartridge with complete control from magazine to chamber. A color-coded magazine follower shows when the brass magazine tube is empty. Receivers are grooved for scope mounting. Other functional features include exposed hammer with half-cock safety, hooded bead front sight, semi-buckhorn rear sight and side ejection of spent cartridges.

Stock and forearm are American walnut with checkering, high-luster finish, and straight-grip design. Internal parts are carefully finished for smoothness of action.

MODEL 9422 WALNUT

Considered one of the world's finest production sporting arms, this lever action rimfire (shown above) holds 21 Short, 17 Long or 15 Long Rifle cartridges.

Model 9422 Walnut Magnum gives exceptional accuracy at longer ranges than conventional 22 rifles. It is designed specifically for the 22 Winchester Magnum Rimfire cartridge and holds 11 cartridges.

Model 9422 Win-Cam Magnum features laminated non-glare, green-shaded stock and forearm. American hardwood stock is bonded to withstand all weather and climates. **Model 9422 Win-Tuff** is also available to ensure resistance to changes in weather conditions, or exposure to water and hard knocks.

SPECIFICATIONS

Model	Caliber	Magazine Capacity	Barrel Length	Overall Length	Nominal Length Of Pull	Nominal Drop At Comb	Heel	Nominal Weight (Lbs.)	Rate of Twist 1 Turn In	Sights	Prices
9422 WALNUT	22	21S,17L,15LR	20½″	37⅛″	13½″	1⅛″	1⅞″	6¼	16″	Rifle	$323.00
	22WMR	11	20½	37⅛	13½	1⅛	1⅞	6¼	16	Rifle	338.00
9422 WIN-TUFF	22	21S,17L,15LR	20½″	37⅛″	13½″	1⅛″	1⅞″	6¼	16″	Rifle	335.00
	22WMR	11	20½	37⅛	13½	1⅛	1⅞	6¼	16	Rifle	349.00
9422 WIN-CAM	22WMR	11	20½″	37⅛″	13½″	1⅛″	1⅞″	6¼	16″	Rifle	349.00

WMR-Winchester Magnum Rimfire. S-Short, L-Long, LR-Long Rifle. Drops are measured from center line of bore.

WINSLOW RIFLES

SPECIFICATIONS

Stock: Choice of two stock models. **The Plainsmaster** offers pinpoint accuracy in open country with full curl pistol grip and flat forearm. **The Bushmaster** offers lighter weight for bush country; slender pistol with palm swell; beavertail forend for light hand comfort. Both styles are of hand-rubbed black walnut. Length of pull—13½ inches; plainsmaster ⅜ inch castoff; Bushmaster 3/16 inch castoff; all rifles are drilled and tapped to incorporate the use of telescopic sights; rifles with receiver or open sights are available on special order; all rifles are equipped with quick detachable sling swivel studs and white-line recoil pad. All Winslow stocks incorporate a slight castoff to deflect recoil, minimizing flinch and muzzle jump. **Magazine:** Staggered box type, four shot. (Blind in the stock has no floor-plate). **Action:** Mauser Mark X Action. **Overall length:** 43″ (Standard Model); 45″ (Magnum); all Winslow rifles have company name and serial number and grade engraved on the action and caliber engraved on barrel. **Barrel:** Douglas barrel premium grade, chrome moly-type steel; all barrels, 20 caliber through 35 caliber, have six lands and grooves; barrels larger than 35 caliber have eight lands and grooves. All barrels are finished to (.2 to .4) micro inches inside the lands and grooves. **Total weight** (without scope): 7 to 7½ lbs. with 24″ barrel in standard calibers 243, 308, 270, etc; 8 to 9 lbs. with 26″ barrel in Magnum calibers 264 Win., 300 Wby., 458 Win., etc. Winslow rifles are made in the following calibers:

Standard cartridges: 22-250, 243 Win., 244 Rem., 257 Roberts, 308 Win., 30-06, 280 Rem., 270 Win., 25-06, 284 Win., 358 Win., and 7mm (7×57).

Magnum cartridges: 300 Weatherby, 300 Win., 338 Win., 358 Norma, 375 H.H., 458 Win., 257 Weatherby, 264 Win., 270 Weatherby, 7mm Weatherby, 7mm Rem., 300 H.H., 308 Norma.

Left-handed models available in most calibers.

WINSLOW BASIC RIFLE

The Basic Rifle, available in the Bushmaster stock, features one ivory diamond inlay in a rose-wood grip cap and ivory trademark in bottom of forearm. Grade 'A' walnut jeweled bolt and follower. **Price: $1750.00 and up.** With **Plainsmaster stock: $100.00** extra. **Left-hand model: $1850.00 and up.**

WINSLOW VARMINT

This 17-caliber rifle is available with Bushmaster stock or Plainsmaster stock, which is a miniature of the original with high roll-over cheekpiece and a round leading edge on the forearm, modified spoon billed pistol grip. Available in 17/222, 17/222 Mag. 17/233, 222 Rem. and 223. Regent grade shown. With **Bushmaster stock: $1750.00 and up.** With **Plainsmaster stock: $100.00** extra. **Left-hand model: $1850.00 and up.**

ANTONIO ZOLI RIFLES

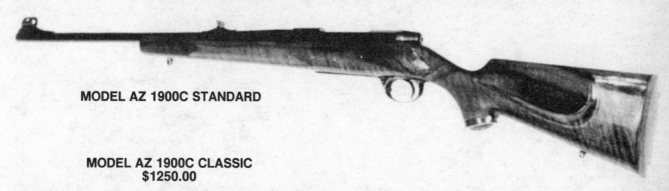

MODEL AZ 1900C STANDARD

MODEL AZ 1900C CLASSIC
$1250.00

This bolt-action rifle features a blued finish, jeweled and polished bolt body, and blued receiver (drilled and tapped for scope mounts). Also, a double safety bolt lock release permits the user to clear the chamber and unload the gun without taking the firearm off safe. For specifications, see the table below.

MODEL AZ 1900C MAGNUM

MODEL AZ 1900C SPECIFICATIONS

	Standard Calibers	Magnum calibers
Barrel length	21''	24''
Overall length	41 $^3/_4$''	44''
Length of pull	13 $^1/_2$	13 $^1/_2$
Sights	Furnished not mounted barrel drilled and tapped	
Stock	Hand rubbed finely checkered Turkish circassian walnut	
Materials	Barrel: hardened - high tensile chrome molybdenum steel-polished blued. Action: same as barrel	
Calibers and rate of twist	Standard: 243W - 6.5×55 mm - 270W - 308Win. - 30.06 Magnum: 7 m.rm.Rem. Mag - 300 Win. Mag.	
Magazine capacity	5	
Nominal weight	7 $^1/_4$''	7 $^5/_7$''

Shotguns

FOR ADDRESSES AND PHONE
NUMBERS OF MANUFACTURERS AND
DISTRIBUTORS INCLUDED IN THIS
SECTION, SEE *DIRECTORY OF
MANUFACTURERS AND SUPPLIERS*

AMERICAN ARMS

SPECIAL SIDE-BY-SIDE
$609.00

SPECIAL OVER/UNDER

MODEL	GAUGE	BBL LGTH.	CHAMBER	CHOKES	AVG. WGT.	PRICES
WT/OU	10	26″	3 1/2″	CT-2	9 lbs. 15 oz.	$839.00
WS/OU	12	28″	3 1/2″	CT-3	6 lbs. 15 oz.	599.00
TS/SS	10	26″	3 1/2″	CT-2	10 lbs. 13 oz.	649.00
TS/SS	12	26″	3 1/2″	CT-3	7 lbs. 6 oz.	559.00
WS/SS	10	32″	3 1/2″	SF/SF	10 lbs. 5 oz.	599.00

CT-3 = Choke tubes IC/M/F   CT-2 = Choke tubes F/F
SF = Steel Full Choke   SST = Single Selective Trigger
ASE = Auto selective ejector
Drop at Comb = 1 1/8″   Drop at Heel = 2 3/8″

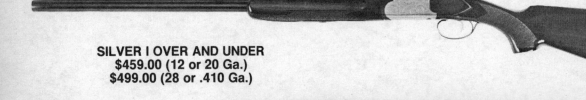

SILVER I OVER AND UNDER
$459.00 (12 or 20 Ga.)
$499.00 (28 or .410 Ga.)

SILVER II
(W/Choke Tubes & Automatic
Selective Ejectors) $599.00

SPECIFICATIONS
Gauges: 12, 20, 28 or .410
Chambers: 3″ (2³/₄″ in 28 ga.)
Barrel lengths: 26″, choked IC/M (all gauges); 28″, choked M/
F (12 and 20 ga.)
Trigger: Single selective

Weight: 6 lbs. 15 oz. (12 ga.); 6 lbs. 10 oz. (20 ga.); 5 lbs. 14
oz. (28 ga.); 6 lbs. 6 oz. (.410 ga.)
Stock: Hand-checkered, walnut, pistol-grip stock and forend
Length of pull: 14¹/₈″
Drop at comb: 1³/₈″
Drop at heel: 2³/₈″
Features: Fitted recoil pad; ¹/₄″ vent rib; manual thumb safety;
scroll-engraved, precision-made boxlocks; one-piece, steel-
forged receiver; locking cross bolt; monobloc chrome-lined
barrels; extractors
Also available: 28 and .410 gauge IC/M (28″ barrels): **$879.00**

AMERICAN ARMS

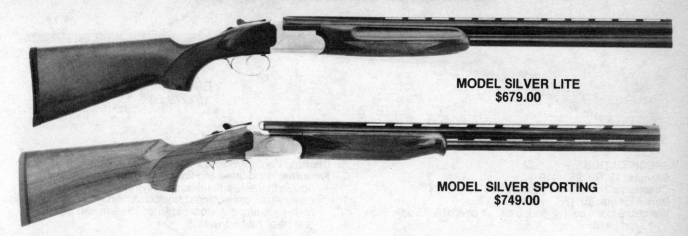

MODEL SILVER LITE
$679.00

MODEL SILVER SPORTING
$749.00

SPECIFICATIONS

MODEL	GAUGE	BBL. LENGTH	CHAMBER	CHOKES	AVG. WEIGHT
SILVER I	12	26"–28"	3"	IC/M-M/F	6 lbs. 15 oz.
	20	26"–28"	3"	IC/M-M/F	6 lbs. 10 oz.
	28	26"	2 3/4"	IC/M	6 lbs. 7 oz.
	.410	26"	3"	IC/M	6 lbs. 7 oz.
SILVER II	12	26"–28"	3"	CT-3	6 lbs. 15 oz.
	20	26"	3"	CT-3	6 lbs. 10 oz.
	28	26"	2 3/4"	IC/M	6 lbs. 7 oz.
	.410	26"	3"	IC/M	6 lbs. 7 oz.
	28/410 Set	26"	2 3/4"–3"	IC/M	6 lbs. 5 oz.
SILVER LITE	12	26"	2 3/4"	CT-3	6 lbs. 0 oz.
	20	26"	2 3/4"	CT-3	5 lbs. 14 oz.
SPORTING	12	28"	2 3/4"	CT-4	7 lbs. 6 oz.

CT-3 Choke Tubes IC/M/F   CT-4 Choke Tubes SK/IC/M/F   Cast Off = 3/8"
SILVER I: Pull = 14 1/8"; Drop at Comb = 1 3/8"; Drop at Heel = 2 3/8"
SILVER II: Pull = 14 1/8"; Drop at Comb = 1 3/8"; Drop at Heel = 2 3/8"
SILVER LITE: Pull = 14 1/8"; Drop at Comb = 1 1/2"; Drop at Heel = 2 1/2"
SILVER SPORTING: Pull = 14 3/8"; Drop at Comb = 1 1/2"; Drop at Heel = 2 3/8"

SHOTGUNS

BRITTANY
$659.00

SPECIFICATIONS
Gauges: 12, 20
Chamber: 3"
Barrel lengths: 25" and 27"
Weight: 6 lbs. 7 ozs. (25"); 6 lbs. 15 oz. (27")
Chokes: Tubes IC/M/F

Features: Engraved case-colored frame; single selective trigger with top tang selector; automatic selective ejectors; manual safety; hard chrome-lined barrels; walnut English-style straight stock and semi-beavertail forearm w/cut checkering and oil-rubbed finish; ventilated rubber recoil pad; and choke tubes with key

AMERICAN ARMS

GRULLA #2
$2279.00

SPECIFICATIONS
Gauges: 12, 20, 28, .410
Chambers: 2³/₄″ (12 & 28 ga.); 3″ (20 & .410 ga.)
Barrel length: 26″ (28″ also in 12 ga.)
Weight: 6 lbs. 4 oz. (12 ga.); 5 lbs. 11 oz. (20 & 28 ga.); 5 lbs. 13 oz. (.410)

Chokes: IC/M (M/F also in 12 ga.)
Features: Hand-fitted and finished high-grade classic double; double triggers; automatic selective ejectors; fixed chokes; concave rib; case-colored sidelock action w/engraving; English-style straight stock; splinter forearm and checkered butt of oil rubbed walnut

GENTRY SIDE-BY-SIDE
$499.00 (12, 16 or 20 Ga.)
$549.00 (28 or .410 Ga.)

Features boxlocks with engraved English-style scrollwork on side plates; one-piece, steel-forged receiver; chrome barrels; manual thumb safety; independent floating firing pin.

SPECIFICATIONS
Gauges: 12, 16, 20, 28, .410
Chambers: 3″ (except 28 gauge, 2³/₄″)
Barrel lengths: 26″, choked IC/M (all gauges); 28″, choked M/F (12, 16 and 20 gauges)

Weight: 6 lbs. 14 oz. (12 and .410 ga.); 6 lbs. 4 oz. (20 and 28 ga.)
Drop at comb: 1³/₈″
Drop at heel: 2³/₈″
Other features: Fitted recoil pad; flat matted rib; walnut pistol-grip stock and beavertail forend with hand-checkering; gold front sight bead

DERBY SIDE-BY-SIDE
Single Trigger

Features functioning side locks with English-style hand engraving on side plates; one-piece, steel-forged receiver; chrome barrels; automatic safety

SPECIFICATIONS
Gauges: 12, 20, 28, .410 (20/28 gauge in two-barrel set)
Chambers: 3″
Barrel lengths: 26″, choked IC/M (all gauges); 28″, choked M/F (12 and 20 gauges)
Weight: 7 lbs. 1 oz. (12 ga.); 6¹/₄ lbs. (20, 28 and .410 ga.)

Sights: Gold bead front sight
Stock: Walnut and splinter forend with hand-checkering
Length of pull: 14¹/₈″
Drop at comb: 1³/₈″
Drop at heel: 2³/₈″
Finish: Hand-rubbed oil finish wood
Prices:
12 or 20 ga. single trigger	$ 839.00
28 or .410 ga. single trigger	879.00
20/28 ga. single trigger set	1099.00

AMERICAN ARMS/FRANCHI SHOTGUNS

BLACK MAGIC SERIES

BLACK MAGIC GAME
$629.00

BLACK MAGIC SKEET & TRAP
$669.00 (Skeet)
$689.00 (Trap)

BLACK MAGIC SPORTING HUNTER & LIGHTWEIGHT HUNTER
$1189.00 (Lightweight Hunter)
$1229.00 (Hunter)

BLACK MAGIC SPECIFICATIONS

Model	Ga.	Action Type	Barrel Length	Chamber	Choke	Length of Pull	Drop at Comb	Drop at Heel	Nominal weight (lbs.)
Game	12	SA	26″ or 28″	3″	FC	14 1/4″	1 1/2″	2 3/8″	7
Trap	12	SA	30″	2 3/4″	FC	14 1/2″	1 1/4″	1 5/8″	7 1/2
Skeet	12	SA	26″	2 3/4″	SK	14 1/2″	1 1/2″	2 1/4″	7 1/4
Sporting Hunter	12	O/U	26″ or 28″	3″	FC	14 1/4″	1 1/2″	2 3/8″	7
Lightweight	12	O/U	26″ or 28″	2 3/4″	FC	14 1/4″	1 1/2″	2 3/8″	6

ARMSPORT SHOTGUNS

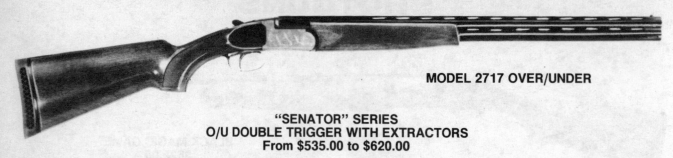

MODEL 2717 OVER/UNDER

"SENATOR" SERIES
O/U DOUBLE TRIGGER WITH EXTRACTORS
From $535.00 to $620.00

The Armsport over/unders with double triggers are lightweight, well balanced and are chambered for 3" Mag. shells. The special grade steel barrels are chrome-lined, with both an upper vent rib and lateral vent rib. The fine grain walnut stock has a palm swell pistol grip and both the stock and schnabel-type forend have a deep, sure-grip checkering. The beautifully engraved antique silver receiver is engineered from the finest gun steel. The double trigger instantly allows the shooter his barrel choice.

Available in:
Model 2701 12 Ga. 28" O/U 3" Mag. 2 Trig. Ext. Mod. & Full
Model 2703 20 Ga. 26" O/U 3" Mag. 2 Trig. Ext. Imp. & Mod.
Model 2705 .410 Ga. 26" O/U 3" Mag. 2 Trig. Ext. Imp. & Mod.
Model 2707 28 Ga. 26" O/U 2 Trigger Full & Full
Also available:
SINGLE SELECTIVE TRIGGER MODELS 2717, 2719, 2720, 2725
SINGLE SELECTIVE TRIGGER MODELS 2727 & 2729 w/ auto ejectors

MODELS 1050 and 1053
SIDE-BY-SIDE DOUBLE BARREL
ITALIAN SHOTGUNS
$575.00

Chambered for 3" magnum with hard chrome-lined barrels, these shotguns feature center ribs, fluorescent front sights, Italian boxlock actions and gloss finish stocks and forends. Also antique silver finish receivers engraved with bird scenes. Model 1050 is 12 gauge with 28" barrel with Modified & Full choke. Model 1053 is 20 gauge with 26" barrel with Imp. & Modified choke.
Also available: **MODEL 1054** (.410 ga.) and **MODEL 1055** (28 ga.) w/26" barrels: **$635.00**

MODELS 2699 and 2700
10 GAUGE OVER & UNDER GOOSE GUN
$950.00 ($1050.00 w/Interchangeable Choke Tubes)

This 10 gauge 3½" "Fowler" Magnum Boss-type action O/U Goose gun has two bottom locking lugs on its OM8 steel barrels attached to an antiqued silver finished action. Three Canada geese scenes are engraved on the two sides and bottom of the receiver. The hard chrome-lined barrels have an extra wide 12mm top vent rib with a fluorescent front sight and a brass mid-bead sight. Both the 32" barrels choked full and the 28" barrels choked Imp. and Mod. will shoot steel BB's effectively. The walnut stock with rubber recoil pad and matching forend are hand-checkered.
Also available:
MODEL 2701 (12 ga., 28" barrel) and **2703** (20 ga., 26" barrel): **$535.00**
MODELS 2705 (.410 ga., 26" barrel) and **2707** (28 ga., 26" barrel): **620.00**

ARMSPORT SHOTGUNS

MODEL 2900
THREE-BARREL SHOTGUN "TRILLING"
$2900.00

The only three-barrel shotgun being manufactured, Model 2900 features 28″ barrels (12 gauge) lined and chambered for 3″ magnum shells choked improved, modified and full. The front trigger fires the top two barrels and the rear trigger fires the bottom barrel. Made on a boss type action from special steel, the shotgun frame has two bottom locking lugs. The select grain walnut palm swell pistol grip stock and forend has a rubber recoil pad, high gloss finish and checkering.

MODELS 2730 & 2731
"PRESIDENT SUPERIMPOSED SERIES"
O/U SINGLE SELECTIVE TRIGGER
WITH AUTO EJECTORS
$775.00

Milled from special high-strength steel, these shotguns feature engraved antique silver finished boss-type receiver fitted to special steel barrels with jeweled engine turned barrel lugs and hand-checkered walnut stock with rubber recoil pad, palm swell full pistol grip and matching checkered semi-schnabel forend. Also, extra-wide 12mm top vent rib with front fluorescent sight and brass mid-bead sight, plus lateral vent rib. All President models have single selective triggers and are chambered 3″ magnum. Barrel lengths are 26″ in 20 gauge and 27″ in 12 gauge. Chokes are Skeet and Skeet 6 Interchangeable Deluxe.

Also available:
Model 2741 12 Ga. 26″ O/U Mod. & Full **$675.00**
Model 2743 20 Ga. 26″ O/U Imp. & Mod. 675.00
Model 2742 12 Ga. 28″/3 Interchangeable
    Chokes IC-M-F 765.00
Model 2744 20 Ga. 26″/3 Interchangeable
    Chokes IC-M-F 765.00

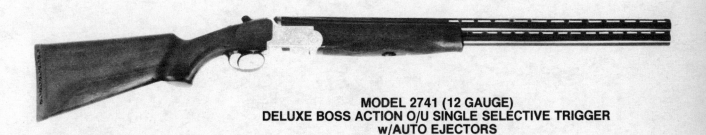

MODEL 2741 (12 GAUGE)
DELUXE BOSS ACTION O/U SINGLE SELECTIVE TRIGGER
w/AUTO EJECTORS

ARMSPORT SHOTGUNS

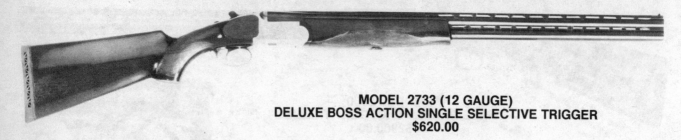

MODEL 2733 (12 GAUGE)
DELUXE BOSS ACTION SINGLE SELECTIVE TRIGGER
$620.00

This is a superbly designed, handsomely engraved over-and-under shotgun with ventilated rib. The single selective trigger allows you to fire either barrel at will. It has exceptionally fine hand-picked walnut stock and forend, hand-crafted and fitted for generations of fine shooting. Gloss or oil finish. 12 gauge. 28-inch barrels choked Mod. and Full (Extractors). 3-inch Mag. shells.

Also available:
Model 2735 20 Ga. 26" O/U 3" Mag. Imp. & Mod. Deluxe Boss Action **$620.00**

MODELS 1126, 1127 & 1128
TAKEDOWN SINGLE BARREL SHOTGUNS
$90.00

Machined from solid block of gun steel drop forging. Features a bottom lever takedown opening action and a complete iron cross removable forend. Barrels are chambered for 3" magnum shells with hard chrome-lined barrels and bores for steel shot use. High-gloss walnut finish stock and forend are checkered.

Models 1125 and 1126 are 12 gauge with 28" barrels (Model 1125 has Modified choke; Model 1126 has Full). **Model 1127** is 20 gauge with 26" barrel, Modified choke. **Model 1128** is .410 gauge with full choke.

BENELLI SHOTGUNS

M1 SUPER 90 SERIES

MODEL M1 SUPER 90 DEFENSE
$669.00 (w/Pistol Grip)
$716.00 (w/Ghost-Ring Sighting System)

MODEL M1 SUPER 90 SLUG
$631.00 ($677.00 w/Ghost-Ring Sighting System)

MODEL M1 SUPER 90 FIELD
(shown with extended magazine)
$675.00

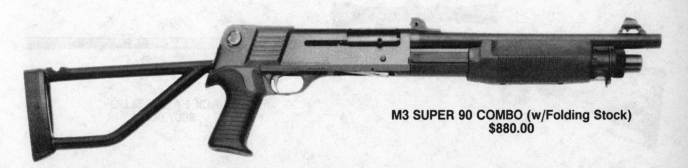

M3 SUPER 90 COMBO (w/Folding Stock)
$880.00

BENELLI SHOTGUNS

MONTEFELTRO SUPER 90 SLUG GUN

MONTEFELTRO SUPER 90 (Standard Hunter)
$685.00 ($745.00 Left Hand)

The Montefeltro Super 90 combines the fast firing characteristics of the M1 Super 90 with the look of a classic sporting shotgun. The heart of this Benelli remains the Montefeltro rotating bolt system, a rugged and simple inertia recoil design that functions with all types of 3″ and 2³/₄″ loads. A drop adjustment kit allows the stock to be custom-fitted to any shooter. See table for specifications.

Also available:
MONTEFELTRO SUPER 90 SLUG GUN w/24″ barrel, satin finish stock, and scope mount. **Price: $685.00**
MONTEFELTRO SUPER 90 UPLANDER GUN with 21″ or 24″ vent. rib and satin finish stock. **Price: $685.00**

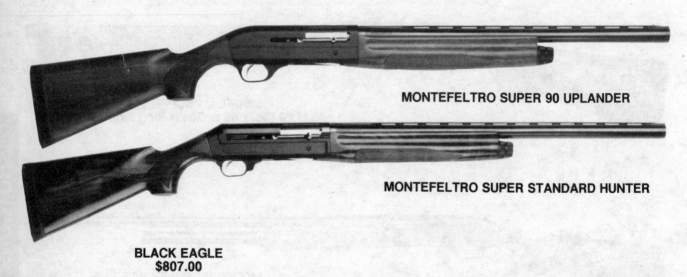

MONTEFELTRO SUPER 90 UPLANDER

MONTEFELTRO SUPER STANDARD HUNTER

BLACK EAGLE
$807.00

Benelli's new Black Eagle shotgun combines the best technical features of the Montefeltro Super 90 and the classic design of the old SL 80 Series. It comes standard with a specially designed two-piece receiver of steel and aluminum, adding to its reliability and resistance to wear. A premium high-gloss walnut stock and gold-plated trigger are included, along with a Montefeltro rotating bolt. The Black Eagle has no complex cylinders and pistons to maintain. See table for specifications.

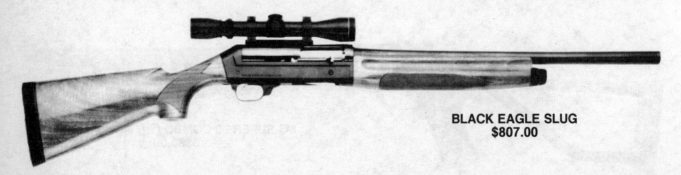

BLACK EAGLE SLUG
$807.00

BENELLI SHOTGUNS

BENELLI M3 SUPER 90
COMBINATION PUMP/AUTO (19³/₄″ barrel)
$813.00
$860.00 w/Ghost-Ring Sighting

SPECIFICATIONS

	GAUGE	OPERATING SYSTEM	MAGAZINE CAPACITY	BARREL LENGTH	OVERALL LENGTH	WEIGHT	CHOKE	STOCK	SIGHTS
M1 Super 90 Slug 3″ chamber*	12	Inertia Recoil, Montefeltro rotating bolt	7	19³/₄″	41″	6 lb. 13 oz.	Cylinder	High impact polymer, standard buttstock	Rifle (ghost ring sights also available)
M1 Super 90 DEFENSE 3″ chamber*	12	Inertia Recoil, Montefeltro rotating bolt	7	19³/₄″	41″	7 lb. 2 oz.	Clyinder	High impact polymer Pistol Grip	Rifle (ghost ring sights also available)
M1 Super 90 FIELD (Extended Magazine available with 26 & 28″ models) 3″ chamber	12	Inertia Recoil, Montefeltro rotating bolt	3 (7 with extended magazine)	28″ 26″ 24″ 21″	49¹/₂″ 47¹/₂″ 45¹/₂″ 42¹/₂″	7 lb. 7 oz. 7 lb. 5 oz. 7 lb. 3 oz. 7 lb. Long tube add 1 oz.	Full Improved Mod. Modified Improved Cyl. Skeet	High impact, polymer, Standard Buttstock	Bead
Montefeltro Super 90 3″ chamber	12	Inertia Recoil, Montefeltro rotating bolt	4	28″ (Std) 26″ (Std) 28″ (Left) 26″ (Left) 24″ (Up) 21″ (Up) 24″ (Slug)	49¹/₂″ 47¹/₂″ 49¹/₂″ 47¹/₂″ 45¹/₂″ 42¹/₂″ 45¹/₂″	7 lb. 5 oz. .7 lb. 7 lb. 5 oz. 7 lb. 6 lb. 14 oz. 6 lb. 13 oz. 7 lb.	Set of Full, Improved Mod., Modified, Improved Cyl., Skeet (Slug Gun has smoothbore cyl.)	Walnut with drop adjustment kit	Bead (Slug Gun has scope mount and rifle sights)
Black Eagle 3″ chamber*	12	Inertia Recoil, Montefeltro rotating bolt	4	28″ 26″ 24″ 21″ 24″ Slug	49¹/₂″ 47¹/₂″ 45¹/₂″ 42¹/₂″ 45¹/₂″	7 lb. 5 oz. 7 lb. 3 oz. 7 lb. 1 oz. 7 lb. 7 lb. 2 oz.	Set of Full, Improved Mod., Mod., I.C., & Skeet (Black Eagle slug has rifled barrel)	Walnut with drop adjustment	Bead
M3 Super 90 Combination PUMP/AUTO 3″ chamber*	12	Semi-automatic & pump, Inertia Recoil, Montefeltro rotating bolt	7	19³/₄″	41″	7 lb. 14 oz.	Cylinder	High impact polymer Pistol Grip	Rifle (ghost ring sights also available)

* All models accept 2³/₄″ chamber.

BERETTA SHOTGUNS

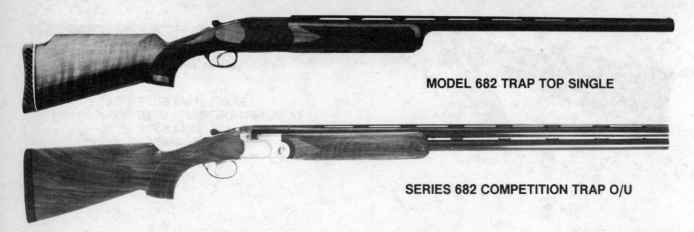

MODEL 682 TRAP TOP SINGLE

SERIES 682 COMPETITION TRAP O/U

Available in Competition Mono, Over/Under or Mono Trap-O/U Combo Set, the 12-gauge 682X trap guns boast premium-grade hand-checkered walnut stock and forend with International or Monte Carlo left- or right-hand stock and choice of 3 stock dimensions.

Features: Adjustable gold-plated, single selective sliding trigger for precise length of pull fit; fluorescent competition front sight; step-up top rib; Bruniton non-reflective black matte finish; low profile improved boxlock action; manual safety with barrel selector; 2³/₄″ chambers; auto ejector; competition recoil pad butt plate; light hand-engraving; stock with silver oval for initials; silver inscription inlaid on trigger guard; handsome fitted case. **Weight:** Approx. 8 lbs.

Barrel length/Choke	Prices
30″ Imp. Mod./Full (Silver)	$2053.00
30″ or 32″ Mobilchoke (Black or Silver)	2120.00
Top Single 32″ or 34″ Mobilchoke	2187.00
Combo.: 30″ or 32″ Mobilchoke (Top)	2827.00
30″ or 32″ IM/F (Top or Mono)	2773.00
30″ or 34″ Mobilchoke (Mono)	2827.00
32″ or 34″ Mobilchoke (Top)	2827.00
30″ Pigeon (Silver)	2175.00

682 COMPETITION W/MONO AND COMBO O/U BARRELS

682 COMPETITION SKEET O/U
26″ or 28″ SK/SK $2073.00
4-Barrel Set (28″) $4913.00
12, 20, 28, .410 Gauge

This skeet gun sports hand-checkered premium walnut stock, forged and hardened receiver, manual safety with trigger selector, auto ejector, stock with silver oval for initials, silver inlaid on trigger guard. Price includes fitted case.
Action: Low profile hard chrome-plated boxlock
Trigger: Single adjustable sliding trigger
Barrels: 26″ or 28″ rust blued barrels with 2³/₄″ chambers
Stock dimensions: Length of pull 14³/₈″; drop at comb 1¹/₂″; drop at heel 2¹/₃″
Sights: Fluorescent front and metal middle bead
Weight: Approx. 8 lbs.

MODEL 682 COMPETITION SKEET

BERETTA SHOTGUNS

MODELS 626/627 SIDE-BY-SIDE FIELD GRADES

These good-looking field models feature low profile solid boxlock design, hand-fitted stocks and forends of handsome European walnut with deep diamond hand-checkering, tang-mounted safety/barrel selectors, single-selective trigger, metal bead sight and knurled rib. 12 gauge barrels are chambered 2¾"; 20 gauge barrels, 3" Mag. **Model 626** has bright chrome finish, full hand-engraving. **Model 627** boasts hand-engraved side plates.

MODEL 626 ONYX SERIES

The **Model 626 Onyx** has a full-figured American walnut stock, lustrous black semi-matte finish on the barrels and receiver, and front and center sighting beads on a vent rib.

Model 626 Onyx $1533.00
12 ga., 26" and 28" Mobilchoke
12 ga., 28" (3½" chamber) Mobilchoke
20 ga., 26" and 28" Mobilchoke

Model 627EL Field $2600.00 (add **$55.00** for 3" chamber)
12 ga., 26" Imp. Cyl./Mod.
12 ga., 28" Mod./Full

Model 627EELL $4453.00 (add **$42.00** for 3" chamber)
12 ga. 28" Mod./Full (w/ or w/o Straight Stock)
12 ga. 26" Imp. Cyl./Mod. (w/ or w/o Straight Stock)

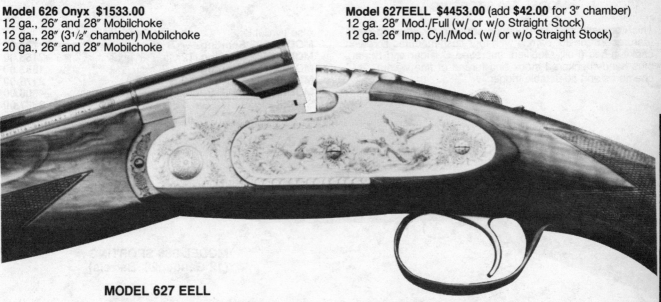

MODEL 627 EELL

MODEL 686 GOLDEN ONYX FIELD SHOTGUNS
$1167.00

SPECIFICATIONS
Gauges: 12, 20
Chamber: 3" or 3½" (add **$33.00**)
Barrel lengths: 26" and 28"
Chokes: Full, Modified and Improved Cylinder
Stock: American walnut with recoil pad
Features: Mobilchoke Screw-in Choke System; automatic ejectors; vent ribs; Golden Onyx features game birds on both sides of the receiver

BERETTA SHOTGUNS

SPORTING CLAY SHOTGUNS 12 GAUGE

MODEL 682 SPORTING

MODEL 682 SPORTING

This competition-style 12-gauge shotgun for sporting clays features 28″ or 30″ barrels with four flush-mounted screw-in choke tubes (Full, Modified, Improved Cylinder and Skeet), plus hand-checkered stock and forend of fine walnut, 2³/₄″ chambers and adjustable trigger.

Also available:
MODEL 303 Sporting . . . . $ 733.00
MODEL 682 Sporting (12 Ga., 30″ bbl.) 2153.00
MODEL 686 Sporting 1653.00
MODEL 687 Sporting (12 or 20 Ga.) 2173.00
MODEL 687 EELL Sporting 4000.00
SUPER SPORT (12 Ga., 28″ or 30″ bbl.) 2287.00

MODEL 686 SPORTING
(12 Gauge; 28″ Barrels)

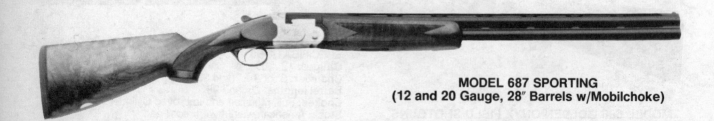

MODEL 687 SPORTING
(12 and 20 Gauge, 28″ Barrels w/Mobilchoke)

BERETTA SHOTGUNS

MODEL 686 FIELD OVER/UNDER
$1147.00 (28 Gauge)

SPECIFICATIONS
Barrels/chokes: 26″ with Imp. Cyl./Mod.; 28″ with Mod./Full. Vent. rib with metal bead sight
Action: Low profile, improved boxlock
Trigger: Selective single trigger, auto safety
Extractors: Auto ejectors
Stock: Choice walnut, hand-checkered and hand-finished with a tough gloss finish
Weight: Less than 7 lbs.

MODEL 687L FIELD GRADE O/U
12 & 20 Gauge (Mobilchoke)
$1573.00

The **687L** features Mobilchoke in 12 and 20 gauge; strong boxlock action handsomely tooled with floral hand-engraved decorative side plates, finest quality walnut stock accented with silver monogram plate, selective auto ejectors and fitted case.

SPECIFICATIONS
Barrels/chokes: 26″ and 28″ with Mobilchoke
Action: Low-profile improved boxlock
Trigger: Single selective with manual safety
Extractors: Auto ejectors
Weight: 7 lbs. 2 oz.
Also available: Model 687EELL, featuring a special premium walnut, custom-fitted stock and exquisitely engraved side-plate, game-scene motifs.
Model 687EELL with Imp. Cyl./Mod. $3767.00
Model 687EELL with Mobilchoke 3820.00
Model 687EL (12 and .410 Ga., 26″ or 28″ bbl.) . . . 2607.00
Model 687L Onyx (26″ and 28″) 1590.00
Model 687EL Onyx (26″ and 28″) 2660.00

MODEL 1200M
$527.00

This All-Weather 12 gauge semiautomatic shotgun features space-age technopolymer stock and forend. Lightweight (only 7+ pounds), it has a 28″ barrel chamber for 2³/₄″ shells and sports a unique weather-resistant matte black finish to reduce glare, resist corrosion and aid in heat dispersion.

SPECIFICATIONS
Gauge: 12
Chamber: 3″
Barrel length: 28″
Choke: Modified
Weight: 7.3 lbs.
Length of pull: 14³/₈″
Mag. Capacity: 6

Also available: **MODEL 1200 RIOT** (Law Enforcement) with 20″ barrel (2³/₄″ or 3″ shells) and Improved Cylinder choke (7-round capacity). **Price: $580.00**

BERETTA SHOTGUNS

MODEL 303 YOUTH GUN

MODEL 303 SEMIAUTOMATIC

This unique autoloader features flush-mounted, screw-in choke tubes, and a magazine cut off that allows shooters to hand-feed a lighter or heavier load into the breech without emptying the magazine. Disassembly takes one minute.

GENERAL 303 SPECIFICATIONS

Weight: 7 lbs. (12 gauge) and 6 lbs. (20 gauge)
Safety: Cross bolt
Action: Locked breech, gas operated
Sight: Vent. rib with front metal bead
Stock length: 14⁷/₈″ length of pull
Capacity: Plugged to 2 rounds

303 YOUTH
Gauge: 20 (3″ chamber)
Barrel length: 24″
Chokes: F, M, IC
Length of pull: 13¹/₂″

MODEL 303 COMPETITION TRAP (not shown)
$673.00 ($727.00 w/Mobilchoke)

The Beretta A303 Trap is the competition version of the proven A303 semiautomatic. Its gas-operated system lessens recoil; other features include wide floating vent rib with flourescent front and mid-rib bead sights, plus Monte Carlo stock fitted with American trap pad. The A303 also comes with hand-checkered stock and forend of select European walnut, plus gold-plated trigger.

SPECIFICATIONS
Gauge: 12
Barrel lengths: 30″ and 32″ (Full or Mobilchoke)

Prices:

303 Field w/Mobilchoke, 12 & 20 ga., 2³/₄″ or 3″ Magnums	$653.00
303 Slug	680.00
303 Youth	733.00
303 Skeet 12 & 20 ga., 2³/₄″, 26″ Skeet	673.00
303 Sporting 12 ga., 2³/₄″, 28″	733.00
303 Trap 12 ga., 2³/₄″, 30″ Full	673.00
303 Trap w/Monte Carlo 12 ga., 2³/₄″, 30″ and 32″ Mobilchoke	727.00
303 Upland 12 ga., 2³/₄″, 24″ Mobilchoke	680.00

303 SLUG SPECIFICATIONS
Gauges: 12, 20 (2³/₄″ and 3″ chambers)
Barrel lengths: 22″
Choke: Slug (C)
Weight: 7 lbs.

Sight: Ventilated rib with fluorescent front bead, metal middle bead
Action: Semiautomatic, locked breech, gas operated
Safety: Cross bolt
Ejector: Auto
Trigger: Gold plated
Stock: Select walnut
Weight: 8 lbs.
Butt plate: Special trap recoil pad
Chamber: 2³/₄″

BERNARDELLI SHOTGUNS

Bernardelli shotguns are the creation of the Italian firm of Vincenzo Bernardelli, known for its fine quality firearms and commitment to excellence for more than a century. Most of the long arms featured below can be built with a variety of options, customized for the discriminating sportsman. With the exceptions indicated for each gun respectively, options include choice of barrel lengths and chokes; pistol or straight English grip stock; single selective or non-selective trigger; long tang trigger guard; checkered butt; beavertail forend; hand-cut rib; automatic safety; custom stock dimensions; standard or English recoil pad; extra set of barrels; choice of luggage gun case.

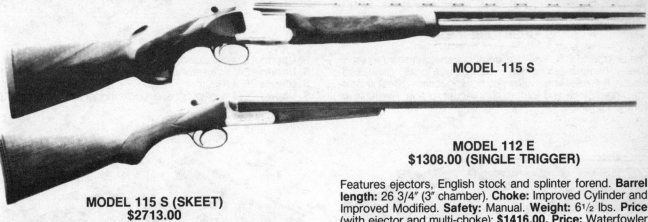

MODEL 115 S

MODEL 112 E
$1308.00 (SINGLE TRIGGER)

Features ejectors, English stock and splinter forend. **Barrel length:** 26 3/4″ (3″ chamber). **Choke:** Improved Cylinder and Improved Modified. **Safety:** Manual. **Weight:** 6½ lbs. **Price** (with ejector and multi-choke): **$1416.00**. **Price:** Waterfowler (3½″ chamber): **$1444.00**

MODEL 115 S (SKEET)
$2713.00

Features inclined plane lockings, ejectors, selective or non-selective triggers, multi-choke. **Model 115 L** has rich relief engravings (**Price: $4201.00**). **Model 115 E** has deluxe engraved side plates (**Price: $6827.00**).

BRESCIA SIDE-BY-SIDE
$1838.00

Available in 12, 16, or 20 gauge, the Brescia side-by-side features Greener or Purdey locks, small engravings, hardened marbled mounting, chrome-lined barrels, finely grained stock. Prices on request.

SLUG SIDE-BY-SIDE
$1575.00 W/EXTRACTOR
$1640.00 W/SINGLE TRIGGER

Especially designed to pattern well with slugs and buckshot, this 12 gauge side-by-side has Anson & Deeley action, Purdey-type locks, reinforced breech, richly engraved hunting scene on white-finish receiver, automatic ejectors, rear adjustable sight with overturning leafs, cheekpiece, double triggers. Deluxe model has fully engraved sideplates. Also available: **SLUG LUSSO** w/Ejectors and Side Plates. **Price: $2188.00** (**$2253.00** w/Single Trigger)

HEMINGWAY SIDE-BY-SIDE
$1663.00
W/Single Non-selective Trigger $1728.00

An elegant and light 12 gauge side-by-side suitable for upland bird hunting, the Hemingway features 23½-inch barrels without monobloc, right bore open and left one slightly Improved Cylinder, automatic ejectors, special rib with white bead front sight, hinged front trigger, woodcock hunting scenes engraved, long-type trigger guard and forend, hand-checkered walnut woods, metal shield for intials. Special steel frame and barrels. **Weight:** 6¼ lbs. Also available:
HEMINGWAY DELUXE w/Ejectors & Side
Plates (**$1990.00** w/Single Trigger) **$1925.00**

BERNARDELLI SHOTGUNS

S. UBERTO SERIES

The S. Uberto F.S. side-by-side offers shotgunners Anson & Deeley hammerless action, Purdey-style locks, reinforced breech, fine relief engravings with hunting scenes, finest walnut checkered stock and forend, right trigger folding. Available in 12 and 20 gauge.

S. UBERTO F.S. WITH EJECTORS
$1357.00

S. Uberto 1E w/ejectors **$1357.00**
S. Uberto 1EM w/ejectors and single trigger 1421.00
S. Uberto 2E w/ejectors 1427.00
S. Uberto 2EM w/ejectors and single trigger 1491.00

HOLLAND LUSSO
$11,202.00

HOLLAND-HOLLAND TYPE SIDELOCK

These 12 gauge Holland & Holland style sidelock side-by-sides feature sidelocks with double safety levers, reinforced breech, three round Purdey locks, automatic ejectors, right trigger folding, striker retaining plates, best-quality walnut stock and

HOLLAND V.B. LISCIO
$8052.00

finely chiselled high-grade engravings. The eight shotguns in this series differ only in the amount and intricacy of engravings. Prices range from $8052.00 to $44,635.00 (gold engravings).

MODEL 192 OVER/UNDER
$1320.00 (12 Gauge)

High-quality hunting over/under shotgun with special steel integral frame, strong cross hinge pin and locks on the lumps, automatic ejectors, ventilated rib, special steel barrels with chrome-plated bores, richly engraved frame, hand-checkered selected walnut stock and forend. Available with double trigger or single selective trigger. **Gauge:** 12; 2¾" or 3" chambers. **Weight:** 6¾ pounds. Prices on request.
Also available: **MODEL 192 WATERFOWLER.** Single selective trigger, multi-choke (3), 3½" Magnum. **Price: $1444.00**

ROMA 6E

ROMA 6E (WITH EJECTORS)
$2008.00

Available in 12, 16, 20 and 28 gauge, the Roma Series is Bernardelli's premier boxlock and a most popular model. These side-by-side shotguns feature Anson & Deeley action with Purdey-style locks, sideplated and coin-finished receivers with elaborate scroll engravings covering 100% of the action, precision-bored barrels made of superior chromium steel, double triggers with front hinged trigger, hand-selected European walnut stocks and forends with fine, hand-cut checkering. Prices range from $1479.00 to $2008.00

BROWNING AUTOMATIC SHOTGUNS

AUTO-5

The Browning Auto-5 Shotgun is offered in an unusually wide variety of models and specifications. The Browning 12-gauge 3-inch Magnum accepts up to and including the 3-inch, 1⅞ ounce, 12-gauge Magnum load, which contains only ⅛ ounce of shot less than the maximum 3½-inch 10-gauge load. The 2¾-inch Magnums and 2¾-inch high velocity shells may be used with equal pattern efficiency. Standard features include a special shock absorber and a hunting-style recoil pad. The Auto-5 is also available with the Invector screw-in choke system.

Browning also offers the 20 gauge in a 3-inch Magnum model. This powerful, light heavyweight offers maximum versatility to 20-gauge advocates. It handles the 20-gauge, 2¾-inch high velocity and Magnums, but it literally thrives on the 3-inch, 1¼-ounce load which delivers real 12-gauge performance in a 20-gauge package.

"SWEET SIXTEEN" AUTO-5

The 12-gauge Auto-5, chambered for regular 2¾-inch shells, handles all 12-gauge, 2¾-inch shells, from the very lightest 1 ounce field load to the heavy 1½-ounce Magnums. The Browning 20-gauge Auto-5 is lightweight and a top performer for the upland hunter. Yet, with 2¾-inch high velocity or 2¾-inch Magnums, it does a fine job in the duck blind. 24-inch barrels are available as an accessory.

Hunting Models	Prices
Light 12, Sweet 16 and Light 20 gauge, Invector	$712.95
Light 12 Buck Special	724.95
3" Magnum 12 and Magnum 20 gauge, Invector	742.95
3" Magnum 12 ga., Buck Special	747.95

BT-99 SINGLE SHOT TRAP SPECIAL

SPECIFICATIONS
Receiver: Machined steel, tastefully hand-engraved and richly blued
Barrel: Choice of 32" or 34" lengths; choke choice of Full or Invector; chambered for 12 gauge, 2¾" shells only; choke tubes supplied (Full, Imp. Mod. and Mod.)
Trigger: Gold-plated, crisp, positive, pull approximately 3½ lbs.
Stock and forearm: Select French walnut, hand-rubbed finish, sharp 20-line hand-checkering; Monte Carlo or conventional stock available; full pistol grip; length of pull 14⅜"; drop at comb 1⅜"; drop at heel 2"; full beavertail forearm

Safety: No manual safety, a feature preferred by trap shooters
Sights: Ivory front and center sight beads
Rib: High post, ventilated, full floating, matted, 11/32" wide
Recoil pad: Deluxe, contoured trap style
Weight: 8 lbs. with 32" barrel; 8 lbs. 3 oz. with 34" barrel
Automatic ejection: Fired shell ejected automatically on opening action, unfired shell elevated from chamber for convenient removal

Grade I Competition, Invector (32" or 34" bbl.)	$1005.00
Grade I Competition, Non-Invector	981.00

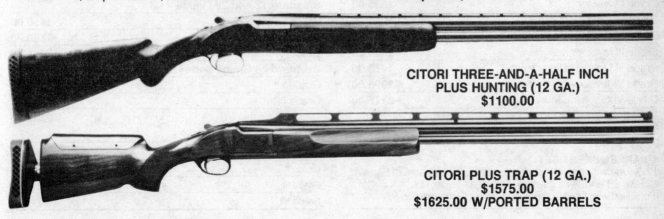

CITORI THREE-AND-A-HALF INCH PLUS HUNTING (12 GA.)
$1100.00

CITORI PLUS TRAP (12 GA.)
$1575.00
$1625.00 W/PORTED BARRELS

BROWNING SHOTGUNS

CITORI STANDARD

FIELD GRADE

Gauge: 12, 20, 28 and .410 gauge
Barrels: 24", 26", 28", or 30" in 12 gauge; 28" in 16 gauge; 24", 26", or 28" in 20 gauge; ventilated rib with matted sighting plane; medium raised German nickel-silver sight bead; 26" or 28" in 28 gauge; 26" or 28" in .410 gauge
Overall length: All gauges 41" with 24" barrels; 43" with 26" barrels; 45" with 28" barrels; 47" with 30" barrels
Chokes: Mod.-Full, Invector in 30" barrels; choice of Invector, Mod.-Full or Imp. Cyl.-Mod. in 28" and 26" barrels
Trigger: Single selective; gold-plated, fast and crisp
Chamber: All 20-gauge Field models and all 12-gauge Field models accept all 3" Magnum loads as well as 2³/₄" loads; 16 and 28-gauge accepts 2³/₄" loads; .410-gauge accepts 2¹/₂", 3", or 3" Mag. loads
Safety: Manual thumb safety; combined with barrel selector mechanism

Automatic ejectors: Fired shells thrown out of gun; unfired shells are elevated for easy removal
Approximate Weight:

	12 gauge	16 gauge	20 gauge
24" barrels	6 lbs. 9 oz.		5 lbs. 12 oz.
26" barrels	7 lbs. 9 oz.		6 lbs. 11 oz.
28" barrels	7 lbs. 11 oz.	7 lbs.	6 lbs. 13 oz.
30" barrels	7 lbs. 13 oz		

Stock and forearm: Dense walnut; skillfully checkered; full pistol grip; hunting Beavertail forearm; field-type recoil pad installed on 12 gauge models.

	12 gauge	20 gauge
Length of pull	14¹/₄"	14¹/₄"
Drop at comb	1⁵/₈"	1¹/₂"
Drop at heel	2¹/₂"	2³/₈"

CITORI HUNTING, LIGHTNING, SUPERLIGHT & UPLAND SPECIAL MODELS*

HUNTING & LIGHTNING 28 GA., .410 BORE	PRICES
Grade I Hunting	$1025.00
Grade I Lightning	1035.00
Grade III Lightning	1620.00
Grade VI Lightning	2265.00
SUPERLIGHT 12 & 20 GA. (UPLAND SPECIAL)	
Grade I Invector	1055.00
Grade III Invector	1480.00
Grade VI Invector	2140.00
HUNTING & LIGHTNING 12 & 20 GA.	
Grade I Invector	1035.00
Grade I Lightning Invector	1045.00
Gran Lightning Invector 12 & 20 ga.	1380.00
Grade III Invector	1455.00
Grade III Lightning Invector	1475.00
Grade VI Invector	2095.00
Grade VI Lightning Invector	2125.00

*NOTE: All Invector model Citori's are available in the High Grades, except Upland Special (Grade I only)

SUPERLIGHT 28 GAUGE & .410 BORE	
Grade I	$1025.00
Grade III	1600.00
Grade VI	2235.00
TRAP MODELS (High Post Target Rib)	
Standard 12 Gauge	
Grade I Invector	$1160.00
Grade III Invector	1600.00
Grade VI Invector	2235.00
SKEET MODELS (High Post Target Rib)	
Standard 12 and 20 Gauge	
Grade I Invector	1150.00
Grade III Invector	1600.00
Grade VI Invector	2235.00
Standard 28 Gauge and .410 Bore	
Grade I	1155.00
Grade III	1600.00
Grade VI	2235.00

4-BARREL SKEET SET

12 Gauge with one removable forearm and four sets of barrels, 12, 20, 28 and .410 gauges, high post target rib.
(Furnished with fitted luggage case for gun and extra barrels)

Grade 1	$3710.00
Grade III	4230.00
Grade VI	4740.00

BROWNING SHOTGUNS

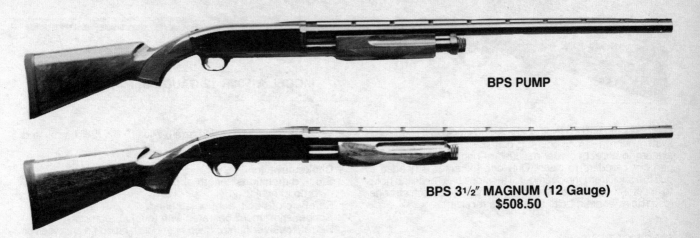

BPS PUMP

BPS 3½" MAGNUM (12 Gauge)
$508.50

BPS PUMP SHOTGUN

Gauge: 10, 12 and 20
Barrels: Choice of 22", 26", 28", 30" or 32" lengths with high-post ventilated rib; Hunting model has German nickel sight bead
Action: Pump action with double-action bars; bottom loading and ejection; serrated slide release located at rear of trigger guard
Choke: Invector only
Trigger: Crisp and positive; let-off at 4½ lbs.
Chamber: 3" chamber in Hunting models accepts all 2¾", 2¾" Magnum and 3" Magnum shells; target models 2¾" shells only
Safety: Convenient knurled-thumb, top-receiver safety; slide forward to shoot
Approximate weight: 7 lbs. 12 oz. with 28" barrel

Overall length: 42¾" with 22" barrel; 46¾" with 26" barrel; 48¾" with 28" barrel; 50¾" with 30" barrel
Stock and forearm: Select walnut, weather-resistant finish, sharp 18-line checkering; full pistol grip; semi-beavertail forearm with finger grooves; length of pull 14¼"; drop at comb 1½"; drop at heel 2½"
Prices:

Invector Hunting, 12 and 20 ga., V.R.	$433.50
Invector Hunting, 10 ga.	534.95
Invector PLUS Hunting & Stalker	534.95
Upland Special, 22" barrel with Invector, 12 and 20 ga., V.R.	433.50
Invector Stalker, 12 ga. only	433.50
Buck Special, 12 ga. only	439.50
Buck Special, 10 ga. & 3½" 12 ga.	538.95

BPS YOUTH & LADIES MODEL

SPECIFICATIONS
Chamber: 20 gauge only
Barrels: 22" invector w/ventilated rib; interchangeable within gauge
Overall length: 41¾"
Weight (approx.): 6 lbs. 11 oz.
Stock and forearm: Straight grip stock of select walnut in durable gloss finish

Length of pull: 13¼"
Drop at comb: 1½"
Drop at heel: 2½"

BPS Youth & Ladies Model $433.50

BROWNING SHOTGUNS

MODEL A-500R 12 GAUGE SEMIAUTOMATIC

Designed and built in Belgium, the A-500 employs a short recoil system with a strong four-lug bolt design. There is no gas system to collect powder residues or grime, and no pistons, ports or cylinders to clean. Only one extractor is needed to pull the shell from the chamber. The stock has no drilled holes to accommodate action springs, making it that much stronger (especially where it bolts against the receiver).

Weight: 7 lbs. 3 oz. (26″ barrel); 7 lbs. 5 oz. (28″ barrel) and 7 lbs. 7 oz. (30″ barrel)
Chamber: 3″
Choke: Invector
Stock dimensions: length of pull 14¼″; drop at comb 1½″; drop at heel 2½″
Safety: cross bolt, right or left hand
Action: short recoil operated with four lug rotary bolt
Barrel/receiver finish: deep high polish blued finish; receiver lightly engraved with scroll pattern

SPECIFICATIONS
Barrel lengths: 26″, 28″ and 30″
Overall lengths: 45½″, 47½″ and 49½″

MODEL A-500 . . . . **$559.95**
Extra barrels **199.95**

MODEL A-500G GAS OPERATED SHOTGUN
$639.95

Browning's patented gas metering system allows reliable shooting with all loads and utilizes the proper amount of gas energy needed to operate the action. A unique gas regulation valve uses only enough gas to operate the action consistently.

SPECIFICATIONS

Gauge	Model	Chamber	Barrel Length	Overall Length	Average Weight	Chokes Available[1]
12	Hunting	3″	30″	51½″	8 lbs. 2 oz.	Invector
12	Hunting	3″	28″	49½″	8 lbs.	Invector
12	Hunting	3″	26″	47½″	7 lbs. 14 oz.	Invector
12	Buck Special	3″	24″	45½″	7 lbs. 12 oz.	Slug/buckshot

[1]All models are fitted with standard invector Choke Tube System: Full Choke installed; Modified, Improved Cylinder and wrench included. Improved Modified, Skeet and Cylinder choke tubes are available as accessories.

Additional features:
Safety: Cross bolt, right or left hand
Capacity: 4 rounds (2¾″) or 3 rounds (3″) with plug removed (with plug installed, 2 round in magazine, one in chamber)
Recoil pad: Ventilated style, standard
Stock and forearm: Select walnut, full pistol grip stock with gloss finish and cut checkering
Barrel and receiver finish: Deep, high polish blued finish; gold accents on receiver
Trigger: gold colored
Stock dimensions: Length of pull 14⅜″; drop at comb 1½″; drop at heel 2″
Action: Gas operated with 4-lug rotary bolt

BROWNING SHOTGUNS

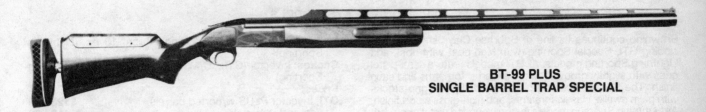

BT-99 PLUS
SINGLE BARREL TRAP SPECIAL

SPECIFICATIONS
Gauge: 12 (2¾" shells only)
Barrel length: 34" (.745 over bore; barrel porting optional)
Weight: 8 lbs. 12 oz.
Choke: Invector Plus system (Invector Plus Full, Imp. Mod., and Modified tubes and wrench included)
Rib: High post, ventilated, tapered, target rib; matted sight plane

Stock & Forearm: Select walnut with high-gloss finish and cut checkering; Monte Carlo stock; modified beavertail forearm; stock fully adjustable for length of pull (14-14½"), drop at comb (2½-2") and drop at Monte Carlo (2⅜-1⅛")
Prices:
MODEL BT-99 PLUS $1570.00
   Without ported barrels 1520.00

MODEL 12 PUMP SHOTGUN

After more than 75 years, the ageless Winchester Model 12, one of the most popular shotguns ever produced (over 2 million), is offered as part of Browning's Limited Edition Model 12 Program. The first Model 12 is available in 20 gauge, with 28 gauge and .410 bore (Model 42) to follow. A total of 12,500 20 gauge Model 12's will be produced, including 8,500 Grade I models and 4,000 Grade V's.

SPECIFICATIONS
Gauge: 20
Barrel length: 26"
Overall length: 45"
Chamber: 2¾"
Choke: Modified
Weight: 7 lbs. 1 oz.
Length of pull: 14"

Drop at heel: 2½"
Drop at comb: 1½"
Trigger: Approx. 4½ lbs. trigger pull
Capacity: 5 loads in magazine (w/plug removed), one in chamber; 2 loads in magazine (w/plug installed), one in chamber
Receiver: Grade I: deeply blued. Grade V: engraved with gold game scenes
Stock and forearm: Grade I: select walnut w/semi-gloss finish and cut checkering. Grade V: select high grade walnut with high gloss finish (both grades include steel grip cap)
Prices:
GRADE I 20 ga. . . . . $ 734.95
GRADE I 28 ga. 771.95
GRADE V 20 ga. 1187.00
GRADE V 28 ga. 1246.00

SHOTGUNS

BROWNING SHOTGUNS

SPORTING CLAYS MODELS

Browning continues its line of Sporting Clays shotguns, including GTI, Special Sporting (with high post vent ribs), and Lightning Sporting models. All GTI models feature semi-pistol grips with slightly grooved semi-beavertail forearms and satin finish. The Special Sporting guns have full pistol grip stocks with palm swells, classic forearms, and high-gloss wood finish. All Lightning Sporting models feature rounded pistol grips with classic forearms and high-gloss wood finish.

Gauge: 12
Barrel lengths: 28″ & 30″ (GTI); 28″, 30″ & 32″ (Special Sporting); 30″ (Lightning)
Overall lengths: 45″ & 47″ (GTI); 45″, 47″ & 49″ (Special Sporting); 47″ (Lightning Sporting)
Weight: 8 lbs. & 8 lbs. 2 oz. (GTI); 8 lbs. 1 oz., 8 lbs. 3 oz. & 8 lbs. 5 oz. (Special Sporting); 8 lbs. 10 oz. (Lightning Sporting)
Chokes: Invector (GTI); IC/M (Special Sporting and Lightning Sporting)
Prices:
GTI, Invector PLUS w/ported barrels **$1230.00**
  w/o ported barrels **1180.00**
GRADE I SPECIAL SPORTING, Invector PLUS,
  ported barrels **1240.00**
  w/o ported barrels **1190.00**
GRADE I LIGHTNING SPORTING, Invector PLUS,
  high rib, ported barrels **1240.00**
  w/o ported barrels **1190.00**
  Same as above w/low rib & ported barrel **1190.00**
  Same as above w/o ported barrels **1140.00**

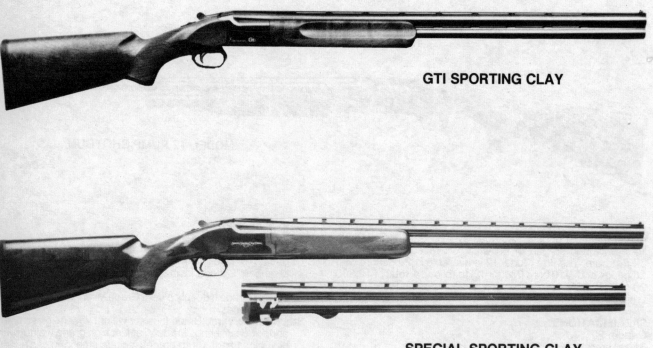

GTI SPORTING CLAY

SPECIAL SPORTING CLAY

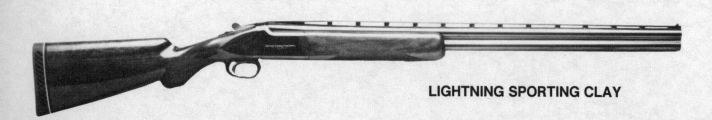

LIGHTNING SPORTING CLAY

CHAPUIS SHOTGUNS

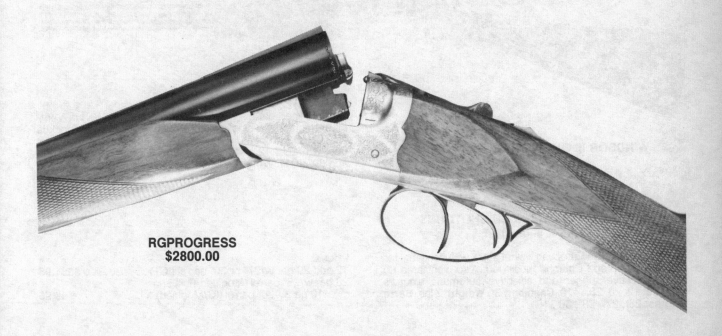

RGPROGRESS
$2800.00

CHAPUIS SIDE-BY-SIDE & OVER/UNDER SHOTGUNS

Manufactured in France by Chapuis Armes, these side-by-side and over/under double shotguns are distributed in the U.S. by Armes de Chasse (see Directory of Manufacturers & Distributors for details). All Chapuis shotguns feature notched action zone, long trigger guard, coin metal finish, automatic ejectors or extractors, barrels with double hook, Blitz system center side lock, and choice of raised or solid rib, ventilated rib, or ultra light rib; plus deluxe French walnut, hand-cut checkering, and oil finish.

SPECIFICATIONS
Gauges: 12, 16 and 20
Barrel lengths: 22″, 23.6″, 26.8″, 27.6″ & 31.5″
Weight: 5 to 10 lbs. (depending on gauge)
Stock: French walnut with pistol and English grips
Price: **$3000.00** (Side-by-Side)
　　　　$3500.00 (Over/Under)

WINDSOR III OVER/UNDER SHOTGUNS
$624.95

Chrome-lined barrels handle both lead and steel shot. Vent-rib extractors and single select trigger are standard. Stock is checkered European walnut with schnabel forend and pistol grip. **Gauges:** 12 and 20. **Chamber:** 3″. **Barrel lengths:** 27″ and 30″ (ICT). **Weight:** 7 lbs. 3 oz.

WINDSOR IV OVER/UNDER SHOTGUNS
(not shown)

Features checkered European walnut stock with schnabel forend, pistol grip and Churchill recoil pad. Also, ventilated rib, single selective trigger and selective automatic ejectors. **Gauges:** 12, 20, 28, .410. **Chamber:** 3″. **Weight:** 7 lbs. **Barrel lengths:** 26″, 27″, 28″, 30″.

Prices:

12 and 20 ga. w/27″ or 30″ barrel (ICT) **$851.95**
28 ga. w/28″ barrel (Modified/Full) and
   .410 ga. w/26″ barrel (IC/Modified) **799.95**

COMPETITION SHOTGUNS
$962.95
$999.95 (w/Imp./Full Trap)

Available in trap or skeet, both guns feature select European walnut stocks with oil finish, 28-line checkering and sculpted schnabel forend. Receiver is engraved. Other features include selective automatic ejectors, single selective triggers, top tang safety, wide vent ribs. **Gauges:** 12 and 20. **Chamber:** 2³/₄″. **Barrel lengths:** 26″ and 30″. **Weight:** 8 lbs. **Chokes:** Skeet/Skeet (26″ barrel w/o recoil pad) and IM/Full (30″ barrel, 12 ga.).

REGENT V OVER/UNDER SHOTGUNS (not shown)
$1099.95

Extra select European walnut stock has an oil-rubbed finish with 22-line checkering on forend and pistol grip. Features an 11mm-wide vent rib, single selective trigger, selective automatic ejectors, automatic top tang safety, interchangeable choke tubes. Barrels are chrome-lined. **Gauges:** 12 and 20. **Barrel length:** 27″. **Chamber:** 3″. **Weight:** 7 lbs. 5. oz. **Choke:** ICT.

MONARCH OVER/UNDER SHOTGUNS (not shown)

Silver receiver features scroll engraving. Stock is checkered, European walnut with hard matte finish. Other features: Gold selective trigger, extractors and vent rib. **Gauges:** 12, 20, 28, .410. **Chamber:** 3″. **Barrel lengths:** 24″, 25″, 26″, 28″. **Weight:** 7 lbs.

Prices:

12 and 20 ga. w/26″ and 28″ barrels
   (IC-Modified & Modified/Full) **$528.95**
.410 ga. w/26″ barrel (Modified/Full) **596.95**
28 ga. w/25″ barrel (IC/Modified or
   w/28″ barrel (Modified/Full) **495.95**
12 ga. Turkey w/24″ barrel **569.95**

CHURCHILL SHOTGUNS

ROYAL SIDE X SIDE SHOTGUNS

Chromed barrel with concave rib, double-hinged triggers, extractors, casehardened receiver and English-style walnut stock (checkered with splinter forend) are all included in this hunting gun. **Gauges:** 12, 20, 28, .410. **Barrel lengths:** 25″, 26″, 28″. **Chamber** 3″. **Weight:** 6 lbs. 4 oz.

Prices:
12 and 20 ga. w/26″ or 28″ barrels,
  Modified/Full or IC/Modified $539.95
28. ga. w/25″ barrel, Modified/Full 570.95
.410 ga. w/26″ barrel, Full/Full 613.95

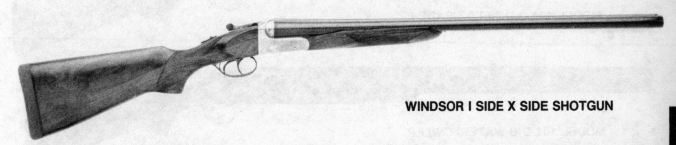

WINDSOR I SIDE X SIDE SHOTGUN

This handsome side-by-side offers hand-checkered European walnut stock with Churchill recoil pad and scroll-engraved antique silver receiver. Also double triggers, automatic top tang, safety and extractors. **Gauges:** 10, 12, 16, 20, 28, .410. **Barrel lengths:** 25″, 26″, 28″, 32″. **Chamber:** 3″ (16 ga. has 2¼″). **Weight:** 8 lbs.

Prices:
12, 16 and 20 ga. w/26″ and 28″ barrels,
  Modified/Full or IC/Modified . . . . , ... $652.95
28 ga. w/25″ barrel (Skeet/Skeet) and
  410 ga. w/26″ barrel (Mod./Full) 707.95

AUTOMATIC SHOTGUNS
$549.95 (Standard)
$569.95 (Turkey)

Gauge: 12. **Barrel lengths:** 24″ (Standard & Turkey); 26″ and 28″ (Standard only)
Stock: Hand checkered walnut w/satin finish. **Features:** Magazine cut-off (shoots all loads interchangeably w/o alterations); non-glare finish; vent rib w/mid-bead and gold trigger; ICT choke system.

CLASSIC DOUBLES

MODEL 101 OVER/UNDER

Formerly distributed by Olin/Winchester, Model 101 has been acquired by Classic Doubles International. These guns will continue to be produced in Japan by OK Firearms. All models feature chrome molybdenum steel barrels with chrome-lined chambers and bores suitable for steel shot, plus forged steel frames and trigger guards, single selective triggers, and top-grade semi-fancy American walnut.

Included in the new Classic Doubles line is Olin/Winchester's former Model 23 side-by-side, which is now Model 201. Prices and specifications for all models are listed below.

Prices:
MODEL 101 FIELD GRADE I **$2335.00**
  Waterfowler 1865.00

MODEL 101 FIELD GRADE II	**2685.00**
Field Set	4190.00
MODEL 101 SPORTERS	2425.00
Combo (28″ and 30″ Barrels)	3610.00
MODEL 101 TRAP SINGLE BARREL	2535.00
Over/Under	2335.00
Combo (Over/Under Single)	3460.00
MODEL 101 SKEET	2335.00
Four-Barrel Set (12, 20, 28, .410)	5840.00
MODEL 201 SIDE/SIDE GRADE I (12 Ga.)	2335.00
20 Ga. Skeet/Skeet Choke	2830.00
Set (28 & .410 Ga.)	4500.00

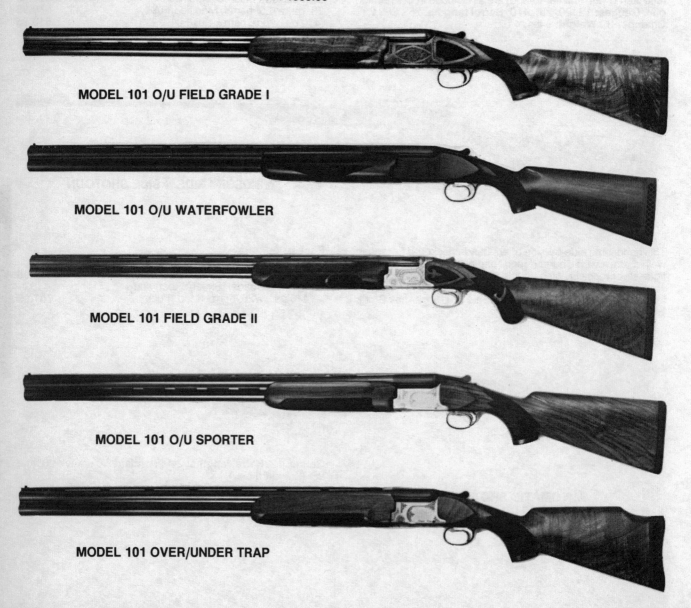

MODEL 101 O/U FIELD GRADE I

MODEL 101 O/U WATERFOWLER

MODEL 101 FIELD GRADE II

MODEL 101 O/U SPORTER

MODEL 101 OVER/UNDER TRAP

CLASSIC DOUBLES

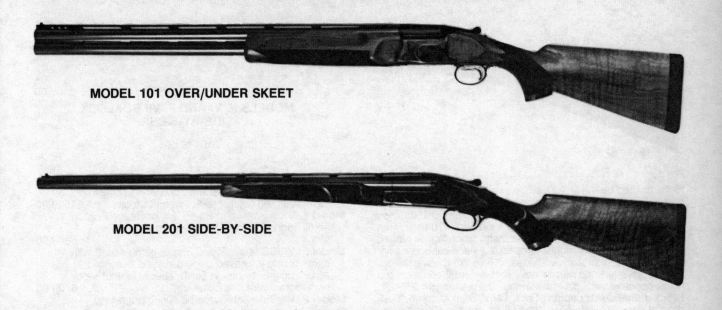

MODEL 101 OVER/UNDER SKEET

MODEL 201 SIDE-BY-SIDE

Model	Symbol	Gauge	BBL Lgth.	O/A Lgth.	Lgth. of Pull	Drop at Comb	Drop at Heal	Nominal Weight	Choke	Stock
M101 Field-	B1012W	12	28"	44$^7/_8$"	14½"	1½"	2¼"	7	In Choke 6	Standard
Grade I	B1012EW	12	25½"	42¼"	14½"	1½"	2½"	6¾	In Choke 6	Straight English
	B1015W	20	28"	44$^7/_8$"	14½"	1½"	2¼"	6½	In Choke 4	Standard
	B1015EW	20	25½"	42¼"	14½"	1½"	2½"	6¼	In Choke 4	Straight English
M101 Field-	A1012W	12	28"	44$^7/_8$"	14½"	1½"	2¼"	7	In Choke 6	Standard
Grade II	A1015W	20	28"	44$^7/_8$"	14½"	1½"	2¼"	6½	In Choke 4	Standard
	A1017W	28	28"	44$^7/_8$"	14½"	1½"	2¼"	6½	In Choke 4	Standard
	A1019	410	28"	44$^7/_8$"	14½"	1½"	2¼"	6¼	M/F	Standard
SET	A10128W2	12/20	28"/26"	44$^7/_8$"/42$^7/_8$"	14½"	1½"	2¼"	7/6½	In Choke 6/4	Standard
M101 Waterfowler	101CWF	12	30"	46$^7/_8$"	14½"	1½"	2¼"	7½	In Choke 4	Standard
M101 Sporter	101SP28W	12	28"	44$^7/_8$"	14½"	1½"	2$^1/_8$"	7	In Choke 6	Standard
New Model	101SP20W	12	30"	46$^7/_8$"	14½"	1½"	2$^1/_8$"	7¼	In Choke 6	Standard
COMBO	101SP28W2	12	28"/30"	44$^7/_8$"/46$^7/_8$"	14½"	1½"	2$^1/_8$"	7/7¼	In Choke 6	Standard
M101 Trap Single	101T014M	12	34"	51¼"	14½"	1$^7/_{16}$"	2$^3/_{16}$"	8½	In Choke 4	Monte Carlo
Single	101T014S	12	34"	51¼"	14½"	1$^7/_{16}$"	1$^7/_{16}$"	8½	In Choke 4	Standard
Single	101T0112M	12	32"	49¼"	14½"	1$^7/_{16}$"	2$^3/_{16}$"	8½	In Choke 4	Monte Carlo
Single	101T012S	12	32"	49¼"	14½"	1$^7/_{16}$"	1$^7/_{16}$"	8½	In Choke 4	Standard
O/U	101T20M	12	30"	47¼"	14½"	1$^3/_8$"	2$^1/_8$"	8¾	In Choke 4	Monte Carlo
O/U	101T20S	12	30"	47¼"	14½"	1$^3/_8$"	1$^3/_8$"	8¾	In Choke 4	Standard
O/U	101T22M	12	32"	49¼"	14½"	1$^3/_8$"	2$^1/_8$"	9	In Choke 4	Monte Carlo
O/U	101T22S	12	32"	49¼"	14½"	1$^3/_8$"	1$^3/_8$"	9	In Choke 4	Standard
COMBO; O/U-Single	101T30M	12	30"-34"	47¼"-51¼"	14½"	1$^3/_8$"	2$^1/_8$"	9-8¾	In Choke 4	Monte Carlo
O/U-Single	101T30S	12	30"-34"	47¼"-51¼"	14½"	1$^3/_8$"	1$^3/_8$"	9-8¾	In Choke 4	Standard
O/U-Single	101T302M	12	30"-32"	47¼"-49¼"	14½"	1$^3/_8$"	2$^1/_8$"	9-8¾	In Choke 4	Monte Carlo
O/U-Single	101T302S	12	30"-32"	47¼"-49¼"	14½"	1$^3/_8$"	1$^3/_8$"	9-8¾	In Choke 4	Standard
O/U-Single	101T32M	12	32"-34"	49¼"-51¼"	14½"	1$^3/_8$"	2$^1/_8$"	9-8¾	In Choke 4	Monte Carlo
O/U-Single	101T32S	12	32"-34"	49¼"-51¼"	14½"	1$^3/_8$"	1$^3/_8$"	9-8¾	In Choke 4	Standard
M101 Skeet	101527W	12	27½"	44$^5/_8$"	14¼"	1$^3/_8$"	2$^1/_8$"	7¼	In Choke 4	Standard
	101557	20	27½"	44$^5/_8$"	14¼"	1$^3/_8$"	2$^1/_8$"	6½	SK/SK	Standard
	10154	12,20,28,410	27½"	44$^5/_8$"	14¼"	1½"	2$^1/_8$"	7½	SK/SK	Standard
M201 Side-by-Side	201C2	12	26"	43¼"	14½"	1½"	2¼"	7	IC/M	Standard
	201C2W	12	26"	43¼"	14½"	1½"	2¼"	7	In Choke 6	Standard
New Model	201C5	20	26"	43¼"	14½"	1½"	2¼"	7	IC/M	Standard
	201C5E	20	26"	43¼"	14½"	1½"	2¼"	7	IC/M	Straight English
SET	201C79	28/410	28"	45¼"	14½"	1½"	2¼"	6½/5$^7/_8$	IC/M, M/F	Standard

FERLIB SHOTGUNS

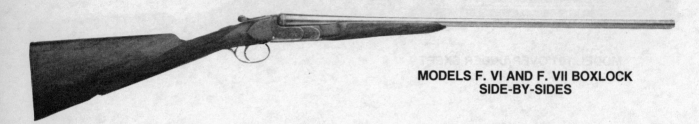

MODELS F. VI AND F. VII BOXLOCK SIDE-BY-SIDES

Hand-crafted by the small European artisan firm of the same name, Ferlib shotguns are high-quality, hand-fitted side-by-sides. With Anson & Deeley boxlock design, all Ferlib doubles are available in 12, 16, 20 and 28 gauge and .410 bore, with automatic ejectors, double triggers with front trigger hinged (non-selective single trigger is optional), hand-rubbed oil-finished straight grip stock with classic forearm (beavertail optional). Dovetail lump barrels have soft-luster blued finish; top rib is concave with file-cut matting. **Barrel length:** 25″-28″. **Stock dimensions:** Length of pull, 14 1/2″; drop at comb, 1 1/2″; drop at heel, 2 1/4. **Weight:** 12 ga., 6 lbs. 8 oz.—6 lbs. 14 oz.; 16 ga., 6 lbs. 4 oz.—6 lbs. 10 oz.; 20 ga., 5 lbs. 14 oz.—6 lbs. 4 oz.; 28 ga. and .410, 5 lbs. 6 oz.—5 lbs. 11 oz.

Model F. VI w/scalloped frame, border-line engraving, casehardened colors, select walnut stock **$4500.00**
Model F. VII w/scalloped frame, full-coverage English scroll engraving, coin finish, select walnut stock **5300.00**
Model F. VII/SC w/scalloped frame, game scene with either bulino engraved or gold inlayed birds and scroll accents with coin finish, special walnut stock with extra figure and color **6700.00**
Model F. VII/Sideplate w/game scene engraving, gold inlayed birds and coin finish, special walnut stock, extra figure and color **9400.00**

FRANCHI AUTOLOADING SHOTGUNS

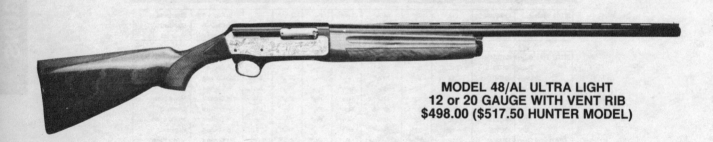

MODEL 48/AL ULTRA LIGHT
12 or 20 GAUGE WITH VENT RIB
$498.00 ($517.50 HUNTER MODEL)

Model 48/AL Ultra Lights feature specially selected European stock, forend; screw-in chokes; fully engraved light weight receiver covered by a lifetime guarantee; the automatic safety, which securely locks the hammer, is silent and positive; hand safety can be reversed for left-handed shooters; chrome-lined barrel for light weight and maximum strength; checkered pistol grip; reliable recoil action requiring no maintenance and no cleaning. Chambered for 2 3/4 shells.

SPECIFICATIONS
Gauge: 12 or 20
Barrel lengths (and chokes): 26″ or 28″ w/choke tubes
Mechanism: Recoil
Chamber: 2 3/4″
Overall length: 47 7/8″ (w/28″ barrel)
Weight: 6 lbs. 4 oz. (12 ga); 5 lbs. 2 oz. (20 ga)
Capacity: 5 shots
Safety: Lateral push button safety
Stock: Stock and forearm have machine cut diamond checkering (Magnum models equipped with recoil pads)

FRANCOTTE SHOTGUNS

SIDELOCK SHOTGUN SIDE BY SIDE
$22,629.00–$24,891.00

BASIC SPECIFICATIONS
Gauges: 12, 16, 20 (28 ga. & .410 ga. also available)
Barrel length: 26″ to 29″
Chambers: 2¹/₂″, 2³/₄″ or 3″
Action: H&H true sidelock mechanism
Forend length: 8¹/₂″ (splinter- or beavertail-shaped)
Stock: Deluxe walnut (straight or pistol grip)

Features: Bead front sight; double trigger, front-hinged; free or automatic safety; modeled tang; marked fences; independent firing pins; Purdey lock; checkered forend; H&H ejectors; English scroll engraving; checkered butt plate and grip; choice of rib (plunging or straight)
Also available: BOXLOCK SHOTGUN SIDE BY SIDE. Same specifications as Sidelock Model. **Price: $12,960.00–$13,989.00**

ENGRAVING ON 12 GAUGE SIDELOCK MODEL
(locks are detachable)

GARBI SIDELOCK SHOTGUNS

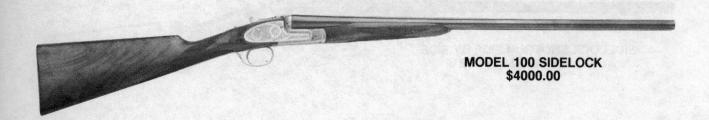

MODEL 100 SIDELOCK
$4000.00

Like this Model 100 shotgun, all Spanish-made Garbi models featured here are Holland & Holland pattern sidelock ejector guns with chopper lump (demibloc) barrels. They are built to English gun standards with regard to design, weight, balance and proportions, and all have the characteristic "feel" asso- ciated with the best London guns. All of the models offer fine 24-line hand-checkering, with outstanding quality wood-to-metal and metal-to-metal fit. The Model 100 is available in 12, 16, 20 and 28 gauge and sports Purdey-style fine scroll and rosette engraving, partly done by machine.

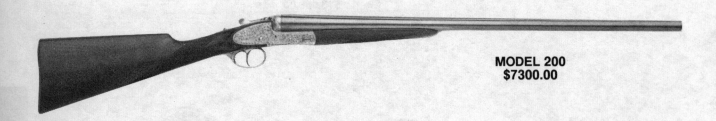

MODEL 200
$7300.00

MODELS 101, 103A and 120 (not shown)

Available in 12, 16, 20, and 28 gauge, the sidelocks are hand-crafted with hand-engraved receiver and select walnut straight grip stock.

SPECIFICATIONS
Barrels: 25″ to 30″ in 12 ga.; 25″ to 28″ in 16, 20 and 28 ga.; high-luster blued finish; smooth concave rib (optional Chur-chill or level, file-cut rib)
Action: Holland & Holland pattern sidelock; automatic ejectors; double triggers with front trigger hinged; case-hardened
Stock/forend: Straight grip stock with checkered butt (optional pistol grip); hand-rubbed oil finish; classic (splinter) forend (optional beavertail)

Weight: 12 ga. game, 6 lbs. 8 oz. to 6 lbs. 12 oz.; 12 ga. pigeon or wildfowl, 7 lbs.—7lbs. 8 oz.; 16 ga., 6 lbs. 4 oz. to 6 lbs. 10 oz.; 20 ga., 5 lbs. 15 oz.—6 lbs. 4 oz.; 28 ga., 5 lbs. 6 oz.—5 lbs. 10 oz.
Prices:
Model 101 . . . . **$4100.00**
Model 103A 5500.00
Model 120 . . . . 7000.00
Also available:
MODEL 200 in 12, 16, 20 or 28 gauge; features Holland pattern stock ejector double, heavy-duty locks, Continental-style floral and scroll engraving, walnut stock.

ITHACA SHOTGUNS

MODEL 87 FIELD GRADES

Made in much the same manner as 50 years ago, Ithaca's Model 37 pump (now designated as Model 87) features Roto-forged barrels hammered from 11″ round billets of steel, then triple-reamed, lapped and polished. The receivers are milled from a solid block of ordnance grade steel, and all internal parts—hammer, extractors, slides and carriers—are milled and individually fitted to each gun.

Prices:
MODEL 87 w/Supreme Vent Rib **$819.00**
MODEL 87 w/Deluxe Vent Rib and choke tubes . . . **495.00**
MODEL 87 ULTRA DELUXE w/Choke Tubes . . . **514.00**
MODEL 87 Deluxe Combo **582.00**
MODEL 87 FIELD **458.00**
MODEL 87 ULTRAFIELD **481.00**

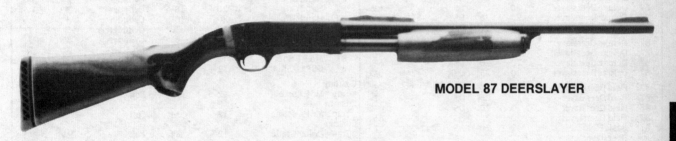

MODEL 87 DEERSLAYER

The first shotgun developed to handle rifled slugs successfully, Ithaca's Deerslayer shotgun remains first choice for many big-game hunters around the world. The Deerlayer's design results in an "undersized" cylinder bore—from the forcing cone all the way to the muzzle. This enables the slug to travel smoothly down the barrel with no gas leakage or slug rattle. The new Deerslayer II features the world's first production rifled barrel for shotguns; moreover, the Deerslayer's barrel is permanently screwed into the receiver for solid frame construction, which insures better accuracy to about 85 yards.

Prices:
MODEL 87 DEERSLAYER **$391.00**
MODEL 87 DEERSLAYER ULTRA **444.00**
MODEL 87 MONTE CARLO DEERSLAYER II
  w/Rifled Barrel **525.00**
MODEL 87 DELUXE DEERSLAYER **462.00**
MODEL 87 FIELD DEERSLAYER **407.00**

MODEL 87 TURKEY GUN
(Camo-seal Finish)

See Specifications for Ithaca 87 Models on following page.

SHOTGUNS

ITHACA SHOTGUNS

SPECIFICATIONS: ITHACA MODEL 87 SHOTGUNS

Model	Grade	Gauge	Barrel Length	Choke*	Chamber	Weight (lbs.)
87	Supreme	12	30"	3 Tubes	3"	7
87	Supreme	12	28"	3 Tubes	3"	7
87	Supreme	12	26"	3 Tubes	3"	7
87	Supreme	20	26"	3 Tubes	3"	6¾
87	Deluxe	12	30"	3 Tubes	3"	7
87	Deluxe	12	28"	3 Tubes	3"	7
87	Deluxe	12	26"	3 Tubes	3"	7
87	Deluxe	20	26"	3 Tubes	3"	6¾
87	Field	12	30"	3 Tubes	3"	7
87	Field	12	28"	3 Tubes	3"	7
87	Field	12	26"	3 Tubes	3"	7
87	Field	20	26"	3 Tubes	3"	6¾
87	Ultra Deluxe	12	26"	3 Tubes	3"	6
87	Ultra Deluxe	20	26"	3 Tubes	3"	5
87	Ultra Deluxe	20	24"	3 Tubes	3"	5
87	Ultra Field	12	26"	3 Tubes	3"	6
87	Ultra Field	20	26"	3 Tubes	3"	5
87	Ultra Field	20	24"	3 Tubes	3"	5
87	Camo Field	12	28"	3 Tubes	3"	7
87	Deluxe Deerslayer	12	20"	DS	3"	7
87	Deluxe Deerslayer	12	25"	DS	3"	7
87	Deluxe Deerslayer	20	20"	DS	3"	6¾
87	Deluxe Deerslayer	20	25"	DS	3"	6¾
87	Ultra Deerslayer	20	20"	DS	3"	5
87	Deluxe Deerslayer	12	20"	DSR	3"	7
87	Deluxe Deerslayer	12	25"	DSR	3"	7
87	Deluxe Deerslayer	20	20"	DSR	3"	6¾
87	Deluxe Deerslayer	20	25"	DSR	3"	6¾
87	Field Deerslayer	12	20"	DS	3"	7
87	Field Deerslayer	12	25"	DS	3"	7
87	Field Deerslayer	20	20"	DS	3"	6¾
87	Field Deerslayer	20	25"	DS	3"	6¾
87	Basic Field Deerslayer	12	20"	DS	3"	7
87	Basic Field Deerslayer	12	25"	DS	3"	7
87	Monte Carlo Deerslayer II	12	25"	DS II	3"	7
		12	20"	DS II	3"	7
		20	20"	DS II	3"	6¾

*3 tubes furnished are Improved Cylinder, Modified, and Full.
DS = Deer, Special Bore   DSR = Deer, Rifled Bore   DS II = Deer, Rifled Barrel

Model	Grade	Gauge	Barrel Length	Choke*	Chamber	Weight (lbs.)
87	Deluxe Combo	20	28" & 20"	3 Tubes/DS	3"	6¾
87	Deluxe Combo	12	28" & 20"	3 Tubes/DS	3"	7
87	Deluxe Combo	12	28" & 20"	3 Tubes/DSR	3"	7
87	Deluxe Combo	12	28" & 25"	3 Tubes/DSR	3"	7
87	Deluxe Combo	20	28" & 20"	3 Tubes/DSR	3"	6¾
87	Deluxe Combo	20	28" & 25"	3 Tubes/DSR	3"	6¾
87	Basic Field/C	12	28" & 20"	Mod Tube/DS	3"	7
87	Basic Field/C	12	28" & 25"	Mod Tube/DS	3"	7
87	Basic Field/C	20	28" & 20"	Mod Tube/DS	3"	6¾
87	Basic Field/C	12	28" & 20"	Mod Tube/DSR	3"	7
87	Basic Field/C	12	28" & 25"	Mod Tube/DSR	3"	7
87	Basic Field/C	20	28" & 20"	Mod Tube/DSR	3"	6¾
87	Basic Field/C	20	28" & 25"	Mod Tube/DSR	3"	6¾
87	Turkey Gun Matte Blue	12	24"	Full Tube	3"	7
87	Turkey Gun Matte Blue	12	24"	Full Choke	3"	7
87	Turkey Gun Camo	12	24"	Full Tube	3"	7
87	Turkey Gun Camo	12	24"	Full Choke	3"	7
87	Hand Grip	12	18½"	Cylinder	3"	5¼
87	Hand Grip	20	18½"	Cylinder	3"	4½
87	Hand Grip	20	18½"	Cylinder	3"	4½
87	M&P	12	20"	Cylinder	3"	7
87	M&P	12	18½"	Cylinder	3"	7
87	DSPS	12	20"	DS	3"	7
87	M&P 8 Shot	12	20"	Cylinder	3"	7
87	DSPS 8 Shot	12	20"	DS	3"	7

Model	Grade	Gauge	Barrel Length	Choke*	Chamber	Weight (lbs.)
Custom Trap	M5E Custom	12	32"	Full	2¾"	8½
Custom Trap	M5E Custom	12	34"	Full	2¾"	8½
Custom Trap	Dollar Grade	12	32"	Full	2¾"	8½
Custom Trap	Dollar Grade	12	34"	Full	2¾"	8½

Model	Grade	Caliber	Barrel Length	Choke*	Chamber	Weight (lbs.)
Pistol	Pistol	.22	10"	N/A	N/A	3½
Pistol	Pistol	.44	10"	N/A	N/A	3½
Pistol	Pistol	.44	15"	N/A	N/A	3½
Pistol	Pistol Combo	.22/.44	10" & 15"	N/A	N/A	3½
Pistol	Pistol Combo	.22/.44	10" & 10"	N/A	N/A	3½

CUSTOM TRAP

Prices:
CUSTOM TRAP 32" and 34" Barrel . . . . $ 7,500.00
DOLLAR TRAP w/Grade AA Fancy American
walnut stock & forend 10,000.00

SINGLE BARREL CUSTOM TRAP
SPECIFICATIONS

Model	Gauge	Chamber	Barrel Length	Choke	Weight (Lbs.)
Custom	12	2¾"	32"	Full	8½
	12	2¾"	34"	Full	8½
Trap	12	2¾"	32"	Full	8½
	12	2¾"	34"	Full	8½

Standard dimensions are: Length of pull is 14⅜" with 1¾" drop at both comb and heel. Custom stock fitting at no extra charge.

KBI/KASSNAR SHOTGUNS

KBI/KASSNAR GRADE I OVER/UNDER
$440.00–$600.00

SPECIFICATIONS
Gauges: 12, 20, 28, .410
Barrel lengths: 26″ (IC/M); 28″ (M/F, W/ICT)
Weight: 7½ lbs. (12 ga.); 6½ lbs. (20 ga.)

Stock: European walnut with checkered pistol grip and forend
Features: Single selective trigger; blued engraved receiver; ventilated rib; chrome-lined barrels; hinged floorplate for easy loading; positive non-slip thumb-type safety (locks the trigger but allows bolt to be opened safely for unloading and inspection of chamber; available with or without deluxe sights; rear sight adjustable for windage and elevation; swivel posts; recoil pad

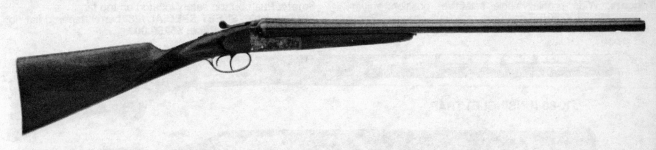

KBI/KASSNAR GRADE II SIDE BY SIDE
$575.00–$665.00

Gauges: 10, 12, 20, 28, .410
Barrel lengths: 32″ (10 ga., F/F); 26″ (12 ga. & 20 ga.; IC/M); 28″ (12 ga. & 20 ga., IC/M); 28″ (16 ga. & 28 ga., M/F); 26″ (.410 ga. F/F)

Weight: 9 lbs. (10 ga.); 6½ lbs. (12 ga.); 6 lbs. (20 ga.); 5¼ lbs. (28 ga.); 5 lbs. (.410 ga.)
Stock: Checkered European walnut
Features: Double hinged triggers; automatic top tang safety; extractors; concave rib; case hardened receivers; chromed barrels; antique silver receiver with fine scroll engraving

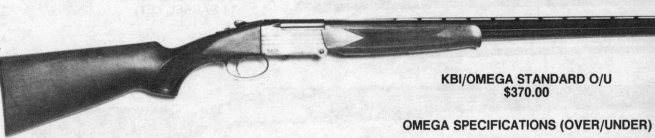

KBI/OMEGA DELUXE O/U
$415.00

The Omega over/under is truly a premium shotgun featuring single trigger, automatic safety, ventilated rib and checkered European walnut stock.

KBI/OMEGA STANDARD O/U
$370.00

OMEGA SPECIFICATIONS (OVER/UNDER)

Movel	Gauge	Barrel Length	Chokes	Weight
Deluxe	12	28″	M/F	7 lbs. 6 oz.
Deluxe	12	26″	IC/M	7 lbs. 2 oz.
Standard	12	28″	M/F	7 lbs. 6 oz.
Standard	12	26″	IC/M	7 lbs. 2 oz.
Standard	20	28″	M/F	6 lbs. 2 oz.
Standard	20	26″	IC/M	6 lbs.
Standard	28	26″	IC/M	6 lbs. 1 oz.
Standard	28	26″	M/F	6 lbs. 1 oz.
Standard	.410	26″	F/F	6 lbs.

SHOTGUNS

KRIEGHOFF SHOTGUNS

(See following page for additional Specifications and Prices)

MODEL K-80 TRAP, SKEET, SPORTING CLAY AND LIVE BIRD

Barrels: Made of Boehler steel; free-floating bottom barrel with adjustable point of impact; standard Trap and Live Pigeon ribs are tapered step; standard Skeet, Sporting Clay and International ribs are tapered or parallel flat.

Receivers: Hard satin-nickel finish; casehardened; blue finish available as special order

Triggers: Wide profile, single selective, position adjustable; **Model K-80/RT** features removable trigger (**Price:** $1200.00)

Weight: 8½ lbs. (Trap); 8 lbs. (Skeet)

Ejectors: Selective automatic

Sights: White pearl front bead and metal center bead

Stocks: Hand-checkered and epoxy-finished Select European walnut stock and forearm; quick-detachable palm swell stocks available in five different styles and dimensions

Safety: Push button safety located on top tang.

Also available: **SKEET SPECIAL** (28″ barrel; tapered flat rib; 2 choke tubes). **Price: $5250.00**

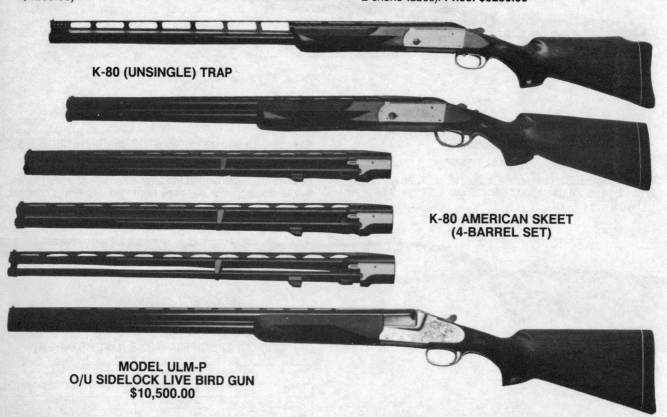

K-80 (UNSINGLE) TRAP

**K-80 AMERICAN SKEET
(4-BARREL SET)**

**MODEL ULM-P
O/U SIDELOCK LIVE BIRD GUN
$10,500.00**

SPECIFICATIONS

Gauge: 12

Chamber: 2¾″

Barrel: 28″ or 30″ long; tapered, ventilated rib

Choke: Top, Full; bottom, Imp. Mod.

Trigger action: Single trigger, non-selective bottom-top; hand-detachable sidelocks with coil springs; optional release trigger

Stock: Selected fancy English walnut, oil finish; length, 14⅜″; drop at comb, 1⅜″; optional custom-made stock

Forearm: Semi-beavertail

Engraving: Light scrollwork; optional engravings available

Weight: Approx. 8 lbs.

Also available in Skeet (28″) and Trap (30″) models (same prices as above)

KRIEGHOFF SHOTGUNS

SPECIFICATIONS AND PRICES

Model	Description	Bbl Length	Choke	Standard	Bavaria	Danube	Gold Target	Extra Barrels
Trap	Over & Under	30″/32″	IM/F	$4995.00	$8,685.00	$10,750.00	$13,995.00	$1950.00
	Unsingle	32″/34″	Full	5845.00	9,350.00	11,500.00	14,865.00	2625.00
	Top Single	34″ only	Full	5495.00	8,995.00	11,150.00	14,500.00	2275.00
	Combo (unsingle)	30″ + 32″ / 30″ + 34″	IM/F+F	7500.00	11,195.00	13,400.00	16,700.00	
		32″ + 34″	CT/CT + CT	8325.00	11,995.00	14,225.00	17,525.00	
Skeet	4-Barrel Set	28″/12 ga.	Tula	9985.00	13,995.00	16,100.00	20,900.00	2150.00
		28″/20 ga.	Skeet	9985.00	13,995.00	16,100.00	20,900.00	2100.00
		28″/28 ga.	Skeet	9985.00	13,995.00	16,100.00	20,900.00	2100.00
		28″/.410 ga.	Skeet	9985.00	13.995.00	16,100.00	20,900.00	2100.00
	2-Barrel Set	28″/12 ga.	Tula	8700.00	12,450.00	14,750.00	18,100.00	3400.00
	Lightweight	28″/12 ga.	Skeet	4890.00	8,540.00	10,595.00	N/A	1950.00
	Standardweight	28″/12 ga.	Tula	5090.00	8,740.00	10,795.00	14,195.00	2150.00
		28″/12 ga.	Skeet	4890.00	8,540.00	10,595.00	13,995.00	1950.00
	International	28″/12 ga.	Tula	5250.00	8,875.00	10,900.00	14,380.00	2150.00
Sporting Clays	Over/Under w/screw-in tubes (5)	28″/12 ga.	Tubes	5550.00	9150.00	11,190.00	14,650.00	2440.00
Live Bird	Live Bird	28″/29″/30″	IM/SF	4995.00	8685.00	10,750.00	14,865.00	1950.00
Optional engravings: Super Scroll								650.00

Optional Features:*
Screw-in chokes (O/U, Top or Unsingle) $335
Single factory release   285.00
Double factory release   490.00

* Choke tubes in single barrel (w/tubes): add $335.00. In O/U barrel (5 tubes) add $490.00.

SPECIFICATIONS
Gauge: 12
Chamber: 2³/₄″
Barrel length: 32″ or 34″
Choke: Full; optional screw-in chokes
Rib: Tapered step; ventilated
Trigger: Weight of pull adjustable; optional release
Receiver: Casehardened; satin grey finished in electroless nickel; now available in blue
Grade: Standard; engraved models on special order
Weight: Approximately 8.6-8.8 lbs.
Case: Aluminum
Price: With full choke and case **$2750.00**
With screw-in choke and case 3085.00
Screw-in choke barrels 1785.00
Regular barrels **1450.00**

MODEL KS-5

The KS-5 is a single barrel trap gun with a ventilated, tapered and adjustable step rib, casehardened receiver in satin grey matte or blue, finished in electroless nickel. It features an adjustable point of impact by means of different optional front-hangers. Screw-in chokes and adjustable stock are optional. Trigger is adjustable externally for poundage.
Also available: **KS-5 SPECIAL.** Same as **KS-5** except barrel has fully adjustable rib and stock. **Price: $3655.00**

LAURONA SHOTGUNS

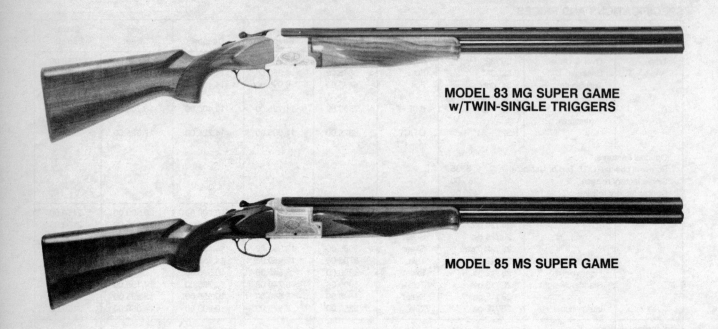

**MODEL 83 MG SUPER GAME
w/TWIN-SINGLE TRIGGERS**

MODEL 85 MS SUPER GAME

MODEL 83 MG SUPER GAME
$1215.00

SPECIFICATIONS
Gauges: 12 and 20
Chamber: 2³/₄″ or 3″
Barrel lengths: 26″ or 28″ (20 ga.) and 28″ (12 ga.)
Chokes: Multichokes (screw-in)
Rib: ⁵/₁₆″
Frame finish: Old Silver

Weight: 6 lbs. 10 oz. (20 ga.); 7 lbs. (12 ga.)
Features: Non-rusting Black-chrome barrel finish; extra-long forcing cones
Also available: **Model 85 MS** (12 and 20 Gauge). Specifications same as Model 83, but with selective single trigger. **Price: $1215.00 ($1630.00 for 2-barrel set).**

MODEL 85 MS SUPER TRAP

MODEL 85 MS SUPER TRAP
$1390.00

SPECIFICATIONS
Gauge: 12
Chamber: 2³/₄″
Barrel length: 29″
Choke: Multichoke/Full
Rib: ¹/₂″ aluminum

Frame finish: Old silver
Weight: 7 lbs. 12 oz.
Also available: **MODEL 85 MS SUPER PIGEON** (12 ga.). Same specifications as Super Trap model except **Barrel length:** 28″ and **Weight:** 7 lbs. 4 oz. **Price: $1370.00**

LAURONA SHOTGUNS

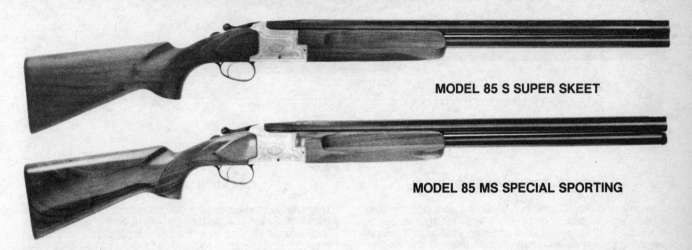

MODEL 85 S SUPER SKEET

MODEL 85 MS SPECIAL SPORTING

MODEL 85 S SUPER SKEET
$1300.00

SPECIFICATIONS
Gauge: 12
Chamber: 2³/₄″
Barrel length: 28″
Choke: Skeet/Skeet
Rib: ¹/₂″ aluminum

Frame finish: Old silver
Weight: 7 lbs. 1 oz.
Features: Black-chrome barrel finish; extra-long forcing cones
Also available: MODEL 85 MS SPECIAL SPORTING (12 ga.). Same specifications as Super Skeet model but with IM-Multi-choke. **Weight:** 7 lbs. 4 oz. **Price:** $1325.00

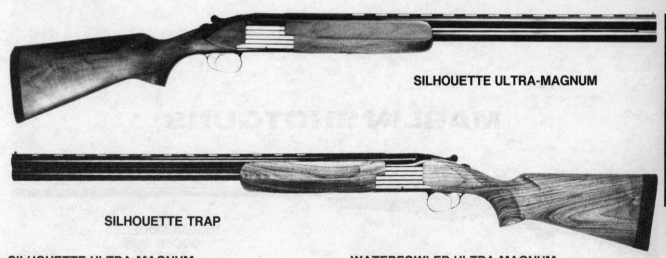

SILHOUETTE ULTRA-MAGNUM

SILHOUETTE TRAP

SILHOUETTE ULTRA-MAGNUM
$1265.00

SPECIFICATIONS (Game, Trap & Sporting Clay Models)
Gauge: 12
Chamber: 3¹/₂″ Magnum
Barrel length: 28″
Choke: Multichoke
Rib: ⁷/₁₆″ steel
Weight: 7 lbs. 12 oz.

WATERFOWLER ULTRA-MAGNUM
$1265.00

SPECIFICATIONS
Gauge: 12
Chamber: 3¹/₂″
Rib: ⁷/₁₆″ steel
Finish: Non-glare Black-chrome
Rib: ⁷/₁₆″
Ejectors: Automatic selective ejectors
Stock: Full pistol grip
Weight: 8 lbs. (7 lbs. 15 oz. in Trap; 7 lbs. 12 oz. in Sporting Clays)

LAURONA SHOTGUNS

GRAND TRAP MODEL GTU

GRAND TRAP MODEL GTO

Laurona's new Trap Combo gun features a unique 10mm steel rib designed for interception of shot with rising target at approx. 40 yards. The 34″ barrel is chambered 2³/₄″ with a special elongated forcing cone with flush-style screw-in chokes. The bottom chamber area is fitted with a buffered recoil system. The forend is full beavertail style with finger grooves. Butt stock is a Monte Carlo comb with full orthopedic pistol grip and a white-line, curved trap pad.
Price: $590.00

GRAND TRAP MODEL GTU

This combo gun features a 34″ bottom single barrel with a 10mm steel high-rise, floating rib with matching walnut inserts fitted into the forearm area. The barrel is supplied with a screw-in full choke. Forearm is slightly rounded with a tear-drop cross section. Butt stock comes with a full orthopedic pistol grip, straight comb, and a white line black-carved trap recoil pad.
Price: $670.00

Both models—GTO and GTU—are supplied with 29″ O/U barrels with 11mm steel rib, flush-style screw-in chokes plus Black-Chrome finish, mechanical triggers and extra long forcing cones.
Prices:
TRAP O/U Barrels (29″): **$450.00**
FIELD O/U Barrels (28″, 12 or 20 ga.): **$425.00**

MARLIN SHOTGUNS

MARLIN MODEL 55 GOOSE GUN $228.95

High-flying ducks and geese are the Goose Gun's specialty. The Marlin Goose Gun has an extra-long 36-inch full-choked barrel and Magnum capability, making it the perfect choice for tough shots at wary waterfowl. It also features a quick-loading 2-shot clip magazine, a convenient leather carrying strap and a quality ventilated recoil pad.

SPECIFICATIONS
Gauge: 12; 2³/₄″ Magnum, 3″ Magnum or 2³/₄″ regular shells

Choke: Full
Capacity: 2-shot clip magazine
Action: Bolt action; positive thumb safety; red cocking indicator
Stock: Walnut-finish hardwood with pistol grip and ventilated recoil pad; swivel studs; tough Mar-Shield® finish
Barrel length: 36″
Sights: Bead front sight and U-groove rear sight
Overall length: 56³/₄″
Weight: About 8 lbs.

MAROCCHI AVANZA SHOTGUNS

SPECIFICATIONS

GAUGE	BARREL LENGTH	CHOKES	LENGTH O/A	WEIGHT	PRICES
12	28″	M & F	44½″	6 lbs. 9 oz.	$ 879.00
12	28″	IC & M & F Interchokes	44½″	6 lbs. 13 oz.	979.00
12	26″	IC & M	42½″	6 lbs. 6 oz.	879.00
12	26″	IC & M & F Interchokes	42½″	6 lbs. 9 oz.	979.00
20	28″	M & F	44½″	6 lbs. 8 oz.	910.00
20	28″	IM & M & F Interchokes	44½″	6 lbs. 12 oz.	1010.00
20	26″	IC & M	42½″	6 lbs. 5 oz.	910.00
20	26″	IC & M & F Interchokes	42½″	6 lbs. 8 oz.	1010.00

Features: Single selective trigger (5½ lb. pull); stock is select walnut with cut checkering; ribs are top and middle ventilated; 3″ chambers; mechanism is lightweight, all steel with Mono-Block boxlock, automechanical barrel cycling, selective automatic ejectors/extractors, automatic safety

MAVERICK PUMP ACTION SHOTGUNS

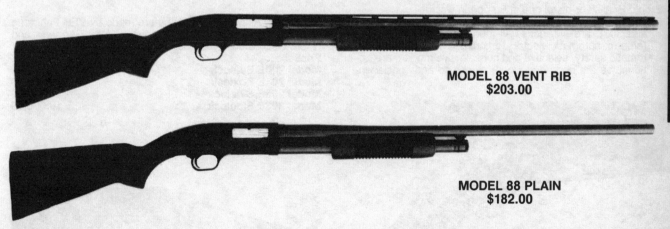

MODEL 88 VENT RIB
$203.00

MODEL 88 PLAIN
$182.00

SPECIFICATIONS
Gauge: 12
Chamber: 2¾″ or 3″
Barrel length: 28″ (Modified); 30″ (Full)
Overall length: 48″ (w/28″ barrel)
Weight: 7¼ lbs. (w/28″ barrel)
Capacity: 6 shots (2¾″); 5 shots (3″)

Features: Rubber recoil pad; positive crossbolt safety; interchangeable barrels without tools; durable black synthetic stock and matching forend; high strength aluminum alloy receiver; steel-to-steel lockup between hardened barrel extension and bolt lock

MERKEL OVER/UNDER SHOTGUNS

Merkel over-and-unders are the first hunting guns with barrels arranged one above the other, and they have since proved to be able competitors of the side-by-side gun. Merkel superiority lies in the following details:

- Available in 12, 16, 20 and .410 gauges
- Lightweight (5¾ to 6¾ lbs.)
- The high, narrow forend protects the shooter's hand from the barrel in hot or cold climates.
- The forend is narrow and therefore lies snugly in the hand to permit easy and positive swinging.

- The slim barrel line provides an unobstructed field of view and thus permits rapid aiming and shooting.
- The over-and-under barrel arrangement reduces recoil error; the recoil merely pushes the muzzle up vertically.

Additional specifications on the following page. For details and prices on Merkel options, contact Armes de Chasse (see Directory of Manufacturers & Suppliers).

MODEL 200E SIDELOCK

MODEL 201E SIDELOCK

MERKEL OVER/UNDER SHOTGUN SPECIFICATIONS

Gauges: 12, 16, 20, 28, .410
Barrel lengths: 26″, 26¾″, 28″
Weight: 5.5 to 7 lbs.
Stock: English or pistol grip in European walnut
Features: Models 200E and 201E are boxlocks; Models 203E and 303E are sidelocks. All models include three-piece forearm, automatic ejectors, articulated front triggers. Automatic safety, selective and nonselective triggers are optional, as are upgraded wood, recoil pad and special engraving. All Merkel shotguns are made by VEB Fahrzeug and Jagdwaffenwerk Ernst Thalman, West Germany, and are distributed in the U.S. by Armes de Chasse.

Prices:

Model 200E Boxlock	$ 3500.00
Model 201E Boxlock	4500.00
Model 203E Sidelock	9000.00
Model 303E Sidelock	10,000.00

MODEL 203E SIDELOCK

MODEL 303E SIDELOCK

MERKEL SIDE-BY-SIDE SHOTGUNS

SPECIFICATIONS
Gauges: 12, 16, 20
Barrel lengths: 26″, 26¾″, 28″
Weight: 6 to 7 lbs.
Stock: English or pistol grip in European walnut
Features: Models 47E and 147E are boxlocks; Models 47S, 147S, 247S, 347S, and 447S are sidelocks. All guns have cold hammer-forged barrels, double triggers, double lugs and Greener crossbolt locking systems and automatic ejectors. Choking and patterning for steel shot (using U.S. Steel shotshells), upgraded wood, automatic safety, recoil pad and special engraving are available as options.

Prices:
MODEL 47E	$2000.00
MODEL 147E	2500.00
MODEL 76E	3500.00
MODEL 47S Sidelock	4500.00
MODEL 147S Sidelock	5000.00
MODEL 247S Sidelock	5500.00
MODEL 347S Sidelock	6000.00
MODEL 447S Sidelock	6500.00

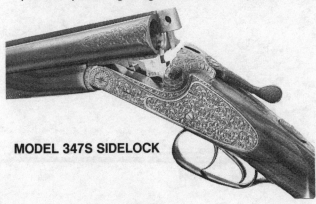

MODEL 347S SIDELOCK

MODEL 147E BOXLOCK

MODEL 47S SIDE-BY-SIDE

MODEL 147S & 247S

MODEL 122E BOXLOCK

MODEL 47E BOXLOCK

MOSSBERG PUMP SHOTGUNS

These slide-action Model 500's offer lightweight action and high tensile-strength alloys. They also feature the famous Mossberg "Safety on Top" and a full range of interchangeable barrels. Stocks are walnut-finished birch with rubber recoil pads with combs checkered pistol grip and forend.

MODEL 500 SPECIFICATIONS

Action: Positive slide-action

Barrel: 12 or 20 gauge and .410 bore with free-floating vent. rib; ACCU-CHOKE II interchangeable choke tubes; chambered for 2¾" standard and Magnum and 3" Magnum shells

Receiver: Aluminum alloy, deep blue/black finish; ordnance steel bolt locks in barrel extension for solid "steel-to-steel" lockup

Capacity: 6-shot (one less when using 3" Magnum shells); plug for 3-shot capacity included

Safety: Top tang, thumb-operated; disconnecting trigger

Stock/forend: Walnut-finished American hardwood with checkering; rubber recoil pad

Standard stock dimensions: 14" length of pull; 2½" drop at heel; 1½" drop at comb

Sights: Metal bead front

Overall length: 48" with 28" barrel

Weight: 12 ga. 7½ lbs.; 20 ga. 6¾ lbs.; .410 bore 6½ lbs.; Slugster 6¾ lbs.; Magnums 8½ lbs. (weight varies slightly due to wood density)

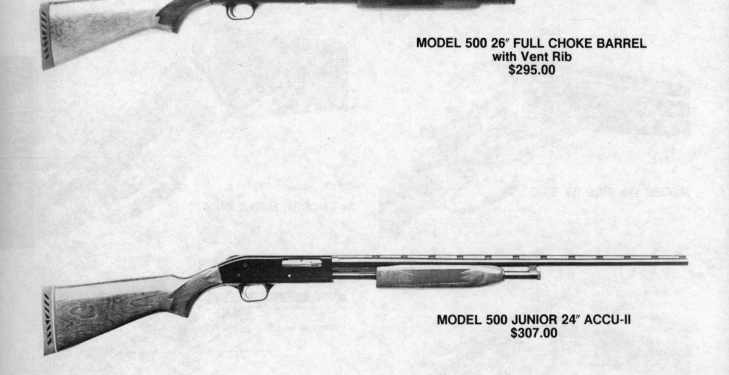

MODEL 500 26″ FULL CHOKE BARREL
with Vent Rib
$295.00

MODEL 500 JUNIOR 24″ ACCU-II
$307.00

MOSSBERG PUMP SHOTGUNS

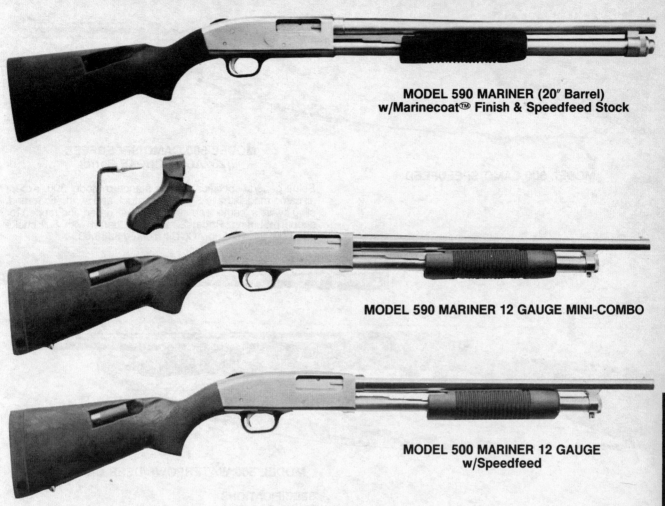

MODEL 590 MARINER (20″ Barrel)
w/Marinecoat™ Finish & Speedfeed Stock

MODEL 590 MARINER 12 GAUGE MINI-COMBO

MODEL 500 MARINER 12 GAUGE
w/Speedfeed

MODEL 500 & 590 MARINER

All carbon steel parts of these 12 gauge shotguns are treated with MARINECOAT™ protective finish, a unique Teflon and metal coating. This finish makes each Mariner 500 shotgun resistant to salt spray and water damage by actually penetrating into the steel pores. All stock and forearms are made of a high-strength synthetic material rather than wood to provide extra durability with minimum maintenance. Mossberg's Speedfeed stock allows shooters to carry up to four extra 2¾″ rounds in the buttstock—two on each side. Mariners are available in a variety of 6- or 9-shot versions. The Mini-Combo offers a full-length buttstock and extra pistol grip. Pistol grip models include heat shields.

SPECIFICATIONS
Gauge: 12
Chambers: 2¾″ and 3″
Capacity: 6-shot model—5-shot (3″ chamber) and 6-shot (2¾″ chamber)
8-shot model—7-shot (3″ chamber) and 8-shot (2¾″ chamber)

Barrel lengths: 18½″ and 20″
Overall length: 40″ w/20″ barrel; 38½″ w/18½″ barrel
Weight: 6½ lbs. w/18½″ barrel
Stock dimensions: 14″ pull; 1½″ drop at comb; 2½″ drop at heel
Features: Double slide bars; twin extractors; dual shell latches; ambidextrous safety

Prices:
MODEL 500 MARINER 6-SHOT
Pistol Grip & Synthetic Field Models **$373.00**
MODEL 590 MARINER 9-SHOT
Pistol Grip & Synthetic Field Models **449.00**
Speedfeed Model **466.00**
MODEL 500 MARINER 6-SHOT MINI-COMBO
Synthetic Field **380.00**
Speedfeed Model **396.00**
MODEL 590 MARINER 9-SHOT MINI-COMBO
Pistol Grip & Synthetic Field Model **441.00**
Speedfeed Model **458.00**

MOSSBERG PUMP SHOTGUNS

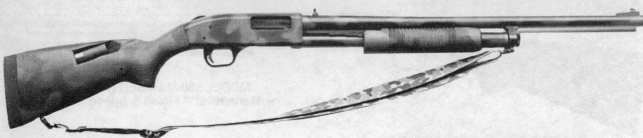

MODEL 500 CAMO/SPEEDFEED

MODEL 500 CAMO/SPEEDFEED
w/20″ ACCU-CHOKE Barrel

Same general specifications as standard Model 500, except all camo models have Speedfeed stock and synthetic forend, sling swivels, camo web strap, receiver drilled and tapped for scope mounting. **Price:** 20″ vent rib barrel with Full choke **$353.00;** 24″ vent rib ACCU II Turkey **$336.00.**

MODEL 500 WATERFOWL/DEER CAMO COMBO

SPECIFICATIONS
Gauge: 12
Barrel length: 28″ (Accu-Choke w/one Accu-Steel choke tube and 20″ Slugster barrel
Features: Synthetic forearm and Speedback buttstock; receiver drilled and tapped for scope mounting; quick disconnect posts and swivels, plus camo web sling, are supplied
Price: $358.00

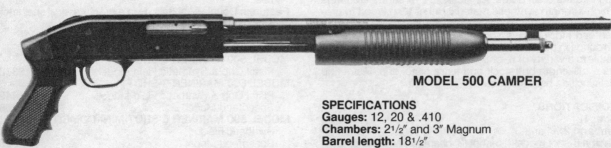

MODEL 500 CAMPER

SPECIFICATIONS
Gauges: 12, 20 & .410
Chambers: 2 1/2″ and 3″ Magnum
Barrel length: 18 1/2″
Weight: 4 1/2 lbs. (.410 ga.); 5 lbs. (20 ga.); 5 1/2 lbs. (12 ga.)
Features: Synthetic pistol grip; camo carrying case
Price: $309.00; in .410 gauge **$316.00**

MOSSBERG PUMP SHOTGUNS

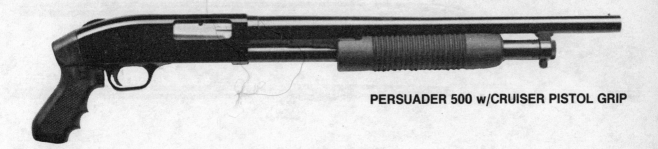

PERSUADER 500 w/CRUISER PISTOL GRIP

12 GAUGE 8-SHOT PERSUADER (20″ Barrel)

12 GAUGE 6-SHOT PERSUADER (18½″ Barrel)

SHOTGUNS

MODEL 500 SLIDE-ACTION LAW ENFORCEMENT "PERSUADER"

These slide-action shotguns are available in 6- or 8-shot versions, chambered for both 2¾-inch and 3-inch shells.

Six-shot models have 18½-inch barrel, overall length of 37¾ inches and a weight of 6¼ pounds with full buttstock. Also available in 20 gauge and .410 bore.

Eight-shot models have 20-inch barrels, overall length of 39¾ inches and weigh 6¾ pounds with full buttstock.

Both 6- and 8-shot models are available in choice of blued, parkerized or nickel metal finish; satin or oiled walnut wood finish. Lightweight aluminum alloy receiver with steel locking bolt into barrel extension affords solid "steel-to-steel" lockup. Heavy-duty rubber recoil pads come on all full stock models; sling swivels on all models. Optional pistol grip and other accessories.

PRICES (6-SHOT MODELS):
PERSUADER 6-SHOT—Blued
With wood stock, bead sights **$276.00**
Synthetic Field stock, blued, bead sight **276.00**
Speedfeed stock, blued (12, 20 ga.) **293.00**
PERSUADER 6-SHOT MINI-COMBO
Blued, 12 and 20 gauge **284.00**
Synthetic Field Model **284.00**

PRICES (8-SHOT MODELS):
PERSUADER 8-SHOT
Synthetic Field Model **$293.00**
With rifle sight **314.00**
PERSUADER 8-SHOT MINI-COMBO Blued **301.00**

MOSSBERG SHOTGUNS

MODEL 5500 MKII
$447.00

Mossberg's semiauto 12-gauge "Shooting System," Model 5500 MKII, is equipped with two barrels—one for non-magnum 2³/₄" 12-gauge loads only, and the other for magnum 2³/₄" or 3" loads. A larger gas port in the non-magnum barrel ensures reliable extraction and ejection with even the lightest target or field loads. The 26" non-magnum barrel is ideal for close cover upland hunting and comes equipped with three ACCU-II choke tubes (Imp. Cyl., Modified, and Full) for lead shot.

The 28" magnum barrel has a smaller gas port designed to regulate the speed of the bolt and tame the recoil of heavy hunting loads. The magnum barrel provides the balance and longer sighting plane preferred by waterfowl hunters. It comes equipped with two ACCU-STEEL choke tubes (Modified and Full). Model 5500 MKII Auto has a full 5-shot capacity and features a high-strength aluminum alloy receiver for good balance and fast handling in the field. The positive tang safety is located in the top rear of the receiver for easy operation by right- or left-hand shooters.

Also available: **CAMO MODEL 5500** (28" Magnum) w/ACCU-II Set and ACCU-Steel Full choke, plus Synthetic Field Camo Stock. **Price: $434.00.**

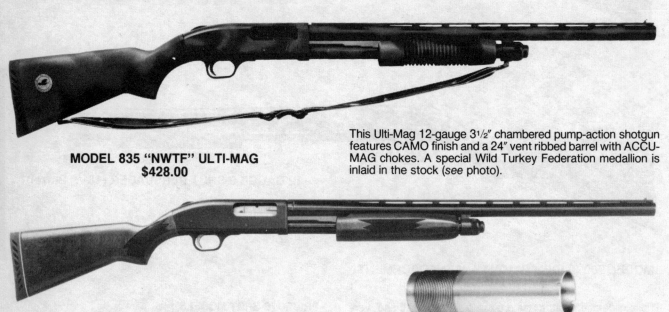

MODEL 835 "NWTF" ULTI-MAG
$428.00

This Ulti-Mag 12-gauge 3¹/₂" chambered pump-action shotgun features CAMO finish and a 24" vent ribbed barrel with ACCU-MAG chokes. A special Wild Turkey Federation medallion is inlaid in the stock (*see* photo).

MODEL 835 ULTI-MAG
$428.00 (Blued) $458.00 (Camo)

The world's first shotgun chambered specifically for Federal Cartridge's 3¹/₂" 12 gauge Magnum shotshell, the **Ulti-Mag** fires all standard 12 gauge 2³/₄" and 3" field and target loads as well. Designed for waterfowlers who need a shotshell capable of delivering larger payloads of steel shot, the high-velocity (1300+ fps) load provides a 23 percent or more increase in steel shot capacity compared to conventional 12 gauge 3" Magnums.

The **Ulti-Mag** also features a "backbored" barrel, thus increasing diameter bore, reducing recoil, and improving patterns. With the ACCU-MAG choke tube system, stainless steel tubes fit flush with the muzzle to handle high-velocity steel shot loads with efficiency. Capacity is five shots with 3" or 3¹/₂" shells, and six shots with 2³/₄" shells. Other features include an ambidextrous safety, solid "steel-to-steel" lockup, and high-strength aluminum alloy receivers with anodized finish.

NAVY ARMS SHOTGUNS

MODEL 96
$530.00

Five fully interchangeable chokes make the Model 96 Over/Under a versatile shotgun, useful for all types of upland and waterfowl hunting as well as target shooting. Italian made, this 12-gauge gun features 28-inch chrome-lined barrels with 3-inch chambers, ejectors, double ventilated rib construction, an engraved hard chrome reciver, European walnut stock with checkered wrist and forend and gold-plated single trigger. Chokes: Full; Imp. Cyl./ Mod.; Mod.; Imp. Cyl./Skeet; Cyl.

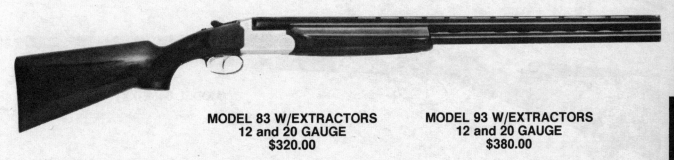

MODEL 83 W/EXTRACTORS
12 and 20 GAUGE
$320.00

MODEL 93 W/EXTRACTORS
12 and 20 GAUGE
$380.00

The Model 83/93 Bird Hunter is a quality field grade over/under available in 12 or 20 gauge. Manufactured in Italy, it features 28-inch chrome-lined barrels with 3-inch chambers; double vent rib construction, European walnut stock, hand-checkered wrist and forend, chrome engraved receiver and gold-plated triggers. Both gauges available in Mod./Full or Imp. Cyl./ Mod. chokes.

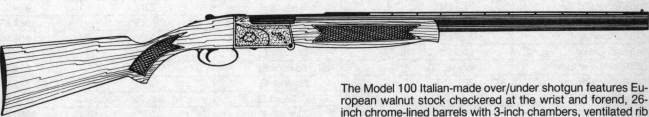

MODEL 100 SHOTGUN
$250.00

The Model 100 Italian-made over/under shotgun features European walnut stock checkered at the wrist and forend, 26-inch chrome-lined barrels with 3-inch chambers, ventilated rib barrel and an engraved, hard chrome receiver. **Chokes:** Full/Full & S/S (.410), Mod./Full & S/S (28 ga.), Imp. Cyl./Mod. & S/S (20 ga.), and Imp. Cyl./Mod. or Mod./Full (12 ga.). **Weight:** 6¼ lbs.

SHOTGUNS

PARKER-HALE SHOTGUNS

Now available in the U.S., Parker-Hale side-by-side shotguns have long been favorites in Great Britain. Superbly crafted by the Spanish gunmaking firm of Ignacio Ugartechea, the "600" Series doubles are available in field grade boxlock models and "best" grade sidelock versions. Field grade models are offered in either extractor or ejector configurations. All models boast stocks of hand-checkered walnut finished with hand-rubbed oil, actions and parts machined from ordnance steel, standard auto safety, forged barrels, deep lustrous bluing and English scroll design engraving. **American** (A) models: Single non-selective trigger, pistol grip, beavertail forend, butt plate, raised matted rib. **English** (E) models: Double triggers, straight grip, splinter forend, checkered butt, concave rib; XXV models have Churchill-type rib. **Chokes:** Imp. Cyl./Mod.; Mod./Full. **Weight:** 12 ga., 6¾-7 lbs.; 20 ga. 5¾ lbs.-6 lbs.; 28 and .410 ga., 5¼-5½ lbs. 3″ chambers on 20 and .410 ga.; 2¾ chambers on others. Bi-Gauge models have two sets of barrels, one set in each gauge.

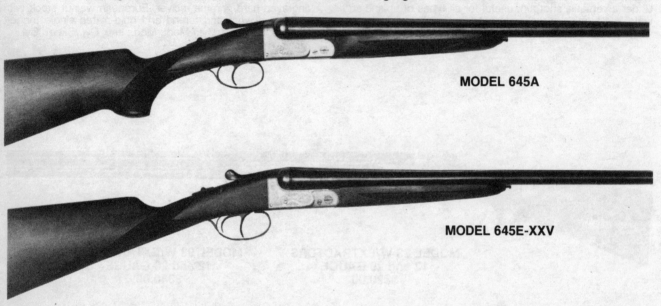

MODEL 645A

MODEL 645E-XXV

PARKER-HALE SIDE-BY-SIDE SHOTGUNS "600" SERIES

Model	Gauges	Action	Barrel Length	Price
640E (English)	12, 16, 20	Boxlock Ex.	26″, 28″	$ 619.95
640E (English)	28, .410	Boxlock Ex.	27″	699.95
640A (American)	12, 16, 20, 28, .410	Boxlock Ex.	26″, 28″	719.95
640A (American)	28, .410	Boxlock Ex.	27″	799.95
640M "Big Ten"	10 Magnum	Boxlock Ex.	26″, 30″, 32″	749.95
645E (Bi-Gauge)	20/28 or 28/410	Boxlock Ej.	26″	1399.95
645E (English)	12, 16, 20	Boxlock Ej.	26″, 28″	784.95
645E (English)	28, .410	Boxlock Ej.	27″	864.95
645A (American)	12, 16, 20	Boxlock Ej.	26″, 28″	884.95
645A (American)	28, .410	Boxlock Ej.	27″	964.95
645A (Bi-Gauge)	20/28 or 28/410	Boxlock Ej.	27″	1499.95
645E-XXV (English)	12, 16, 20	Boxlock Ej.	25″	819.95
645E-XXV (English)	28, .410	Boxlock Ej.	25″	899.95
670E (English)**	12, 16, 20	Sidelock Ej.	26″, 28″	3200.00
670E (English)**	28, .410	Sidelock Ej.	27″	3400.00
680E-XXV (English)**	12, 16, 20	Sidelock Ej.	25″	3150.00
680E-XXV (English)**	28, .410	Sidelock Ej.	25″	3250.00

* Ex.=Extractor; Ej.=Ejector; ** Custom order only

PARKER REPRODUCTIONS

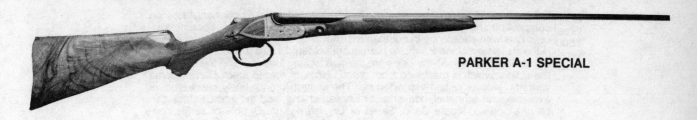

PARKER A-1 SPECIAL

Recognized by the shooting fraternity as the finest American shotgun ever produced, the Parker A-1 Special is again available. Exquisite engraving and rare presentation grade French walnut distinguish the A-1 Special from any other shotguns in the world. Currently offered in 12, 20 and 28 gauge. Each gun is custom-fitted in its own oak and leather trunk case. Two models are offered: Hand Engraved and Custom Engraved. Also available in B and D Grades. For specifications, see the table below.

Standard features: Automatic safety, selective ejectors, skeleton steel butt plate, splinter forend, engraved snap caps, fitted leather trunk case, canvas and leather case cover, chrome barrel interiors, hand-checkering. The A-1 Special also features a 24k gold initial plate or pistol cap, 32 lines per inch checkering, selected wood, and fine hand-engraving. Choose from single or double trigger, English or pistol grip stock (all models). Options include beavertail forend, additional barrels.

Prices:

A-1 SPECIAL

One barrel set . . . . $ 8,740.00
Two barrel set 9,740.00

A-1 SPECIAL CUSTOM ENGRAVED . . . . . From 10,500.00

D-GRADE

One barrel set $2,970.00
Two sets of barrels 3,600.00

SPECIFICATIONS

Gauge	Barrel Length	Chokes	Chambers	Drop At Comb	Drop At Heel	Length of Pull	Nominal Weight	Overall Length
12	26	Skeet I & II or IC/M	2³/₄	1³/₈	2³/₁₆	14½	6³/₄	42⁵/₈
12	28	IC/M or M/F	2³/₄	1³/₈	2³/₁₆	14⅛	6³/₄	44⁵/₈
12	28	IC/M	3	1³/₈	2³/₁₆	14⅛	7+	44⁵/₈
20	26	Skeet I & II or IC/M	2³/₄	1³/₈	2³/₁₆	14³/₈	6½	42³/₈
20	28	M/F	3	1³/₈	2³/₁₆	14³/₈	6½	44⁵/₈
28	26	Skeet I & II or IC/M	2³/₄	1³/₈	2³/₁₆	14³/₈	5½	42⁵/₈
28	28	M/F	2³/₄	1³/₈	2³/₁₆	14⅛	5⅓	44⁵/₈

Note: *Dimensions may vary slightly as each stock is hand-carved.*

PERAZZI SHOTGUNS

For the past 20 years or so, Perazzi has concentrated solely on manufacturing competition shotguns for the world market. Today the name has become synonymous with excellence in competitive shooting. The heart of the Perazzi line is the classic over/under, whose barrels are soldered into a monobloc that holds the shell extractors. At the sides are the two locking lugs that link the barrels to the action, which is machined from a solid block of forged steel. Barrels come with flat, step or raised ventilated rib. The walnut forend, finely checkered, is available with schnabel, beavertail or English styling, and the walnut stock can be of standard, Monte Carlo, Skeet or English design. Double or single non-selective or selective triggers. Sideplates and receiver are masterfully engraved and transform these guns into veritable works of art.

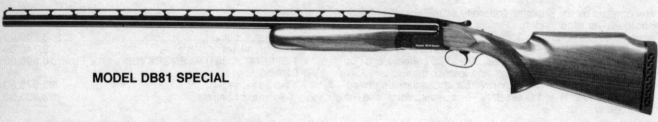

MODEL DB81 SPECIAL

AMERICAN TRAP STANDARD COMBO SET
MODELS MX8 SPECIAL COMBO, MX3 SPECIAL COMBO,
GRAND AMERICAN 88 SPECIAL COMBO & DB81 SPECIAL COMBO

SPECIFICATIONS
Gauge: 12
Chamber: 2³/₄″
Barrel lengths: 29¹/₂″ and 31¹/₂″ (O/U); 32″ and 34″ (single barrel)
Chokes: Mod./Full (O/U); Full (single barrel)
Trigger group: Detachable and interchangeable with flat "V" springs
Stock: Interchangeable and custom made
Forend: Beavertail
Weight: 8 lbs. 6 oz.

Prices:

Standard Grade	$ 6850.00- 8340.00
with Gold Outline	11,280.00-11,900.00
SC3 Grade	10,400.00-12,620.00
SCO Grade	17,200.00-19,310.00
Gold Grade	19,110.00-21,270.00
Grand American 88 Special	7880.00-20,750.00
DB81 Special	8340.00-21,270.00

HUNTING MODEL MX20C

HUNTING MODELS MX12, MX12C, MX20, & MX20C

SPECIFICATIONS
Gauges: 12 (MX12 & MX12C); 20 (MX20 & MX20C); 28 & .410 (MX20)
Chambers: 2³/₄″ (MX20 & MX20C also avail. in 3″)
Barrel lengths: 26″ (except MX12C) and 27″ (MX12 & MX12C only)
Chokes: Mod./Full (MX12 & MX20); Chokes (MX12C & MX20C)
Trigger group: Non-detachable with coil springs and selective trigger

Stock: Interchangeable and custom made
Forend: Schnabel
Weight: 7 lbs. 4 oz. (MX12 & MX12C); 6 lbs. 6 oz. (MX20 & MX20C)
Prices:

Standard Grade	$ 5360.00- 6180.00
With gold outline	7670.00- 8810.00
SC3 Grade	9270.00- 9790.00
SCO Grade	15,660.00-16,220.00

PERAZZI SHOTGUNS

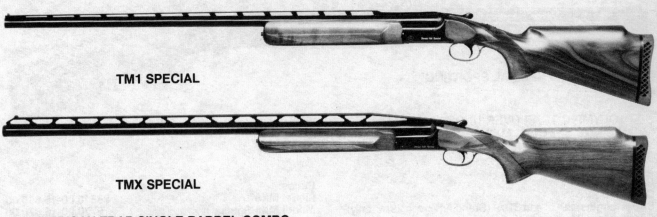

TM1 SPECIAL

TMX SPECIAL

AMERICAN TRAP SINGLE BARREL COMBO
MODELS TM1 SPECIAL & TMX SPECIAL
$4380.00

SPECIFICATIONS
Gauge: 12
Chamber: 2¾"
Barrel lengths: 32" and 34"
Choke: Full

Trigger group: Detachable and interchangeable with coil springs
Stock: Interchangeable and custom made
Forend: Beavertail
Weight: 8 lbs. 6 oz.

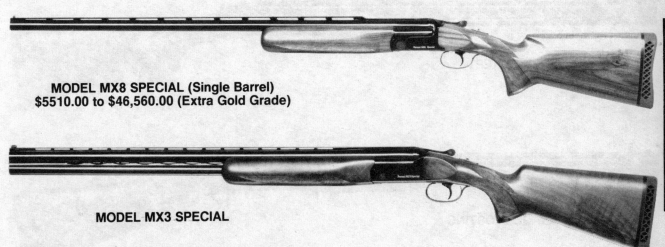

MODEL MX8 SPECIAL (Single Barrel)
$5510.00 to $46,560.00 (Extra Gold Grade)

MODEL MX3 SPECIAL

AMERICAN TRAP SINGLE BARREL MODELS
MX8 SPECIAL, MX3 SPECIAL & GRAND AMERICAN
88 SPECIAL

SPECIFICATIONS
Gauge: 12
Chamber: 2¾"
Barrel lengths: 32" and 34"
Choke: Full
Trigger group: Detachable and interchangeable with flat "V" springs
Stock: Interchangeable and custom made
Forend: Beavertail
Weight: 8 lbs. 6 oz.

Prices:
Standard Grade	$ 4890.00- 5510.00
with Gold Outline	7880.00- 8190.00
SC3 Grade	8240.00- 9370.00
SCO Grade	14,630.00-15,810.00
Gold Grade	16,380.00-17,650.00
Also available:	
SCO & Gold Grade Sideplates	23,480.00-27,040.00
Extra & Extra Gold Grades	43,110.00-46,560.00

PERAZZI SHOTGUNS

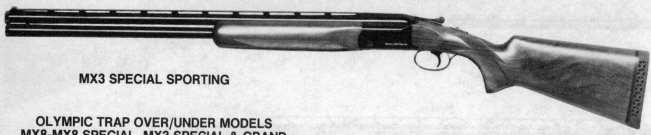

MX3 SPECIAL SPORTING

OLYMPIC TRAP OVER/UNDER MODELS MX8-MX8 SPECIAL, MX3 SPECIAL & GRAND AMERICAN 88 SPECIAL

SPECIFICATIONS
Gauge: 12
Chamber: 2³/₄″
Barrel lengths: 29¹/₂″ and 31¹/₂″ (Grand American 29¹/₂″ only)
Chokes: Imp./Mod. and X Full
Trigger group: Detachable & interchangeable with flat "V" springs
Stock: Interchangeable and custom made
Forend: Beavertail
Weight: 8 lbs. 4¹/₂ oz. (MX8); 8 lbs. 6 oz. (MX3 & Grand American)

Prices:

Model MX8	$5510.00-15,860.00
Model MX8 Special	5770.00-16,070.00
Model MX3 Special	5490.00-15,190.00
Grand American 88 Special	5770.00-16,070.00

Note: Gold Grade, SCO Grade or Gold Sideplates, Extra and Extra Gold Grade and O/U Sidelock Medals are also available at prices ranging from **$17,610.00 to $47,170.00.**

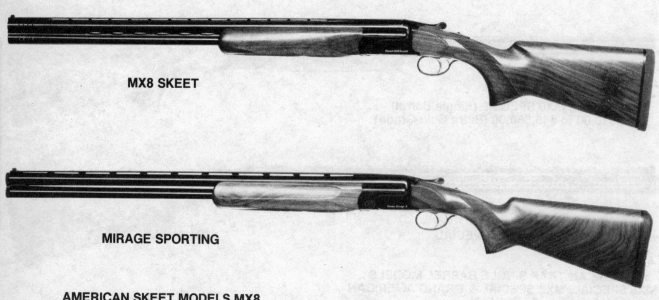

MX8 SKEET

MIRAGE SPORTING

AMERICAN SKEET MODELS MX8 & MIRAGE SPECIAL

SPECIFICATIONS
Gauge: 12
Chamber: 2³/₄″
Barrel length: 27⁵/₈″
Choke: Skeet/Skeet
Trigger group: Detachable and interchangeable with flat "V" springs
Stock: Interchangeable and custom made
Forend: Beavertail

Weight: 7 lbs. 15 oz.
Prices:

Standard Grade	$ 5770.00-	6950.00
with Gold Outline	7880.00-	9940.00
SC3 Grade	9420.00-	9790.00
SCO Grade	15,860.00-	16,330.00
Gold Grade	17,610.00-	18,130.00

PIOTTI SHOTGUNS

One of Italy's top gunmakers, Piotti limits its production to a small number of hand-crafted, best-quality double-barreled shotguns whose shaping, checkering, stock, action and barrel work meets or exceeds the standards achieved in London prior to WWII. The Italian engravings are the finest ever and are becoming recognized as an art form in themselves.

All of the sidelock models exhibit the same overall design, materials and standards of workmanship; they differ only in the quality of the wood, shaping and sculpturing of the action, type of engraving and gold inlay work and other details. The Model Piuma differs from the other shotguns only in its Anson & Deeley boxlock design.

SPECIFICATIONS
Gauges: 10, 12, 16, 20, 28, .410
Chokes: As ordered
Barrels: 12 ga., 25″ to 30″; other gauges, 25″ to 28″; chopper lump (demi-bloc) barrels with soft-luster blued finish; level, file-cut rib or optional concave or ventilated rib
Action: Boxlock, Anson & Deeley; Sidelock, Holland & Holland pattern; both have automatic ejectors, double triggers with front trigger hinged (non-selective single trigger optional), coin finish or optional color case-hardening
Stock: Hand-rubbed oil finish (or optional satin luster) on straight grip stock with checkered butt (pistol grip optional)
Forend: Classic (splinter); optional beavertail
Weight: Ranges from 4 lbs. 15 oz. (.410 ga.) to 8 lbs. (12 ga.)

MODEL PIUMA BOXLOCK
$8900.00

Anson & Deeley boxlock ejector double with chopper lump (demi-bloc) barrels, and scalloped frame. Very attractive scroll and rosette engraving is standard. A number of optional engraving patterns including game scene and gold inlays are available at additional cost.

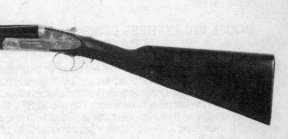

MODEL KING NO. 1 SIDELOCK
$14,800.00

Best-quality Holland & Holland pattern sidelock ejector double with chopper lump barrels, level file-cut rib, very fine, full coverage scroll engraving with small floral bouquets, gold crown in top lever, name in gold, and gold crest in forearm, finely figured wood.

MODEL LUNIK SIDELOCK
$15,800.00

Best-quality Holland & Holland pattern sidelock ejector double with chopper lump (demi-bloc) barrels, level, filecut rib, Renaissance-style, large scroll engraving in relief, gold crown in top lever, gold name, and gold crest in forearm, finely figured wood.

MODEL KING EXTRA (With Gold)
$22,500.00

Best-quality Holland & Holland pattern sidelock ejector double with chopper lump barrels, level filecut rib, choice of either bulino game scene engraving or game scene engraving with gold inlays, engraved and signed by a master engraver, exhibition grade wood.

REMINGTON SHOTGUNS

PARKER AHE SHOTGUN
$14,100.00

Produced by the Parker Gun Works (a division of Remington Arms Company at Ilion, N.Y.), this new version of a time-honored American firearms tradition is available in 20 gauge AHE Grade. It will be handcrafted in limited quantities on special order from the Remington Custom Shop. The Parker model features a new single selective trigger mechanism, the first new side-by-side trigger design in over 60 years. Automatic ejectors have a more simplified and reliable design, as do the updated automatic safeties. Stocks are produced from highly select Circassian or American walnut, and custom checkering

(28 lines/inch) adorns both forend and butt stock, with AHE-grade side panels on each side of the tang. Fine-scroll engraving and game scenes decorate the casehardened receivers.

Additional specifications include **Barrel length:** 28″. **Chambers:** 2³/₄″. **Weight:** 6¹/₂ lbs. Raised ventilated ribs are standard, with front and mid-barrel ivory beads. Customers may specify stock dimensions and any combination of chokes, including Skeet, Improved Cylinder, Modified and Full.

MODEL 870 EXPRESS MAGNUM

MODEL 870 EXPRESS (12 GAUGE)
$261.00

Model 870 Express features the same action as the Wingmaster and is available with 3″ chamber and 28″ vent-rib barrel only. It has a hardwood stock with low-luster finish and solid butt pad. Choke is Modified REM Choke tube and wrench. **Overall length:** 48¹/₂″. **Weight:** 7¹/₄ lbs.

MODEL 870 EXPRESS COMBO (not shown)
$358.00

Model 870 Express offers all the features of the standard Model 870, including twin-action bars, quick-changing barrels, REM Choke plus low-luster, checkered hardwood stock and no-shine finish on barrel and receiver. The Model 870 Combo is packaged with an extra 20″ deer barrel, fitted with rifle sights and fixed, Improved Cylinder choke (additional REM chokes can be added for special applications). The 3-inch chamber handles all 12 gauge ammo without adjustment.

REMINGTON PUMP SHOTGUNS

MODEL 870 "TC" TRAP (12 GAUGE ONLY)
$612.00 ($625.00 w/Monte Carlo Stock)

The **870 "TC"** is a trap version of Model 870 that features REM Choke and a high step-up ventilated rib. REM chokes include regular full, extra full and super full. **Stock:** Redesigned stock and forend of select American walnut with cut-checkering and satin finish; length of pull 14³/₈"; drop at heel 1⁷/₈"; drop at comb 1³/₈". **Weight:** 8¹/₂ lbs. **Barrel length:** 30".

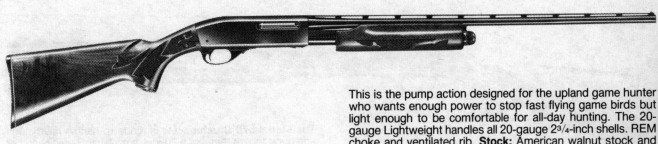

MODEL 870 • 20 GAUGE LIGHTWEIGHT
$469.00

This is the pump action designed for the upland game hunter who wants enough power to stop fast flying game birds but light enough to be comfortable for all-day hunting. The 20-gauge Lightweight handles all 20-gauge 2³/₄-inch shells. REM choke and ventilated rib. **Stock:** American walnut stock and forend. **Barrel lengths:** 26" and 28". **Average weight:** 6 lbs.

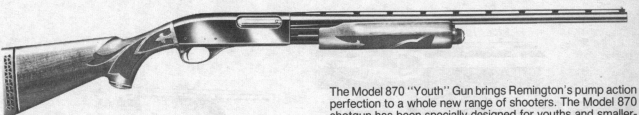

MODEL 870 "YOUTH" GUN
20 Gauge Lightweight
$452.00

The Model 870 "Youth" Gun brings Remington's pump action perfection to a whole new range of shooters. The Model 870 shotgun has been specially designed for youths and smaller-sized adults. It's a 20-gauge lightweight with a 1-inch shorter stock and 5-inch shorter barrel. Yet it is still all 870, complete with REM Choke and ventilated rib barrel. **Barrel length:** 21". **Stock Dimensions:** Length of pull 12¹/₂" (including recoil pad); drop at heel; 2¹/₂" drop at comb 1⁵/₈". **Overall length:** 40". **Average Weight:** 6 lbs. **Choke:** Mod. and Imp. Cyl.

REMINGTON PUMP SHOTGUNS

MODEL 870 WINGMASTER 12 GAUGE
$469.00 ($528.00 Left Hand)

This new restyled 870 "Wingmaster" pump has cut checkering on its satin finished American walnut stock and forend for confident handling, even in wet weather. An ivory bead "Bradley" type front sight is included. Rifle is available with 26", 28" and 30" barrel with REM Choke and handles 3" and 2¾" shells interchangeably. **Overall length:** 46½ (26" barrel), 48½" (28" barrel), 50½" (30" barrel). **Weight:** 7¼ lbs.

Also available: **WINGMASTER LEFT HAND DEER GUN** with Imp. Cyl. and rifle sights, 12 gauge only. **Barrel length:** 20". **Price:** Left-hand model: $485.00

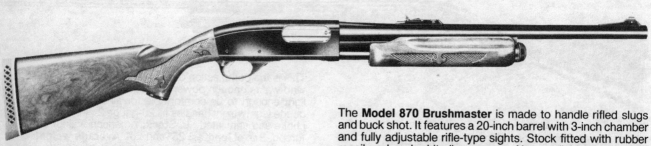

MODEL 870 DEER GUN
$443.00 ($412.00 in Lightweight 20 Ga.)

The **Model 870 Brushmaster** is made to handle rifled slugs and buck shot. It features a 20-inch barrel with 3-inch chamber and fully adjustable rifle-type sights. Stock fitted with rubber recoil pad and white-line spacer. Also available in standard model, but with lacquer finish, no checkering, recoil pad, grip cap; special handy short forend. **Choke:** Imp. Cyl. **Weight:** 6¼ lbs.

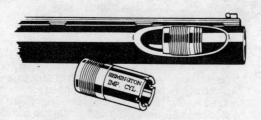

"REM" CHOKE TUBES

TURKEY EXTRA FULL CHOKE TUBE

REMINGTON PUMP SHOTGUNS

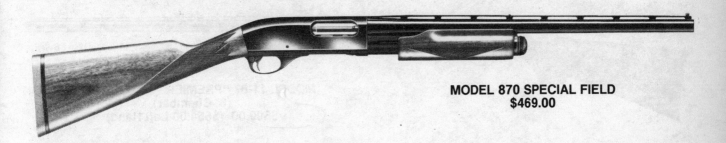

MODEL 870 SPECIAL FIELD
$469.00

The **Model 870 "Special Field"** shotgun combines the traditional, straight-stock styling of years past with features never before available on a Remington pump. Its 21-inch vent rib barrel, slimmed and shortened forend, straight, cut-checkered stock offers upland hunters a quick, fast-pointing shotgun.

The "Special Field" is chambered for 3-inch shells and will also handle all 2¾-inch shells interchangeably. Barrels will not interchange with standard 870 barrels. **Overall length:** 41½". **Weight:** 7 lbs. (12 ga.); 6 lbs. (20 ga.).

MODEL 870 SPECIAL PURPOSE MAGNUM
$469.00

Available in 12 gauge Magnum with 3-inch Mag. chamber, the **Model 870 SP (Special Purpose) Magnum** pump gun has been designed with waterfowlers and turkey hunters in mind. For concealment, all metal surfaces have been finished in non-glare, non-reflective Parkerized black. And all wood surfaces have been given a dull, non-reflective oil finish with a slightly rough feel for firmer grip. For ease of carrying, the SP Mag. Pump comes factory-equipped with a camo-patterned padded

sling, attached at both ends by quick-detachable sling swivels. More than 2 inches wide at the shoulder, the sling is made of durable Du Pont nylon "Cordura." **Barrel:** 26" or 28" chrome-lined barrel bore; ventilated rib. **Choke:** Full. **Stock:** Supplied with dark-colored recoil pad and black line spacers. **Overall length:** 46½" with 26" barrel; 48½" with 28" barrel. **Weight:** Approx. 7¼ lbs.

MODEL 870 SPECIAL PURPOSE DEER GUN
$443.00

Gauge: 12. **Choke:** Imp. Cyl. Equipped with rifle sights, recoil pad. **Barrel length:** 20". **Overall length:** 40½." **Average weight:** 7 lbs.

Also available with cantilever barrel for scope mounting and Extra Full Turkey choke. **Price:** $496.00.

REMINGTON SHOTGUNS

MODEL 11-87 "PREMIER" AUTOLOADER
(3" Chamber)
$599.00 ($654.00 Left Hand)

Model 11-87 "Premier" with REM Choke offers the dependability of a pump along with the easy shootability of an autoloader, the magnum power of a waterfowl gun, and the light handling of an upland gun. This new shotgun's standout attraction to the practical shooter is its ability to handle a broad variety of 12-gauge ammunition interchangeably. Switching from light, 2³/₄" field loads to heavy 3" magnums is simply a matter of inserting different shotgun shells. A new, patented pressure compensating gas system accomplishes this without the need for adjustments. An additional bonus to shooters is a 50 percent increase in overall performance endurance, revealed by extensive testing. Among the factors contributing to this high level of dependability and durability are:

- Extractor 30 percent thicker
- A redesigned, more durable firing pin retractor spring
- Heat treated pistol and piston seal
- Corrosion and rust resistant stainless steel magazine tube

The standard version of the 11-87 "Premier" shotgun is available in three ventilated rib barrel lengths: 26", 28" and 30"—all with REM Choke. A left-hand mirror image version is available in 28" only. The stock is satin finished with new cut-checkering (20 lines per inch), featuring a "floating diamond" motif. Also, there's a solid brown presentation-type butt pad and a grip cap with Remington's new "RA" logo. Forend has the same satin finish and checkering pattern. Barrel and receiver have Bradley-type white-faced front sight and metal bead on barrel.

MODEL 11-87 PREMIER TRAP 12 GAUGE
$662.00
$677.00 (w/Monte Carlo Stock)

A 30" trap barrel offers trap shooters a REM Choke system with three interchangeable choke constrictions: trap full, trap extra full, and trap super full.

MODEL 11-87 PREMIER SHOTGUNS

Gauge	Barrel Length & Choke	Overall length	Avg. Wt. (lbs.)
12	30" REM Choke	50¹/₂	8³/₈
	28" REM Choke	48¹/₄	8¹/₄
	28" REM Choke	48¹/₄	8¹/₄
	26" REM Choke	46	8¹/₈

EXTRA BARRELS. 11-87 barrels are not interchangeable with the Remington Model 1100. Also, target barrels are designed for optimal performance with target loads and therefore are not pressure compensated. These guns will, however, be pressure compensating and shoot all 12-gauge loads when equipped with an 11-87 Premier field barrel.

MODEL 11-87 PREMIER SKEET 12 GAUGE
$654.00

This model features American walnut wood and distinctive cut checkering with satin finish, plus new two-piece butt plate. REM Choke system includes option of two skeet chokes—skeet and improved skeet. Trap and skeet guns are designed for 12-gauge target loads and are set to handle 2³/₄" shells only.

REMINGTON SHOTGUNS

MODEL 11-87 SPECIAL PURPOSE MAGNUM
$599.00

Features non-reflective wood and metal finish for all types of hunting where concealment is critical. Exposed metal surfaces of both barrel and receiver are Parkerized; bolt and carrier have non-glare blackened coloring. **Barrel lengths:** 26″ and 28″. **Chamber:** 3″. **Choke:** REM Choke.

MODEL 11-87 SPECIAL PURPOSE DEER GUN
3″ MAGNUM
$580.00

Features same finish as other SP models plus a padded, camostyle carrying sling of Cordura nylon with Q.D. sling swivels. Barrel is 21″ with rifle sights and rifled and IC choke (handles all 2¾″ and 3″ rifled slug and buckshot loads as well as high-velocity field and magnum loads; does not function with light 2¾″ field loads).

Also available with cantilever barrel and rings for scope mount. Includes interchangeable rifled and IC ''REM'' chokes. **Price: $621.00.**

SP-10 MAGNUM SHOTGUN
$1265.00

Remington's new SP-10 Magnum is the only gas-operated semiautomatic 10 gauge shotgun made today. Engineered to shoot steel shot, the SP-10 delivers up to 34 percent more pellets to the target than standard 12 gauge shotgun and steel shot combinations. This autoloader features a non-corrosive, stainless steel gas system, in which the cylinder moves—not the piston. This reduces felt recoil energy by spreading the recoil over a longer period of time. The SP-10 has a ³/₈″ vent rib with middle and front sights for a better sight plane. It is also designed to appear virtually invisible to the sharp eyes of waterfowl. The American walnut stock and forend have a protective, low-gloss satin finish that reduces glare, and positive deep-cut checkering for a sure grip. The receiver and barrel have a matte finish, and the stainless steel breech bolt features a non-reflective finish. Remington's new autoloader also has a brown vented recoil pad and a padded camo sling of Cordura nylon for easy carrying. The receiver is machined from a solid billet of ordnance steel for total integral strength. The SP-10 vented gas system reduces powder residue buildup and makes cleaning easier.

Gauge: 10. **Barrel lengths & choke:** 26″ REM Choke and 30″ REM Choke. **Overall length:** 51½″ (30″ barrel) and 47½″ (26″ barrel). **Weight:** 11¼ lbs. (30″ barrel) and 11 lbs. (26″ barrel).

REMINGTON AUTOLOADING SHOTGUNS

MODEL 1100 AUTOLOADING SHOTGUNS

The Remington Model 1100 is a 5-shot gas-operated autoloading shotgun with a gas metering system designed to reduce recoil effect. This design enables the shooter to use all 2¾-inch standard velocity "Express" and 2¾-inch Magnum loads without any gun adjustments. Barrels, within gauge and versions, are interchangeable. The 1100 is made in gauges of 12, Lightweight 20, 28 and .410. All 12 and 20 gauge versions include REM Choke; interchangeable choke tubes in 26" and 28" (12 gauge only) barrels. The solid-steel receiver features decorative scroll work. Stocks come with fine-line checkering in a fleur-de-lis design combined with American walnut and a scratch-resistant finish. Features include white-diamond inlay in pistol-grip cap, white-line spacers, full beavertail forend, fluted-comb cuts, chrome-plated bolt and metal bead front sight. Made in U.S.A.

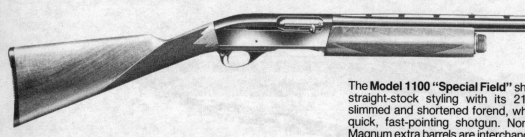

MODEL 1100 SPECIAL FIELD (12 GAUGE)
$583.00

The **Model 1100 "Special Field"** shotgun combines traditional, straight-stock styling with its 21-inch vent-rib barrel and slimmed and shortened forend, which offer upland hunters a quick, fast-pointing shotgun. Non-engraved receiver; non-Magnum extra barrels are interchangeable with standard Model 1100 barrels. **Overall length:** 41". **Stock dimensions:** Length of pull 14⅛"; drop at comb 1½"; drop at heel 2½". **Choke:** REM Choke system. **Weight:** 7¼ lbs. (12 ga.); 6½ lbs. (20 ga.).

MODEL 1100 3″ MAGNUM
20 Lightweight Gauge
$583.00

Designed for 3-inch and 2¾-inch Magnum shells; accepts and functions with any 1100 standard 2¾-inch chambered barrel. Available in 20 gauge, 26" or 28" (ventilated rib optional) barrels. **Stock dimensions:** 14" long including pad; 1½" drop at comb; furnished with recoil pad. **Weight:** About 7 lbs.

MODEL 1100 DEER GUN
Lightweight 20 Gauges
$525.00

Features 20-inch (LT-20 gauge) barrels, Improved Cylinder choke. Rifle sights adjustable for windage and elevation. Recoil pad. Choked for both rifled slugs and buck shot. **Weight:** 6½ lbs. **Overall length:** 40".

REMINGTON AUTOLOADING SHOTGUNS

MODEL 1100 TOURNAMENT SKEET
$662.00

The world's winningest skeet gun, with high-grade positive cut-checkering on selected American walnut stock and forend. The LT-20, 28 and .410 gauge Model 1100 Tournament Skeet guns have a higher vent rib to match the sight picture of the 12-gauge model. A true "matched set," with all the reliability, superb balance, and low recoil sensation that make it the choice of over 50% of the entrants in the world skeet shooting championships. **Barrel length:** 26" 5. **Choke:** REM Choke (20 ga.) and Skeet choke (28 and .410 ga.). **Weight:** 6³/₄ lbs. (20 ga.), 6¹/₂ lbs. (28 ga.), 7¹/₄ lbs. (.410 ga.).

MODEL 1100 VENTILATED RIB
28 and .410 Gauges
$625.00

The Remington Model 1100 Autoloading shotguns in 28 and .410 gauges are scaled-down models of the 12-gauge version. Built on their own receivers and frames, these small gauge shotguns are available in full (.410 only) and modified chokes with ventilated rib barrels.

SPECIFICATIONS. Type: Gas-operated. **Capacity:** 5-shot with 28 ga. shells; 4-shot with 3" .410 ga. shells; 3-shot plug furnished. **Barrel:** 25" of special Remington ordnance steel; extra barrels interchangeable within gauge. **Chamber:** 3" in .410, 2³/₄" in 28 ga. **Overall length:** 45". **Safety:** Convenient cross-bolt type. **Receiver:** Made from solid steel, top matted, scroll work on bolt and both sides of receiver. **Stock dimensions:** Walnut; 14" long; 2¹/₂" drop at heel; 1¹/₂" drop at comb. **Average weight:** 6¹/₂ lbs. (28 ga.); 7 lbs. (.410).

MODEL 1100 LT-20 YOUTH GUN • LIGHTWEIGHT
20 Gauge Only
$569.00

The Model 1100 LT-20 Youth Gun autoloading shotgun features a shorter barrel (21") and stock. **Overall length:** 39¹/₂". **Weight:** 6¹/₂ lbs.

REMINGTON SHOTGUNS

MODEL 90-T SINGLE BARREL TRAP GUN

Remington's new Model 90-T Single Barrel Trap gun features a top-lever release and internal, full-width, horizontal bolt lockup. Barrels are overbored, with elongated forcing cones, and are available in 30″, 32″ and 34″ lengths (an optional, heavier 34″ barrel can also be ordered). Shooters can choose barrels with either fixed chokes or Remington's interchangeable Trap Choke system. A medium-high, tapered, ventilated rib includes a white, Bradley-type front bead and stainless steel center bead. Choice of stocks includes Monte Carlo style with 1³/₈″, 1¹/₂″ or 1¹/₄″ drop at comb, or a conventional straight stock with 1¹/₂″ drop. Standard length of pull is 14³/₈″. Stocks and modified beavertail forends are made from semi-fancy American walnut. Wood finish is low-lustre satin with positive, deep-cut checkering 20 lines to the inch. All stocks come with black, vented-rubber recoil pads. A standard Model 90-T Super Single weighs approx. 8³/₄ lbs. **Price: $2595.00**

ROSSI SHOTGUNS

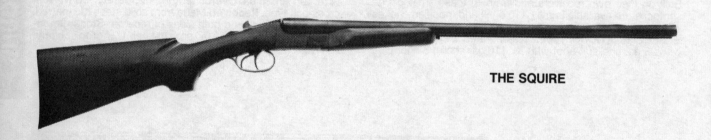

THE SQUIRE

SQUIRE DOUBLE. Available in .410 bore or 12 or 20 gauge, the Squire has 3-inch chambers to handle the full range of shotgun loads. Features double triggers, raised matted rib, beavertail forend and pistol grip. Twin underlugs mesh with synchronized sliding bolts for double-safe solid lockup.

Gauge	Barrel Length	Choke	Price
12	20″	IC&M	**$350.00**
12	28″	M&F	**350.00**
20	26″	IC&M	**350.00**
.410 bore	26″	F&F	**360.00**

RUGER SHOTGUNS

RUGER RED LABEL OVER/UNDER 20 GAUGE
$1102.50

Hardened chrome molybdenum, other alloy steels and music wire coil springs are used throughout. Features single-selective trigger, automatic top safety, standard gold bead front sight. Stock and semi-beavertail forearm are shaped from American walnut with hand-cut checkering (20 lines per inch). Pistol grip cap and rubber recoil pad are standard, and all wood surfaces are polished and beautifully finished. Stainless steel receiver available on 12 gauge version; 20 gauge is satin polished and blued. Also available in 12 gauge with **stainless receiver: $1102.50**

RUGER SCREW-IN CHOKE INSERTS

Designed especially for the popular 12 gauge "Red Label" over/under shotgun. Easily installed with a key wrench packaged with each shotgun. Choke fits flush with the muzzle. Every shotgun is equipped with a Full, Modified, Improved Cylinder and two Skeet screw-in chokes. The muzzle edge of the chokes has been slotted for quick identification in or out of the barrels. Full choke has 3 slots; Modified has 2 slots, and Improved Cylinder has 1 slot (Skeet has no slots).

SPECIFICATIONS
OVER & UNDER SHOTGUNS WITH SCREW-IN CHOKES

Catalog Number	Gauge	Chamber	Choke	Barrel Length	Overall Length	Length of Pull	Drop at Comb	Drop at Heel	*Sights	Approx. Weight (pounds)
KRL-1226	12	3″	F,M,IC,S	26″	42⁷⁄₈	14″	1¹⁄₂″	2¹⁄₂″	GBF	7¹⁄₂
KRL-1227	12	3″	F,M,IC,S	28″	44⁷⁄₈	14″	1¹⁄₂″	2¹⁄₂″	GBF	7¹⁄₂
KRL-2029	20	3″	F,IM,C,S	26″	43″	14″	1¹⁄₂″	2¹⁄₂″	GBF	7
KRL-2030	20	3″	F,M,IC,S	28″	45″	14″	1¹⁄₂″	2¹⁄₂″	GBF	7

F-Full, M-Modified, IC-Improved Cylinder; S-Skeet, GBF-Gold Bead Front Sight.

SAVAGE SHOTGUNS

MODEL 312 FIELD

MODEL 312 TRAP

MODEL 312 SPORTING CLAY

MODEL 312 OVER & UNDERS

Savage's new Model 312 over/under shotguns feature select walnut stocks and fine cut checkering. The 312 also features internal hammers with an unbreakable coil mainspring and positive extraction. The safety also acts as a barrel selector. All three versions—Field, Trap and Sporting Clay—have a ventilated rib and ivory bead front sights. All specifications are listed in the table below.

Prices:
MODEL 312F (FIELD) **$779.61**
MODEL 312T (TRAP) **828.24**
MODEL 312SC (SPORTING CLAY) **850.20**

SPECIFICATIONS

Shotgun	Gauge	Chamber	Chokes	Barrel Length	O.A. Length	Pull	Avg. Wt. Lbs.	Stock
312 Field	12	2³/₄ & 3″	Full Mod IC with wrench	26″ or 28″	43″ or 45″	14″	7	Cut Checkered Walnut with Recoil Pad
312 Trap	12	2³/₄ & 3″	Full (2) Mod with wrench	30″	47″	14″	7¹/₄	Cut Checkered Walnut Monte Carlo with Recoil Pad
312 Sporting Clays	12	2³/₄ & 3″	Full IC(2) Mod (2) #1 Skeet (1) #2 Skeet (1) with wrench	28″	45″	14″	7	Cut Checkered Walnut with Recoil Pad

Features: Ivory bead front sights, metal bead mid sight, internal hammers, positive extraction & manually operated top tang safety that acts as a barrel selector, (312 field has automatic safety feature.)

SKB SHOTGUNS

GAS-OPERATED AUTOMATICS FOR FIELD & TRAP

MODEL 1900
$682.50

Same specifications as Model 1300, but includes Field Outdoor Scene engraved on receiver with gold trigger and Interchoke. Also available: **Deluxe Auto Trap** (12 ga. only with 2³/₄″ chamber). **Price: $695.50**

MODEL 1300 UPLAND (not shown)
$643.50

SPECIFICATIONS
Gauges: 12 and 20
Chambers: 3″
Choke: Interchoke
Barrel lengths: 26″ and 28″ (Field); 30″ (Trap)
Overall length: 48¹/₄″ (Field); 50¹¹/₁₆″ (Trap)
Weight: 6 lbs. 6 oz. (20 ga.); 7 lbs. 4 oz. (12 ga.)
Also available: **SLUG GUN** with sights (22″ barrel), 12 ga. only.
Price: $643.50

OVER & UNDER FIELD HUNTING GUNS

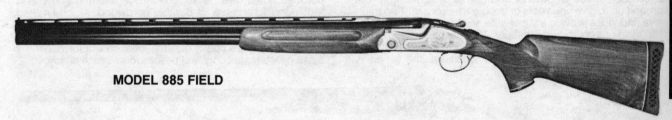

MODEL 885 FIELD

MODEL 885
SPECIFICATIONS
Gauge: 12
Chambers: 2³/₄″
Choke: Interchoke
Barrel lengths: 30″, 32″, 34″
Overall length: 47³/₈″
Weight: 8 lbs. 2 oz.
Stock: Standard or Monte Carlo
Finish: Silver engraved receiver
Also available: **MODEL 605**—Same specifications as Model 885, but without engraving on side plate. **MODEL 505**—Same specifications as Models 885 and 605, but with blued receiver.

Prices:

MODEL 885 FIELD	$1735.50
MODEL 885 TRAP or SKEET	1750.00
MODEL 885 SPORTING CLAY	1775.00
MODEL 605 FIELD	1280.00
MODEL 605 TRAP or SKEET	1295.00
MODEL 605 SPORTING CLAY	1315.00
MODEL 505 DELUXE FIELD	1038.50
MODEL 505 DELUXE TRAP or SKEET	1072.50
Also available: **THREE-BARREL SKEET SETS**	
MODEL 885	$3250.00
MODEL 605	2645.00
MODEL 505	2457.00

STOEGER SHOTGUNS

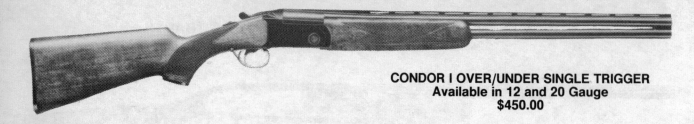

CONDOR I OVER/UNDER SINGLE TRIGGER
Available in 12 and 20 Gauge
$450.00

The **STOEGER OVER/UNDER SINGLE TRIGGER** is a work-horse of a shotgun, designed for maximum dependability in heavy field use. The super-safe lock-up system makes use of a sliding underlug, the best system for over/under shotguns. A massive monobloc joins the barrel in a solid one-piece assembly at the breech end. Reliability is assured, thanks to the mechanical extraction system. Upon opening the breech, the spent shells are partially lifted from the chamber, allowing easy removal by hand. Stoeger barrels are of chrome-moly steel with micro-polished bores to give tight, consistent patterns.

They are specifically formulated for use with steel shot where Federal migratory bird regulations require. Atop the barrel is a sighting rib with an anti-glare surface. The buttstock and forend are of durable hardwood, hand-checkered and finished with an oil-based formula that takes dents and scratches in stride.

The Stoeger over/under shotgun is available in 12 or 20 gauge with 26-inch barrels choked Imp. Cyl./Mod. with 3-inch chambers; 12 or 20 gauge with 28-inch barrels choked Mod./Full, 3-inch chambers; 12 or 20 gauge with 26" barrels choked Skeet/Skeet.

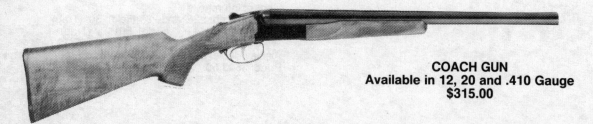

COACH GUN
Available in 12, 20 and .410 Gauge
$315.00

The **STOEGER CLASSIC SIDE-BY-SIDE COACH GUN** sports a 20-inch barrel. Lightning fast, it is the perfect shotgun for hunting upland game in dense brush or close quarters. This endurance-tested workhorse of a gun is designed from the ground up to give you years of trouble-free service. Two massive underlugs provide a super-safe, vise-tight locking system for lasting strength and durability. The mechanical extraction of spent shells and double-trigger mechanism assure reliability. The automatic safety is actuated whenever the action is

opened, whether or not the gun has been fired. The polish and blue is deep and rich, and the solid sighting rib is matte-finished for glare-free sighting. Chrome-moly steel barrels with micro-polished bores give dense, consistent patterns. The classic stock and forend are of durable hardwood . . . oil finished, hand-rubbed and hand-checkered.

Improved Cylinder/Modified choking and its short barrel make the Stoeger coach gun the ideal choice for hunting in close quarters, security and police work. 3-inch chambers.

UPLANDER SIDE-BY-SIDE
Available in 12, 20, 28 and .410 gauge
$330.00

The **STOEGER SIDE-BY-SIDE** is a rugged shotgun, endurance-tested and designed to give years of trouble-free service. A vise-tight, super-safe locking system is provided by two massive underlugs for lasting strength and durability. Two design features which make the Stoeger a standout for reliability are its positive mechanical extraction of spent shells and its traditional double-trigger mechanism. The safety is automatic

in that every time the action is opened, whether the gun has been fired or not, the safety is actuated. The polish and blue is deep and rich. The solid sighting rib carries a machined-in matte finish for glare-free sighting. Barrels are of chrome-moly steel with micro-polished bores to give dense, consistent patterns. The stock and forend are of classic design in durable hardwood . . . oil finished, hand-rubbed and hand-checkered.

STOEGER SHOTGUNS

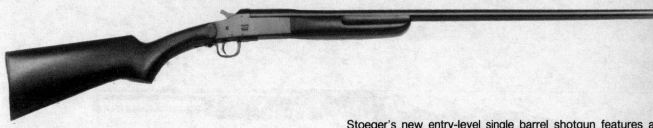

SINGLE BARREL
$110.00

Stoeger's new entry-level single barrel shotgun features a unique locking system. By pulling rearward on the trigger guard, the underlug engagement is released, thus opening the action. Single mechanical extraction makes for convenient removal of spent shells. For ease of operation and maximum safety, this single barrel shotgun is equipped with an exposed hammer, which must be cocked manually. A half-cocked setting on the hammer provides the safety mode.

The buttstock and semi-beavertail forearm are of durable Brazilian hardwood. Stoeger's new single barrel shotgun is available in 12, 20 gauge, and .410 bore.

STOEGER SHOTGUN SPECIFICATIONS

Model	Gauge	Chokes	Chamber	Barrel Length	Length of Pull	Drop at Comb	Drop at Heel	Approx. Average Weight	Safety	Extractors
Single Barrel	12	M, F, IC	2³/4″	28″/26″	14¹/2″	1¹/2″	2¹/2″	5¹/8 lbs.	Manual	Yes
	20	M, F, IC	3″	28″/26″	14¹/2″	1¹/2″	2¹/2″	5¹/8 lbs.	Manual	Yes
	.410	F	3″	26″	14¹/2″	1¹/2″	2¹/2″	5¹/8 lbs.	Manual	Yes
Side-by-Side	12	M/F IC&M	3″	28″/26″	14¹/2″	1¹/2″	2¹/2″	7 lbs.	Automatic	Yes
	20	M/F IC&M	3″	28″/26″	14¹/2″	1¹/2″	2¹/2″	6³/4 lbs.	Automatic	Yes
	28	IC/M	2³/4″	26″	14¹/2″	1¹/2″	2¹/2″	7 lbs.	Automatic	Yes
	.410	F/F	3″	26″	14¹/2″	1¹/2″	2¹/2″	7 lbs.	Automatic	Yes
Over/Under	12	M/F IC&M	3″	28″/26″	14¹/2″	1¹/2″	2¹/2″	7 lbs.	Manual	Yes
	20	M/F IC/M	3″	28″/26″	14¹/2″	1¹/2″	2¹/2″	7 lbs.	Automatic	Yes
Coach Gun	12	IC&M	3″	20″	14¹/2″	1¹/2″	2¹/2″	6¹/2 lbs.	Automatic	Yes
	20	IC&M	3″	20″	14¹/2″	1¹/2″	2¹/2″	6¹/2 lbs.	Automatic	Yes
	.410	IC/M	3″	20″	14¹/2″	1¹/2″	2¹/2″	6³/4 lbs.	Automatic	Yes

SHOTGUNS

TIKKA SHOTGUNS

TIKKA 412S SHOTGUN/RIFLE
$1135.00

Tikka's unique 412S Shotgun/Rifle combination continues to be the most popular gun of its type in the U.S. Its features are identical to the 412S Field Grade over/under shotguns, including strong steel receiver, superior sliding locking mechanism with automatic safety, cocking indicators, mechanical triggers and two-piece firing pin. In addition, note the other features of this model—

Barrel regulation: Adjusts for windage simply by turning the screw on the muzzle. Elevation is adjustable by regulating the sliding wedge located between the barrels.

Compact: 24-inch barrels mounted on the low-profile receiver limit the overall length to 40 inches (about 5″ less than most bolt-action rifles with similar 24-inch barrels).

Single selective trigger: A barrel selector is located on the trigger for quick, easy selection. Double triggers are also available.

Choice of calibers: Choose from 222 or 308. Both are under the 12 gauge, 3″ chamber with Improved Modified choke.

Sighting options: The vent rib is cross-filed to reduce glare. The rear sight is flush-folding and permits rapid alignment with the large blade front sight. The rib is milled to accommodate Tikka's one-piece scope mount with 1″ rings. Scope mount is of ''quick release'' design and can be removed without altering zero.

American walnut stock: Stocks are available with palm swell for greater control and comfort. Quick detachable sling swivel. Length or pitch adjustable with factory spacers. Semi-Monte Carlo design.

Interchangeability: Receiver will accommodate Tikka's 12 and 20 gauge over/under shotgun barrels and double-rifle barrels with minor initial fitting.

SPECIFICATIONS
Gauge/Caliber: 12/222 or 12/308
Chamber: 3″ with Improved Modified choke
Barrel length: 24″
Overall length: 40″
Weight: 8 lbs.
Stock: American walnut with semi-Monte Carlo design

TIKKA SHOTGUNS

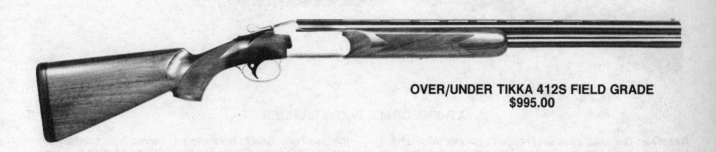

OVER/UNDER TIKKA 412S FIELD GRADE
$995.00

Designed for the experienced hunter, Tikka's 412S represents the pride and skill of "Old World" European craftsmanship. The barrels are polished to a mirror finish and deeply blued. Select American walnut stock and forearm highlight fine, deep-cut checkering. Other features include:

Time-proven action: Designed to handle large centerfire calibers for more durability and reliability.

Mechanical trigger: Fires two shots as fast as you can pull the trigger. Does not rely on the inertia from the recoil of the first shot to set the trigger for the second. In the event of a faulty primer or light hit, inertia trigger shotguns cannot function on the second round.

Single selective trigger: Selector button is located on the trigger for fast, easy selection.

Large trigger guard opening: Designed for cold weather shooting; permits easy finger movement when wearing gloves.

American walnut stock and forearm: Add greatly to overall appearance.

Superior stock design: A palm swell provides additional hand comfort. Length and angle (pitch) can be altered for a perfect fit with addition of factory spacers. Fine, deep-cut checkering.

Palm-filling forearm: Rounded and tapered for comfort and smooth, true swing, plus fine, deep-cut checkering.

Automatic ejectors: Select and eject fired rounds. Raise unfired shells for safe removal.

Chrome-lined barrels: For more consistent patterns. Eliminates pitting and corrosion, extends barrel life even with steel shot.

Stainless steel choke tubes: Added strength over regular carbon and alloy materials. Easily handles steel shot. Recessed so as not to detract from appearance. Tight tolerances enable truer patterns and enhance choke versatility.

Sliding locking bolt: Secure lockup between receiver and barrels. Wears in, not loose.

Matte nickel receiver: Non-glare and more resistant to wear and corrosion.

Wide vent rib: Cross-file pattern reduces glare. Fluorescent front and middle beads.

Automatic safety: Goes to safe position automatically when gun is opened.

Cocking indicators: Allow shooter to determine (through sight or feel) which barrel has been fired.

Steel receiver: Forged and machined for durability.

Chamber: 3-inch on all models

Two-piece firing pin: For more durability

Versatility: Change from 12 to 20 gauge simply by adding a barrel. Change from over/under shotgun to shotgun/rifle, trap, skeet or double rifle. Precision tolerances require only minor initial fitting.

SPECIFICATIONS
Gauge: 12
Chambers: 3"
Weight: 7¼ lbs. w/26" barrels; 7½ lbs. w/28" or 30" barrels
Barrel lengths/chokes:
   26", 5 chokes (F, M, IM, IC & Skeet)
   28", 5 chokes (F, M, IM, IC & Skeet)

WEATHERBY SHOTGUNS

ATHENA GRADE IV OVER/UNDER

Receiver: The Athena receiver houses a strong, reliable box-lock action, yet it features side lock-type plates to carry through the fine floral engraving. The hinge pivots are made of a special high strength steel alloy. The locking system employs the time-tested Greener cross-bolt design. **Single selective trigger:** It is mechanically rather than recoil operated. This provides a fully automatic switchover, allowing the second barrel to be fired on a subsequent trigger pull, even in the event of a misfire. A flick of the trigger finger and the selector lever, located just in front of the trigger, is all the way to the left enabling you to fire the lower barrel first, or to the right for the upper barrel. The Athena trigger is selective as well. **Barrels:** The breech block is hand-fitted to the receiver, providing closest possible tolerances. Every Athena is equipped with a matted, ventilated rib and bead front sight. **Selective automatic ejectors:** The Athena contains ejectors that are fully automatic both in selection and action. **Slide safety:** The safety is the traditional slide type located conveniently on the upper tang on top of the pistol grip. **Stock:** Each stock is carved from specially selected Claro walnut, with fine line hand-checkering and high luster finish. Trap model has Monte Carlo stock only. *See Athena and Orion table for additional information and specifications.*

GRADE IV PRICES:
Fixed Choke:
Field, 28 or .410 Ga.	**$1675.00**
Skeet, 12 or 20 Ga.	**1690.00**

IMC Multi Choke:
Field, 12 or 20 Ga.	**1675.00***
Trap, 12 Ga.	**1695.00**
Trap, single barrel, 12 Ga.	**1695.00**
Trap Combo, 12 Ga.	**2240.00**
Athena Master Skeet (tube set w/case)	**3360.00**

* Available in **GRADE V** with custom
metal engraving **2100.00**

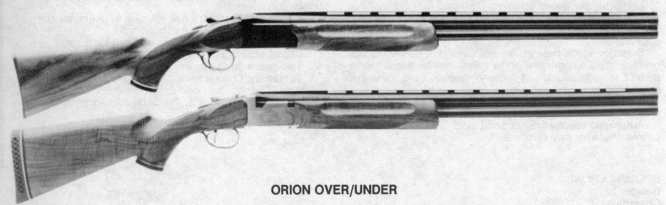

ORION OVER/UNDER

For greater versatility, the Orion incorporates the integral multichoke (IMC) system. Available in Extra-full, Full, Modified, Improved Modified, Improved Cylinder and Skeet, the choke tubes fit flush with the muzzle without detracting from the beauty of the gun. Three tubes are furnished with each gun. The precision hand-fitted monobloc and receiver are machined from high-strength steel with a highly polished finish. The boxlock design uses the Greener cross-bolt locking system and special sears maintain hammer engagement. Pistol grip stock and forearm are carved of Claro walnut with hand-checkered diamond inlay pattern and high-gloss finish. Chrome moly steel barrels, and the receiver, are deeply blued. The Orion also features selective automatic ejectors, single selective trigger, front bead sight and ventilated rib. The trap model boasts a curved trap-style recoil pad and is available with Monte Carlo stock only. **Weight:** 12 ga. Field, 7½ lbs.; 20 ga. Field, 7½ lbs.; Trap, 8 lbs.

ORION PRICES:
Grade I
IMC Multi- Choke, Field, 12 or 20 Ga.	**$ 900.00**

Grade II
Fixed Choke, Field, 28 or .410 Ga.	**1055.00**
Fixed Choke, Skeet, 12 or 20 Ga.	**1070.00**
IMC Multi Choke, Field, 12 or 20 Ga.	**1055.00**
IMC Multi Choke, Trap, 12 Ga.	**1100.00**

Grade III
IMC Multi-choke, Field, 12 or 20 Ga.	**1160.00**

WEATHERBY SHOTGUNS

ATHENA & ORION OVER/UNDER SHOTGUN SPECIFICATIONS

Model	Chamber	Bbl Length	Chokes	Overall Length	Length Of Pull	Comb	Drop at Heel	**MC	Bead Sights	*Approx. Weight
IMC MULTI-CHOKE FIELD MODELS (12 GA., 20 GA.)										
Field	3″	26″	M/IC/Sk	43¼″	14¼″	1½″	2½″		Brilliant Front	6½-7½ lbs.
Field	3″	28″	F/M/IC	45¼″	14¼″	1½″	2½″		Brilliant Front	6½-7½ lbs.
Field (12 Ga. only)	3″¾	30″	F/M/F	47¼″	14¼″	1½″	2½″		Brilliant Front	7½-8 lbs.
FIXED CHOKE FIELD MODELS (28 GA., .410 GA.)										
28 Ga.	2¾	26″	M/IC	43¼″	14¼″	1½″	2½″		Brilliant Front	6½-7½ lbs.
28 Ga.	2¾″	28″	F/M	45¼″	14¼″	1½″	2½″		Brilliant Front	6½-7½ lbs.
.410	3″	26″	M/IC	43¼″	14¼″	1½″	2½″		Brilliant Front	6½-7½ lbs.
.410	3″	28″	F/M	45¼″	14¼″	1½″	2½″		Brilliant Ford	6½-7½ lbs.
IMC MULTI CHOKE TRAP MODELS (12 GA. only)**										
Trap	2¾″	30″	F/M/IM	47½″	14⅜″	1⅜″	2⅛″	1¾	White Fr/Mid Br	8-8½ lbs.
Trap	2¾″	32″	F/M/IM	49½″	14⅜″	1⅜″	2⅛″	1¾	White Fr/Mid Br	8-8½ lbs.
†Sgl Bbl Trap	2¾″	32″	F/M/IM	49½″	14⅜″	1⅜″	2⅛″	1¾ ·	White Fr/Mid Br	8-8½ lbs.
†Sgl Bbl Trap	2¾″	34″	F/M/IM	51½″	14⅜″	1⅜″	2⅛	1¾	White Fr/Mid Br	8½-9 lbs.
Single barrel trap available in combo set with 30″ or 32″ O/U barrels.										
FIXED CHOKE SKEET MODELS (12 GA., 28 GA., .410 GA.)										
12 Ga.	2¾″	26″	S/S	43½″	14¼″	1½″	2½″		White Fr/Mid Br	6½-7½ lbs.
12 Ga.	2¾″	28″	S/S	45¼″	14¼″	1½″	2½″		White Fr/Mid Br	6½-7½ lbs.
20 Ga.	2¾″	26″	S/S	43¼″	14¼″	1½″	2½″		White Fr/Mid Br	6½-7½ lbs.
28 Ga.	2¾″	26″	S/S	43¼″	14¼″	1½″	2½″		White Fr/Mid Br	6½-7½ lbs.
.410	3″	26″	S/S	43¼″	14¼″	1½″	2½″		White Fr/Mid Br	6½-7½ lbs.
ATHENA MASTER SKEET TUBE SET (12 GA. Shotgun with 20 GA., 28 GA, and .410 GA. tubes)										
12 Ga.	2¾″***	28″ & 26″	S/S	45¼″	14¼″	1½″	2½″		White Fr/Mid Br	7-8 lbs.
***.410 tube has 2½ chamber.										
Three choke tubes shown are furnished with IMC model. An Extra Full tube is also available as a separate item (12 ga. only).										
*Weight varies due to wood density.										
**TRAP STOCKS AVAILABLE ONLY WITH MONTE CARLO										
†Available in Athena Model only.										

WINCHESTER SECURITY SHOTGUNS

This trio of tough 12-gauge shotguns provides backup strength for security and police work as well as all-around utility. The action is one of the fastest second-shot pumps made. It features a front-locking rotating bolt for strength and secure, single-unit lock-up into the barrel. Twin-action slide bars prevent binding.

All three guns are chambered for 3-inch shotshells. They handle 3-inch Magnum, 2¾-inch Magnum and standard 2¾-inch shotshells interchangeably. They have cross-bolt safety, walnut-finished hardwood stock and forearm, black rubber butt pad and plain 18-inch barrel with Cylinder Bore choke. All are ultra-reliable and easy to handle.

Special chrome finishes on Police and Marine guns are actually triple-plated: first with copper for adherence, then with nickel for rust protection, and finally with chrome for a hard finish. This triple-plating assures durability and quality. Both guns have a forend cap with swivel to accommodate sling.

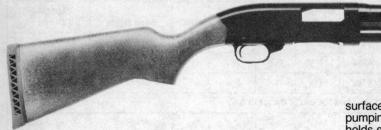

MODEL 1300 DEFENDER
$261.00

surfaces and features a traditional ribbed forearm for sure pumping grip. It has a metal bead front sight. The magazine holds eight 12-gauge. 3″ Magnum shells.

Also available with a shotshell capacity of five 3″ Magnum shells with metal bead front sight or rifle type (front and rear): **$256.00.**

Defender Combo (see table): **$346.00**

Security Defender™ is ideal for home security use. The compact 38⅝″ overall length (28½″ w/pistol grip) handles and stores easily. The Defender has a deep blued finish on metal

Model	Symbol Number	Gauge	Chamber	Shotshell Capacity*	Choke	Barrel Length & Type	Overall Length	Nominal Length of Pull	Nominal Drop At Comb	Heel	Nominal Weight (Lbs.)	Sights
1300 DEFENDER	7566	12	3″Mag.	8[1]	Cyl.	18″	38⅝	14″	1⅜″	2¾″	6¾	MBF
1300 PISTOL GRIP	7616	12	3 Mag.	8[1]	Cyl.	18	28½	14	—	—	—	MBF
1300 DEFENDER	7665	12	3 Mag.	5	Cyl.	18	38⅝	14	1⅜	2¾	6¼	MBF
1300 DEFENDER COMBO With Extra Barrel: Vent Rib-Winchoke	7814	12 12	3 Mag. 3 Mag.	5 5	Cyl. W1M	18 28 VR	38⅝ —	14 —	1⅜ —	2¾ —	6¼ —	MBF MBF

* Includes one shotshell in chamber when ready to fire. VR-Ventilated rib. Cyl-Cylinder Bare. W1M-Modified tube. MBF-Metal bead front.
[1] Subtract one for 3″ shells.

MODEL 1300 STAINLESS MARINE
DEFENDER $423.00

Comes in 12 gauge with multiple-plated chrome-finish ordnance stainless steel 18″ barrel. Receiver and internal parts are coated with Sandstrom 9A corrosion-inhibiting dry film lubricant. Stock and forend are made of corrosion and moisture-resistant material. **Capacity:** 7 shells (2¾″). **Sights:** Bead front (sling swivels incl.). Additional specifications same as Defender model described above.

SPECIFICATIONS MODEL 1300 STAINLESS MARINE

Model	Symbol Number	Gauge	Chamber	Shotshell Capacity*	Choke	Barrel Length & Type	Overall Length	Nominal Length of Pull	Nominal Drop At Comb	Heel	Nominal Weight (Lbs.)	Sights
1300 STAINLESS MARINE *New*	7475	12	3″Mag.	7[1]	Cyl.	18″	38⅝	14″	1⅜″	2¾″	7	MBF
1300 PISTOL GRIP *New*	7483	12	3 Mag.	7[1]	Cyl.	18	28⅝	14	—	—	6	MBF

* Includes one shotshell in chamber when ready to fire. [1] Subtract one shell capacity for 3″ shells. Cyl.-Cylinder Bare. MBF-Metal bead front.

WINCHESTER SHOTGUNS

MODEL 1300 PUMP DEER SLUG GUNS
$403.00

Winchester's Model 1300 Walnut Slug Hunter pump action shotgun features a rifled barrel with 8 lands and grooves, rifle-type sights, and a receiver that is factory-drilled and tapped for scope. Also available is a Model 1300 WinTuff Slug Hunter, featuring a Winchester Proof steel-rifled barrel with rifle-type sights. Model 1300 Walnut Slug Hunter has a smooth-bore barrel that comes with an extra long Sabot-rifled choke tube. Also included is an improved Cylinder Winchoke tube for traditional slug or buckshot shooting.

The Walnut models feature sculptured, cut-checkered forends, while the brown laminated WinTuff models have the tra-

ditional ribbed corn cob-style forend. All models have honey-comb recoil pad and a crossbolt safety. The lockup is a chrome molybdenum high-speed, four-slug rotary bolt and barrel extension system (lockup does not require use of the receiver top as part of the locking system). The Model 1300 receiver is made of lightweight, corrosion-resistant, space age alloy. Because the rotary lockup is concentric with the bore of the barrel, recoil forces are used to unlock the bolt and drive both bolt and forend rearward to help the shooter set up the next shot.

MODEL 1300 WALNUT SLUG HUNTER (with Sabot Tube)

MODEL 1300 WALNUT SLUG HUNTER (fully rifled) Sights Drilled and Tapped

SPECIFICATIONS

Model	Symbol Number	Gauge	Chamber	Shotshell Capacity*	Choke	Barrel Length & Type	Overall Length	Nominal Length of Pull	Nominal Drop At Comb	Heel	Nominal Weight (Lbs.)	Rate of Twist 1 Turn in	Sights
1300 WALNUT *New*	6204	12	3"Mag.	5	Cyl	22"Rifled	42¾	14"	1½"	2½"	7	35"	Rifle
1300 WALNUT Sabot Tube *New*	6253	12	3 Mag.	5	W2	22 Smooth	42¾	14	1½	2½	7	—	Rifle
1300 WINTUFF *New*	6220	12	3 Mag.	5	Cyl	22 Rifled	42¾	14	1½	2½	7	35	Rifle

* Includes one shotshell in chamber when ready to fire. W2-Improved Cylinder and rifled Sabot choke tubes. Drilled and Tapped-Bases included.

SHOTGUNS

WINCHESTER SHOTGUNS

MODEL 1300
PISTOL GRIP SLIDE-ACTION DEFENDER
$261.00

Winchester Security shotguns are also available with high-strength pistol grip and forearm. The pistol grip features finger grooves and checkering for sure, fast handling. The shorter forearm is ribbed for positive grip and pumpability. Both pistol grip and forearm are high-impact-resistant ABS plastic with non-glare matte black finish. The Pistol Grip series is lighter in weight, compact, easily stored and fast handling.

MODEL 1300
RANGER SEMIAUTOMATIC SHOTGUN
$277.00 ($276.00 w/22″ Barrel Deer)

Gauge: 12 and 20; 2³/₄″ chamber; 3-shot magazine. **Barrel:** 28″ vent rib with Full, Modified and Improved Cylinder Winchoke tubes or 28″ plain barrel Modified. **Weight:** 7 to 7¹/₄ pounds. **Overall length:** 48⁵/₈″. **Stock:** Walnut-finished hardwood with cut-checkering. **Sights:** Metal bead front. **Features:** Cross-bolt safety; front-locking rotating bolt; black serrated butt plate, gas-operated action. Also available in deer barrel.

Also available:
Model 1300 Ranger Deer Combo with 28l barrel and Winchoke set: **$358.00**
Model 1300 Ranger Waterfowl, 12 and 20 gauge with 28″ barrel: **$268.00**

SPECIFICATIONS: MODEL 1300 RANGER & LADIES/YOUTH

Model	Symbol Number	Gauge	Chamber	Shotshell Capacity*	Choke	Barrel Length & Type	Overall Length	Nominal Length of Pull	Nominal Drop At Comb	Heel	Nominal Weight (Lbs.)	Sights
1300 RANGER	6519	12	3″Mag.	5	W3	28″VR	48⁵/₈″	14″	1¹/₂″	2¹/₂″	7¹/₄	MBF
	6568	20	3 Mag.	5	W3	28 VR	48⁵/₈	14	1¹/₂	2¹/₂	7¹/₄	MBF
1300 RANGER DEER COMBO 12 ga. Extra Barrel	6618	12 12	3 Mag. 3 Mag.	5 5	Cyl. W3	22 28 VR	42⁵/₈	14	1¹/₂	2¹/₂	6¹/₂	RT MBF
1300 RANGER DEER COMBO 20 ga. Extra Barrel	6667	20 20	3 Mag. 3 Mag.	5 5	Cyl. W3	22 28 VR	42³/₄	14	1¹/₂	2¹/₂	6¹/₂	RT MBF
1300 RANGER DEER GUN	6717	12	3 Mag.	5	Cyl.	22	42³/₄	14	1¹/₂	2¹/₂	6¹/₂	RT
	6766	20	3 Mag.	5	Cyl.	22	42³/₄	14	1¹/₂	2¹/₂	6¹/₂	RT
1300 RANGER	6816	12	3 Mag.	5	W1M	28 VR	48⁵/₈	14	1¹/₂	2¹/₂	7¹/₄	MBF
	6865	20	3 Mag.	5	W1M	28 VR	48⁵/₈	14	1¹/₂	2¹/₂	7¹/₄	MBF
	6923	12	3 Mag.	5	W1F	28 VR	50⁵/₈	14	1¹/₂	2¹/₂	7¹/₂	MBF
1300 WALNUT LADIES/YOUTH *New*	6402	20	3 Mag.	5	W3	22 VR	41⁵/₈	13	1¹/₂	2³/₈	6	MBF
1300 RANGER LADIES/YOUTH	7111	20	3 Mag.	5	W3	22 VR	41⁵/₈	13	1¹/₂	2³/₈	6¹/₄	MBF

* Includes one shotshell in chamber when ready to fire. VR-Ventilated rib. Cyl.-Cylinder Bore. R-Rifled Barrel. MBF-Metal bead front. RT-Rifle type front and rear sights. Model 1300 and Ranger pump action shotguns have factory-installed plug which limits capacity to three shells. Ladies/Youth has factory-installed plug which limits capacity to one, two or three shells as desired. Extra barrels for Model 1300 and Ranger shotguns are available in 12 gauge, plain or ventilated rib, in a variety of barrel lengths and chokes; interchangeable with gauge. Winchoke sets with wrench come with gun as follows: W3W-Extra Full, Full, Modified tubes. W3-Full, Modified, Improved Cylinder tubes. W1M-Modified tube. W1F-Full tube.

WINCHESTER SHOTGUNS

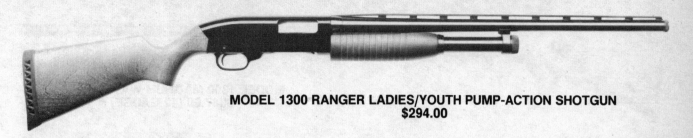

MODEL 1300 RANGER LADIES/YOUTH PUMP-ACTION SHOTGUN
$294.00

Gauge: 20 gauge only; 3″ chamber; 5-shot magazine. **Barrel:** 22″ barrel w/vent. rib; Winchoke (Full, Modified, Improved Cylinder). **Weight:** 6½ lbs. **Length:** 41⅝″. **Stock:** Walnut or American hardwood with ribbed forend. **Sights:** Metal bead front. **Features:** Cross-bolt safety; black rubber butt pad; twin-action slide bars; front-locking rotating bolt; removable segmented magazine plug to limit shotshell capacity for training purposes.

MODEL 1300 PUMP-ACTION WALNUT SHOTGUNS
$355.00

Whether hunting rabbits or pheasants with the 12 gauge, or going after doves or quail with the 20 gauge, Model 1300 Walnut with its beavertail forend is a versatile performer. This model features Winchester's Armor-Lock rotary-bolt lockup, which provides better balance, faster pointing and easier carrying. It also means that a new round is cycled into the chamber as fast as the pump can be operated. The trigger-blocking cross bolt safety is located at the front of the trigger guard. Single pin take-down provides easy field maintenance and cleaning. The floating ventilated rib assures consistent point-of-impact. The special ventilated rubber recoil pad on all 12 gauge models provides maximum recoil absorption.

Each barrel (22″ or 28″) is equipped with Winchoke Tubes, which extend ¼″ past the muzzle so that choice of choke tube can be identified easily; it also protects the muzzle of the barrel from getting crimped or accidentally damaged. All Winchester Model 1300 Walnut shotguns feature diamond point cut checkering. Stocks are American walnut with satin finish and diamond point cut checkering on the pistol grip.

Model		Symbol Number	Gauge	Chamber	Shotshell Capacity*	Choke	Barrel Length & Type	Overall Length	Nominal Length Of Pull	Nominal Drop At		Nominal Weight (Lbs.)	Sights
										Comb	Heel		
1300 WALNUT		6014	12	3″Mag.	5	W3	28″VR	48⅝″	14″	1½″	2½″	7⅛	MBF
	New	6022	20	3 Mag.	5	W3	28 VR	48⅝	14	1½	2½	7⅛	MBF
		6063	12	3 Mag.	5	W3	22 VR	42⅝	14	1½	2½	6¾	MBF
		6113	20	3 Mag.	5	W3	22 VR	42⅝	14	1½	2½	6¾	MBF

* Includes one shotshell in chamber when ready to fire. VR-Floating ventilated rib. MBF-Metal bead front. Winchokes sets with wrench come with gun as follows: W3-Full, Modified, Improved Cylinder tubes.

SHOTGUNS

WINCHESTER SHOTGUNS

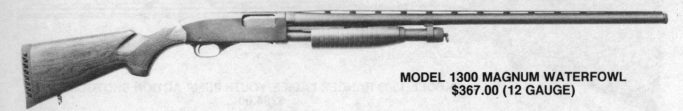

MODEL 1300 MAGNUM WATERFOWL
$367.00 (12 GAUGE)

The Model 1300 Magnum Waterfowl pump is designed specifically for hunting ducks and geese. It features a 28-inch ventilated rib barrel with the Winchoke System of interchangeable choke tubes (Extra Full, Full and Modified). Stock and forearm are of American walnut with a low-luster protective finish. All exterior metal surfaces have a special non-glare matte finish to aid in hunter concealment. Other features include metal front bead sight, cross-bolt safety, rubber recoil pad and sling swivels. **Chamber:** 3" Mag. **Barrel length:** 28". **Overall length:** 48⅝". **Stock dimensions:** Length of pull, 14"; drop at comb, 1½"; drop at heel, 2½"; **Weight:** 7 lbs. Also available with WIN-TUFF brown laminated stock and forearm.

MODEL 1300 TURKEY SHOTGUN
$384.00

Available in 12 gauge only, the Model 1300 Turkey gun comes equipped with a 22-inch ventilated rib barrel, which includes the Winchester Winchoke system with Extra Full, Full and Modified choke tubes and wrench. Its walnut stock and forearm have a special low-luster protective finish; the receiver, barrel and all exterior metal surfaces feature a non-glare matte finish. The receiver is roll engraved. The pistol grip has deep-cut checkering; the contoured forearm is ribbed for sure gripping and has been modified for positioning and comfort. Other features include cross-bolt safety with red indicator blocks and metal bead sights. The 1300 Turkey Gun handles 3" magnum, 2¾" Magnum and 2¾" standard shotshells interchangeably. See table below for complete specifications.

Also available:
Model 1300 Walnut Stock with satin finish, checkered, beavertail forend, and floating vent rib: **$338.00.**
Model 1300 Walnut Ladies/Youth with scaled-down checkered stock with forend positioned rearward: **$338.00 ($403.00 w/green camo, Winchoke Sling, 20 ga.)**

SPECIFICATION: MODEL 1300 TURKEY

Model		Symbol Number	Gauge	Chamber	Shotshell Capacity*†	Choke	Barrel Length & Type	Overall Length	Nominal Length of Pull	Nominal Drop At Comb	Heel	Nominal Weight (Lbs.)	Sights
1300 NWTF TURKEY GUN WINCAM Series II	*New*	6311**	12	3"Mag.	5	W3W	22"VR	42⅝"	14"	1½"	2½"	6⅜	MBF
1300 TURKEY GUN WINCAM		6295	12	3 Mag.	5	W3W	22 VR	42⅝	14	1½	2½	6⅜	MBF
1300 LADIES/YOUTH TURKEY GUN	*New*	6378	20	3 Mag.	5	W3	22 VR	41⅝	13	1½	2⅜	6	MBF

WINCHESTER MODEL 1300 WATERFOWL SHOTGUNS

Model		Symbol Number	Gauge	Chamber	Shotshell Capacity*†	Choke	Barrel Length & Type	Overall Length	Nominal Length of Pull	Nominal Drop At Comb	Heel	Nominal Weight (Lbs.)	Sights
1300 WATERFOWL WALNUT		6162	12	3"Mag.	5	W3	28"VR	48⅝"	14"	1½"	2½"	7	MBF
1300 WATERFOWL WINTUFF		6196	12	3 Mag.	5	W3	28 VR	48⅝	14	1½	2½	7	MBF

  * Includes one shotshell in chamber when ready to fire. VR-Ventilated rib. MBF-Metal bead front. Winchoke sets with wrench come with gun as follows: W3W-Extra Full, Full, Modified tubes. W3-Full, Modified, Improved Cylinder tubes. Cordura® is a registered trademark of E. I. duPont deNemours & Co.

  † Includes one shotshell in chamber when ready to fire. VR-Floating ventilated rib. MBF-Metal bead front. Winchoke sets with wrench come with gun as follows: W3-Full, Modified, Improved Cylinder tubes.

WINCHESTER SHOTGUNS

MODEL 1400 SEMIAUTO SHOTGUNS

The self-compensating gas-operated action in these shotguns enables the hunter to deliver follow-up shots as fast as the trigger can be pulled. A military-style lockup (armor-Lock) assures high strength and low receiver weight. Front-locking rotary bolt is machined from solid chrome molybdenum steel and locks directly into a chrome molybdenum steel barrel extension by means of four locking bolts. The barrel is Winchester Proof steel; receiver is extruded from high strength, corrosion-resistant alloy; positive cross-bolt safety is located at the front of the trigger guard (blocking the trigger when "on," which in turn blocks the hammer). For other specifications, see the table below.

MODEL 1400 SEMIAUTO WALNUT
(22″ Barrel, 12 Ga.)
$399.00

**MODEL 1400 SEMIAUTO
SLUG HUNTER
$442.00**

Also available:
MODEL 1400 RANGER (12 or 20 ga., 28″ barrel) w/walnut-finished hardwood stock $358.00
MODEL 1400 RANGER DEER GUN (12 ga.,
22″ barrel) 349.00
MODEL 1400 DEER COMBO 440.00

SPECIFICATIONS: MODEL 1400 SEMI-AUTO

Model		Symbol Number	Gauge	Chamber	Shotshell Capacity*	Choke	Barrel Length & Type	Overall Length	Nominal Length of Pull	Nominal Drop At Comb	Heel	Nominal Weight (Lbs.)	Sights
1400 WALNUT		7186	12	2¾″	3	W3	22″VR	42¾″	14″	1½″	2½″	7	MBF
		7194	20	2¾	3	W3	22 VR	42¾	14	1½	2½	7	MBF
		7202	12	2¾	3	W3	28 VR	48⅝	14	1½	2½	7¾	MBF
	New	7236	20	2¾	3	W3	28 VR	48⅝	14	1½	2½	7	MBF
Sabot tube	New	7244	12	2¾	3	W2	22	42¾	14	1½	2½	7¼	RT
1400 RANGER		7210	12	2¾	3	W3	28 VR	48⅝	14	1½	2½	7¾	MBF
		7228	12	2¾	3	W1	28 VR	48⅝	14	1½	2½	7¾	MBF
		7269	20	2¾	3	W3	28 VR	48⅝	14	1½	2½	7¾	MBF
		7277	20	2¾	3	W1	28 VR	48⅝	14	1½	2½	7¾	MBF
	New	7368	12	2¾	3	Cyl	22	42¾	14	1½	2½	7¾	RT
1400 RANGER DEER New With Combo Extra Barrel		7319	12 12	2¾ 2¾	3 3	Cyl W3	22 28 VR	42¾	14	1½	2½	7¼	RT MBF

* Includes one shotshell in chamber when ready to fire. VR-Ventilated rib. Cyl.-Cylinder Bore. MBF-Metal bead front. RT-Rifle type front and rear sights. Winchoke sets with wrench come with gun as follows: W1-Modified tube. W2 Improved Cylinder and rifled Sabot tubes. W3-Full, Modified, Improved Cylinder tubes.

ANTONIO ZOLI SHOTGUNS

UPLANDER
$1295.00

This traditional European upland game bird gun features a fast-swinging 25″ barrel choked Improved Cylinder and Modified. It is stocked in the traditional English style with straight butt stock and splinter forend of hand-rubbed, finely checkered oil-finished Turkish Circassian walnut. For additional specifications, see table below.

Gauge:	12–20	Top rib:	Tapered from 25/64 to 15/64	Drop at heel:	1½″
Chamber	3″ Magnum	Finish:	Case hardened	Drop at comb:	2⁵⁄₁₆″
Barrel length:	25″	Engraving:	—	Length of pull:	14½″
Chokes:	I.C. + Mod.	Stock:	English	Total weight:	6.25–7.25 lbs.

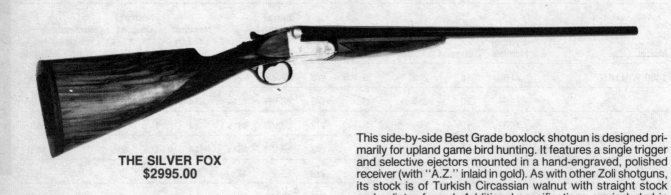

THE SILVER FOX
$2995.00

This side-by-side Best Grade boxlock shotgun is designed primarily for upland game bird hunting. It features a single trigger and selective ejectors mounted in a hand-engraved, polished receiver (with "A.Z." inlaid in gold). As with other Zoli shotguns, its stock is of Turkish Circassian walnut with straight stock and splinter forend. Additional specifications are included in the table below.

SPECIFICATIONS THE SILVER FOX

Gauge:	12–20*	Top rib:	Tapered from 25/64 to 15/64	Drop at heel:	1½″
Chamber	3″ Magnum	Finish:	Antiqued silver	Drop at comb:	2⁵⁄₁₆″
Barrel length:	26″–28″	Engraving:	By hand	Length of pull:	14½″
Chokes:	26″–IC/M 28″–M/F	Stock:	English	Total weight:	From 6.25 lbs. To 7.25 lbs.

* Available only in 26″.

ANTONIO ZOLI SHOTGUNS

SILVER FALCON O/U FIELD
$1395.00

This new Zoli over/under field shotgun features a silver-tone floral engraved receiver, single selective triggers, automatic selective ejectors, and 4 screw-in Zoli chokes in both 12 and 20 gauge. Stock is of Turkish Circassian walnut enhanced by a polyurethane-type weatherproof finish. For specifications, see table below.

SPECIFICATIONS SILVER FALCON

Gauge:	12–20	Screw-in Zoli chokes	4 (IC-M-IM-F)	Drop at heel:	1⁵⁄₁₆″
Chamber	3″ Magnum	Engravings:	Floral	Drop at comb:	2⅛″
Barrel length:	26″–28″	Finish:	Antiqued silver	Length of pull:	14¼″
Top rib:	9⁄32″	Stock:	Pistol grip	Total weight:	6.25–7.25 lbs.

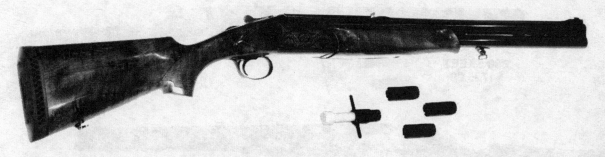

THE WOODSMAN
$1495.00

This over/under field shotgun features a special raised "quarter-rib" with pop-up rifle-type sights for use in hunting birds, deer, turkey, or large game, such as wild boar, in thick cover. The 23″ barrels with center ventilation are regulated to shoot rifled slugs at 55 yards and accept the interchangeable Zoli chokes with 5 tubes. Additional specifications are listed in the table below.

SPECIFICATIONS THE WOODSMAN

Gauge:	12	Finish:	Receiver photoengraved	Length of pull:	14½″
Chamber	3″ Magnum	Engraving:	Floral	Total weight:	6¾ lbs.
Barrel length:	23″	Stock:	Pistol grip	Regulated:	55 yds. with slugs
Chokes:	Screw-in Zoli-chokes (5)	Drop at heel:	1⅜″		
Top rib:	Slug type	Drop at comb:	2⁵⁄₁₆″		

ANTONIO ZOLI SHOTGUNS

Z90 TRAP GUN SERIES

Z90 MONO-TRAP GUN
$1795.00

This top/single barrel trap gun features a black competition receiver, ventilated raised rib barrels with two beads, gold-plated single selective trigger (adjustable to length of pull), and a polyurethane-type weatherproof finish stock of Turkish Cir- cassian walnut, select grade, with Monte Carlo butt stock and rounded tip forend. For additional specifications see table be- low.

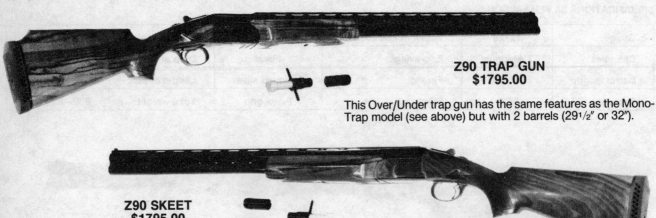

Z90 TRAP GUN
$1795.00

This Over/Under trap gun has the same features as the Mono-Trap model (see above) but with 2 barrels (29½" or 32").

Z90 SKEET
$1795.00

SPORTING CLAYS
$1595.00

Models	Gauge	BBL length	Chokes	Top rib	Stock	Action frame	Total weight
Z90-Trap	12	29½"–32"	Screw-in Zoli chokes	7/16"	Pistol deluxe walnut	Black	8½ lbs.
Z90-Skeet	12	28"	SK-SK	7/16"	Pistol deluxe walnut	Black	7¾ lbs.
Z90-Mono trap	12	32"–34"	Screw-in Zoli chokes	7/16"	Pistol deluxe walnut	Black	8½ lbs.
Z90-Sporting	12	28"	Screw-in Zoli chokes	Tapered	Pistol deluxe walnut	Antique silver side plated	7⅓ lbs.

Black Powder Guns

FOR ADDRESSES AND PHONE NUMBERS OF MANUFACTURERS AND DISTRIBUTORS INCLUDED IN THIS SECTION, SEE *DIRECTORY OF MANUFACTURERS AND SUPPLIERS*

ARMSPORT
REPLICA REVOLVERS

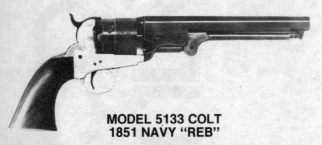

MODEL 5133 COLT
1851 NAVY "REB"

A modern replica of a Confederate percussion revolver, this has a polished brass frame, rifled blued barrel and polished walnut grips. **Price: $120.00** (Kit: **$110.00**).

MODEL 5136 COLT
1851 NAVY STEEL

This authentic reproduction of the Colt Navy Revolver, which helped shape the history of America, features a rifled barrel, blued steel frame, engraved cylinder, polished brass trigger guard and walnut grips. **Price: $165.00** (Kit: **$150.00**).

MODEL 5120 NEW REMINGTON ARMY
44 CALIBER STEEL REVOLVER

One of the most accurate cap-and-ball revolvers of the 1880's. Its rugged steel frame and top strap made this the favorite of all percussion cap revolvers. **Price: $165.00** (Kit: **$150.00**). With brass frame: **$120.00**.

MODEL 5138 REMINGTON ARMY
STAINLESS STEEL 44 CALIBER

This stainless-steel version of the 44-caliber Remington New Army Revolver is made for the shooter who seeks the best. Its stainless steel frame assures lasting good looks and durability. **Price: $285.00**.

MODEL 5139 COLT 1860 ARMY
44 CALIBER

This authentic reproduction offers the same balance and ease of handling for fast shooting as the original 1860 Army model. **Price: $165.00** (Kit: **$150.00**).

MODEL 5140 COLT 1860 ARMY
(Not shown)

Same as the Model 5139 Colt Army replica, but with brightly polished brass frame. **Price: $120.00** (Kit: **$110.00**).

REPLICA REVOLVERS Description	Model No. Finished	Barrel Length	Caliber	Recommended Ball Dia.
New Remington Army Stainless Steel	5138	8″	44	.451
New Remington Army	5120	8″	44	.451
1851 Navy Reb Brass	5133	7″	36	.376
1851 Navy Reb Brass	5134	7″	44	.451
1851 Navy Steel	5135	7″	36	.376
1851 Navy Steel	5136	7″	44	.451
1860 Colt Army	5139	8″	44	.451

ARMSPORT

MODEL 5145 COLT 1847 WALKER
$220.00

The largest of all Colt revolvers, this true copy of the original weighs 4½ lbs., making it also the most powerful revolver made at the time. **Caliber:** 44.

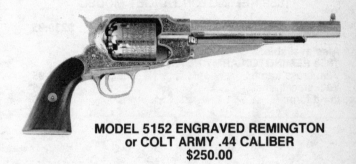

MODEL 5152 ENGRAVED REMINGTON
or COLT ARMY .44 CALIBER
$250.00

MODEL 5153 ENGRAVED COLT ARMY
$250.00

MODEL 5155 REMINGTON BUFFALO
TARGET SIGHTS (not shown)
$185.00   (Kit $165.00)

MODEL 5154 ENGRAVED COLT NAVY
$250.00

Also available:
Model 5134 1851 Colt Navy Brass (36 & 44 Cal.) . **$120.00**
  Kit **110.00**
Model 5135 1851 Colt Navy Steel (36 & 44 Cal.) . . **165.00**
  Kit **150.00**
Model 5150 1860 Colt Army SS **285.00**

BLACK POWDER

CVA REVOLVERS

1858 REMINGTON ARMY STEEL FRAME REVOLVER
$213.95

Caliber: 44
Cylinder: 6-shot
Barrel length: 8″ octagonal
Overall length: 13″
Weight: 38 oz.
Sights: Blade front; groove in frame (rear)
Grip: Two-piece walnut

1858 REMINGTON TARGET MODEL

With adjustable target sights: **$239.95**

Also available:
1858 REMINGTON ARMY REVOLVER
With brass frame: **$173.95**
With steel frame: 221.95
In Kit form:. 151.95

COLT WALKER REVOLVER
$287.95

Caliber: 44
Barrel: 9″ rounded with hinged-style loading lever
Cylinder: 6-shot engraved
Overall length: 15½″
Weight: 72 oz.
Grip: One-piece walnut
Front sight: Blade
Finish: Solid brass trigger guard

NEW MODEL POCKET REMINGTON
Finished $127.95
Kit $95.95

This single-action 31-caliber percussion revolver is a reproduction of a valued collector's item. Manufactured originally in the mid-1800s, the five-shot revolver was most effective at close ranges. Its brass frame and 4-inch blued barrel provide beauty as well as ruggedness.

Caliber: 31 percussion
Barrel length: 4″ octagonal
Cylinder: 5 shots
Overall length: 7½″
Sights: Post in front; groove in frame in rear
Weight: 15 oz.
Finish: Solid brass frame

CVA REVOLVERS

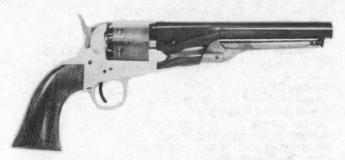

1861 COLT NAVY BRASS-FRAMED REVOLVER
Finished $145.95
Kit $127.95

Calibers: 36 and 44
Barrel length: 7¹/₂″ rounded; creeping style
Weight: 44 oz.
Cylinder: 6-shot, engraved
Sights: Blade front; hammer notch rear
Finish: Solid brass frame, trigger guard and backstrap; blued barrel and cylinder
Grip: One-piece walnut

Also available in 36 caliber with steel frame: **$205.95**

**1851 COLT NAVY
BRASS-FRAMED REVOLVER**
Finished $139.95
Kit $123.95

Caliber: 36
Barrel length: 7¹/₂″ octagonal; hinged-style loading lever
Overall length: 13″
Weight: 44 oz.
Cylinder: 6-shot, engraved
Sights: Post front; hammer notch rear
Grip: One-piece walnut
Finish: Solid brass frame, trigger guard and backtrap; blued barrel and cylinder; color casehardened loading lever and hammer

Also available with steel frame: **$205.95**

COLT SHERIFF'S MODEL REVOLVER
Brass Frame $157.95
Steel Frame $185.95
Kit $137.95

Caliber: 36
Barrel length: 5¹/₂″ (rounded w/creeping-style loading lever)
Overall length: 11¹/₂″
Weight: 40¹/₂ oz.
Cylinder: 6-shot semi-fluted
Grip: One-piece walnut
Sight: Hammer notch in rear
Finish: Solid brass frame, trigger guard and backstrap

Also available: **Engraved Nickel Plated Model** (with matching flask) **$223.95.**

1860 COLT ARMY REVOLVER
$221.95 (Steel Frame Only)

Caliber: 44
Barrel length: 8″ rounded; creeping-style loading lever
Overall length: 13″
Weight: 44 oz.
Cylinder: 6-shot, engraved and rebated
Sights: Blade front; hammer notch rear
Grip: One-piece walnut
Finish: Solid brass trigger guard; blued barrel and cylinder with color casehardened loading lever, hammer and frame

BLACK POWDER

CVA REVOLVERS

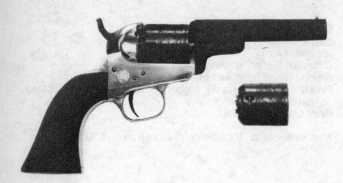

WELLS FARGO MODEL COLT
Brass Frame $127.95   Steel Frame $191.95
Kit $109.95 (Brass)

Caliber: 31
Capacity: 5-shot cylinder (engraved)
Barrel length: 4″ octagonal
Overall length: 9″
Weight: 28 oz. (w/extra cylinder)
Sights: Post front; hammer notch rear
Grip: One-piece walnut

COLT POCKET POLICE
Brass Frame $143.95   Steel Frame $195.95
Kit $121.95 (Brass)

Caliber: 36
Capacity: 5-shot cylinder
Barrel length: 5½″ (octagonal, with creeping-style loading lever)
Overall length: 10½″
Weight: 26 oz.
Sights: Post front; hammer notch rear

THIRD MODEL COLT DRAGOON
Steel Frame $245.95

Caliber: 44
Cylinder: 6-shot engraved
Barrel length: 7½″ rounded with hinged-style loading lever
Overall length: 14″
Weight: 66 oz.
Sights: Blade front; hammer notch rear
Grip: One-piece walnut

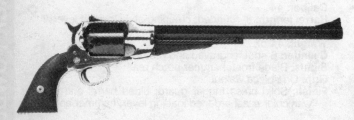

REMINGTON BISON
$259.95

Caliber: 44
Cylinder: 6-shot
Barrel length: 10¼″ octagonal
Overall length: 18″
Weight: 48 oz.
Sights: Fixed blade front; screw adjustable target rear
Grip: Two-piece walnut
Finish: Solid brass frame

CVA PISTOLS

KENTUCKY PISTOL
Finished $149.95
Percussion Kit $97.95

Caliber: 50 percussion
Barrel: 10¼", rifled, octagonal
Overall length: 15½"
Weight: 40 oz.
Finish: Blued barrel, brass hardware
Sights: Brass blade front; fixed open rear
Stock: Select hardwood
Ignition: Engraved, color casehardened percussion lock, screw adjustable sear engagement
Accessories: Brass-tipped, hardwood ramrod; stainless steel nipple or flash hole liner

COLONIAL PISTOL
Finished $113.95
Percussion Kit $83.95

Caliber: 45 percussion
Barrel: 6¾", rifled, octagon
Overall length: 12¾"
Weight: 31 oz.
Finish: Casehardened lock; blued barrel; brass hardware
Sights: Dovetail rear; brass blade front
Stock: Select hardwood
Ignition: Engraved, color casehardened lock
Accessories: Steel ramrod, stainless steel nipple; kits available for percussion and flintlock

PHILADELPHIA DERRINGER
Finished $93.95
Kit $57.95

Caliber: 45 percussion
Barrel: 3¼" rifled, octagonal
Overall length: 7⅛"
Weight: 16 oz.
Finish: Brass hardware; blued barrel
Stock: Select hardwood
Ignition: Color casehardened and engraved, coil-spring back-action lock
Accessories: Stainless steel nipple

HAWKEN PISTOL
Finished $153.95
Kit $111.95

Caliber: 50 percussion
Barrel length: 9¾", octagonal
Overall length: 16½"
Weight: 50 oz.
Trigger: Early-style brass
Sights: Beaded steel blade front; fully adjustable rear (click adj. screw settings lock into position)
Stock: Select hardwood
Finish: Solid brass wedge plate, nose cap, ramrod thimbles, trigger guard and grip cap

VEST POCKET DERRINGER
Finished $61.95
Kit $53.95

Caliber: 31
Barrel length: 2½" (single shot) brass
Overall length: 5"
Weight: 16 oz.
Grip: Two-piece walnut
Frame: Brass

SIBER PISTOL
$414.95

Caliber: 45 percussion
Barrel length: 10½", octagonal
Overall length: 16½"
Weight: 38 oz.
Sights: Blade front; rear adjustable for elevation
Stock: Fancy Eutopean walnut
Trigger: Adjustable single-set trigger with rear over-lateral limiting screw
Finish: Polished steel barrel, lock plate, hammer and trigger

CVA RIFLES

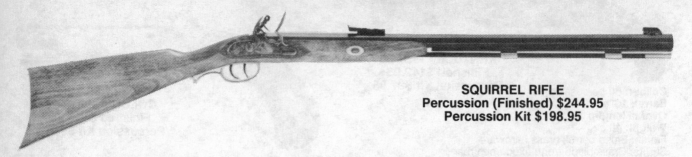

SQUIRREL RIFLE
Percussion (Finished) $244.95
Percussion Kit $198.95

Ignition: Color case-hardened and engraved lockplate; bridle, fly, screw-adjustable sear engagement; authentic V-type mainspring
Caliber: 36 percussion
Stock: Select hardwood
Barrel: 25″ octagonal; 7/8″ across flats; hooked breech for easy take down and cleaning; rifling, one turn in 48″; 8 lands, deep grooves; blued steel
Overall length: 40 3/4″
Weight: 6 lbs.

Trigger: Double set with adj. trigger pull (will fire set or unset)
Front sight: Dovetail, beaded blade
Rear sight: Fully adjustable, open hunting-style dovetail
Finish: Solid brass butt plate, trigger guard, wedge plates and thimbles
Accessories: Stainless steel nipple or flash hole liner; aluminum ramrod with brass tips, cleaning jag
Also available:
SQUIRREL RIFLE HUNTING COMBO KIT (36 and 50 caliber percussion): **$252.95**

BLAZER RIFLE
Finished $178.95
Kit $143.95

Caliber: 50 percussion
Barrel length: 28″ octagonal (15/16″ across flats); in-line breech and nipple
Rifling: 1 turn in 66″ (8 lands and deep grooves)
Overall length: 43 1/2″

Weight: 7 lbs.
Sights: Brass blade front; fixed open rear
Stock: Select hardwood
Lock: Straight-through ignition (removable for cleaning and adjustment)

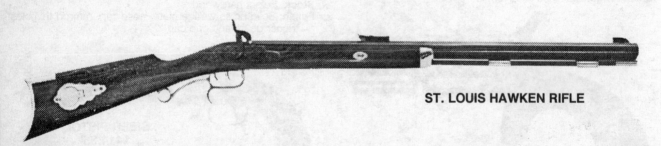

ST. LOUIS HAWKEN RIFLE

Calibers: 50, 54 and 58 percussion or flintlock
Barrel: 28″ octagonal 15/16″ across flats; hooked breech; rifling one turn in 66″, 8 lands and deep grooves
Overall length: 44″
Weight: 8 lbs.
Sights: Dovetail, beaded blade (front); adjustable open hunting-style dovetail (rear)
Stock: Select hardwood with beavertail cheekpiece
Triggers: Double set; fully adjustable trigger pull
Finish: Solid brass wedge plates, nose cap, ramrod thimbles, trigger guard and patch box

Prices:

50 Caliber Flintlock	$297.95
50 Caliber Percussion	278.95
50 Caliber Percussion, Left Hand	297.95
50 Caliber Percussion Kit	223.95
54 & 58 Caliber Percussion	278.95
Percussion Combos (50 and 54 calibers)	265.95
50 Cal./12 Ga. (full choke) Combo	364.95
Same as above in Kit	285.95

CVA RIFLES

APOLLO 90 PERCUSSION RIFLE
$387.95 (Standard Grade)
$513.95 (Premier Grade)

Caliber: 50 percussion
Barrel length: 27″ round, tapered, one-piece
Overall length: 45″
Weight: 7½ lbs.
Trigger: Box-type with hooking tumbler automatic trigger safety system (Premier Grade)

Sights: Front, ramp-mounted brass bead with hood to fit ³/₈″ dovetails; rear, Hunting-style full click adjustable for windage and elevation to fit ³/₈″ dovetail; both sights removable for scope mounting
Stock: Walnut, Monte Carlo-style comb with flutes; fully formed beavertail cheekpiece, pistol-grip handle (Premier Grade); select hardwood (Standard Grade)
Accessories: Stainless steel nipple; fiberglass ramrod with cleaning jag; black ABS trigger guard

HAWKEN RIFLE
$389.95

Caliber: 50 percussion
Barrel length: 28″, octagonal; chrome bore
Overall length: 44″

Weight: 8 lbs.
Stock: Select walnut with fully formed beavertail cheekpiece
Sights: Beaded steel blade front; hunting-style rear, fully click adjustable for windage and elevation
Finish: Solid brass wedge plates, nose cap, ramrod thimbles, trigger guard, butt plate and patchbox

HUNTER HAWKEN
$267.95
Kit $219.95

Calibers: 50 and 54
Barrel length: 28″, blued, octagonal
Overall length: 44″
Weight: 8 lbs.

Sights: Beaded steel blade front; hunting-style rear, fully click adjustable for windage and elevation
Stock: Select hardwood with non-glare finish; rubber recoil pad
Triggers: Double set with fully adjustable trigger pull
Finish: Black nose cap, trigger guard, thimbles and wedge plate
Also available: HUNTER HAWKEN CARBINE (24″ barrel; 40″ overall) **$267.95**

KENTUCKY RIFLE (Full Stock)
$259.95
Kit $165.95

Caliber: 50 percussion
Barrel length: 33½″, octagonal
Overall length: 48″

Weight: 7½ lbs.
Sights: Brass blade front; fixed open rear
Stock: Select hardwood
Trigger: Early-style brass
Finish: Solid brass trigger guard, butt plate, toe plate, front sight, nose cap and thimble
Also available: KENTUCKY HUNTER (Half Stock) **$274.95**

CVA

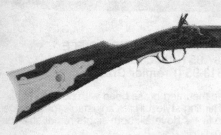

PENNSYLVANIA LONG RIFLE
Percussion (Finished) $516.95
Flintlock $536.95

Caliber: 50 percussion or flintlock
Stock: Select walnut
Barrel: 40″ octagonal, ⁷/₈″ across flats; rifling 8 lands, deep grooves
Overall length: 55³/₄″
Weight: 8 lbs.
Trigger: Double set (will fire set or unset)
Rear sight: Fixed semi-buckhorn, dovetail
Finish: Brass butt plate, patchbox, trigger guard, thimbles and nose cap
Ignition: Color casehardened and engraved lockplate; bridle, fly, screw-adjustable sear engagement; authentic V-type mainspring
Accessories: Color casehardened nipple or flash hole liner; hardwood ramrod and brass tips

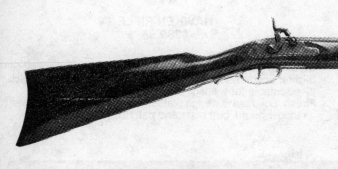

FRONTIER CARBINE
Finished $228.95
Kit $164.95

Caliber: 50 percussion
Barrel length: 24″ octagonal (¹⁵/₁₆″ across flats)
Rifling: 1 turn in 48″ (8 lands and deep grooves)
Overall length: 40″
Weight: 6 lbs. 9 oz.
Sights: Brass blade front; fixed open rear
Trigger: Early-style brass with tension spring
Stock: Select hardwood
Finish: Solid brass butt plate, trigger guard wedge plate, nose cap and thimble
Accessories: Stainless steel nipple, hardwood ramrod with brass tips and cleaning jag

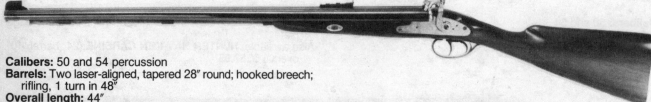

Calibers: 50 and 54 percussion
Barrels: Two laser-aligned, tapered 28″ round; hooked breech; rifling, 1 turn in 48″
Overall length: 44″
Weight: 10 lbs.
Locks: Plate is color hardened and engraved; includes bridle, fly, screw-adjustable sear engagement
Triggers: Double, color casehardened
Sights: Fully adjustable for windage and elevation, hunting style (rear); dovetail, beaded blade (front)
Stock: Select hardwood
Finish: Polished steel wedge plates; color casehardened locks, hammers, triggers and trigger guard; engraved locks, hammers and tang
Also available: Accessory barrel (12 Ga. Modified Choke) **$198.00.**

EXPRESS DOUBLE BARREL RIFLE
Finished $547.95
Kit $468.95

CVA RIFLES

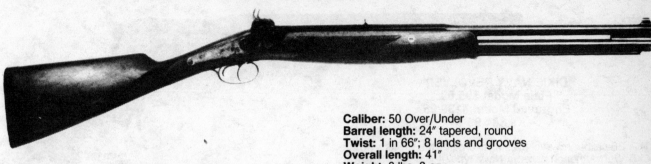

OVER/UNDER CARBINE
$579.95

Caliber: 50 Over/Under
Barrel length: 24″ tapered, round
Twist: 1 in 66″; 8 lands and grooves
Overall length: 41″
Weight: 8 lbs. 8 oz.
Features: Checkered fancy-grade walnut stock; ventilated rubber recoil pad; color casehardened nipples

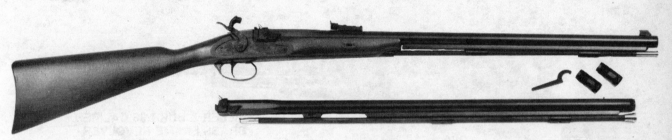

TRAPPER COMBO
3 Interchangeable Chokes
Finished Combo $416.95
Single Barrel $348.95

Gauge: 12
Barrel length: 28″ round, smoothbore
Chokes: Interchangeable Improved, Modified and Full
Overall length: 46″
Weight: 6 lbs.
Trigger: Early-style steel
Sight: Brass bead in front
Stock: Select hardwood; English-style straight grip
Finish: German silver wedge plates; color-hardened engraved lock plates, hammer, trigger guard and tang
Features: Casehardened steel nipple, wooden ramrod with brass tip

OZARK MOUNTAIN RIFLE
(Premier Grade)
$397.95 (Chrome Bore)

Calibers: 50 and 54 percussion
Barrel length: 32″ octagonal (15/16″ across flats); with hooked breech for easy takedown and cleaning
Rifling: 1 turn in 66″ (8 lands and deep grooves)
Overall length: 48″
Weight: 9 lbs.
Sights: German silver blade front; screw adjustable ramp rear
Triggers: Double set, fully adjustable trigger pull
Stock: Select hardwood
Finish: Pewter nose cap, trigger guard and butt plate
Lock: Plate is color casehardened and engraved; internal features include bridle, fly, screw-adjustable sear engagement, V-type mainspring
Accessories: Stainless steel nipple, hardwood ramrod with aluminum tips
Also available: Standard model (not chromed) with select finished hardwood stock and low cheekpiece in 50 or 54 caliber **$306.95.**

BLACK POWDER

DIXIE

DIXIE NAVY REVOLVER
Plain Model $95.00
Engraved Model $139.95
Kit $84.95

This 36-caliber revolver was a favorite of the officers of the Civil War. Although called a Navy type, it is somewhat misnamed since many more of the Army personnel used it. Made in Italy; uses .376 mold or ball to fit and number 11 caps. Blued steel barrel and cylinder with brass frame.

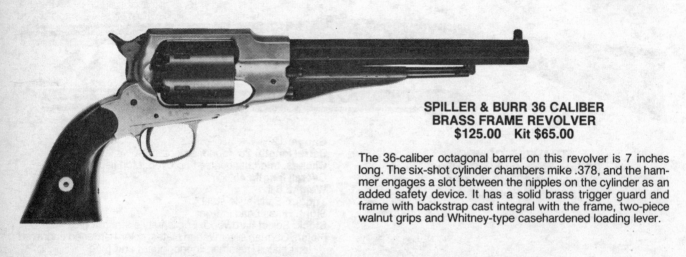

SPILLER & BURR 36 CALIBER
BRASS FRAME REVOLVER
$125.00   Kit $65.00

The 36-caliber octagonal barrel on this revolver is 7 inches long. The six-shot cylinder chambers mike .378, and the hammer engages a slot between the nipples on the cylinder as an added safety device. It has a solid brass trigger guard and frame with backstrap cast integral with the frame, two-piece walnut grips and Whitney-type casehardened loading lever.

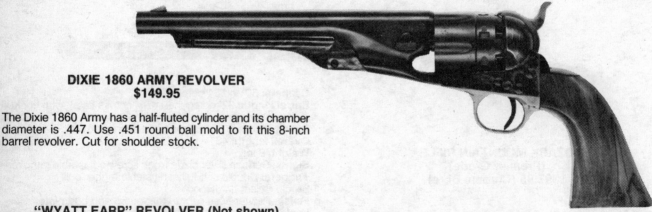

DIXIE 1860 ARMY REVOLVER
$149.95

The Dixie 1860 Army has a half-fluted cylinder and its chamber diameter is .447. Use .451 round ball mold to fit this 8-inch barrel revolver. Cut for shoulder stock.

"WYATT EARP" REVOLVER (Not shown)
$130.00

This 44-caliber revolver has a 12-inch octagon rifled barrel and rebated cylinder. Highly polished brass frame, backstrap and trigger guard. The barrel and cylinder have a deep blue luster finish. Hammer, trigger, and loading lever are case-hardened. Walnut grips. Recommended ball size is .451.

DIXIE

RHO200 WALKER REVOLVER
$195.00   Kit $169.00

This 4½-pound, 44-caliber pistol is the largest ever made. Steel backstrap; guard is brass with Walker-type rounded-to-frame walnut grips; all other parts are blued. Chambers measure .445 and take a .450 ball slightly smaller than the originals.

RHO301 THIRD MODEL DRAGOON
$195.00

This engraved-cylinder, 4½-pounder is a reproduction of the last model of Colt's 44 caliber "horse" revolvers. Barrel measures 7⅜ inches, ⅛ inch shorter than the original; color case-hardened steel frame, one-piece walnut grips. Recommended ball size: .454.

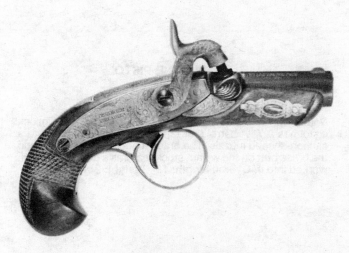

DSB-58 SCREW BARREL DERRINGER
(Not shown)
$89.00   Kit $58.95

Overall length: 6½". Unique loading system; sheath trigger, color case-hardened frame, trigger and center-mounted hammer; European walnut, one-piece, "bag"-type grip. Uses #11 percussion caps.

LINCOLN DERRINGER
$285.00   Kit $89.95

This 41-caliber, 2-inch browned barrel gun has 8 lands and 8 grooves and will shoot a .400 patch ball.

DIXIE BRASS FRAMED "HIDEOUT" DERRINGER
(Not shown)
Plain $49.95   Engraved $85.95
Kit $42.50

This small handgun sports a brass frame and walnut grips, and fires a .395 round ball.

FHO201 FRENCH CHARLEVILLE FLINT PISTOL
(Not shown)
$164.95

Reproduction of the Model 1777 Cavalry, Revolutionary War-era pistol. Has reversed frizzen spring; forend and lock housing are all in one; casehardened, round-faced, double-throated hammer; walnut stock; casehardened frizzen and trigger; shoots .680 round ball loaded with about 40 grains FFg black powder.

ABILENE DERRINGER (Not shown)
$81.50   Kit $51.95

An all-steel version of Dixie's brass-framed derringers. The 2½-inch, 41-caliber barrel is finished in a deep blue black; frame and hammer are case-hardened. Bore is rifled with 6 lands and grooves. Uses a tightly patched .395 round ball and 15 or 20 grains of FFFg powder. Walnut grips. Comes with wood presentation case.

DIXIE

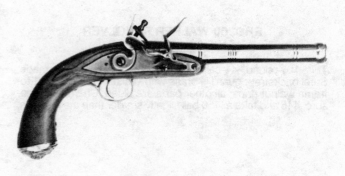

LePAGE PERCUSSION DUELING PISTOL
$225.00

This percussion pistol features a blued 10″ octagonal barrel with 12 lands and grooves. The 45-caliber sidearm has a brass-bladed front sight with open rear sight dovetailed into the barrel. Trigger guard and butt cap are polished silver plating. Right side of barrel is stamped "LePage á Paris." Double-set triggers are single screw adjustable. **Overall length:** 16″. **Weight:** 2½ lbs.

QUEEN ANNE PISTOL
$144.00
Kit $119.95

Named for the Queen of England (1702-1714), this flintlock pistol has a 7½″ barrel that tapers from rear to front with a cannon-shaped muzzle. The brass trigger guard is fluted and the brass butt on the walnut stock features a grotesque mask worked into it. **Overall length:** 13″. **Weight:** 2¼ lbs.

PEDERSOLI ENGLISH DUELING PISTOL
(Not shown)
$250.00

This reproduction of an English percussion dueling pistol, created by Charles Moore of London, features a European walnut halfstock with oil finish and checkered grip. The 45-caliber octagonal barrel is 11″ with 12 grooves and a twist of 1 in 15″. Nose cap and thimble are silver. Barrel is blued; lock and trigger guard are color casehardened.

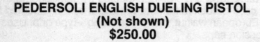

PEDERSOLI MANG TARGET PISTOL
(Not shown)
$545.00

Designed specifically for the precision target shooter, this 38-caliber pistol has a 10⁷⁄₁₆″ octagonal barrel with 7 lands and grooves. Twist is 1 in 15″. Blade front sight is dovetailed into the barrel, and rear sight is mounted on the breech-plug tang, adjustable for windage. **Overall length:** 17¼″. **Weight:** 2½ lbs.

DIXIE PENNSYLVANIA PISTOL (Not shown)
Percussion $124.95   Kit $95.00
Flintlock $134.95   Kit $115.00

Available in 44-caliber percussion or flintlock. The bright luster blued barrel measures 10 inches long; rifled, ⁷⁄₈-inch octagonal and takes .430 ball; barrel is held in place with a steel wedge and tang screw; brass front and rear sights. The brass trigger guard, thimbles, nose cap, wedge plates and side plates are highly polished. Locks are fine quality with early styling. Plates measure 4¾ inches × ⁷⁄₈ inch. Percussion hammer is engraved and both plates are left in the white. The flint is an excellent style lock with the gooseneck hammer having an early wide thumb piece. The stock is walnut stained and has a wide bird's-head-type grip.

DIXIE

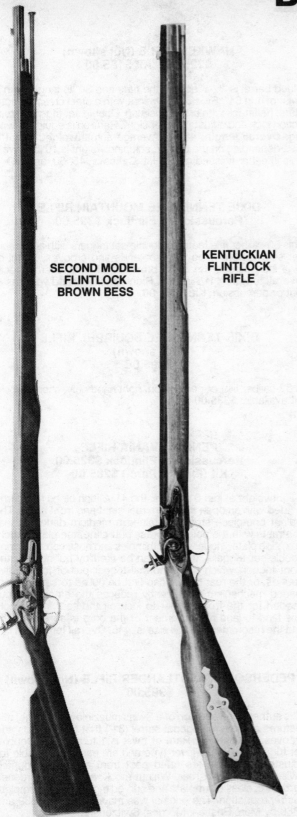

**SECOND MODEL
FLINTLOCK
BROWN BESS**

**KENTUCKIAN
FLINTLOCK
RIFLE**

SECOND MODEL BROWN BESS MUSKET
$450.00

This 75-caliber Brown Bess has a 41¾-inch smoothbore barrel that takes a .730 round ball. In keeping with the traditional musket, it has brass furniture on a walnut-stained stock. The lock is marked "Tower" and has the crown with the "GR" underneath. Barrel, lock and ramrod are left bright.
Kit: $375.00

THE KENTUCKIAN RIFLE
Flintlock $225.00
Percussion $210.00

This 45-caliber rifle, in flintlock or percussion, wears a 33½-inch blued octagonal barrel that is ¹³/₁₆ inch across the flats. The bore is rifled with 6 lands and grooves of equal width and about .006 inch deep. Land-to-land diameter is .453 with groove-to-groove diameter at. 465. Ball size ranges from .445 to .448. The rifle has a brass blade front sight and a steel open rear sight. The Kentuckian is furnished with brass butt plate, trigger guard, patch box, side plate, thimbles and nose cap plus case-hardened and engraved lock plate. Highly polished and finely finished stock in European walnut. **Overall length: 48″. Weight:** Approx. 6¼ lbs.

DIXIE DOUBLE BARREL MAGNUM
MUZZLE LOADING SHOTGUN (Not shown)

A full 12-gauge, high-quality, double-barreled percussion shotgun with 30-inch browned barrels. Will take the plastic shot cups for better patterns. Bores are choked modified and full. Lock, barrel tang and trigger are case-hardened in a light gray color and are nicely engraved. In **12 Gauge: $357.95** (Kit **$280.00**). Also available: **10 Gauge Magnum** with double barrel (right-hand = cyl. bore; left-hand = Mod.), otherwise same specs as above: **$399.00** (Kit **$335.00**).

DIXIE

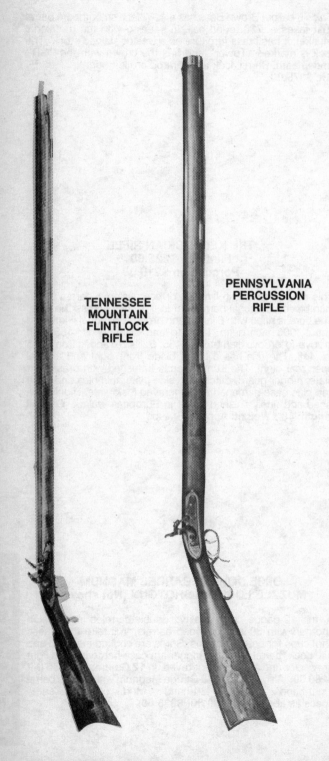

TENNESSEE MOUNTAIN FLINTLOCK RIFLE

PENNSYLVANIA PERCUSSION RIFLE

HAWKEN RIFLE (Not shown)
$225.00   Kit $185.00

Blued barrel is 15/16″ across the flats and 30″ in length with a twist of 1 in 64″. Stock is of walnut with a steel crescent buttplate, halfstock with brass nosecap. Double set triggers, front action lock and adjustable rear sight. Ramrod is equipped with jag. **Overall length:** 46½″. Average actual **weight:** about 8 lbs., depending on the caliber; shipping weight is 10 lbs. Available in either finished gun or kit. **Calibers:** 45, 50, and 54.

DIXIE TENNESSEE MOUNTAIN RIFLE
Percussion or Flintlock $395.00

This 50-caliber rifle features double-set triggers with adjustable set screw, bore rifled with six lands and grooves, barrel of 15/16 inch across the flats, brown finish and cherry stock. **Overall length:** 41½ inches. Right- and left-hand versions in flint or percussion. **Kit: $335.00.**

DIXIE TENNESSEE SQUIRREL RIFLE
(Not shown)
$395.00

In 32-caliber flint or percussion, right hand only, cherry stock. Kit available: **$335.00**

PENNSYLVANIA RIFLE
Percussion or Flintlock $325.00
Kit (Flint or Perc.) $285.00

A lightweight at just 8 pounds, the 41½-inch blued rifle barrel is fitted with an open buckhorn rear sight and front blade. The walnut one-piece stock is stained a medium darkness that contrasts with the polished brass butt plate, toe plate, patchbox, side plate, trigger guard, thimbles and nose cap. Featuring double-set triggers, the rifle can be fired by pulling only the front trigger, which has a normal trigger pull of four to five pounds; or the rear trigger can first be pulled to set a spring-loaded mechanism that greatly reduces the amount of pull needed for the front trigger to kick off the sear in the lock. The land-to-land measurement of the bore is an exact .450 and the recommended ball size is .445. **Overall length:** 51½″.

PEDERSOLI WAADTLANDER RIFLE (Not shown)
$995.00

This authentic re-creation of a Swiss muzzleloading target rifle features a heavy octagonal barrel (31″) that has 7 lands and grooves. **Caliber:** 45. Rate of twist is 1 turn in 48″. Double-set triggers are multi-lever type and are easily removable for adjustment. Sights are fitted post front and tang-mounted Swiss-type diopther rear. Walnut stock, color casehardened hardware, classic buttplate and curved trigger guard complete this reproduction. The original was made between 1839 and 1860 by Marc Bristlen, Morges, Switzerland.

DIXIE

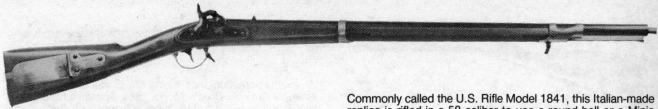

PRO401 MISSISSIPPI RIFLE
$430.00

Commonly called the U.S. Rifle Model 1841, this Italian-made replica is rifled in a 58 caliber to use a round ball or a Minie ball; 3 grooves and regulation sights; solid brass furniture; casehardened lock.

This 44-40 caliber gun can use modern or black powder cartridges. **Overall length:** 39″. **Barrel:** 20″ round. Its full tubular magazine will hold 11 shots. The walnut forearm and buttstock complement the high-luster bluing of the all steel parts such as the frame, barrel, magazine, loading lever and butt plate. Comes with the trap door in the butt for the cleaning rod; leaf rear sight and blade front sight. This carbine is marked "Model 1873" on the tang and caliber "44-40" on the brass carrier block.

WINCHESTER '73 CARBINE
$495.00
ENGRAVED WINCHESTER '73 RIFLE
$625.00

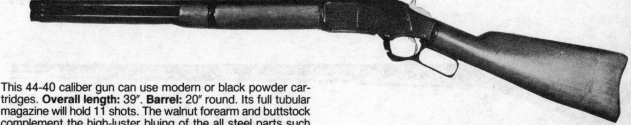

WESSON RIFLE
$425.00

The lock work for this rifle is housed in a steel frame or receiver. Barrel is a heavy $1\frac{1}{8}″ \times .50$ caliber measuring 28″ and fitted with a false muzzle. Two-piece European walnut stock is hand checkered at wrist and forearm. Barrel and underrib are finished in bright blue; receiver is case colored. Double set triggers and adjustable rear sight. **Overall length:** $43\frac{1}{2}″$. **Weight:** $10\frac{1}{4}$ lbs.

TRYON CREEDMOOR RIFLE (Not shown)
$495.00

This updated version of the Tryon rifle features a high-quality back-action lock, double-set triggers, steel buttplate, patchbox, toe plate and curved trigger guard. **Caliber:** 45. **Barrel:** $32\frac{3}{4}″$, octagonal, with 1 twist in 20.87″. **Sights:** Hooded post front fitted with replaceable inserts; rear is tang-mounted and adjustable for windage and elevation.

DIXIE

U.S. MODEL 1861 SPRINGFIELD PERCUSSION RIFLE-MUSKET
$450.00   Kit $420.00

An exact re-creation of an original rifle produced by Springfield National Armory, Dixie's Model 1861 Springfield .58-caliber rifle features a 40″ round, tapered barrel with three barrel bands. Sling swivels are attached to the trigger guard bow and middle barrel band. The ramrod has a trumpet-shaped head with swell; sights are standard military rear and bayonet-attachment lug front. The percussion lock is marked "1861" on the rear of the lockplate with an eagle motif and "U.S. Springfield" in front of the hammer. "U.S." is stamped on top of buttplate. All furniture is "National Armory Bright." **Overall length:** 55$\frac{13}{16}$″. **Weight:** 8 lbs.

1862 THREE-BAND ENFIELD RIFLED MUSKET
$395.00

One of the finest reproduction percussion guns available, the 1862 Enfield was widely used during the Civil War in its original version. This rifle follows the lines of the original almost exactly. The .58 caliber musket features a 39-inch barrel and walnut stock. Three steel barrel bands and the barrel itself are blued; the lock plate and hammer are case colored and the remainder of the furniture is highly polished brass. The lock is marked, "London Armory Co." **Weight:** 10$\frac{1}{2}$ lbs. **Overall length:** 55 inches.

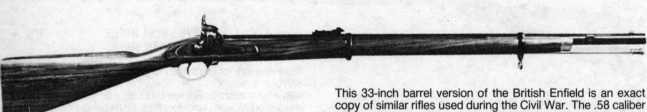

1858 TWO-BAND ENFIELD RIFLE
$325.00

This 33-inch barrel version of the British Enfield is an exact copy of similar rifles used during the Civil War. The .58 caliber rifle sports a European walnut stock, deep blue-black finish on the barrel, bands, breech-plug tang and bayonet mount. The percussion lock is color casehardened and the rest of the furniture is brightly polished brass.

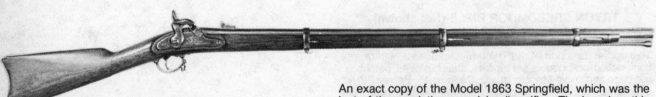

1863 SPRINGFIELD CIVIL WAR MUSKET
$475.00   Kit $330.00

An exact copy of the Model 1863 Springfield, which was the last of the regulation muzzleloading rifles. The barrel on this .58 caliber gun measures 40 inches. The action and all metal furniture is finished bright. The oil-finished walnut-stain stock is 53 inches long. **Overall length:** 56 inches. **Weight:** 9$\frac{1}{2}$ lbs.

EMF

MODEL 1860 ARMY REVOLVER
$148.00 (Brass) $200.00 (Steel)

SPECIFICATIONS
Caliber: 44 Percussion
Barrel length: 8"
Overall length: 13⁵/₈"
Weight: 41 oz.
Frame: Casehardened
Finish: High-luster blue with walnut grips
Also available as a **cased set** with steel frame, wood case, flask and mold: **$318.00**

MODEL 1862 POLICE REVOLVER
$220.00

SPECIFICATIONS
Caliber: 36 Percussion
Capacity: 5-shot
Barrel length: 6¹/₂"
Also available as a **cased set: $338.00**

SHERIFF'S MODEL 1851 REVOLVER
$130.00 (Brass) $180.00 (Steel)

SPECIFICATIONS
Caliber: 36 Percussion
Ball diameter: .376 round or conical, pure lead
Barrel length: 5"
Overall length: 10¹/₂"
Weight: 39 oz.
Sights: V-notch groove in hammer (rear); truncated cone in front
Percussion cap size: #11
Also available in complete **cased set** (36 caliber steel frame): **$298.00**

MODEL 1851 STEEL NAVY REVOLVER
36 Caliber $180.00

SECOND MODEL 44 DRAGOON
$248.00

SPECIFICATIONS
Caliber: 44
Barrel length: 7¹/₂" (round)
Overall length: 14"
Weight: 4 lbs.
Finish: Steel casehardened frame

EUROARMS OF AMERICA

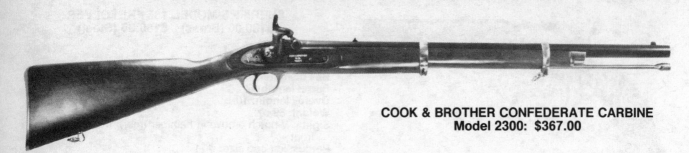

COOK & BROTHER CONFEDERATE CARBINE
Model 2300: $367.00

Classic re-creation of the rare 1861, New Orleans-made Artillery Carbine. The lockplate is marked "Cook & Brother N.O. 1861" and is stamped with a Confederate flag at the rear of the hammer.

Caliber: 58
Barrel length: 24"
Overall length: 40 1/3"

Weight: 7 1/2 lbs.
Sights: Adjustable dovetailed front and rear sights
Ramrod: Steel
Finish: Barrel is antique brown; butt plate, trigger guard, barrel bands, sling swivels and nose cap are polished brass; stock is walnut
Recommended ball sizes: .575 r.b., .577 Minie and .580 maxi; uses musket caps

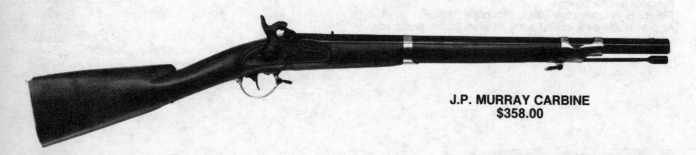

J.P. MURRAY CARBINE
$358.00

Caliber: 58 percussion
Barrel length: 23"
Features: Brass barrel bands and butt plate; oversized trigger guard; sling swivels

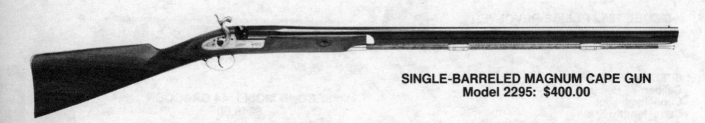

SINGLE-BARRELED MAGNUM CAPE GUN
Model 2295: $400.00

Euroarms of America offers a beautiful reproduction of a classic English-styled single-barreled shotgun. The lock is left in the white and displays a scroll engraving, as does the bow of the trigger guard. Uses #11 percussion caps and recommended wads are felt overpowder and cardboard overshot.

Gauge: 12
Barrel: 32", open choke
Overall length: 47 1/2"
Weight: 7 1/2 lbs.
Stock: English style; European walnut with satin oil finish; moderate recoil, even with relatively heavy powder charges
Finish: Barrel, underrib, thimbles, nose cap, trigger guard and butt plate are deep, rich blue

EUROARMS OF AMERICA

LONDON ARMORY COMPANY
2-BAND RIFLE MUSKET
Model 2270: $382.00

Caliber: 58
Barrel length: 33", blued and rifled
Overall length: 49"
Weight: 8½ to 8¾ lbs., depending on wood density
Stock: One-piece walnut; polished "bright" brass butt plate, trigger guard and nose cap; blued barrel bands
Sights: Inverted 'V' front sight; Enfield folding ladder rear
Ramrod: Steel

LONDON ARMORY COMPANY
ENFIELD MUSKETOON
Model 2280: $350.00

Caliber: 58; Minie ball
Barrel length: 24"; round high-luster blued barrel
Overall length: 40½"
Weight: 7 to 7½ lbs., depending on density of wood
Stock: Seasoned walnut stock with sling swivels
Ramrod: Steel
Ignition: Heavy-duty percussion lock
Sights: Graduated military-leaf sight
Furniture: Brass trigger guard, nose cap and butt plate; blued barrel bands, lock plate, and swivels

LONDON ARMORY COMPANY
3-BAND ENFIELD RIFLED MUSKET
Model 2260: $447.00

Caliber: 58
Barrel length: 39", blued and rifled
Overall length: 54"
Weight: 9½ to 9¾ lbs., depending on wood density
Stock: One-piece walnut; polished "bright" brass butt plate, trigger guard and nose cap; blued barrel bands
Ramrod: Steel; threaded end for accessories
Sights: Traditional Enfield folding ladder rear sight; inverted 'V' front sight

EUROARMS OF AMERICA

1803 HARPERS FERRY RIFLE

1803 HARPERS FERRY FLINTLOCK RIFLE
$512.00

Caliber: 54 Flintlock
Barrel length: 33″, octagonal
Features: Walnut halfstock with cheekpiece; browned barrel

1841 MISSISSIPPI RIFLE

1841 MISSISSIPPI RIFLE
$463.00

Caliber: 58 percussion
Barrel length: 33″, octagonal
Features: Walnut stock; brass barrel bands and buttplate;
   sling swivels

**1863 ZOUAVE RIFLE
RANGE GRADE**

1863 ZOUAVE RIFLE (2-Barrel Bands)
$406.00 (Range Grade)
$323.00 (Field Grade)

Caliber: 58 percussion
Barrel length: 33″, octagonal
Overall length: 48½″
Weight: 9½ to 9¾ lbs.
Sights: U.S. Military 3-leaf rear; blade front
Features: Two brass barrel bands; brass buttplate and nose
   cap; sling swivels

EUROARMS OF AMERICA

MODEL 1005

ROGERS & SPENCER ARMY REVOLVER
Model 1006 (Target)
$234.00

Caliber: 44; takes .451 round or conical lead balls; #11 percussion cap
Weight: 47 oz.
Barrel length: 7¹/₂″
Overall length: 13³/₄″
Finish: High-gloss blue; flared walnut grip; solid-frame design; precision-rifled barrel
Sights: Rear fully adjustable for windage and elevation; ramp front sight

ROGERS & SPENCER REVOLVER
Model 1007, London Gray
$234.00

Revolver is the same as Model 1005, except for London Gray finish, which is heat treated and buffed for rust resistance; same recommended ball size and percussion caps.

ROGERS & SPENCER REVOLVER
Model 1005
$192.00

Caliber: 44 Percussion; #11 percussion cap
Barrel length: 7¹/₂″
Sights: Integral rear sight notch groove in frame; brass truncated cone front sight
Overall length: 13³/₄″
Weight: 47 oz.
Finish: High-gloss blue; flared walnut grip; solid-frame design; precision-rifled barrel
Recommended ball diameter: .451 round or conical, pure lead

MODEL 1006

MODEL 1020

REMINGTON 1858 NEW MODEL ARMY REVOLVER
Model 1020: $164.00

This model is equipped with blued steel frame, brass trigger guard in 44 caliber.

Weight: 40 oz.
Barrel length: 8″
Overall length: 14³/₄″
Finish: Deep luster blue rifled barrel; polished walnut stock; brass trigger guard.
MODEL 1010: Same as Model 1020, except with 6¹/₂″ barrel and in 36 caliber: **$164.00**

REMINGTON 1858 NEW MODEL ARMY ENGRAVED
Model 1040: $275.00

Classical 19th-century style scroll engraving on this 1858 Remington New Model revolver.

Caliber: 44 Percussion; #11 cap
Barrel length: 8″
Overall length: 14³/₄″
Weight: 41 oz.
Sights: Integral rear sight notch groove in frame; blade front sight
Recommended ball diameter: .451 round or conical, pure lead

BLACK POWDER

EUROARMS OF AMERICA

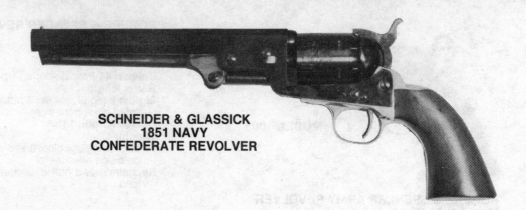

**SCHNEIDER & GLASSICK
1851 NAVY
CONFEDERATE REVOLVER**

SCHNEIDER & GLASSICK
1851 NAVY CONFEDERATE REVOLVER
Model 1050 (36 Cal.): $104.00

A modern replica of a Confederate Percussion Army Revolver. Polished brass frame, rifled high-luster blued, octagonal barrel and polished walnut grips.

Weight: 40 oz.
Barrel length: 7¹/₂"
Overall length: 13"
Finish: Brass frame, backstrap and trigger guard; blued rifled barrel; casehardened hammer and loading lever; engraved cylinder with naval battle scene

SCHNEIDER & GLASSICK
1851 NAVY (Not shown)
Model 1120: $137.00

Caliber: .36 percussion, #11 cap
Barrel length: 7¹/₂", octagonal barrel, precision rifled
Overall length: 13"
Weight: 42 oz.
Finish: Blued barrel and frame; backstrap and trigger guard are polished brass; walnut grips.

GONIC ARMS

**MODEL GA-87 RIFLE
$447.99 Standard
$478.44 Deluxe**

SPECIFICATIONS
Caliber: 458 Express and 308 Spitfire
Barrel lengths: 26" (Rifle); 24" (Carbine)
Overall length: 43" (Rifle); 41" (Carbine)
Weight: 6¹/₂ lbs. (Rifle); 6 lbs. (Carbine)
Sights: Bead front; open rear (adjustable for windage and elevation); drilled and tapped for scope bases

Stock: American walnut
Length of pull: 14"
Trigger: Single stage (4-lb. pull)
Mechanism type: Closed-breech muzzleloader
Features: Ambidextrous safety; non-glare satin finish; newly designed loading system; all-weather performance guaranteed; faster lock time

LYMAN

LYMAN PLAINS PISTOL
$184.95
Percussion Kit $154.95

This replica of the pistol carried by the Western pioneers of the 1830s features a pistol-sized Hawken lock with dependable coil spring and authentic rib and thimble styling. It has a richly stained walnut stock, blackened iron furniture and polished brass trigger guard and ramrod tips. Equipped with a spring-loaded trigger and a fast twist (1 in 30 inches both calibers) barrel for target accuracy. **Caliber:** 50 or 54 percussion.

DEERSTALKER RIFLE
$275.00

Lyman's new Deerstalker rifle incorporates many features most desired by muzzleloading hunters, including the following: higher comb for better sighting plane • non-glare hardware • 24″ octagonal barrel • casehardened side plate • Q.D. sling swivels • Lyman sight package (37MA beaded front; fully adjustable fold-down 16A rear) • walnut stock with 1/2″ black recoil pad • single trigger. **Calibers:** 50 and 54, flintlock or percussion. **Weight:** 7 1/2 lbs.

GREAT PLAINS RIFLE
Percussion $339.95   (Kit $269.95)
Flintlock $359.95   (Kit $289.95)

The Great Plains Rifle has a 32-inch deep-grooved barrel and 1 in 66-inch twist to shoot patched round balls. Blued steel furniture including the thick steel wedge plates and steel toe plate; correct lock and hammer styling with coil spring dependability; and a walnut stock without a patch box. A Hawken-style trigger guard protects double-set triggers. Steel front sight and authentic buckhorn styling in an adjustable rear sight. A fixed primitive rear sight is also included. **Calibers:** 50 and 54.

LYMAN TRADE RIFLE
Percussion $254.95   (Kit $204.95)
Flintlock $279.95   (Kit $234.95)

The Lyman Trade Rifle features a 28-inch octagonal barrel, rifled one turn at 48 inches, designed to fire both patched round balls and the popular maxistyle conical bullets. Polished brass furniture with blued finish on steel parts; walnut stock; hook breech; single spring-loaded trigger; coil-spring percussion lock; fixed steel sights; adjustable rear sight for elevation also included. Steel barrel rib and ramrod ferrrule. **Caliber:** 50 or 54 percussion and flint. **Overall length:** 45″.

BLACK POWDER

MITCHELL ARMS REVOLVERS

1851 COLT NAVY

SPECIFICATIONS
Calibers: 36 and 44
Barrel length: 7½" (brass or steel)
Frame: Polished solid brass or color case steel
Grips: Walnut
Price: $169.95

SPILLER & BURR

SPECIFICATIONS
Caliber: 36
Barrel length: 7½" (blue steel)
Frame: Brass
Grips: Walnut
Price: $169.95

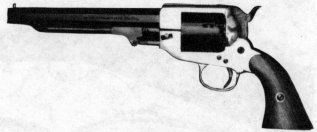

REMINGTON NEW MODEL ARMY

SPECIFICATIONS
Calibers: 36 and 44
Barrel length: 8"
Frame: Blued steel
Grips: Walnut
Features: Progressive rifling; brass trigger guard
Price: $179.95

1860 COLT ARMY MODEL

SPECIFICATIONS
Caliber: 44
Barrel length: 7½" (round rebated cylinder)
Weight: 2 lbs. 11 oz.
Frame: Steel
Grips: Walnut
Features: Detachable shoulder stock (optional)
Price: $169.95

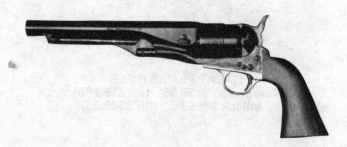

REMINGTON "TEXAS" MODEL

SPECIFICATIONS
Calibers: 36 and 44
Barrel length: 8" octagonal; blued steel
Frame: Bright brass
Grips: Walnut
Price: $179.95

Also available:
1861 COLT NAVY (36 or 44 cal.) $169.95
'51 NAVY SHERIFF'S MODEL (36 or 44 cal.) 169.95

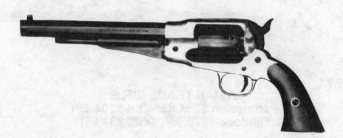

MODERN MUZZLE LOADING

KNIGHT MK-85 RIFLE

The Knight MK-85 muzzleloading rifle (designed by William A. "Tony" Knight of Schuyler County, Missouri) is a handcrafted, lightweight rifle capable of 1½-inch groups at 100 yards. It features a one-piece, in-line bolt assembly, patented double safety system, Timney featherweight deluxe trigger system, recoil pad, and Lothar Walther barrels (1 in 32″ twist in 50 and 54 caliber; 1 in 17″ twist in 45 caliber).

SPECIFICATIONS
Calibers: 45, 50 and 54
Barrel lengths: 20″, 22″ and 24″
Weight: 7 lbs.
Sights: Adjustable high-visibility open sights
Stock: Classic walnut, laminated, or composite
Features: Swivel studs installed; LS&B Perfect Memory nylon ramrod; combo tool; flush valve; hex keys, and more.
Prices:
KNIGHT MK-85 HUNTER (Walnut) **$500.00**
KNIGHT MK-85 STALKER (Laminated) 565.00
KNIGHT MK-85 PREDATOR (Stainless) 630.00
Also available:
BACKCOUNTRY CARBINE (20″ barrel) 565.00
   Stainless Steel 630.00
MODEL BK-89 SQUIRREL RIFLE (24″ barrel, 36 cal.) 480.00

NAVY ARMS REVOLVERS

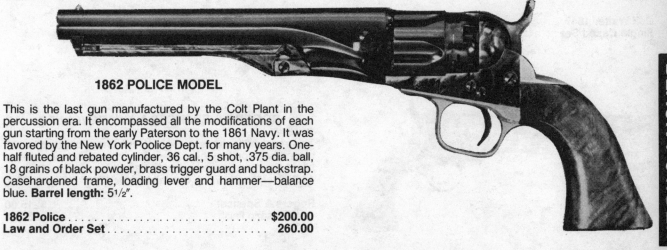

1862 POLICE MODEL

This is the last gun manufactured by the Colt Plant in the percussion era. It encompassed all the modifications of each gun starting from the early Paterson to the 1861 Navy. It was favored by the New York Poolice Dept. for many years. One-half fluted and rebated cylinder, 36 cal., 5 shot, .375 dia. ball, 18 grains of black powder, brass trigger guard and backstrap. Casehardened frame, loading lever and hammer—balance blue. **Barrel length:** 5½″.

1862 Police $200.00
Law and Order Set 260.00

BLACK POWDER

NAVY ARMS REVOLVERS

LE MAT REVOLVERS

Once the official sidearm of many Confederate cavalry officers, this 9 shot .44 caliber revolver with a central single shot barrel of approx. 65 caliber gave the cavalry man 10 shots to use against the enemy. **Barrel length:** 7⅝". **Overall length:** 14". **Weight:** 3 lbs. 7 oz.

Cavalry Model $595.00
Navy Model 595.00
Army Model 595.00

ARMY MODEL

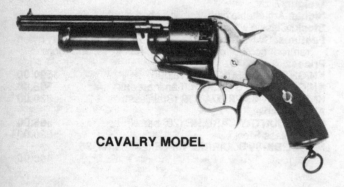

CAVALRY MODEL

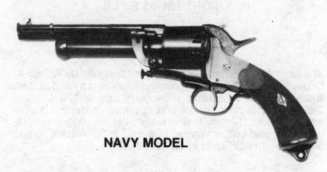

NAVY MODEL

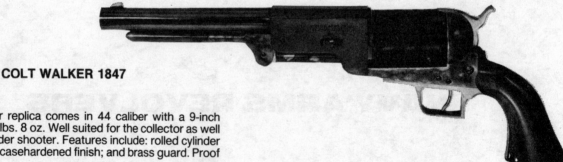

COLT WALKER 1847

The 1847 Walker replica comes in 44 caliber with a 9-inch barrel. **Weight:** 4 lbs. 8 oz. Well suited for the collector as well as the black powder shooter. Features include: rolled cylinder scene; blued and casehardened finish; and brass guard. Proof tested.

Colt Walter 1847 . . . . $195.00
Single Cased Set 295.00

ROGERS & SPENCER NAVY REVOLVER

This revolver features a six-shot cylinder, octagonal barrel, hinged-type loading lever assembly, two-piece walnut grips, blued finish and case-hardened hammer and lever. **Caliber:** 44. **Barrel length:** 7½". **Overall length:** 13¾". **Weight:** 3 lbs.

Rogers & Spencer $215.00
  With satin finish 230.00

NAVY ARMS REVOLVERS

REB MODEL 1860

A modern replica of the confederate Griswold & Gunnison percussion Army revolver. Rendered with a polished brass frame and a rifled steel barrel finished in a high-luster blue with genuine walnut grips. All Army Model 60's are completely proof-tested by the Italian government to the most exacting standards. **Calibers:** 36 and 44. **Barrel length:** 7¼″. **Overall length:** 13″. **Weight:** 2 lbs. 10 oz.-11 oz. **Finish:** Brass frame, backstrap and trigger guard, round barrel hinged rammer on the 44 cal. rebated cylinder.

Reb Model 1860	$100.00
Single Cased Set	190.00
Double Cased Set	300.00
Kit	80.00

COLT ARMY 1860

These guns from the Colt line are 44 caliber and all six-shot. The cylinder was authentically roll engraved with a polished brass trigger guard and steel strap cut for shoulder stock. The frame, loading lever and hammer are finished in high-luster color case-hardening. Walnut grips. **Weight:** 2 lbs. 9 oz. **Barrel length:** 8″. **Overall length:** 13⅝″. **Caliber:** 44. **Finish:** Brass trigger guard, steel back strap, round barrel creeping cylinder, rebated cylinder engraved. Navy scene. Frame cut for s/stock (4 screws). Also available with full fluted cylinder and in 5½″ barrel (Sheriff's Model).

Army 1860	$150.00
Single Cased Set	240.00
Double Cased Set	365.00
Kit	125.00

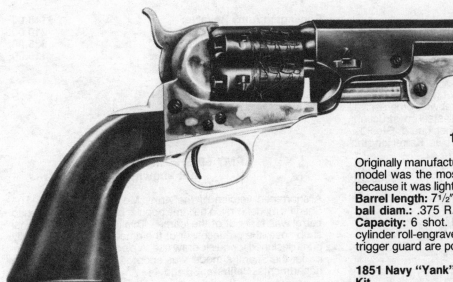

1851 NAVY "YANK"

Originally manufactured by Colt from 1850 through 1876, this model was the most popular of the Union revolvers, mostly because it was lighter and easier to handle than the Dragoon. **Barrel length:** 7½″. **Overall length:** 14″. **Weight:** 2 lbs. **Rec. ball diam.:** .375 R.B. (.451 in 44 cal) **Calibers:** 36 and 44. **Capacity:** 6 shot. **Features:** Steel frame, octagonal barrel, cylinder roll-engraved with Naval battle scene, backstrap and trigger guard are polished brass.

1851 Navy "Yank"	$130.00
Kit	110.00
Single Cased Set	215.00
Double Cased Set	340.00

BLACK POWDER

NAVY ARMS REVOLVERS

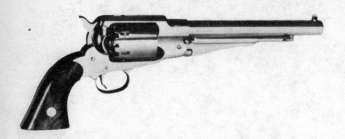

STAINLESS STEEL 1858 REMINGTON

Exactly like the standard 1858 Remington except that every part with the exception of the grips and trigger guard is manufactured from corrosion-resistant stainless steel. This gun has all the style and feel of its ancestor with all of the conveniences of stainless steel. **Caliber:** 44.

1858 Remington Stainless **$220.00**

TARGET MODEL REMINGTON REVOLVER

With its top strap and frame, the Remington Percussion Revolver is considered the magnum of Civil War revolvers and is ideally suited to the heavy 44-caliber charges. Based on the Army Model, the target gun has target sights for controlled accuracy. Ruggedly built from modern steel and proof tested.

Remington Percussion Revolver **$155.00**

DELUXE 1858 REMINGTON-STYLE 44 CALIBER

Built to the exact dimensions and weight of the original Remington 44, this model features an 8″ barrel with progressive rifling, adjustable front sight for windage, all-steel construction with walnut stocks and silver-plated trigger guard. Steel is highly polished and finished in rich charcoal blue. **Barrel length:** 8″. **Overall length:** 14¹/₄″. **Weight:** 2 lbs. 14 oz.

Deluxe 1858 Remington-Style 44 Cal. **$300.00**

REMINGTON NEW MODEL ARMY REVOLVER
(not shown)

This rugged, dependable, battle-proven Civil War veteran with its top strap and rugged frame was considered the magnum of C.W. revolvers, ideally suited for the heavy 44 charges. Blued finish. **Caliber:** 44. **Barrel length:** 8″. **Overall length:** 14¹/₄″. **Weight:** 2 lbs. 8 oz.

Remington Army Revolver **$140.00**
Single cased set 210.00
Double cased set 335.00
Kit 115.00

ARMY 60 SHERIFF'S MODEL
(not shown)

A shortened version of the Army Model 60 Revolver. The Sheriff's model version became popular because the shortened barrel was fast out of the leather. This is actually the original snub nose, the predecessor of the detective specials or belly guns designed for quick-draw use. A piece of traditional Americana, the Sheriff's model was adopted by many local police departments. **Calibers:** 36 and 44.

Army 60 Sheriff's Model **$100.00**
Kit 80.00

NAVY ARMS PISTOLS

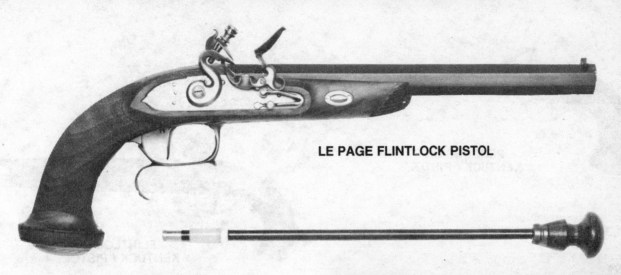

LE PAGE FLINTLOCK PISTOL

LE PAGE FLINTLOCK PISTOL
(45 Caliber)

The Le Page pistol is a beautifully hand-crafted reproduction featuring hand-checkered walnut stock with hinged buttcap and carved motif of a shell at the forward portion of the stock. Single-set trigger and highly polished steel lock and furniture together with a brown finished rifled barrel make this a highly desirable target pistol. **Barrel length:** 10½″. **Overall length:** 17″. **Weight:** 2 lbs. 2 oz.

Le Page Flintlock (rifled or smoothbore) **$435.00**
Single Cased Set 625.00

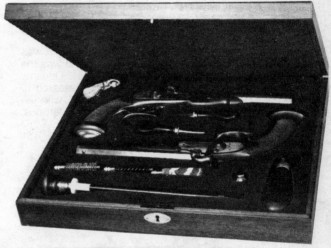

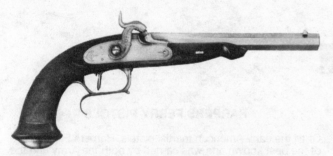

LE PAGE PERCUSSION PISTOL
(45 Caliber)

The tapered octagonal rifled barrel is in the traditional style with 7 lands and grooves. Fully adjustable single-set trigger. Engraved overall with traditional scrollwork. The European walnut stock is in the Boutet style. Spur-style trigger guard. Fully adjustable elevating rear sight. Dovetailed front sight adjustable for windage. **Barrel length:** 9″. **Overall length:** 15″. **Weight:** 2 lbs. 2 oz. **Rec. ball diameter:** 440 R.B.

Le Page Percussion **$355.00**

CASED LE PAGE PISTOL SETS
(45 Caliber)

The case is French-fitted and the accessories are the finest quality to match.

Double Cased Flintlock Set **$1100.00**

Double Cased Set
French-fitted double-cased set comprising two Le Page pistols, turn screw, nipple key, oil bottle, cleaning brushes, leather covered flask and loading rod.

Double Cased Percussion Set **$930.00**

Single Cased Set
French-fitted single-cased set comprising one Le Page pistol, turn screw, nipple key, oil bottle, cleaning brushes, leather covered flask and loading rod.

Single Cased Percussion Set **$540.00**

NAVY ARMS PISTOLS

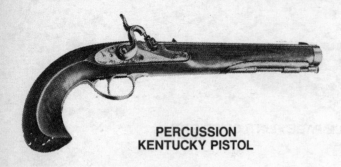

**PERCUSSION
KENTUCKY PISTOL**

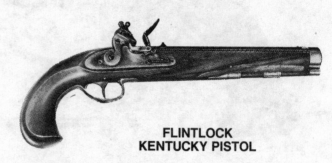

**FLINTLOCK
KENTUCKY PISTOL**

KENTUCKY PISTOLS

The Kentucky Pistol is truly a historical American gun. It was carried during the Revolution by the Minutemen and was the sidearm of "Andy" Jackson in the Battle of New Orleans. Navy Arms Company has conducted extensive research to manufacture a pistol truly representative of its kind, with the balance and handle of the original for which it became famous.

Prices:

Flintlock	**$145.00**
Single Cased Flintlock Set	230.00
Double Cased Flintlock Set	350.00
Percussion	125.00
Single Cased Percussion Set	205.00
Double Cased Percussion Set	330.00

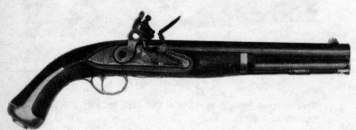

HARPERS FERRY PISTOLS

Of all the early American martial pistols, Harpers Ferry is one of the best known and was carried by both the Army and the Navy. Navy Arms Company has authentically reproduced the Harper's Ferry to the finest detail, providing a well-balanced and well-made pistol. **Weight:** 2 lbs. 9 oz. **Barrel length:** 10″. **Overall length:** 16″. **Caliber:** 58 smoothbore. **Finish:** Walnut stock; casehardened lock; brass-mounted browned barrel.

Harpers Ferry **$195.00**

NAVY ARMS RIFLES

PARKER-HALE WHITWORTH MILITARY TARGET RIFLE

Recreation of Sir Joseph Whitworth's deadly and successful sniper and target weapon of the mid-1800s. Devised with a hexagonal bore with a pitch of 1 turn in 20 inches. Barrel is cold-forged from ordnance steel, reducing the build-up of black powder fouling. Globe front sight; open military target rifle rear sight has interchangeable blades of different heights. Walnut stock is hand-checkered. **Caliber:** 451. **Barrel length:** 36″. **Weight:** 9½ lbs.

Parker-Hale Whitworth Military Target Rifle **$815.00**

PARKER-HALE 451 VOLUNTEER RIFLE

Originally designed by Irish gunmaker William John Rigby, this relatively small-caliber rifle was issued to volunteer regiments during the 1860s. Today it is rifled by the cold-forged method, making one turn in 20 inches. Sights are adjustable: globe front and ladder-type rear with interchangeable leaves; hand-checkered walnut stock. **Weight:** 9½ lbs.

Parker-Hale 451 Volunteer Rifle **$750.00**
    Same as above with 3-band barrel 815.00

Other Parker-Hale muskets available:
2-BAND MUSKET MODEL 1858
    Barrel length: 33″. **Overall length:** 48½″. **Weight:** 8½ lbs. 550.00
MUSKETOON MODEL 1861
    Barrel length: 24″. **Overall length:** 40¼″. **Weight:** 7½ lbs. 450.00
3-BAND MUSKET MODEL 1853
    Barrel length: 39″. **Overall length:** 55″. **Weight:** 9 lbs. 585.00

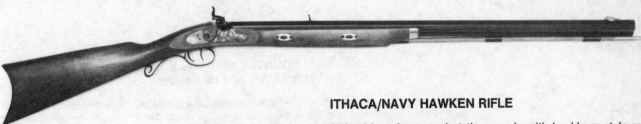

ITHACA/NAVY HAWKEN RIFLE

Features a 31½″ octagonal blued barrel crowned at the muzzle with buckhorn-style rear sight, blade front sight. Color casehardened percussion lock is fitted on walnut stock. Furniture is all steel and blued (except for nose cap and escutcheons). Available in 50 and 54 cal.

Ithaca/Navy Hawken Rifle **$355.00**
Kit 315.00

BLACK POWDER

NAVY ARMS RIFLES

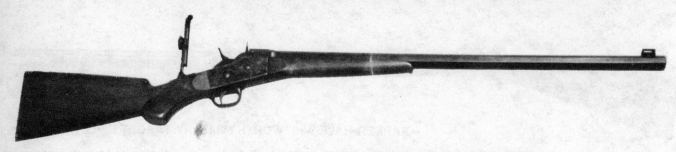

No. 2 CREEDMOOR TARGET RIFLE

Features a color casehardened rolling block receiver, checkered walnut stock and forend, 30″ tapered barrel in 45/70 caliber with blued finish, hooded front sight and Creedmoor tang sight. **Barrel length: 30″. Overall length: 46″. Weight: 9 lbs.**

No. 2 Creedmoor Target Rifle	$640.00
Rolling Block Action	125.00

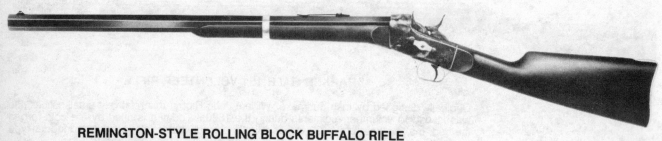

REMINGTON-STYLE ROLLING BLOCK BUFFALO RIFLE

Features 26″ or 30″ octagonal/half-round barrel; color casehardened receiver; solid brass trigger guard, walnut stock and forend. Available in 45/70 caliber only. Tang is drilled and tapped for Creedmoor sight.

Remington-Style Rolling Block Buffalo Rifle	$485.00

COUNTRY BOY RIFLE
(32, 36, 45, and 50 Caliber)

An authentic copy of one of the most effective percussion systems ever devised. The simple lock is trouble-free and with the nipple directly on the barrel gives fast, positive ignition. The quickest handling, fastest shooting rifle on the market today; ideal for the young beginner shooter. Features hooked breech and fully adjustable hunting sights. Simple, efficient and trustworthy. **Barrel length: 26″. Weight: 5½ lbs.**

Country Boy Rifle	$165.00
Rifle Kit (50 caliber only)	145.00

NAVY ARMS RIFLES

1853 ENFIELD RIFLE MUSKET

The Enfield Rifle Musket marked the zenith in design and manufacture of the military percussion rifle and this perfection has been reproduced by Navy Arms Company. This and other Enfield muzzleloaders were the most coveted rifles of the Civil War, treasured by Union and Confederate troops alike for their fine quality and deadly accuracy. **Caliber:** 557. **Barrel length:** 39″. **Weight:** 9 lbs. **Overall length:** 55″. **Sights:** Fixed front; graduated rear. **Rifling:** 3 groove, cold forged. **Stock:** Seasoned walnut with solid brass furniture.

1853 Enfield Rifle Musket **$400.00**

1858 ENFIELD RIFLE

In the late 1850s the British Admiralty, after extensive experiments, settled on a pattern rifle with a 5-groove barrel of heavy construction, sighted to 1100 yards, designated the Naval rifle, Pattern 1858. In the recreation of this famous rifle Navy Arms has referred to the original 1858 Enfield Rifle in the Tower of London and has closely followed the specifications even to the progressive depth rifling. **Caliber:** 557. **Barrel length:** 33″. **Weight:** 8 lbs. 8 oz. **Overall length:** 48.5″. **Sights:** Fixed front; graduated rear. **Rifling:** 5-groove; cold forged. **Stock:** Seasoned walnut with solid brass furniture.

1858 Enfield Rifle **$350.00**

1861 ENFIELD MUSKETOON

The 1861 Enfield Musketoon is a Limited Collector's edition, individually serial numbered with certificate of authenticity. **Caliber:** 557. **Barrel length:** 24″. **Weight:** 7 lbs. 8 oz. **Overall length:** 40.25″. **Sights:** Fixed front; graduated rear. **Rifling:** 5-groove; cold forged. **Stock:** Seasoned walnut with solid brass furniture.

1861 Enfield Musketoon **$300.00**
Kit **250.00**

BLACK POWDER

NAVY ARMS RIFLES

MISSISSIPPI RIFLE MODEL 1841

The historic percussion lock weapon that gained its name as a result of its performance in the hands of Jefferson Davis' Mississippi Regiment during the heroic stand at the Battle of Buena Vista. Also known as the "Yager" (a misspelling of the German Jaeger), this was the first rifle adopted by Army Ordnance to fire the traditional round ball. In 58 caliber, the Mississippi is handsomely furnished in brass, including patch box for tools and spare parts. **Weight:** 9½ lbs. **Barrel length:** 32½". **Overall length:** 48½". **Caliber:** 58. **Finish:** Walnut finish stock, brass mounted.

Mississippi Rifle Model 1841 . . . . **$425.00**

RIGBY-STYLE TARGET RIFLE

This affordable reproduction of the famed Rigby Target Rifle of the 1880s features a 32-inch blued barrel, target front sight with micrometer adjustment, fully adjustable vernier rear sight (adjustable up to 1000 yards), hand-checkered walnut stock color casehardened breech plug, hammer lock plate, and escutcheons. This .451 caliber gun comes with loading accessories. including bullet starter and sizer and special ramrod.

Rigby-Style Target Rifle **$645.00**

1863 SPRINGFIELD RIFLE

An authentically reproduced replica of one of America's most historical firearms, the 1863 Springfield rifle features a full-size, three-band musket and precision-rifled barrel. **Caliber:** 58. **Barrel length:** 40". **Overall length:** 56". **Weight:** 9½ lbs. **Finish:** Walnut stock with polished metal lock and stock fittings.

1863 Springfield Rifle **$550.00**
Springfield Kit 450.00

NAVY ARMS RIFLES

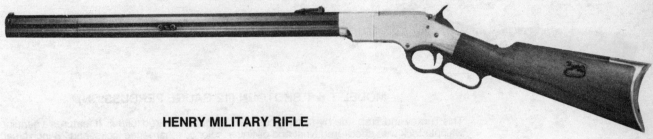

HENRY MILITARY RIFLE

Features a highly polished brass frame, blued barrel and walnut stock. Sling swivels to the original specifications are located on left side. Availale in calibers 44-40 and .44 Rimfire. **Barrel length:** 24″. **Weight:** 9¼ lbs. **Overall length:** 43″.

Henry Military Rifle **$765.00**

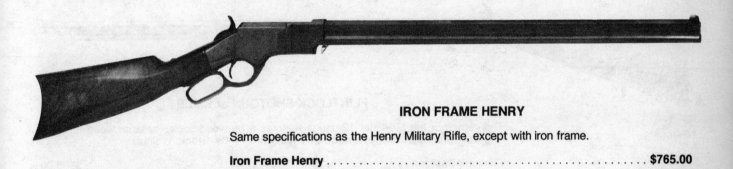

IRON FRAME HENRY

Same specifications as the Henry Military Rifle, except with iron frame.

Iron Frame Henry **$765.00**

HENRY TRAPPER MODEL

This short, lightweight 44/40 is ideal for the hunter. **Barrel length:** 16½″. **Overall length:** 34½″. **Weight:** 7¼ lbs.

Henry Trapper Model **$765.00**

HENRY CARBINE

The arm first utilized by the Kentucky Cavalry. Available in either original 44 rimfire caliber or in 44/40 caliber. Oil-stained American walnut stock, blued finish with brass frame. **Barrel length:** 23⅝″. **Overall length:** 45″.

Henry Carbine **$765.00**

NAVY ARMS SHOTGUNS

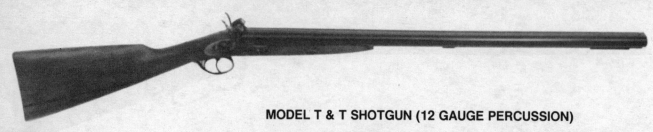

MODEL T & T SHOTGUN (12 GAUGE PERCUSSION)

This Turkey and Trap side-by-side percussion shotgun is choked full/full. It features a genuine walnut stock with checkered wrist and oil finish, color casehardened locks, and 28-inch blued barrels. It will pattern a load of #6 shot size in excess of 85% in a 30-inch circle at 30 yards and in excess of 65% at 40 yards, using 96 grains of FFg, 1¼ oz. #6 shot and 13 gauge overshot, over powder and cushion wads.

Model T & T Shotgun **$315.00**

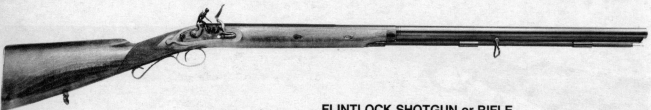

FLINTLOCK SHOTGUN or RIFLE

This replica of the Mortimer 12-gauge features a browned barrel, casehardened furniture and waterproof pan. **Barrel length:** 36″. **Weight:** 7½ lbs. **Stock:** Walnut.

Flintlock Shotgun **$500.00**
Flintlock Rifle (54 caliber) 535.00

FOWLER (12 GAUGE)

This traditional side-by-side percussion field gun features blued barrels and English-style straight stock design. It also sports a hooked breech, engraved and color casehardened percussion locks, double triggers and checkered walnut stained stock. **Gauge:** 12. **Chokes:** Cylinder/Cylinder. **Barrel length:** 28″. **Overall length:** 44½″. **Weight:** 7½ lbs.

Fowler (12 Gauge) **$285.00**

STEEL SHOT FOWLER (10 GAUGE)

Same general specifications as 12-Gauge Fowler (above), but with heavier barrels and designed for steel shot.

Steel Shot Fowler **$350.00**
Extra 10-Gauge Barrels 165.00

SHILOH SHARPS

MODEL 1874 BUSINESS RIFLE
$725.00

Calibers: 45-70, 45-90, 45-120, 50-70, 50-90 and 50-140. **Barrel:** 28-inch heavy-tapered round; dark blue. Double-set triggers adjustable set. **Sights:** Blade front, and sporting rear with leaf. Buttstock is straight grip rifle butt plate, forend sporting schnabel style. Receiver group and butt plate case-colored; wood is American walnut oil-finished. **Weight:** 9 lbs. 8 oz.

MODEL 1874 MILITARY RIFLE
$845.00

Calibers: 45-70 and 50-70. **Barrel:** 30-inch round; dark blue. Blade front and Lawrence-style sights. Military-style forend with 3 barrel bands and 1¼-inch swivels. Receiver group, butt plate and barrel bands case-colored. Wood is oil finished. **Weight:** 8 lbs. 2 oz.
Also available: **1874 MILITARY CARBINE** with 22″ round barrel. **Weight:** 7 lbs. 8 oz. **Price: $765.00.**

MODEL 1874 CARBINE "CIVILIAN"
$725.00

Calibers: 45-70 and 45-90. **Barrel:** 24-inch round; dark blue. Single trigger, blade front and sporting rear sight, buttstock straight grip, steel rifle butt plate, forend sporting schnabel style. Case-colored receiver group and butt plate; wood has oil finish. **Weight:** 8 lbs. 4 oz.

SHARPS MODEL 1874 RIFLE and CARTRIDGE AVAILABILITY TABLE

MODEL	CALIBERS										
	40-50 1¹¹/₁₆″BN	40-70 2¹/₁₀″BN	40-90 2⁵/₈″BN	45-70 2¹/₁₀″ST	45-90 2⁴/₁₀″ST	45-100 2⁶/₁₀″ST	45-110 2⁷/₈″ST	45-120 3¹/₄″ST	50-70 1³/₄″ST	50-100 2¹/₂″ST	40-65 Win
Long Range Express	★	★	★	★	★	★	★	★	★	★	★
No. 1 Sporting Rifle	★	★	★	★	★	★	★	★	★	★	★
No. 3 Sporting Rifle	★	★	★	★	★	★	★	★	★	★	★
Business Rifle	★	★	★	★	★	★	★	★	★	★	★
Carbine, Civilian	★	★	★	★	★						★
1874 Military Rifle	★	★	★	★					★		★
1874 Saddle Rifle	★	★	★	★	★				★		★
1874 Military Carbine	★	★	★	★							★

SHILOH SHARPS

MODEL 1863 SPORTING RIFLE
$740.00

Caliber: 54. **Barrel:** 30″ tapered octagonal. Blade front sight, sporting rear with elevation leaf; double-set triggers with adjustable set; curved trigger plate, pistol grip buttstock with steel butt plate, forend schnable style; optional Tang sight. **Weight:** 9 lbs.
Also available:
MODEL 1863 PERCUSSION MILITARY RIFLE $850.00
MODEL 1863 PERCUSSION CARBINE 740.00

MODEL 1874 SPORTING RIFLE NO. 1
$820.00

Calibers: 45-70, 45-90, 45-120, 50-70, 50-90 and 50-140. Features 28-inch or 30-inch tapered octagon barrel. Double-set triggers with adjustable set, blade front sight, sporting rear with elevation leaf and sporting tang sight adjustable for elevation and windage. Buttstock is pistol grip, shotgun butt, sporting forend style. Receiver group and butt plate case colored. Barrel is high finish blue-black; wood is American walnut oil finish. **Weight:** 10 lbs.

MODEL 1874 SPORTING RIFLE NO. 3
$725.00

Calibers: 45-70, 45-90, 45-120, 50-70, 50-90 and 50-140. **Barrel:** 30-inch tapered octagonal; with high finish blue-black. Double-set triggers with adjustable set, blade front sight, sporting rear with elevation leaf and sporting tang sight adjustable for elevation and windage. Buttstock is straight grip with rifle butt plate; trigger plate is curved and checkered to match pistol grip. Forend is sporting schnabel style. Receiver group and butt plate is case colored. Wood is American walnut oil-finished. **Weight:** 9 lbs. 8 oz.

Also available:
MODEL 1874 ROUGHRIDER $725.00
    With Semi-fancy Wood 810.00
MODEL 1874 "JAEGER" HUNTING RIFLE 795.00
HARTFORD MODEL 915.00

MODEL	CALIBERS										
	30-40 KRAG	30-30 WIN	.307 WIN	40-50 1-¹¹/₁₆″ BN	40-70 2-¹/₁₀″ BN	45-70 2-¹/₁₀″ ST					
1874 "Roughrider" Rifle	★	★	★	★	★						
Shiloh Jaeger	★	★									★
Hartford Model	★	★	★	★	★	★	★	★	★	★	
Military Carbine	★	★		★					★		

THOMPSON/CENTER

PENNSYLVANIA HUNTER

For the hunter who prefers (or is required to use) a round ball, the Pennsylvania Hunter offers a firearm designed especially for that purpose. Its 31″ barrel is cut rifled (.010″ deep) with 1 turn in 66″ twist. The outer contour of the barrel is distinctively stepped from octagon to round. Sights are fully adjustable for both windage and elevation. The single hunting style trigger with large trigger guard bow allows the rifle to be fired with gloves on. Stocked with select American black walnut; metal hardware is all blued steel. Features a hooked breech system and coil spring lock. **Caliber:** Caplock and flintlock models are available in 50 caliber only. **Overall length:** 48″. **Weight:** Approx. 7.6 lbs.

Pennsylvania Hunter Caplock 50 caliber $275.00
Pennsylvania Hunter Flintlock 50 caliber 290.00

THE NEW ENGLANDER RIFLE

This percussion rifle features a 26″ round, 50 or 54 caliber rifled barrel (1 in 48″ twist). **Weight:** 7 lbs. 15 oz.

New Englander Rifle $235.00
    With Rynite stock (24″ barrel, right-hand only) 215.00
Kit 195.00
Left-Hand Model 250.00

THE NEW ENGLANDER SHOTGUN

This 12-gauge muzzleloading percussion shotgun weighs only 5 lbs. 2 oz. It features a 28-inch (improved cylinder) round barrel and is stocked with selected American black walnut.

New Englander Shotgun $235.00
    With Rynite stock (26″ barrel, right-hand only) 215.00
Left-Hand Model 250.00

THOMPSON/CENTER

THE HAWKEN
45, 50 and 54 caliber

Similar to the famous Rocky Mountain rifles made during the early 1800's, the Hawken is intended for serious shooting. Button-rifled for ultimate precision, the Hawken is available in 45, 50 or 54 caliber, flintlock or percussion. It features a hooked breech, double-set triggers, first-grade American walnut stock, adjustable hunting sights, solid brass trim and color casehardened lock. Beautifully decorated. **Weight:** Approx. 8½ lbs.

Hawken Caplock 45, 50 or 54 caliber	$345.00
Hawken Flintlock 50 caliber	360.00
Kit: Caplock	240.00
Flintlock	255.00

White Mountain Caplock Carbine

White Mountain Flintlock Carbine

WHITE MOUNTAIN CARBINE

This hunter's rifle features a single trigger with a wide trigger guard bow that allows the shooter to fire the rifle in cold weather without removing his gloves. It's stock is of select American black walnut finished off with a rifle-type rubber recoil pad, and equipped with swivel studs and quick detachable sling swivels. A soft leather hunting-style sling is included. The barrel's outer surface is stepped from octagonal to round. **Caliber:** 50 (Hawken or Renegade loads). **Barrel length:** 21″. **Overall length:** 38″. **Weight:** 6½ lbs. **Sights:** Open hunting (Patridge) style, fully adjustable. **Lock:** Heavy-duty coil springs; decorated with floral design and color-cased. **Breech:** Hooked breech system.

White Mountain Carbine–Caplock (right-hand only)	$295.00
White Mountain Carbine–Flintlock (right-hand only)	310.00

THOMPSON/CENTER

THE RENEGADE

Available in 50 or 54 caliber percussion, the Renegade was designed to provide maximum accuracy and maximum shocking power. It is constructed of superior modern steel with investment cast parts fitted to an American walnut stock, featuring a precision-rifled (26-inch carbine-type) octagonal barrel, hooked-breech system, coil spring lock, double-set triggers, adjustable hunting sights and steel trim. **Weight:** Approx. 8 lbs.

Renegade Caplock 50 and 54 caliber	$295.00
Renegade Caplock Left Hand	305.00
Renegade Caplock Kit (right-hand)	210.00
Renegade Caplock Kit (left-hand)	220.00
Renegade Flintlock 50 caliber (R.H. only)	305.00
Renegade Flintlock Kit (R.H. only)	225.00

RENEGADE SINGLE TRIGGER HUNTER
50 and 54 Caliber

This single trigger hunter model, fashioned after the double triggered Renegade, features a large bow in the shotgun-style trigger guard. This allows shooters to fire the rifle in cold weather without removing their gloves. The octagon barrel measures 26″ and the stock is made of select American walnut. **Weight:** About 8 pounds.

Renegade Hunter	$275.00

THE CHEROKEE

A light percussion sporting rifle with interchangeable barrels. **Caliber:** 32 or 45. **Barrel length:** 24″. **Weight:** About 6 lbs. Sights are open hunting style fully adjustable for windage and elevation. Stock is American walnut with contoured cheekpiece on left-hand side.

Cherokee Caplock	$280.00
Kit	220.00
Interchangeable barrels (w/ramrod) in 32 and 45 caliber	122.00
Kit barrels	100.00

THOMPSON/CENTER

SCOUNT CARBINE

SCOUT CARBINE & PISTOL

Thompson/Center's new Scout Carbine & Pistol introduces a new "in-line ignition system" with a special vented breech plug that produces constant pressures from shot to shot, thereby improving accuracy. The patented trigger mechanism consists of only two moving parts—the trigger and the hammer—thus providing ease of operation and low maintenance. Both the carbine and pistol are available in 50 and 54 caliber. The carbine's 21″ barrel and the pistol's 12″ barrel are easily removable and readily interchangeable in either caliber. Their lines are reminiscent of the saddle guns and pistols of the "Old West," combining modern-day engineering with the flavor of the past. Both are suitable for left-hand shooters. Price not set.

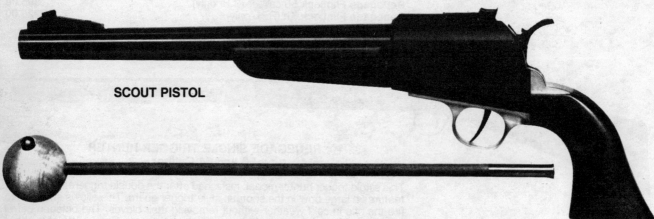

SCOUT PISTOL

TRADITIONS

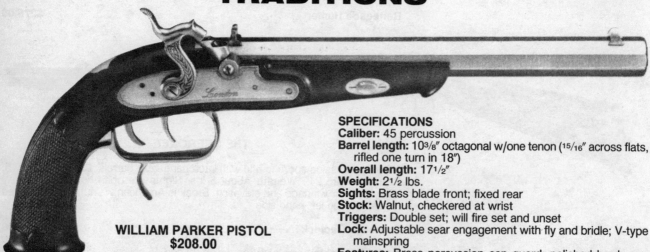

WILLIAM PARKER PISTOL
$208.00

SPECIFICATIONS
Caliber: 45 percussion
Barrel length: 10³/₈″ octagonal w/one tenon (¹⁵/₁₆″ across flats, rifled one turn in 18″)
Overall length: 17¹/₂″
Weight: 2¹/₂ lbs.
Sights: Brass blade front; fixed rear
Stock: Walnut, checkered at wrist
Triggers: Double set; will fire set and unset
Lock: Adjustable sear engagement with fly and bridle; V-type mainspring
Features: Brass percussion cap guard; polished hardware, brass inlays

TRADITIONS

FRONTIER SCOUT
$187.00 (Percussion)

SPECIFICATIONS
Calibers: 36, 45 and 50
Barrel length: 24″ (36 caliber); 26″ (45 and 50 caliber); octagonal (⅞″ across flats) with tenon; rifled 1 turn in 66″; hooked breech
Overall length: 39⅛″ (36 caliber); 41⅛″ (45 and 50 caliber)
Weight: 6 lbs.
Length of pull: 12¼″
Sights: Primitive, adjustable rear, brass blade front
Stock: Beech
Lock: Adjustable sear engagement with fly and bridle
Furniture: Solid brass, blued steel

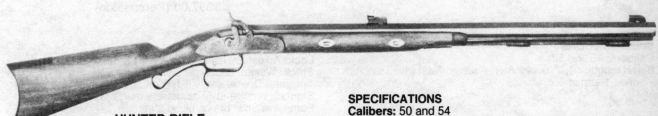

HUNTER RIFLE
$350.00 (Percussion)

SPECIFICATIONS
Calibers: 50 and 54
Barrel length: 28¼″; octagonal (1″ across flats) with 2 tenons; hooked breech, rifled 1 turn in 66″ (1 turn in 48″ optional)
Overall length: 46″
Weight: 8 lbs.
Lock: Adjustable sear engagement with fly and bridle
Stock: Walnut with contoured beavertail cheekpiece
Sights: Beaded blade front; hunting-style rear adjustable for windage and elevation
Furniture: Black-chromed brass with German silver wedge plates and stock ornaments

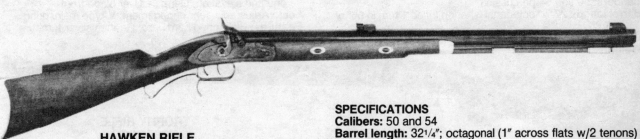

HAWKEN RIFLE
$342.00 (Percussion)
$225.00 (Kit, 54 caliber only)

SPECIFICATIONS
Calibers: 50 and 54
Barrel length: 32¼″; octagonal (1″ across flats w/2 tenons)
Overall length: 50″
Weight: 9 lbs.
Lock: Adjustable sear engagement with fly and bridle
Stock: Walnut, beavertail cheekpiece
Triggers: Double set; will fire set and unset
Sights: Beaded blade front; hunting-style rear adjustable for windage and elevation
Furniture: Solid brass, blued steel

BLACK POWDER

TRADITIONS

HAWKEN WOODSMAN
$225.00 (Percussion)
$173.00 (Kit)

SPECIFICATIONS
Calibers: 50 and 54
Barrel length: 28″ (octagonal); hooked breech; rifled 1 turn in 66″ (1 turn in 48″ optional)
Overall length: 45³/₄″

Weight: 7 lbs.
Triggers: Double set; will fire set or unset
Lock: Adjustable sear engagement with fly and bridle
Stock: Beech
Sights: Beaded blade front; hunting-style rear, fully screw adjustable for windage and elevation
Furniture: Solid brass, blued steel

PENNSYLVANIA RIFLE
$410.00 (Flintlock)
$387.00 (Percussion)

SPECIFICATIONS
Calibers: 45 and 50
Barrel length: 40¹/₄″; octagonal (⁷/₈″ across flats) with 3 tenons; rifled 1 turn in 66″

Overall length: 57¹/₂″
Weight: 9 lbs.
Lock: Adjustable sear engagement with fly and bridle
Stock: Walnut, beavertail style
Triggers: Double set; will fire set and unset
Sights: Primitive-style adjustable rear; brass blade front
Furniture: Solid brass, blued steel

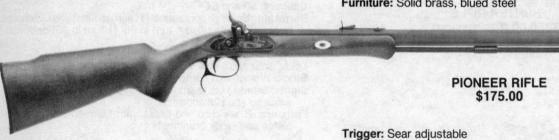

PIONEER RIFLE
$175.00

SPECIFICATIONS
Calibers: 50 and 54 percussion
Barrel length: 27¹/₄″ octagonal w/tenon (rifled 1 turn in 66″ or 48″)
Overall length: 44″
Weight: 7 lbs.

Trigger: Sear adjustable
Stock: Beech
Sights: Buckhorn rear with elevation ramp, ajustable for windage and elevation; German silver blade front
Lock: Adjustable sear engagement; V-type mainspring
Features: Blackened hardware; German silver furniture

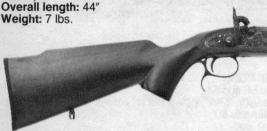

TROPHY RIFLE
$350.00

SPECIFICATIONS
Calibers: 50 and 54
Barrel length: 27¹/₄″ octagonal-to-round with tenon (rifled 1 turn in 48″ or 66″)
Overall length: 44³/₄″

Weight: 7 lbs.
Lock: Adjustable sear engagement with bridle, claw mainspring
Trigger: Sear adjustable
Stock: Walnut with cheekpiece
Sights: Hunting-style rear, click adjustable for windage and elevation; Patridge-style blade front
Features: Sling swivel, fiberglass ramrod, blackened furniture

TRADITIONS

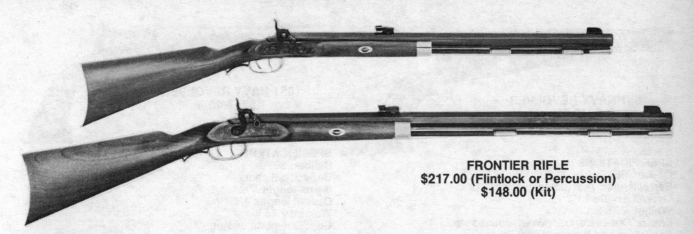

FRONTIER RIFLE
$217.00 (Flintlock or Percussion)
$148.00 (Kit)

SPECIFICATIONS
Calibers: 45 and 50
Barrel length: 28″ octagonal ($^{15}/_{16}$″ across flats) with tenon;
   hooked breech, rifled 1 turn in 66″ (1 turn in 48″ optional)
Overall length: 44$^3/_4$″
Weight: 8 lbs.
Lock: Adjustable sear engagement with fly and bridle
Triggers: Double set; will fire set and unset
Stock: Beech

Sights: Beaded blade front; hunting-style rear, adjustable for
   windage and elevation
Furniture: Solid brass, blued steel
Also available:
FRONTIER CARBINE with 24″ barrel, 40$^1/_2$″ overall length;
   weight 6$^1/_2$ lbs.; percussion only in 45 or 50 caliber. **Price:**
$200.00. Kit **$148.00.**

TRAPPER RIFLE
$200.00 (Percussion)

SPECIFICATIONS
Calibers: 36 and 50
Barrel length: 24″; rifled 1 turn in 66″; hooked breech; octag-
   onal ($^7/_8$ across flats)
Overall length: 40$^5/_8$″
Weight: 6 lbs.

Stock: Beech
Lock: Adjustable sear engagement with fly and bridle
Triggers: Double set, will fire set and unset
Sights: Fully screw adjustable for windage and elevation;
   beaded blade front with Patridge-style open rear
Furniture: Solid brass, blued steel

TRAPPER PISTOL
$140.00 (Percussion)
$107.00 (Kit)

SPECIFICATIONS
Calibers: 45 and 50
Barrel length: 9$^3/_4$″; octagonal ($^7/_8$″ across flats) with tenon
Overall length: 16″
Weight: 2$^3/_4$ lbs.
Stock: Beech
Lock: Adjustable sear engagement with fly and bridle
Triggers: Double set, will fire set and unset
Sights: Primitive-style adjustable rear; brass blade front
Furniture: Solid brass; blued steel on assembled pistol

A. UBERTI

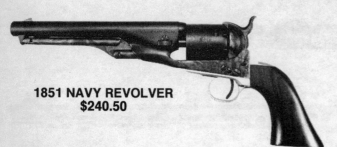

1851 NAVY REVOLVER
$240.50

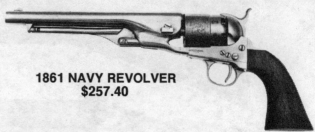

1861 NAVY REVOLVER
$257.40

SPECIFICATIONS
Caliber: 36
Barrel length: 7¹/₂″ (octagonal, tapered)
Overall length: 13″
Weight: 2.75 lbs.
Frame: One-piece, color casehardened steel
Backstrap and trigger guard: Brass
Cylinder: 6 shots (engraved)
Grip: One-piece walnut

SPECIFICATIONS
Caliber: 36
Capacity: 6 shots
Barrel length: 7¹/₂″
Overall length: 13″
Weight: 2.75 lbs.
Grip: One-piece walnut
Frame: Color casehardened steel

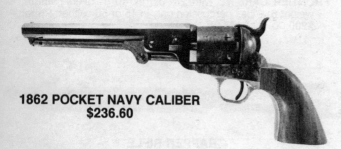

1862 POCKET NAVY CALIBER
$236.60

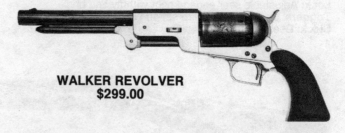

WALKER REVOLVER
$299.00

SPECIFICATIONS
Caliber: 36
Barrel lengths: 5¹/₂″ and 6¹/₂″ (round, tapered)
Cylinder: 5 shots (engraved)
Overall length: 10¹/₂″
Weight: 1.59 lbs. (1.68 lbs. w/6¹/₂″ barrel)
Frame: Color casehardened steel
Backstrap and trigger guard: Brass
Grip: One-piece walnut

SPECIFICATIONS
Caliber: 44
Barrel length: 9″ (round in front of lug)
Overall length: 15³/₄″
Weight: 4.41 lbs.
Frame: Color casehardened steel
Backsstrap: Steel
Cylinder: 6 shots (engraved with "Fighting Dragoons" scene)
Grip: One-piece walnut

SPECIFICATIONS
Caliber: 44
Capacity: 6 shots
Barrel length: 7¹/₂″ round forward of lug
Overall length: 13¹/₂″
Weight: 4 lbs.
Frame: Color casehardened steel
Grip: One-piece walnut
Features: Brass backstrap and trigger guard; engraved cylinder
Also available:
2nd Model Dragoon w/square cylinder bolt shot . . **$250.00**
3rd Model Dragoon w/loading lever latch, steel
  backstrap, cut for shoulder stock **273.00**

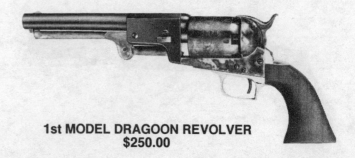

1st MODEL DRAGOON REVOLVER
$250.00

A. UBERTI

1858 Remington 44 Revolver (7⅞″ barrel) **$208.00**
  With stainless steel 292.50
  Target Model, black finish 245.70
  Target Model, stainless steel 325.00

**1858 REMINGTON
44 REVOLVER**

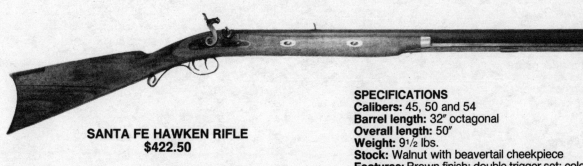

**SANTA FE HAWKEN RIFLE
$422.50**

SPECIFICATIONS
Calibers: 45, 50 and 54
Barrel length: 32″ octagonal
Overall length: 50″
Weight: 9½ lbs.
Stock: Walnut with beavertail cheekpiece
Features: Brown finish; double trigger set; color casehardened
    lockplate; German silver wedge plates and stock turrule
Also available:
Flintlock Hawken (50 and 54 caliber only) **$474.50**

ULTRA LIGHT ARMS

**MODEL 90
$950.00**

This new muzzleloader comes with a 28″ button-rifled barrel (1 in 48″ twist) and a length of pull at 13½″. Fast ignition with in-line action and fully adjustable Timney trigger create smooth, consistent shots. Available in 45 or 50 caliber, each rifle has a Kevlar/Graphite stock (colors optional) and Williams sights, plus integral side safety. Recoil pad, sling swivels and a hard case are included. **Overall weight:** 6 lbs.

Sights & scopes

FOR ADDRESSES AND PHONE NUMBERS OF MANUFACTURERS AND DISTRIBUTORS INCLUDED IN THIS SECTION, SEE *DIRECTORY OF MANUFACTURERS AND SUPPLIERS*

ACTION ARMS SIGHTS

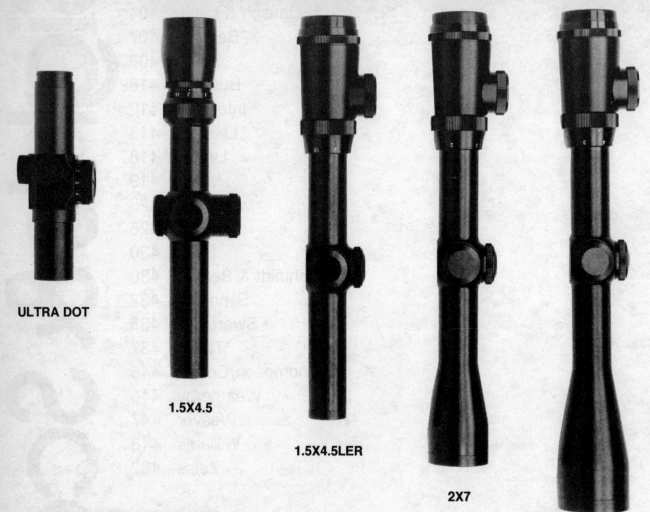

ULTRA DOT

1.5X4.5

1.5X4.5LER

2X7

3X9

MICRO DOT SIGHTS

Micro Dot's red aiming point allows the hunter to aim with confidence even when he can no longer see the crosshairs. These 1″, waterproof sights feature an extended eye relief model, one-piece tube and coated optics. *See* table below for specifications.

Prices:

1½X4½ pistol sight	$265.00
1½X4½ rifle sight	270.00
2X7 rifle sight	290.00
3X9 rifle sight	295.00

ULTRA DOT SIGHTS

The Ultra Dot is lighter and more compact than the Micro Dot sight. Its battery pack is built right into the small, click adjustable brightness control. Mounts easily with 1″ scope mounts on any firearm. *See* table below for specifications.

Price (Black or Silver)**$195.00**

MICRO DOT SCOPES & ULTRA DOT SIGHT SPECIFICATIONS

Model	Length	Tube Dia.	Weight	Objective Dia.	Eye Relief
3 × 9	12.2″	1″	13.3 oz.	40mm	3″
2 × 7	11.0″	1″	12.1 oz.	32mm	3″
1.5 × 4.5	9.8″	1″	10.5 oz.	20mm	3″
1.5 × 4.5 LER	8.8″	1″	9.5 oz.	20mm	12–24″
Ultra Dot	5.1″	1″	4.0 oz.	1″	unlimited

AIMPOINT RED DOT SIGHTS

SERIES 1000 ELECTRONIC SIGHT
$189.95 (Black or Stainless)

LASERPOINT
$379.95

SERIES 1000 SPECIFICATIONS
Weight: 7.95 oz.
Length: 6″
Magnification: 1X
Scope Attachment: 3X
Battery Choices: Lithium CR 1/3 N, 2L76, DL 1/3 N, Mercury (2) MP 675 or SP 675, Silver Oxide (2) D 375 H, Alkaline (2) LR 44
Material: Anodized Aluminum, Blue or Stainless Finish
Mounting: Clamps to Weaver Bases (except for Weaver handgun mounts)

LASERPOINT

Laserpoint allows the shooter to project an intense red dot of visible laser light onto the target quickly and accurately. Its compact, lightweight design enables Laserpoint to withstand heavy recoil and demanding conditions. Can be mounted on pistols, rifles, shotguns, air rifles, and bows.

SPECIFICATIONS
Length: 7″
Weight: 5.95 oz.
Diameter: 1″
Switch pad: 6⅞″ cable and pressure switch
Adjustment: Each click = 1/4″ at 50 yards
Output beam: Wavelength 670 nm; output aperture approx. 1/4″; beam divergence 0.5 mRad
Batteries: 3 X AAA Alkaline (LR03)
Battery life: Up to 9 hrs continuous (16 hrs in pulse mode @ 10 pulses per sec.
Mounting: Standard 1″ rings

SERIES 3000 SHORT
$249.95 (Black or Stainless)

SERIES 3000 SHORT SPECIFICATIONS
Weight: 5.15 oz.
Length: 5½″
Magnification: 1X
Battery Choices: Lithium CR 1/3 N, 2L76, DL 1/3 N, Mercury (2) MP 675 or SP 675, Silver Oxide (2) D 375 H, Alkaline (2) LR 44
Material: Anodized Aluminum, Blue or Stainless Finish
Mounting: 1″ Rings

SERIES 3000 LONG SPECIFICATIONS
Weight: 5.85 oz.
Length: 6⅞″
Magnification: 1X
Scope Attachment: 3X
Battery Choices: Lithium CR 1/3 N, 2L76, DL 1/3 N, Mercury (2) MP 675 or SP 675, Silver Oxide (2) D 375 H, Alkaline (2) LR 44
Material: Anodized Aluminum, Blue or Stainless Finish
Mounting: 1″ Rings (Medium or High)

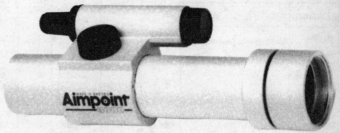

SERIES 3000 LONG
$259.95 (Black or Stainless

BAUSCH & LOMB SCOPES

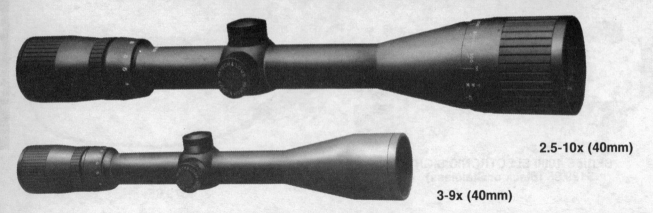

2.5-10x (40mm)

3-9x (40mm)

BALVAR RIFLESCOPES SPECIFICATIONS

Model	Special Features	Actual Magnification	Obj. Lens Aperture (mm)	Field of View at 100 yds. (ft.)	Weight (oz.)	Length (in.)	Eye Relief (in.)	Exit pupil (mm)	Click Value at 100 yds. (in.)	Adjust Range at 100 yds. (in.)	Selections
64-1238	Matte finish, fine crosshair reticle, compact design, high contrast filter, 5" sunshade	12x-32x	40	8.6@12x 3.6@32x	18.9	13.5	3	3.3@12x 1.3@32x	.125	±14	Precise, ultra long range shooting. Parallax focus adjustment for target and silhouette ranges.
64-6244	Semi-turret target adjustments. Matte finish sunshades.	6x-24x	40	18@6x 4.5@24x	20.9	16.8	3.3	6.7@6x 1.7@24x	.125	±13	Varmint, target and silhouette long range capability with all steel target adjustments for pin-point accuracy. Parallax focus adjustments.
64-2540	Adj. obj.	2.5x-10x	40	43.5@2.5x 11.2@10x	16.4	13.7	3.3	16@2.5x 4@10x	.25	±50	All purpose hunting scope with 4 times zoom range for close-in brush and long range shooting, parallax focus adjustment
64-2548	Matte finish Adj. obj.										
64-0394		3x-9x	40	36@3x 12@9x	16.5	13	3.2	13.3@3x 4.4@9x	t.25	±30	All purpose variable excellent for use at any range. Extra brightness for low light conditions. Large exit pupil for quick sighting.
64-0398	Matte finish										
64-3940TD	Tapered dot reticle										
64-3948TD	Matte finish, tapered dot reticle										
64-1563		1.5x-6x	32	70@1.5x 18@6x	12.7	11.5	3.3	21.3@1.5x 5.3@6x	.25	±50	Compact wide angle for close-in and brush hunting. Maximum brightness and extra large exit pupil for quick sighting. Versatile four times zoom ratio.
64-1598	Matte finish										

Model 64 Balvar Riflescope

6-24x40mm	$654.95	1.5-6x32mm	549.95
3-9x40mm	523.95	2.5-10x40mm	601.95
3-9x40mm Tapered Dot Reticle	554.95	12-32x40mm	778.95

BAUSCH & LOMB

TARGET RIFLESCOPES

Model	Special Features	Actual Magnification	Obj. Lens Aperture (mm)	Field of View at 100 yds. (ft.)	Weight (oz.)	Length (in.)	Eye Relief (in.)	Exit pupil (mm)	Click Value at 100 yds. (in.)	Adjust Range at 100 yds. (in.)	Selections
64-364D	$1/8$ M.O.A. dot reticle 2 sets of turret adjustments 2 matte finish sunshades	36x	40	3.1	17.6	15	3.2	1.1	.125	±15	Excellent for target, silhouette, and long range shooting with all steel target adjustments for precise repeatability. Parallax focus adjustment for pin-point accuracy.
64-3640CH	Fine crosshair reticle 2 sets of turret adjustments 2 matte finish sunshades	36x	40	3.1	17.6	15	3.2	1.1	.125	±15	
64-2440CH	Fine crosshair reticle 2 sets of turret adjustments 2 matte finish sunshades	24x	40	4.7	17.6	15	3.2	1.7	.125	±15	Excellent for varmint, target and silhouette. Long range capability with all steel target adjustments for precise repeatability. Parallax focus adjustment for pin-point accuracy.
64-2440D	$1/8$ M.O.A. dot reticle 2 sets of turret adjustments 2 matte finish sunshades	24x	40	4.7	17.6	15	3.2	1.7	.125	±15	

36x(40mm) Dot Reticle $758.95
36x(40mm) Fine Crosshair Reticle 758.95
24x(40mm) Dot Reticle 732.95
24x(40mm) Fine Crosshair Reticle 732.95
10x(40mm) w/Ranging Reticle 1667.95

TARGET SCOPE
36x(40mm)

COMPACTS

Offer same features and performance as full-size Bausch & Lomb riflescopes in lightweight design. Include four times zoom ratio, resettable 1/4" MOA click adjustments, hard surface multi-coated optics, one-piece body tube. Fogproof and waterproof.

2x-8x(32mm) Balvar Compact $471.95
4x(32mm) Balfor Compact 356.95

COMPACT RIFLESCOPE
4x(32mm) Balfor

HANDGUN SCOPES

Feature one-piece body tube, resettable 1/4" MOA click adjustments, wide margin of eye relief, hard surface, multi-coated optics. Fogproof and waterproof.

4x(28mm) $340.95
2x(28mm) 329.95
Add **$26.00** for Matte Silver.

HANDGUN SCOPES

BAUSCH & LOMB

SCOPECHIEF RIFLESCOPES

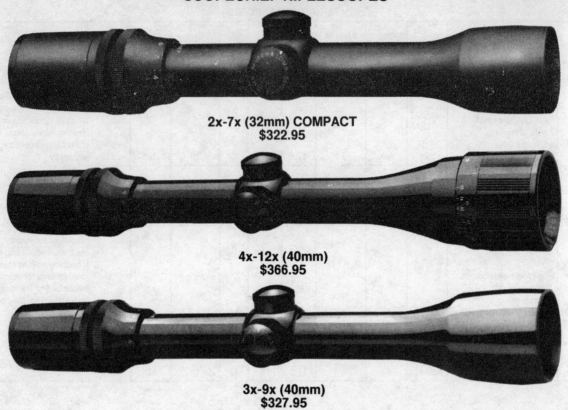

2x-7x (32mm) COMPACT
$322.95

4x-12x (40mm)
$366.95

3x-9x (40mm)
$327.95

BAUSCH & LOMB SCOPECHIEF RIFLESCOPES SPECIFICATIONS

Model	Special Features	Actual Magnifi-cation	Obj. Lens Aperture (mm)	Field of View at 100 yds. (ft.)	Weight (oz.)	Length (in.)	Eye Relief (in.)	Exit Pupil (mm)	Click Value at 100 yds. (in.)	Adjust Range at 100 yds. (in.)	Selection
63-4124	Adjustable objective	4x-12x	40	29@4x 10@12x	15.4	13.5	3.2	10@4x 3.3@12x	.25	±40	Medium to long-range variable makes superb choice for varmint or big game shooting. Parallax focus adjustment.
63-3940		3x-9x	40	39@3x 13@9x	13.9	12.6	3.3	13.3@3x 4.4@9x	.25	±45	For the full range of hunting. From varmint to big game. Tops in versatility.
63-3948	Matte										
63-2732		2x-7x	32	49.7@2x 14.2@7x	12.7	11.2	3.3	16@2x 4.5@7x	.25	±25	Compact variable for close-in-brush or medium range shooting.
63-2738	Matte										
63-1545		1.5x-4.5x	32	69.9@1.5x 23.3@4.5	10	9.6	3.3	21@1.5x 7.1@4.5x	.25	±25	Low power variable for close-in-brush at medium range shooting.
63-1548	Matte										
63-0440		4x	40	37.3	12	12.3	3	10	.25	±30	All purpose riflescope.

BEEMAN SCOPES

SS-3 SERIES

Offers 1.5-4x zoom power for greater flexibility. Glare-free black matte finish is anodized into metal for deep sheen and extra toughness. Instant action dial around front of scope dials away parallax error and dials in perfect focus from 10 feet to infinity. Scope measures only 5¾ inches in length and weighs only 8.5 ounces. **SS-3 Series: $250.00**

SS-1 AND SS-2 SERIES

Beeman SS-1 and SS-2 short scopes are extra compact and rugged, due largely to breakthroughs in optical engineering and computer programming of lens formulas. Less than 7 inches long, both scopes pack 11 lenses that actually gather light for bigger, brighter targets than ''projected spot'' targets. Scope body and built-in mounts are milled as a single unit from a solid block of hi-tensile aircraft aluminum. Almost identical in appearance to Beeman SS-2L ''Skylite'' scope pictured above (right).

SS-1 Series: $179.50
SS-2 Series: $225.00

BEEMAN SS-2L "SKYLITE" RIFLESCOPE

Features a brightly illuminated reticle powered by daylight and even moonlight (no batteries necessary). In addition to standard black reticle, supplementary color filters are available for different lighting and shooting situations. Filter options include: white (for silhouette or target); red (for twilight and general purpose); yellow (for haze, fog and low light); green (for bright light and snow). A small electrical illuminator is also available for use in total darkness.

Beeman SS-2L w/color reticle, 3x	$275.00
Beeman SS-2L w/color reticle, 4x	295.00
Lamp	29.95
Filter Kit (green or yellow)	18.95

BLUE RIBBON AND BLUE RING SCOPES

These versatile scopes have a Range Focus Ring by which parallax error can be dialed away and perfect focus dialed in from 13 feet to infinity. Model 66R also has Speed Dials—extra large windage and elevation knobs that are especially fast and easy to use. Beeman economy scopes (Models 30A, 35R and 45R) are notable for their high lens counts. **Prices:** range from **$36.95 - $379.95**

SCOPE SPECIFICATIONS

Model	Series	Power	Obj. Lens mm	Tube Dia. in. (mm)	Wgt. oz. (gm)	Length in. (mm)	Field of View 100 yds. (100m)	Eye Relief in. (mm)	Reticle
30A	Blue Ring	4	15	¾" (19)	4.5* (128)	10.2 (259)	21 (7m)	2 (50)	5 pt. TL
35R	Blue Ring	3	20	¾" (19)	5.2* (147)	11 (280)	25 (8.3m)	2.5 (64)	5 pt. TL
45R	Blue Ring	3-7	20	¾" (19)	6.3* (179)	10.8 (275)	26-12 (8.7-4m)	2.5 (64)	5 pt. TL
50R	Blue Ribbon	2.5	32	1" (25)	12.3 (350)	12 (305)	33 (11m)	3.5 (90)	5 pt. TL
54R	Blue Ribbon	4	32	1" (25)	12.3 (35)	12 (305)	29' (8.8m)	3.5 (90)	5 pt. TL
66R	Blue Ribbon	2.7	32	1" (25)	14.9 (422)	11.4 (290)	62-16 (18.9-5.3m)	3 (76)	5 pt. TL
66RL	Blue Ribbon	2-7	32	1" (25)	17 (482)	11.4 (290)	30.5'-11' (9.3-3.4m)	3 (76)	5 pt. TL
67R	Blue Ribbon	3-9	40	1" (25)	15.2 (431)	14.4 (366)	43.5-15' (13.3-4.6m)	3 (76)	5 pt. TL
68R	Blue Ribbon	4-12	40	1" (25)	15.2 (431)	14.4 (366)	30.5'-11' (9.3-3.4m)	3 (76)	5 pt. TL
MS-1	Blue Ribbon	4	18	1" (25)	8 (227)	7.5 (191)	23' (7m)	3.5	5 pt. TL
SS-1	Blue Ribbon	2.5	16	⅞" (22)	6.9* (195)	5.5 (137)	32.5 (10.8m)	3 (76)	5 pt. TL
SS-2*	Blue Ribbon	3	21	1.38" (35)	13.6* (385)	6.8 (172)	34.5 (11.5m)	3.5 (90)	5 pt. TL
SS-2**	Blue Ribbon	4	21	1.38" (35)	13.7 (388)	7 (182)	24.6 (8.2m)	3.5 (90)	5 pt. TL
SS-3	Blue Ribbon	1.5-4	16	⅞" (22)	8.6 (241)*	5.75 (146)	44.6'-24.6' (13.6-7.5m)	3 (76)	5 pt. TL

* Includes scope mount in price and weight.   TL = Thin Line reticle.
* SS-2L same as SS-2 3-power except length: 6.8" (172mm) and weight: 14.2 oz.
** SS-2L same as SS-2 4-power except length: 7.2" (186mm) and weight: 13.8 oz.

BURRIS SCOPES

SIGNATURE SERIES 3X-12X PLEX
$491.95

The Signature Series features a computer-designed optical system, using the most advanced optical glass available. All models have Hi-Lume (multi-coated) lenses for maximum light transmission. Also features full-field wide angle field-of-view sight picture.

Prices:

3x-12x	$571.95
3x-12x Plex-Safari	530.95
3x-9x	412.95
3x-9x Safari	427.95
1½-6x Plex	346.95
1½-6x Plex-Safari	359.95
6X	340.95
6X Safari	353.95
4X	325.95
4X Safari	341.95

6x-24x SIGNATURE w/LIGHT COLLECTOR

NEW "LIGHT COLLECTOR" SIGNATURE SERIES

6x-24x Plex	$571.95
6x-24x 2"-.5" Dot	584.95
6x-24x 2"-.5" Dot Silhouette	606.95
6x-24x Fine Flex Silhouette	593.95

GUNSITE SCOUT SCOPE

Made for hunters who need a seven to 14-inch eye relief to mount just in front of the ejection port opening, allowing hunters to shoot with both eyes open. The 15-foot field of view and 2¾x magnification are ideal for brush guns and handgunners who use the "two-handed hold."

1½x Plex XER	$175.95
1½x Plex XER Safari Finish	189.95
1½x German 3 Post XER	193.95
2¾x German 3 Post XER	213.95
2¾x Plex XER	182.95
2¾x Plex XER Safari Finish	195.95

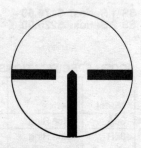

GERMAN 3 POST
For close-in shooting at fast-moving targets under low light conditions

3x-9x FULLFIELD RAC SCOPE
with AUTOMATIC RANGEFINDER RETICLE

Once the crosshair has been zeroed in at 200 yards, it remains there regardless of the power setting. The range reticle automatically moves to a zero at ranges up to 500 yards as power is increased to fit the game between the stadia range wires. No need to adjust elevation knob. Bullet drop adjustment is automatic.

3x-9x Fullfield RAC Crosshair (Dot or Plex)	$334.95
3x-9x RAC CHP Safari Finish	346.95

BURRIS SCOPES

6X-18X

4X-12X FULLFIELD VARIABLE POWER

The ideal scope for long-range varmint hunting and testing hand loads. Can also be used for big-game hunting. Features crisp resolution, accurate parallax settings and a big field of view. Friction-type parallax settings from 50 yards to infinity with positive stop to prevent overturning. Fully sealed to withstand the worst field conditions and designed to deliver years of excellent service.

4x-12x FULLFIELD

Plex	**$368.95**
Fine Plex	366.95
2"–.7" Dot	382.95
ARC Crosshair Fine Plex	388.95
ARC Crosshair Dot	388.95

6X-18X FULLFIELD VARIABLE POWER

This versatile, high-magnification, variable scope can be used for hunting, testing hand loads or shooting bench rest. It features excellent optics, a precise parallax adjustment from 50 yards to infinity, accurate internal adjustments and a rugged, reliable mechanical design that will give years of dependable service. Fully sealed against moisture and dust.

6x-18x FULLFIELD

Plex	**$382.95**
Fine Plex	382.95
2"–.7" Dot	395.95
2"–.7" Dot Silhouette	417.95
Fine Plex Silhouette	405.95

MINI 2X-7X

MINI 6X

MINI 3X-9X

MINI 4X

3X LER

2X LER

MINI SCOPES with PLEX RETICLE:

Mini 4x Plex	**$182.95**
Mini 4x Plex P.A. Airgun	210.95
Mini 4x Plex P.A.	210.95
Mini 4x Plex, Silver Safari	210.95
Mini 6x Plex	200.95
Mini 6x-2" Dot P.A. Airgun	238.95
Mini 6x Plex P.A. Airgun	222.95
Mini 6x Plex P.A.	222.95
Mini 6x 2" Dot P.A.	233.95
Mini 2x-7x Plex	249.95
Mini 3x-9x Plex	254.95
Mini 3x-9x Plex Silver Safari . .	279.95
Mini 4x-12x Plex	337.95
Mini 4x-12x Fine Plex Silhouette	359.95
Mini 4x-12x 1.2-.4 Dot Silhouette	373.95
Mini 3x-9x Plex Safari	267.95

LONG EYE RELIEF SCOPE with PLEX RETICLE:

1½x-4x LER Plex	**$278.95**
1½x-4x LER 3."-1." Dot	310.95
1½x-4x LER Plex, Silver Safari	306.95
2½x-7x LER Plex	289.95
2½x-7x LER Plex P.A.	314.95
2½x-7x LER Plex P.A., Silver Safari	337.95
1x LER Plex	170.95
1x LER 5" Dot	184.95
2x LER Plex	175.95
2x LER Plex P.A.	210.95
2x LER Plex, Silver Safari . . .	202.95
3x LER Plex	192.95
3x LER Plex P.A.	222.95
4x LER Plex	199.95
4x LER Plex P.A.	233.95
4x LER Dot P.A.	246.95
4x LER Plex P.A., Silver Safari	253.95
5x LER Plex	215.95
5x LER Plex P.A.	247.95
5x LER Dot P.A.	264.95

INTERMEDIATE EYE RELIEF SCOPE with PLEX RETICLE:

7X IER	**$233.95**
10x IER	287.95

BUSHNELL RIFLESCOPES

BANNER STANDARD CENTERFIRE RIFLESCOPES

Model	Special Feature	Actual Magnification	Obj. Lens Apert. (mm)	Field of View at 100 yds. (ft.)	Weight (oz.)	Length (oz.)	Eye Relief (in.)	Exit Pupil (mm)	Click Value at 100 yds. (in.)	Adjust. range at 100 yds. (in.)	Selection	Photo
71-3956		3x-9x	56	39@3x 12.5@9x	17.3	13.8	3.5	18.7@3x 6.2@9x	.25	±20	All purpose variable w/ maximum brightness.	A
71-1398		3x-9x	40	33.5@3x 11.5@9x	13.6	13	3.2	13.3@3x 4.4@9x	.25	±35	All purpose variable, excellent for use at close or long ranges.	
71-6102	BDC, WA	3x-9x	40	39@3x 13@9x	13.1	12	3.3	13.3@3x 4.4@9x	.25	±30	All purpose variable, excellent for use from close to long range. Circular view provides a definite advantage over ''TV screen''-type scopes for running game-uphill or down.	B
71-1643		6x	40	19	10.9	13.4	3.1	6.7	.25	±60	For open country. Adequate power for relatively long range, yet light and compact. Excellent for silhouette shooting.	
71-3403	BDC	4x	32	37.3	8.9	11.8	3.1	8	.25	±30	Gen. purpose. Lightwt.	C
71-2520		2.5x	20	44	7.8	10	3.6	8	.25	±50	Shotgun use.	

3x-9x (56mm) **$274.95**
3x-9x (40mm) **167.95**
3x-9x (40mm) Wide Angle, BDC **173.95**

6x (40mm) **189.95**
4x (32mm) BDC **128.95**
2.5x (20mm) Shotgun Scope **100.95**

2.5X (20mm) SHOTGUN SCOPE

3X-9X (40mm)

BUSHNELL TROPHY RIFLESCOPES

4x-12x (40mm) TROPHY WIDE ANGLE
$311.95

Also available:

1.75x-5x (32mm) Trophy Wide Angle Shotgun Scope **$196.95**	2x (32mm) Trophy Handgun Scope **196.95**
2x-6x (32mm) Trophy Handgun Scope **243.95**	2x (32mm) Trophy Handgun Scope (Silver) **209.95**
2x-6x (32mm) Trophy Handgun Scope (Silver) **256.95**	3x-9x (40mm) Trophy Wide Angle **209.95**
2x-7x (32mm) Trophy Wide Angle **233.95**	4x (40mm) Trophy Wide Angle **165.95**
	4x-12x (40mm) Trophy Wide Angle **311.95**
	6x-18x (40mm) Trophy Wide Angle Air Rifle Scope . **327.95**

Model	Special Feature	Actual Magnification	Obj. Lens Apert. (mm)	Field of View at 100 yds. (ft.)	Weight (oz.)	Length (in.)	Eye Relief (in.)	Exit Pupil (mm)	Click Value at 100 yds. (in.)	Adjust. range at 100 yds. (in.)	Selection	Photo
TROPHY HANDGUN SCOPES												
73-2632		2x-6x	32	16.7@2x 5.8@6x	10.9	9.1	9-26	16@2x 5.3@6x	.25	±50	Versatile all-purpose 4 time zoom range for close-in brush and long range shooting.	A
73-2632S	Silver											
73-0232		2x	32	18.5	7.5	8.7	9-26	16	.25	±50	Designed for target and short to medium range hunting. Magnum recoil resistant.	
73-0232S	Silver											
TROPHY SHOTGUN RIFLESCOPE												
73-1500	Wide Angle	1.7x-5x	32	73@1.5x 24.5@5x	10.9	10.8	3.5	18.3@1.75x 6.4@5x	.25	±50	Shotgun, black powder, or centerfire close-in brush hunting.	
TROPHY RIFLESCOPES												
73-4124	Wide Angle w/ adj. obj.	4x-12x	40	30@4x 10.1@12x	16.2	12.5	3	10@4x 3.3@12x	.25	±30	Medium to long range variable for varmint & big game. Parallax adjust.	
73-3940	Wide Angle	3x-9x	40	40@3x 13.4@9x	13.1	12	3	13.3@3x 4.4@9x	.25	±35	All-purpose variable, excellent for use from close to long range. Circular view provides a definite advantage over "TV screen"-type scopes for running game—uphill or down.	B
73-2732	Wide Angle	2x-7x	32	60@2x 18@7x	11.6	10	3	16@2x 4.6@7x	.25	±50	Compact variable for close-in brush & medium range shooting.	C
73-0440	Wide Angle	4x	40	34	12.2	12.6	3	10	.25	±35	General purpose—wide angle field of view.	

INTERAIMS ELECTRONIC RED DOT SIGHTS

The following superior features are incorporated into each model including the NEW MONO TUBE:

- Sharp Red Dot
- Lightweight
- Compact
- Wide Field of View
- Parallaxfree
- True 1 X for Unlimited Eye Relief
- Nitrogen Filled Tube

- Waterproof • Moisture Proof • Shockproof
- Rugged Aluminum Body
- Easy 1″ Ring Mounting
- Manually Adjustable Light Intensity
- Windage and Elevation Adjustments

- Dielectrical Coated Lenses
- Battery - Polarized Filter - Extension Tube - Protective Rubber Eye Piece - All included
- 5 Year Warranty

ONE V
$219.95

MOUNTS INCLUDED

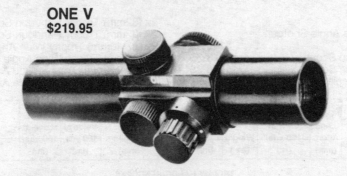

NEW

MONOTUBE CONSTRUCTIONS

Weight	Length	Battery	Finish
3.9 oz.	4½″	(1) 3 V Lithium	Black Satin Nickel

PRO V
$204.95

MARK V
$174.95

Weight	Length	Battery	Finish
4 oz.	4½″	(1) 3 V Lithium	Black Satin Nickel

Weight	Length	Battery	Finish
6 oz.	5″	(2) 1.35V Mercury	Black

LEUPOLD RIFLE SCOPES

VARIABLE POWER SCOPES

VARI-X II 1x4

This scope, the smallest of Leupold's VARI-X II line, is reintroduced in response to consumer demand for its large field of view: 70 feet at 100 yards: **$282.00**

VARI-X II 1x4

VARI-X II 2x7

A compact scope, no larger than the Leupold M8-4X, offering a wide range of power. It can be set at 2X for close ranges in heavy cover or zoomed to maximum power for shooting or identifying game at longer ranges. **$329.00.** With Dot or CPC reticle: **$351.00**

VARI-X II 2x7

VARI-X II 3x9

VARI-X II 3x9

A wide selection of powers lets you choose the right combination of field of view and magnification to fit the particular conditions you are hunting at the time. Many hunters use the 3X or 4X setting most of the time, cranking up to 9X for positive identification of game or for extremely long shots. The adjustable objective eliminates parallax and permits precise focusing on any object from less than 50 yards to infinity for extra-sharp definition. **$354.00.** With Dot or CPC reticle: **$375.00.** Also available with adjustable objective: **$391.00**

VARI-X II 4x12 A.O.

VARI-X II 4x12 (Adj. Objective)

The ideal answer for big game and varmint hunters alike. At 12.25 inches, the 4x12 is virtually the same length as Vari-X II 3x9. **$427.00**

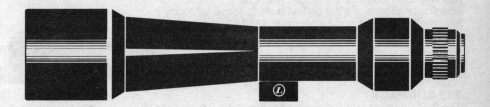

SPOTTING SCOPES

Leupold's Golden Ring 30x60mm Spotting Scope features extraordinary eye relief and crisp, bright roof prism optics housed in a lightweight, sealed, waterproof body. The 12.9-inch, 19.5-ounce Spotting Scope comes complete with a self-storing screw-on sunshade, lens caps, and a green canvas case. **$573.60**

Now available: Leupold's new 20x50mm and 25x50mm compact Waterproof Spotting Scopes with nearly 1" of eye relief for comfortable viewing with or without glasses.

20x50mm Compact Armored $515.00
25x50mm Compact Armored 544.00
   With reticle 573.00

LEUPOLD SCOPES

THE COMPACT SCOPE LINE

The introduction of the Leupold Compacts has coincided with the increasing popularity of the new featherweight rifles. Leupold Compact scopes give a more balanced appearance atop these new scaled-down rifles and offer generous eye relief, magnification and field of view, yet are smaller inside and out. Fog-free.

2.5X COMPACT

2.5X COMPACT
The 2.5X Compact is only 8½ inches long and weighs just 7.4 ounces: **$226.00.**

4X COMPACT
& 4X RF Special

4X COMPACT
The 4X Compact is over an inch shorter than the standard 4X. The 4X RF Special is focused to 75 yards and has a Duplex reticle with finer crosshairs: **$253.00.**

6X COMPACT

6X COMPACT
To make the 6X Compact, Leupold's shaved an ounce and a half and .7 inch off the standard scope of the same magnification: **$271.00.**

6X COMPACT
(with adjustable objective)

6X COMPACT (Adj. Objective)
The popularity of this magnification seems to be growing at the same rate as the availability of lighter or so-called "mountain" rifles. Now available with adjustable objective lens: **$308.00.**

2X7 COMPACT

2X7 COMPACT
Two ounces lighter and a whole inch shorter than its full-size counterpart, this 2x7 is one of the world's most compact variable power scopes. It's the perfect hunting scope for today's trend toward smaller and lighter rifles: **$320.00.**

3x9 COMPACT

3X9 COMPACT
The 3x9 Compact is a full-blown variable that's 3½ ounces lighter and 1.3 inches shorter than a standard 3x9. Also available in flat black, matte finish: **$345.00.**

3X9 COMPACT (Adj. Objective)
Big scope performance in a package compatible with the growing list of scaled down and featherweight rifles: **$382.00.** Now available: **3x9 COMPACT SILVER: $366.00.**

3x9 COMPACT SILVER

LEUPOLD RIFLE SCOPES

VARI-X III LINE

The Vari-X III scopes feature a power-changing system that is similar to the sophisticated lens systems in today's finest cameras. Some of the improvements include an extremely accurate internal control system and a sharp, superb-contrast sight picture. All lenses are coated with Multicoat 4. Reticles are the same apparent size throughout power range, stay centered during elevation/windage adjustments. Eyepieces are adjustable and fog-free.

VARI-X III 1.5x5

Here's a fine selection of hunting powers for ranges varying from very short to those at which big game is normally taken. The exceptional field at 1.5X lets you get on a fast-moving animal quickly. With the generous magnification at 5X, you can hunt medium and big game around the world at all but the longest ranges. **$390.00.** Also available in black matte finish: **$408.00**

VARI-X III 1.5x5

VARI-X III 2.5x8

This is an excellent range of powers for almost any kind of game, inlcuding varmints. In fact, it possibly is the best all-around variable going today. The top magnification provides plenty of resolution for practically any situation. **$440.00.** In matte finish: **$458.00**

VARI-X III 2.5x8

VARI-X III 3.5x10

VARI-X III 3.5x10

The extra power range makes these scopes the optimum choice for year-around big game and varmint hunting. The adjustable objective model, with its precise focusing at any range beyond 50 yards, also is an excellent choice for some forms of target shooting. **$461.00.** With adjustable objective: **$498.00**

VARI-X III 3.5x10-50mm (not shown)

Leupold announces its first hunting scope designed specifically for low-light situations. The 3.5x10-50mm scope, featuring lenses coated with Multicoat 4, is ideal for twilight hunting (especially whitetail deer) because of its efficient light transmission. The new scope delivers maximum available light through its large 50mm objective lens, which translates into an exit pupil that transmits all the light the human eye can handle in typical low-light circumstances, even at the highest magnification: **$535.00**

**VARI-X III 6.5x20
(with adjustable objective)**

VARI-X III 6.5x20

This scope has the widest range of power settings in our variable line, with magnifications that are especially useful to hunters of all types of varmints. In addition, it can be used for any kind of big game hunting where higher magnifications are an aid: **$546.00**

LEUPOLD SCOPES

THE TARGET SCOPE LINE

Shooters using Leupold target scopes are dominating both local and national bench rest and silhouette matches. Fog-free. Adjustable objective.

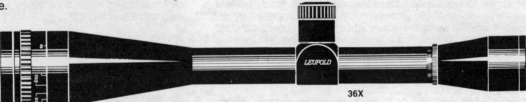

36X

36X TARGET SCOPE
A full 36 power magnification with clear, sharp resolution is possible with Leupold's 36X target scope, all in a package that is only 13.9 inches long and weighs just 15½ ounces. Adjustable objective. **$623.20.** With Target Dot: **$669.00**

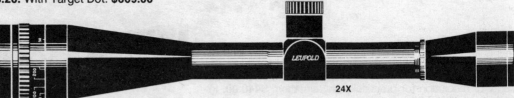

24X

24X TARGET SCOPE
The 24X is just 13.6 inches long and weighs only 14½ ounces. It is compact enough to be receiver mounted and light enough to permit transfer of significant weight from scope to rifle. Adjustable objective. **$648.00.** With ⅛ min. or ½ min. Target Dot: **$669.00**

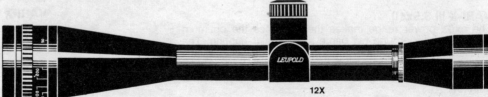

12X

12X TARGET SCOPE
The 12X target scope has the magnification and clear, sharp-contrast sight picture that target shooters need. Two types of redesigned windage/elevation adjustment knobs are included. Adjustable objective. **$445.00.** With CPC reticle or Dot: **$477.00**

VARI-X III 6.5x20

VARI-X III 6.5x20 TARGET SCOPE
The 6.5x20 target allows a shooter to not only change magnifications quickly to match target range, but also rapidly select the windage and elevation needed for each shot, knowing he can unerringly return to a previous setting with ease. Adjustable objective. **$637.00.** With CPC reticle or Dot: **$616.00**

LEUPOLD SCOPES
EXTENDED EYE RELIEF HANDGUN SCOPE LINE

2X EER

With an optimum eye relief of 12-24 inches, the 2X EER is an excellent choice for most handguns. It is equally favorable for carbines and other rifles with top ejection that calls for forward mounting of the scope. Available in black anodized or silver

4X EER

Only 8.4 inches long and 7.6 ounces. Optimum eye relief 12-24 inches. Available in black anodized or silver finish to match stainless steel and nickel-plated handguns. **$241.00.** In silver: **$263.00**

FIXED-POWER SCOPE LINE

4X

The all-time favorite is the 4X, which delivers a widely used magnification and a generous field of view. Also available in new flat black, matte finish. **$253.00.** With CPC reticle or Dot: **$275.00**

6X

Gaining popularity fast among fixed power scopes is the 6X, which can extend the range for big game hunting and double, in some cases, as a varmint scope. **$271.00.** CPC reticle or Dot: **$292.00**

6X42mm

Large 42mm objective lens features increased light gathering capability and a 7mm exit pupil. Great for varmint shooting at night. Duplex or Heavy Duplex: **$316.00.** Post & Duplex: **$338.00**

8X

A true varmint scope, the 8X has the sharp resolution, contrast and accuracy that also make it effective for some types of target shooting. Adjustable objective permits precise, parallax-free focusing. **$361.00.** CPC reticle or Dot: **$382.00**

12X

Superlative optical qualities, outstanding resolution and magnification make the 12X a natural for the varmint shooter. Adjustable objective is standard for parallax-free focusing. **$373.00.** CPC reticle or Dot: **$394.00**

finish to match stainless steel and nickel-plated handguns. **$198.00.** In silver: **$219.00**

2X EER

4X EER

4X

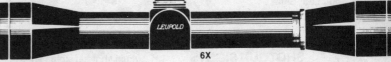

6X

Also available: **8x36mm.** Features a target-style dot and thinner Duplex reticle for long-range use (focused at 300 yds. instead of 150). **$361.00.** With target-style dot: **$382.00.**

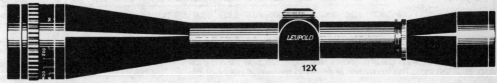

8X

12X

LYMAN SIGHTS

LEAF SIGHTS
NO. 16 FOLDING LEAF SIGHT

Designed primarily as open rear sights with adjustable elevation, leaf sights make excellent auxiliary sights for scope-mounted rifles. They fold close to the barrel when not in use, and they can be installed and left on the rifle without interfering with scope or mount. Two lock screws hold the elevation blade adjustments firmly in place. A sight of this type could save the day if the scope becomes damaged through rough handling. Leaf sights are available in the following heights:

16A—.400″ high; elevates to .500″.
16B—.345″ high; elevates to .445″.
16C—.500″ high; elevates to .600″.

For installation on rifles without a dovetail slot, use Lyman No. 25 Base.

No. 16 Folding Leaf Sight $11.95

BASES
NO. 25 BASES

Permit the installation of dovetail rear sights (such as Lyman 16 leaf sight) on rifles that do not have dovetail cut in barrel. They also supply a higher line of sight when needed. The No. 25 Base is mounted by drilling and tapping the barrel for two 6-48 screws. Screws are supplied with base.

No. 25 Base $8.50

STANDARD BASES	HEIGHT FROM TOP OF BARREL TO BOTTOM OF DOVETAIL	BARREL RADIUS
25A Base (Low)	.025″	.875 or larger
25C Base (High)	.125″	.875 or larger
SPECIAL BASES		
25B Base	.125″	.875 or larger
Fits factory screw holes on Remington 740, 742, 760, 725 & replaces factory rear		

NO. 12 SLOT BLANKS

These blanks fill the standard 3/8-inch barrel dovetail when a receiver sight is installed. They are also available for front sight dovetails and ramps when a scope is being used. **No. 12S** (3/8″×5/8″ long) for standard rear barrel slots. **Price: $3.95**

No. 12S (3/8″ × 5/8″ long) for standard rear barrel slots.

SHOTGUN SIGHTS

Lyman shotgun sights are available for all shotguns. Equipped with oversized ivory beads that give perfect definition on either bright or dull days, they are easy to see under any light conditions. They quickly catch your eye on fast upland targets, and point out the lead on long passing shots. Lyman shotgun sights are available with white bead, and can be fitted to your gun in minutes.

No. 10 Front Sight (press fit) for use on double barrel, or ribbed single
   -barrel guns $4.25
No. 10D Front Sight (screw fit) for use on non-ribbed single-barrel guns;
   supplied with a wrench 5.25
No. 11 Middle Sight (press fit). This small middle sight is intended for use on
   double-barrel and ribbed single-barrel guns 4.25

When you replace an open rear sight with a receiver sight, it is usually necessary to install a higher front sight to compensate for the higher plane of the new receiver sight. The table below shows the increase in front sight height that's required to compensate for a given error at 100 yards.

AMOUNT OF ADJUSTMENT NECESSARY TO CORRECT FRONT SIGHT ERROR																					
DISTANCE BETWEEN FRONT AND REAR SIGHTS		14″	15″	16″	17″	18″	19″	20″	21″	22″	23″	24″	25″	26″	27″	28″	29″	30″	31″	32″	33″	34″
	1	.0038	.0041	.0044	.0047	.0050	.0053	.0055	.0058	.0061	.0064	.0066	.0069	.0072	.0074	.0077	.0080	.0082	.0085	.0088	.0091	.0093
Amount of	2	.0078	.0083	.0089	.0094	.0100	.0105	.0111	.0116	.0122	.0127	.0133	.0138	.0144	.0149	.0155	.0160	.0156	.0171	.0177	.0182	.0188
Error	3	.0117	.0125	.0133	.0142	.0150	.0159	.0167	.0175	.0184	.0192	.0201	.0209	.0217	.0226	.0234	.0243	.0251	.0259	.0268	.0276	.0285
100 Yards	4	.0155	.0167	.0178	.0189	.0200	.0211	.0222	.0234	.0244	.0255	.0266	.0278	.0289	.0300	.0311	.0322	.0333	.0344	.0355	.0366	.0377
Given in	5	.0194	.0208	.0222	.0236	.0250	.0264	.0278	.0292	.0306	.0319	.0333	.0347	.0361	.0375	.0389	.0403	.0417	.0431	.0445	.0458	.0472
Inches	6	.0233	.0250	.0267	.0283	.0300	.0317	.0333	.0350	.0367	.0384	.0400	.0417	.0434	.0450	.0467	.0484	.0500	.0517	.0534	.0551	.0567

EXAMPLE: Suppose your rifle has a 27-inch sight radius, and shoots 4 inches high at 100 yards, with the receiver sight adjusted as low as possible. The 27-inch column shows that the correction for a 4-inch error is .0300 inch. This correction is added to the overall height of the front sight (including dovetail). Use a micrometer or similar accurate device to measure sight height. Thus, if your original sight measured .360 inch, it should be replaced with a sight .390 inch high, such as a J height sight.

MILLETT SIGHTS
RIFLE & SHOTGUN SIGHTS

COLT AR-15 (and similar models)

Riflemen will appreciate this new peep sight system for AR-15's. Fully adjustable for windage and elevation at the rear sight. No more difficult front sight adjustment. The Millett front sight is a serrated post design that provides a sharp, crisp sight picture under all lighting conditions. A real improvement over the round factory front sight. The rear peep sight blade has a large eye piece that blocks out the surrounding light and allows a sharp, crisp image to show through the cone-shaped aperture. Easy to install requiring no special tools.

Combo Peep Sight (Peep Sight Rear/Serrated Ramp Front)	**$62.65**
Rear Only Peep Sight (.080 Dia. Aperture)	51.45
Front Only Serrated Ramp	12.25
Rear Peep Blade (.050 Dia. Aperture)	18.95

RUGER MINI-14

Mini-14 owners will be elated with this new Series 100 adjustable sight system. Precision click adjustments for windage and elevation with easy return to zero. The large eye piece on the peep sight blade blocks out surrounding light to provide a sharp sight picture which greatly improves shooting accuracy. The cone-shaped aperture totally eliminates sighting error caused by reflected light. Easy to install with no special tools or gunsmithing required.

Mini-14 Rear Peep Sight (.080 Dia. Aperture)	**$51.45**
Mini-14 Front Sight	17.85
Mini-14 Combo (Rear peep/post front)	68.25
Rear Peep Blade only; .050 diam. aperture	18.95

OPEN RIFLE SIGHTS
Dovetail Rear Mount

The Series 100 Adjustable Sight System for Dovetail rear mount rifles provide a highly visible sight picture and fast, accurate sightings every time. Precision click adjustments for windage and elevation insure fine sighting. Made of heat treated steel and easy to install. Especially recommended for Marlin 336 owners. Front sights feature blaze orange and white bar enhance contrast, especially in dim light. Rear sight blade provides a sharp horizontal sighting plane with deep notch for fast sighting (choice of white outline or target rear blades). **Rear Sight: $52.95. Front Sight: $11.75.**

SHURSHOT RIBBED SHOTGUN SIGHTS

The greatest deterrent to shotgun accuracy is raising your head from the stock when shooting. With the Millett ShurShot, accuracy is improved by giving the shooter a reference point to align his head position on the stock. The blaze orange inserts are highly visible in low light and aids the eye in picking up the target. Late in the day deer hunters or early morning duck hunters can get on the game quickly and accurately. ShurShot works great with slugs or shot. Shooting is quick and natural. Eye instinct will automatically align and center the rib and sight bar.

ShurShot Shotgun Sight Combo (Orange) Fits Rem. 1100 & 870	SG00001	**$20.95**
ShurShot Shotgun Sight (Rear Only Orange) Fits Rem. 1100 & 870	SG00002	12.50
ShurShot Shotgun Sight (Front Only Orange)	SG00003	8.70
ShurShot Shotgun Combo (Orange)	SG00006	27.40
Other Models ShurShot Shotgun Sight (Rear Only Orange)	SG00005	12.50
Other Models ShurShot Adj. Shotgun Sight Combo (Orange)	SG00004	20.95

MILLET SIGHTS™

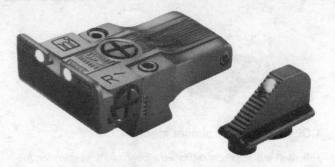

FLUSH-MOUNT SLING SWIVELS

Millett's flush-mount redesigned Pachmayr sling swivels are quick detachable and beautifully styled in heat treated nickel steel. The sling swivel loop has been redesigned to guide the sling into the loop, eliminating twisitng and fraying on edges of sling. Millett flush-mount bases are much easier to install than the old Pachmayr design, with no threading and an easy to use step drill.

Flush-Mount Swivels (pair)	SS00001	**$15.65**
Loops Only	SS00002	**8.70**
Installation Drill	SS00003	**16.75**

HARRIS BIPOD ADAPTER   **STANDARD LOOP 1″**

FLUSH-MOUNT HARRIS BIPOD ADAPTER

Millett's flush-mount sling swivels have a simple-to-use adapter for the Harris bipod, that detaches quickly so the loop can then be installed in the bipod loop receptacle. Will also fit Pachmayr flush-mount bases.

Harris Bipod Adapter	SS00004	**$8.70**

DUAL-CRIMP INSTALLATION TOOL KIT

The Dual-Crimp System is a new revolutionary way of installing front sights on autos. Now it is not necessary to heliarc or silver solder to get a good secure job. Dual-Crimp has a two-post, hollow rivet design that works very much like an aircraft rivet and withstands the heavy abuse of hardball ammo. Your choice of four styles and nine heights. Dual-Crimp is the quick and easy system for professionals. Requires a drill press.

Dual-Crimp Tool Set, Complete	**$142.95**
Application Tool	**76.95**
Reverse counterbore (solid carbide)	**36.85**
³/₁₆″ Drill (solid carbide)	**17.05**
Drill Jig	**21.95**
Complete Tool Kit (Stake-On)	**87.95**

3-DOT SYSTEM SIGHTS

Millett announces 3-Dot System sights for a wide variety of popular handguns.

**3-Dot System Front and Rear Sight
Selection Chart**

DUAL-CRIMP FRONTS
DC 18500	.185 Height
DC 20004	.200 Height
DC 22512	.225 Height
DC31216	.312 Height
DC34020	.340 Height
DC36024	.360 Height

WIDE STAKE-ON FRONTS
(for Colt pistols only, after June 1988)
WS18504	.185 Height
WS20008	.200 Height
WS31220	.312 Height

SPECIAL-APPLICATION PISTOL FRONTS
BE00010	Beretta Accurizer
GL00006	Glock 17, 17L & 19
RP85009	Ruger-P-85
RS22015	Ruger Std. Auto (Fixed Model)
SP22567	Sig Sauer P225/226
SW40513	S&W 3rd Generation, Dovetail
SW46913	S&W 3rd Generation, Dovetail

AUTOPISTOL REAR SIGHTS
BE00003	Beretta
BA00008	Browning Hi-Power, Adjustable
BF00008	Browning Hi-Power, Fixed
CA00008	Colt-Hi-Profile
CC00008	Colt Custom Combat Lo-Profile
MK20008	Colt Mark II Lo-Profile, Fixed
GC00008	Colt Gold Cup
GL00008	Glock 17, 17L & 19
RP85008	Ruger P-85
RS22003	Ruger Std. Auto
SP22005	Sig P220, 225, 226
SW40504	Smith & Wesson, *ALL* Factory Adjustable (incl. 3rd Generation)
SW46904	Smith & Wesson, *ALL* Factory Fixed (incl. 3rd Generation)

MILLET SIGHTS™

REVOLVER SIGHTS

SCOPES

COLT REVOLVER

The Series 100 Adjustable Sight System offers today's discriminating Colt owner the finest quality replacement sight available. 12 crisp click stops for each turn of adjustment, delivers $5/8$″ of adjustment per click at 100 yards with a 6″ barrel. Easy to install, using factory front sight. Guaranteed to give your Colt that custom look.

For Colt Python, Trooper, Diamond Back, and new Frontier single action army.

Rear Only (White Outline)	CR00001	**$46.95**
Rear Only (Target Blade)	CR00002	46.95
Rear Only (Silhouette)	CR00003	46.95

Colt owners will really appreciate the high visibility feature of Colt front sights. Easy to install—just drill 2 holes in the new sight and pin on. All steel. Your choice of blaze orange or white bar. Fits 4″, 6″ & 8″ barrels only.

Colt Python (White or Orange Bar)	FB00007-8	**$12.95**
Trooper, Diamond Back, King Cobra, Peace-maker	FB00015-16	12.95

SMITH & WESSON

The Series 100 Adjustable Sight System for Smith & Wesson revolvers provides the sight picture and crisp click adjustments desired by the discriminating shooter. $1/2$″ of adjustment per click, at 100 yards on elevation, and $5/8$″ on windage, with a 6″ barrel. Can be installed in a few minutes, using factory front sight.

K&N frames manufactured prior to 1974 did not standardize on front screw hole location, so the front hole must be drilled and counterbored on these sights.

Smith & Wesson **N** Frame

N.312—Model 25-5, all bbl., 27-3$1/2$″ & 5″, 28-4″ & 6″
N.360—Model 25, 27, 29, 57, & 629-4, 6 & 6$1/2$″ bbl.
N.410—Model 27, 29, 57, 629 with 8$3/8$″ bbl.

Smith & Wesson **K&L** Frame
K.312—Models 14, 15, 18, 48-4″, & 53
K&L360—Models 16, 17, 19, 48-6″, 8$3/8$″, 66, 686, 586

Smith & Wesson K&L-Frame		
Rear Only .312 (White Outline)	SK00001	**$46.95**
Rear Only .312 (Target Blade)	SK00002	46.95
Rear Only .360 (White Outline)	SK00003	46.95
Rear Only .360 (Target Blade)	SK00004	46.95
Rear Only .410 (White Outline)	SK00005	46.95
Rear Only .410 (Target Blade)	SK00006	46.95
Smith & Wesson K&N Old Style		
Rear Only .312 (White Outline)	KN00001	**$46.95**
Rear Only .312 (Target Blade)	KN00002	46.95
Rear Only .360 (White Outline)	KN00003	46.95
Rear Only .360 (Target Blade)	KN00004	46.95
Rear Only .410 (White Outline)	KN00005	46.95
Rear Only .410 (Target Blade)	KN00006	46.95
Smith & Wesson N-Frame		
Rear Only .312 (White Outline)	SN00001	**$46.95**
Rear Only .312 (Target Blade)	SN00002	46.95
Rear Only .360 (White Outline)	SN00003	46.95
Rear Only .360 (Target Blade)	SN00001	46.95
Rear Only .410 (White Outline)	SN00005	46.95
Rear Only .410 (Target Blade)	KN00006	46.95

RUGER

The high visibility white outline sight picture and precision click adjustments of the Series 100 Adjustable Sight System will greatly improve the accuracy and fast sighting capability of your Ruger. $3/4$″ per click at 100 yard for elevation, $5/8$″ per click for windage, with 6″ barrel. Can be easily installed, using factory front sight or all-steel replacement front sight which is a major improvement over the factory front. Visibility is greatly increased for fast sighting. Easy to install by drilling one hole in the new front sight.

The Red Hawk all-steel replacement front sight is highly visible and easy to pickup under all lighting conditions. Very easy to install. Fits the factory replacement system.

SERIES 100 Ruger Double Action Revolver Sights	
Rear Sight (fits all adjustable models)	**$46.95**
Front Sight (Security Six, Police Six, Speed Six)	12.95
Front Sight (Redhawk and GP-100)	15.25

SERIES 100 Ruger Single Action Revolver Sights	
Rear Sight (Black Hawk Standard & Super; Bisley Large Frame, Single-Six	**$46.95**
Front Sight (Millet Replacement sights not available for Ruger single action revolvers).	

DAN WESSON

This sight is exactly what every Dan Wesson owner has been looking for. The Series 100 Adjustable Sight System provides 12 crisp click stops for each turn of adjustment, with $5/8$″ per click for windage, with a 6″ barrel. Can be easily installed, using the factory front or new Millett high visibility front sights.

Choice of white outline or target blade.

Rear Only (White Outline)	DW00001	**$46.95**
Rear Only (Target Blade)	DW00002	46.95
Rear Only (White Outline) 44 Mag.	DW00003	46.95
Rear Only (Target Blade) 44 Mag.	DW00004	46.95

If you want super-fast sighting capability for your Dan Wesson, the new Millett blaze orange or white bar front is the answer. Easy to install. Fits factory quick-change system. All steel, no plastic. Available in both heights.

Dan Wesson .44 Mag & 15-2 (White Bar) (high)	FB00009	**$12.95**
Dan Wesson .44 Mag & 15-2 (Orange Bar) (high)	FB00010	12.95
Dan Wesson 22 Caliber (White Bar) (low)	FB00011	12.95
Dan Wesson 22 Caliber (Orange Bar) (low)	FB00012	12.95

MILLET SIGHTS ™

PISTOL SIGHTS FOR RUGER P85

Combo (White rear/White front) $66.95
Combo (White rear/Orange front) 66.95
Rear only (White outline) 52.95
Rear, 3-Dot 52.95
Front only (White ramp) 15.25
Front only (Orange ramp) 15.25
Front only (Serrated ramp) 15.25

SCOPE-SITE FOR HANDGUNS

**Colt Python/Trooper/Diamondback/
Peacekeeper** (fully adjustable) $80.25
Dan Wesson (calibers thru 357; fully
adjustable; 2 rings) 80.25
   Same as above fully adjustable 96.20
Ruger Redhawk Engraved (also Ranch Rifle, #1,
#3; adj. for windage, medium) 44.95
   Same as above fully adjustable 79.95
Ruger Super Redhawk Engraved
(also M77; adj. for windage) 44.95
   Same as above fully adjustable 77.95

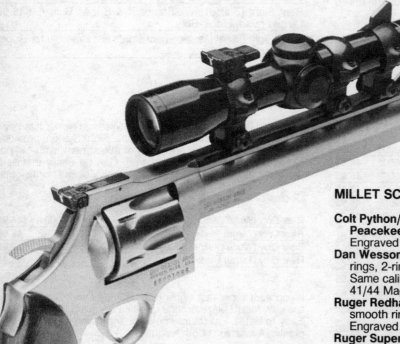

Wide Stake-On Fronts for Colt Semi-Auto (after 6/88)

White Bar	Orange Bar	Serrated Ramp	White Dot

WS18501	.185 Height, White Bar
WS18502	.185 Height, Orange Bar
WS18503	.185 Height, Serrated Ramp
WS18504	.185 Height, White Dot
WS20005	.200 Height, White Bar
WS20006	.200 Height, Orange Bar
WS20007	.200 Height, Serrated Ramp
WS20008	.200 Height, White Dot
WS31217	.312 Height, White Bar
WS31218	.312 Height, Orange Bar
WS31219	.312 Height, Serrated Ramp
WS31220	.312 Height, White Dot

MILLET SCOPE MOUNTS FOR HANDGUNS

**Colt Python/Trooper/Diamondback/
Peacekeeper** (smooth rings) $32.95
   Engraved rings (front and rear, set) 47.25
Dan Wesson (calibers up thru 357; smooth
rings, 2-ring set) 32.95
   Same calibers, engraved rings (2-ring set) 47.25
   41/44 Magnum, smooth rings only (3-ring set) 49.35
Ruger Redhawk (also Ranch Rifle, #1, #3;
smooth rings) 29.65
   Engraved rings (front and rear, set) 44.95
Ruger Super Redhawk (also M77; engraved rings
front & rear) 44.95
   Smooth rings (front & rear, set) 29.65
Smith & Wesson K- and N-Frame smooth rings 32.95
   Same as above w/nickel finish 40.95

MILLETT AUTO PISTOL SIGHTS

SMITH & WESSON 39/59

This sight system provides fast and accurate sighting capability even under low light conditions. The unique white outline rear blade teamed up with the blaze orange or white bar front sight creates a highly visible sight picture, ideal for match or duty use.

Combo (White rear/Dual-Crimp White Front)	SW39591	**$70.50**
Combo (White rear/Dual-Crimp Orange Front	SW39592	**70.50**
Rear Only (White outline)	SW39595	**56.45**
Rear Only (Target Blade)	SW39596	**56.45**

Requires .340 Dual-Crimp Front

SMITH & WESSON 469, 669, 659, 459, 645 AUTOPISTOL SIGHTS

Rear Sight (white outline)	**$54.10**
Front Sight DC 312 white or orange	**15.25**
Rear/Front Combination	**66.95**

SMITH & WESSON 400/500/600 SERIES AUTOPISTOL SIGHTS

Rear Sight (white outline)	**$52.95**
Front Sight DC 312 white or orange	**15.25**
Rear/Front Combination	**68.95**

COLT 45

This Series 100 High Profile Adjustable Sight is rugged, all steel, precision sight which fits the standard factory dovetail with no machine modifications required. This sight provides a highly visible sight picture even under low light conditions. Blaze orange or white bar front sight, precision click adjustments for windage and elevation makes the Colt .45 Auto Combo the handgunner's choice.

Combo (White rear/Stake-On White Front)	CA00001	**$66.95**
Combo (White rear/Stake-On Orange Front)	CA00002	**66.95**
Combo (White rear/Dual-Crimp White Front)	CA00003	**66.95**
Combo (White rear/Dual-Crimp Orange Front)	CA00004	**66.95**
Rear Only (White Outline)	CA00009	**52.95**
Rear Only (Target Blade)	CA00010	**52.95**

Colt Gov. and Com. Require .312 High Front Sight.

BROWNING HI-POWER

The Series 100 Adjustable Sight System for Browning Hi-Power will provide accurate high visibility sighting for both fixed and adjustable slides with no machine modifications required to the dovetail. Most adjustable slide model Hi-Powers can use the factory front sight as shown in the photo. The fixed slide model requires a new front sight installation. We highly recommend the Dual-Crimp front sight installation on this gun.

Browning Hi-Power (Adjustable Slide Model)		
Combo (White rear/Stake-On White Front)	BA00001	**$66.95**
Combo (White rear/Stake-On Orange Front)	BA00002	**66.95**
Combo (White rear/Dual-Crimp White Front)	BA00003	**66.95**
Combo (White rear/Dual-Crimp Orange Front)	BA00004	**66.95**
Rear Only (White Outline)	BA00009	**52.95**
Rear Only (Target Blade)	BA00010	**52.95**

High-Power Requires .340 High Front Sight.

Browning Hi-Power (Fixed Slide Model)		
Combo (White rear/Stake-On White Front)	BF00001	**$66.95**
Combo (White rear/Stake-On Orange Front)	BF00002	**66.95**
Combo (White rear/Dual-Crimp White Front)	BF00003	**66.95**
Combo (White rear/Dual-Crimp Orange Front)	BF00004	**66.95**
Rear Only (White Outline)	BF00009	**52.95**
Rear Only (Target Blade)	BF00010	**52.95**

High-Power Requires .340 High Front Sight.

MODELS CZ75/TZ75/TA90 AUTOPISTOL SIGHTS	
Rear Sight (white and Target) only	**$52.95**

BERETTA ACCURIZER COMBO

This amazing new sight system not only provides a highly visible sight picture but also tunes the barrel lockup to improve your accuracy and reduce your group size by as much as 50%. The Beretta Accurizer sight system fits the 92S, 92SB, 84 and 85 models. Easy to install. Requires the drilling of one hole for installation. Your choice of rear blade styles. Front sight comes in white bar, serrated ramp or blaze orange.

Combo (White Rear/White Bar Front)	BE00001	**$75.35**
Combo (White Rear/Orange Bar Front)	BE00002	**75.35**
Rear Only (White Outline)	BE00005	**53.70**
Rear Only (Target Blade)	BE00006	**53.70**
Front Only (White Bar)	BE00007	**23.95**
Front Only (Orange Bar)	BE00008	**23.95**
Front Only (Serrated Ramp)	BE00009	**23.95**

Fits Models 92S, 92SB, 85, 84

MILLETT AUTO PISTOL SIGHTS

COLT **COLT GOLD CUP** **MARK II HI-PROFILE**

RUGER STANDARD AUTO

The Ruger Standard Auto Combo provides a highly visible sight picture even under low light conditions. The blaze orange or white bar front sight allows the shooter to get on target fast. Great for target use or plinking. Uses Factory Front Sight on adjustable model guns when using Millett target rear only. All other installations use Millett Front Sight. Easy to install.

Combo (White rear/White front)	**$66.95**
Combo (White rear/Orange front)	**66.95**
Rear Only (White Outline)	**52.95**
Rear Only (Silhouette Target Blade)	**52.95**
Front Only (White)	**15.25**
Front Only (Orange)	**15.25**
Front Only (Serrated Ramp)	**15.25**
Front Only (Target-Adjustable Model/White Bar)	**15.25**
Front Only (Target-Adjustable Model/Orange Bar)	**15.25**
Front Only Bull Barrel (White or Orange Ramp)	**16.75**

COLT

Colt Gold Cup Marksman Speed Rear Only (Target .410 Blade)		**$46.95**
Custom Combat Low Profile Marksman Speed Rear Only (Target .410 Blade)		**52.95**
Colt Government & Commander (High Profile) Marksman Speed Rear Only (Target .410 Blade) CA00018		**52.95**
Colt Gold Cup Combo		**61.15**
Colt Mark II Lo-Profile Fixed Combo		**46.95**
Colt Mark II Low-Profile Rear Only		**32.95**

SMITH & WESSON 39-59   **SMITH & WESSON 400, 500, 60**

SMITH & WESSON

Combo (White Rear, Dual-Crimp White Front)	SW39591	70.50
Combo (Whit Rear, Dual-Crimp Orange Front)	SW39592	70.50
Rear, White Outline (Use .340 DC Front)	SW39595	56.45
Rear, Target Blade (Use .340 DC Front)	SW39596	56.45
Combo (White Rear, Dual-Crimp White Front)	SW40501	68.25
Combo (Whit Rear, Dual-Crimp Orange Front)	SW40502	68.25
Rear, White Outline (Use .312 DC Front)	SW40505	54.10
Rear, Target Blade (Use .312 DC Front)	SW40506	54.10
Combo (White Rear, Dual-Crimp White Front)	SW46901	66.95
Combo (Whit Rear, Dual-Crimp Orange Front)	SW46902	66.95
Rear, White Outline (Use .312 DC Front)	SW46905	52.95
Rear, Target Blade (Use .312 DC Front)	SW46906	52.95

SIG/SAUER P-220, P-225, P-226

Now Sig Pistol owners can obtain a Series-100 adjustable sight system for their guns. Precision click adjustment for windage and elevation makes it easy to zero when using different loads. The high visibility features assures fast sight acquisition when under the poorest light conditions. Made of high quality heat treated nickel steel and built to last. Extremely easy to install on P-225 and P-226. The P-220 and Browning BDA 45 require the Dual-Crimp front sight installation.

Sig P220 Combo (White Rear/Dual-Crimp White Front)	SP22001	**$66.95**
Sig P220 Combo (White Rear/Dual-Crimp Orange Front)	SP22002	**66.95**
Sig P220-25-26 Rear Only (White)	SP22003	**52.95**
Sig P220-25-26 Rear Only (Target)	SP22004	**52.95**
Sig P225-6 Combo (White Rear/Dovetail White Front)	SP22561	**66.95**
Sig P225-6 Combo (White Rear/Dovetail Orange Front)	SP22562	**66.95**
Sig P225-6 (White) Dovetail Front	SP22565	**15.25**
Sig P225-6 (Orange) Dovetail Front	SP22566	**15.25**

The Sig P220 Uses .360 Dual-Crimp Front Sight. The Sig P225-6 Uses a Dovetail Mount Front Sight

PENTAX SCOPES

FIXED POWER

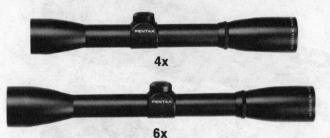

4x

6x

VARIABLE POWER

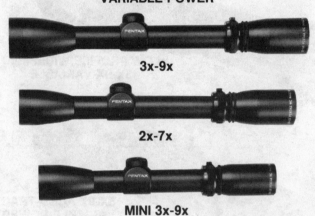

3x-9x

2x-7x

MINI 3x-9x

FIXED POWER RIFLESCOPES

Magnification: 4x
Field of view: 35'
Eye relief: 3.25"
Diameter: 1"
Weight: 12.2 oz.
Length: 11.6"
Prices: $280.00 (Glossy)
　　　　　300.00 (Pro finish)

Magnification: 6x
Field of view: 20'
Eye relief: 3.25"
Diameter: 1"
Weight: 13½ oz.
Length: 13.4"
Prices: $310.00 (Glossy)
　　　　　330.00 (Pro finish)

VARIABLE POWER RIFLESCOPES

Magnification: 1.5x-5x
Field of view: 66'-25'
Eye relief: 3"-3¼"
Diameter: 1"
Weight: 13 oz.
Length: 11"
Price: $330.00 (Matte only)

Magnification: 3x-9x
Field of view: 33'-13½'
Eye relief: 3"-3¼"
Diameter: 1"
Weight: 15 oz.
Length: 13"
Prices: $380.00 (Glossy)
　　　　　400.00 (Pro finish)

Magnification: 2x-7x
Field of view: 42.5'-17'
Eye relief: 3"-3¼"
Diameter: 1"
Weight: 14 oz.
Length: 12"
Prices: $360.00 (Glossy)
　　　　　380.00 (Pro finish)

Magnification: Mini 3x-9x
Field of view: 26½'-10½'
Eye relief: 3¼"
Diameter: 1"
Weight: 13 oz.
Length: 10.4"
Prices: $320.00 (Mini-glossy)
　　　　　350.00 (Mini-Pro
　　　　　finish)

Also available:
4x-12x Mini (glossy): $410.00
6x-12x (glossy): $460.00

PISTOL SCOPES

Magnification: 2x
Field of view: 21'
Eye relief: 10"-24"
Diameter: 1"
Weight: 6.8 oz.
Length: 8¼"
Prices: $240.00 (Glossy)
　　　　　260.00 (Chrome-matte)

Magnification: 1.5x-4x
Field of view: 16'-11'
Eye relief: 11"-25"/11"-18"
Diameter: 1"
Weight: 11 oz.
Length: 10"
Prices: $360.00 (Glossy)
　　　　　390.00 (Chrome-matte)

REDFIELD SCOPES

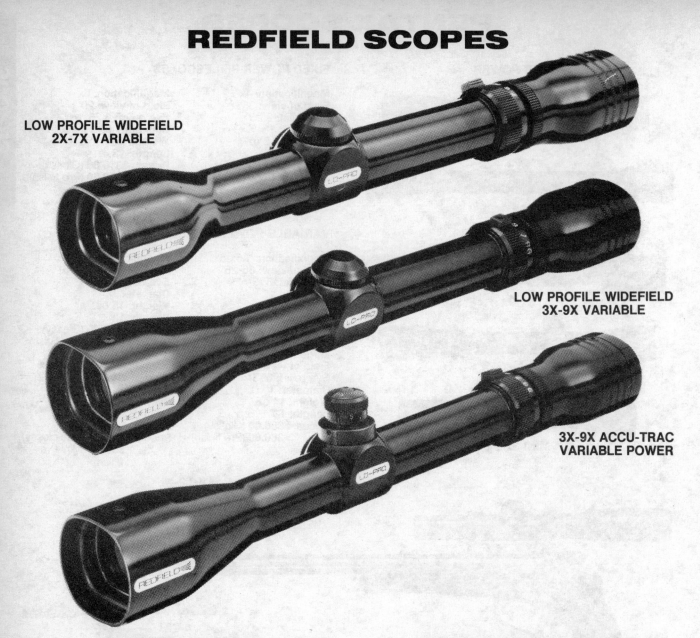

**LOW PROFILE WIDEFIELD
2X-7X VARIABLE**

**LOW PROFILE WIDEFIELD
3X-9X VARIABLE**

**3X-9X ACCU-TRAC
VARIABLE POWER**

LOW PROFILE WIDEFIELD

In heavy cover, game may jump out of the brush 10 feet away or appear in a clearing several hundred yards off, either standing or on the move.

The Widefield®, with 25% more field of view than conventional scopes, lets you spot game quicker, stay with it and see other animals that might be missed.

The patented Low Profile design means a low mounting on the receiver, allowing you to keep your cheek tight on the stock for a more natural and accurate shooting stance, especially when swinging on running game.

The one-piece, fog-proof tube is machined with high tensile strength aluminum alloy and is anodized to a lustrous finish that's rust-free and virtually scratch-proof. Available in 7 models.

WIDEFIELD LOW PROFILE SCOPES

1³/₄x-5x Low Profile Variable Power
113806 1³/₄x-5x 4 Plex **$314.95**
2x-7x Low Profile Variable Power
111806 2x-7x 4 Plex **322.95**
2x-7x Low Profile Accu-Trac Variable Power
111810 2x-7x 4 Plex AT **378.95**
3x-9x Low Profile Variable Power
112806 3x-9x 4 Plex **357.95**
3x-9x Low Profile Accu-Trac Variable Power
112810 3x-9x 4 Plex AT **414.95**
2³/₄x Low Profile Fixed Power
141807 2³/₄x 4 Plex **228.95**
4x Low Profile Fixed Power
143806 4x 4 Plex **255.95**
6x Low Profile Fixed Power
146806 6x 4 Plex **277.95**

REDFIELD SCOPES

GOLDEN FIVE STAR SCOPES

This series of seven scopes incorporates the latest variable and fixed power scope features, including multi-coated and magnum recoil-resistant optical system, plus maximum light-gathering ability. Positive quarter-minute click adjustments for ease of sighting and optimum accuracy. Anodized finish provides scratch-resistant surface.

Golden Five Star Scopes:

1x-4x Variable Power	$251.95
2x-7x Variable Power	264.95
3x-9x Variable Power	282.95
3x-9x Nickel Plated	299.95
4x-12x Variable Power (adj. objective)	362.95
6x-18x Variable Power (adj. objective)	382.95
4x Fixed Power	204.95
6x Fixed Power	222.95

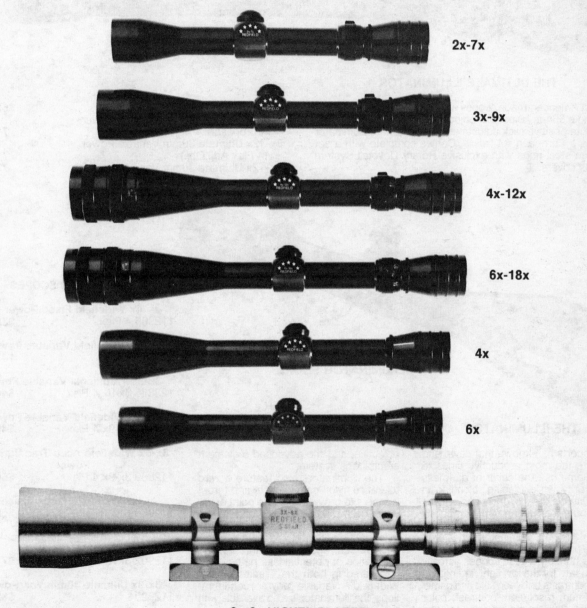

2x-7x

3x-9x

4x-12x

6x-18x

4x

6x

3x-9x NICKEL PLATED

REDFIELD SCOPES

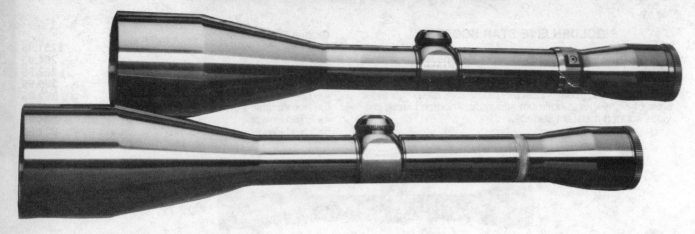

THE ULTIMATE ILLUMINATOR

The first American-made scopes with a 30mm one-piece outer tube and a 56mm adjustable objective. Engineered with quarter-minute positive click adjustments, the Ultimate Illuminator features a European #4 reticle. Comes complete with a set of 30mm steel rings with exclusive Rotary Dovetail System and lens covers.

3x-9x Ultimate 30mm Var. Power $625.95
3x-12x Ultimate 30mm Variable Power
  (European #4 Adj. Obj.) 714.95
3x-12x Ultimate 30mm Variable Power
  (4 Plex Adj. Obj.) 714.95
3x-12x Ultimate 30mm Var. Matte Finish 723.95

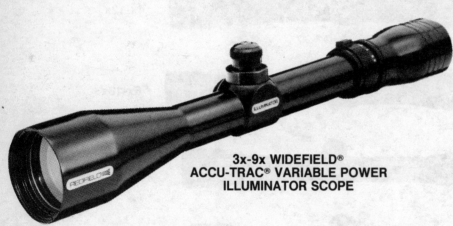

**3x-9x WIDEFIELD®
ACCU-TRAC® VARIABLE POWER
ILLUMINATOR SCOPE**

THE ILLUMINATOR

Every sportsman knows that dawn and dusk are the most productive times to hunt. Game use the cover of darkness for security while feeding, blending in easily with the greens, grays and browns of the outdoors during dim light conditions.

With this new Illuminator series, you can add precious minutes to morning and evening hunting. These scopes actually compensate for the low light, letting you ''see'' contrasts between field and game.

Optimum resolution, contrast, color correction, flatness of field, edge-to-edge sharpness and absolute fidelity are improved by the unique air-spaced, triplet objective, and the advanced 5-element erector lens system.

The Illuminators also feature a zero tolerance nylon cam follower and thrust washers to provide absolute point of impact hold through all power ranges. The one-piece tube construction is virtually indestructible, tested at 1200g acceleration forces, and fog-free through the elimination of potential leak paths.

Offered in both the Traditional and Widefield® variable power configurations, the Illuminator is also available with the Accu-Trac® feature.

Also offered in a 30mm 3x-12x with a 56mm adjustable objective.

ILLUMINATOR SCOPES

4x Widefield Fixed Power
112906 4 Plex   **$382.95**

2x-7x Widefield Variable Power
112910 4 Plex   **$437.95**

3x-9x Traditional Variable Power
123886 3x-9x 4 Plex   **$444.95**

3x-9x Widefield Variable Power
112886 3x-9x 4 Plex   **$493.95**

**3x-9x Widefield Accu-Trac Variable
Power**
112880 3x-9x 4 Plex   **$540.95**

3x9 Widefield Matte Finish
112888   **$501.95**

**3x12 Ultimate Illuminator
Variable Power**
112902 3x12 30mm   **$714.95**

3x-9x Ultimate 30mm Var. Power
112920   **$625.95**

3x-12x Ultimate Var. Power Matte
112908   **$723.95**

REDFIELD SCOPES

THE TRACKER

The Tracker series brings you a superior combination of price and value. It provides the same superb quality, precision and strength of construction found in all Redfield scopes, but at an easily affordable price. Features include the tough, one-piece tube, machined and hand-fitted internal parts, excellent optical quality and traditional Redfield styling.

TRACKER SCOPES

2x-7x Tracker Variable Power
122300 2x-7x 4 Plex $189.95

3x-9x Tracker Variable Power
123300 3x-9x 4 Plex $212.95

4x Tracker Fixed Power
135300 4x 4 Plex $147.95

Matte Finish
122308 2x-7x 4 Plex $199.95
122308 3x-9x 4 Plex   221.95
122308 4x 4 Plex   157.95

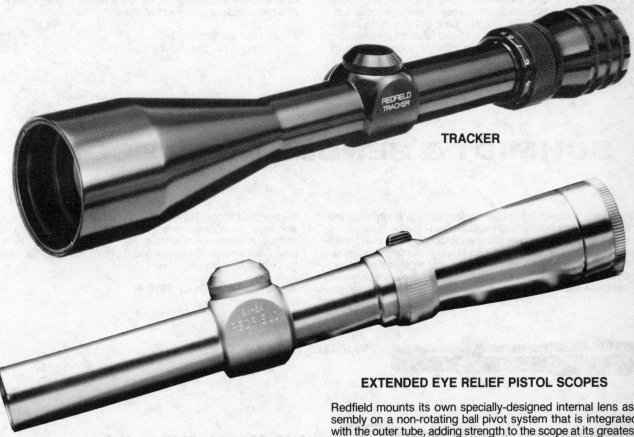

TRACKER

EXTENDED EYE RELIEF PISTOL SCOPES

Redfield mounts its own specially-designed internal lens assembly on a non-rotating ball pivot system that is integrated with the outer tube, adding strength to the scope at its greatest stress point. All pistol scopes feature 1/4-minute click adjustments and 4-plex reticles. A nickel-plated finish is available to match stainless steel pistols and comes in three lengths.

Prices:

2½X **Pistol** Fixed Power $208.95
    Same as above in nickel plate 222.95
4X **Pistol** Fixed Power 221.95
    Same as above in nickel plate 235.95
2X-6X **Pistol** Variable Power 264.95
    Same as above in nickel plate 282.95

SAKO SCOPE MOUNTS

Weighing less than 3 ounces, these new Sako scope mounts are lighter, yet stronger than ever. Tempered steel allows the paring of every last gram of unnecessary weight without sacrificing strength. Like the original mount, these rings clamp directly to the tapered dovetails on Sako rifles, thus eliminating the need for separate bases and screws. Annular grooves inside the rings preclude scope slippage even under the recoil of the heaviest calibers. Nicely streamlined and finished in a rich blue-black to complement any Sako rifle.

Price: Low, medium, or high **$44.50**
Engraved (low, medium, high) **51.25**

SCHMIDT & BENDER RIFLE SCOPES

These fine Schmidt & Bender rifle scopes offer brightness and resolution, color fidelity, and excellent field-of-view. Each model comes with a 30-year guarantee and incorporates the essential ingredients every hunter looks for in rough hunting conditions: recoil-proof, centered reticles; dust and moisture-proof assembly (nitrogen-filled), and precise click adjustments. To guarantee that its scopes will stand up to the most severe hunting conditions, Schmidt & Bender subjects them to vibration tests exceeding the demands of the most powerful cartridges, environmental tests from −40° F to + 122° F, and heavy rain testing. All variable scopes have 30mm center tubes; all fixed power scopes have 1″ tubes.

Also available: 4-12x42: **$650.00**

VARIABLE POWER SCOPE 1¼-4x20
$550.00

VARIABLE POWER SCOPE 1½-6x42
$595.00 (Sniper $925.00)

VARIABLE POWER SCOPE 2½-10x56
$695.00

SCHMIDT & BENDER

FIXED POWER SCOPE 1¹/₂x15
(steel tube w/o mounting rail)
$395.00

FIXED POWER SCOPE 4x36
(steel tube w/o mounting rail)
$450.00

FIXED POWER SCOPE 6x42
(steel tube w/o mounting rail)
$495.00

FIXED POWER SCOPE 12x42
(steel tube w/o mounting rail)
$565.00

FIXED POWER SCOPE 8x56
(steel tube w/o mounting rail)
$525.00

SIMMONS SCOPES

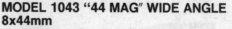

GOLD MEDAL SERIES
MODEL 1044

GOLD MEDAL RIFLESCOPE SERIES

MODEL 1042 "44 MAG" WIDE ANGLE
6x44mm

Field of view: 22.5′
Eye relief: 3.0″
Weight: 14.5 oz.
Price: $220.95

GOLD MEDAL PRESIDENTIAL SERIES

Features "SIMCOAT" multi-coating on all lenses . . . 360°
Wide-angle . . . 44mm Objective lens . . . Anodized high gloss
finish . . . Speed focusing . . . ¼-minute click adjustments

MODEL 1043 "44 MAG" WIDE ANGLE
8x44mm

Field of view: 22.5′
Eye relief: 3.0″
Weight: 14.5 oz.
Price: $220.95

MODEL 1044 "44 MAG" WIDE ANGLE
3-10x44mm

Field of view: 36.2-10.5′
Eye relief: 3.4″ -3.3″
Weight: 16.3 oz.
Price: $273.95

Also available:
Model 1066 (2-7x44mm) $335.95
Model 1067 (3-9x44mm) 360.95
Model 1068 (4-12x44mm) 368.95
Model 1069 (6.5-20x44mm) 392.95

#1066

#1068

#1067

#1069

RIFLESCOPE RINGS

Low 1″ Set **Model 1401** $11.95
Medium 1″ Set **Model 1403** 11.95
High 1″ Set **Model 1404** 11.95
1″ See-Thru Set **Model 1405** 13.95
1″ Rings for 22 Grooved Receiver **Model 1406** 11.95
1″ Rings extention for Compact Scopes
   Model 1409 . . . . 19.95
22 Deluxe Rings for Grooved receivers
   Model 1408 . . . . 14.95

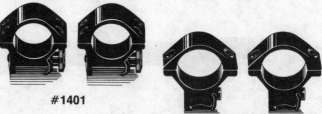

#1401

#1406

#1403

#1409

SIMMONS SCOPES

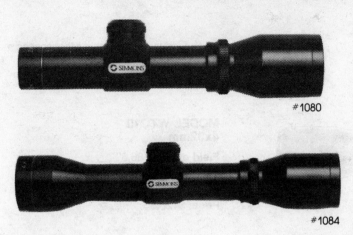

#1080

#1084

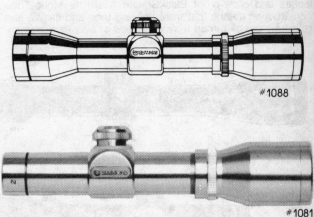

#1088

#1081

SILVER MEDAL PISTOLSCOPE SERIES

Fixed power, variable power and silhouette models are all available in this series in traditional blue or silver finish with multi-coated lenses and one-1/2 piece tubes (to withstand shock of magnum calibers).

Model 1080 2x20	....	**$135.95**
Model 1081 10x20 Polished Alum.	....	135.95
Model 1084 4x32	....	190.95
Model 1088 4x32 Polished Alum.	....	190.95
Model 1089 7x32 w/Adj. Obj. & Tar. Tur.	....	243.95

#1025

#1027

SILVER MEDAL RIFLESCOPE SERIES
QUAD VARIABLES

Model 1023 4x40 Wide Angle	....	**$151.95**
Model 1025 6x40 Wide Angle	....	153.95
Model 1027 2-7x32	....	148.95
Model 1029 3-9x40 Wide Angle	....	170.95
Model 1030 3-9x32 Polished Alum.	....	157.95

#1029

SIMMONS SCOPES

WHITETAIL CLASSIC RIFLESCOPES

Simmons' new Whitetail Classic Series features fully coated lenses and glare-proof BlackGranite finish. Its Mono-Tube construction means that front bell and tube and saddle and rear tube are all turned from one piece of aircraft aluminum.

This system eliminates 3 to 5 joints found in most other scopes in use today. The Whitetail Classic is therefore up to 400 times stronger than comparably priced scopes.

\# WTC10

MODEL WTC10
4x32mm

Field of view: 36.8′
Eye relief: 4″
Length: 12.3″
Weight: 9.8 oz.
Price: $128.95

\# WTC11

MODEL WTC11
1.5-5x20mm

Field of view: 25′-23′
Eye relief: 3.4″
Length: 12 1/2″
Weight: 11.8 oz.
Price: $151.95

\# WTC12

MODEL WTC12
2.5-8x36mm

Field of view: 46.5′-14.5′
Eye relief: 3.1″
Length: 12.6″
Weight: 12.8 oz.
Price: $159.95

\# WTC13

MODEL WTC13
3.5-10x40mm

Field of view: 34′-11.5′
Eye relief: 3.2″
Length: 12.4″
Weight: 12.8 oz.
Price: $173.95

WHITETAIL SERIES

MODEL WT03
3-9x40mm

MODEL WT01

Magnification: 4x32mm
Field of view: 36′ at 100 yds.
Eye relief: 3.7′
Weight: 9.1 oz.
Length: 12″
Price: $89.95

MODEL WT02

Magnification: 3-9x32mm
Field of view: 37′-12.7′ at 100 yds.
Eye relief: 3.1″-2.9″
Weight: 12.8 oz.
Length: 12.8″
Price: $112.95

MODEL WT03

Magnification: 3-9x40mm
Field of view: 37′-12.7′ at 100 yds.
Eye relief: 3.1″-2.9″
Weight: 14.2 oz.
Length: 12.8″
Price: $130.95

SWAROVSKI

HABICHT NOVA TELESCOPIC SIGHTS

These fine Austrian-made sights feature brilliant optics with high-quality lens coating and optimal sighting under poor light and weather conditions. The Nova ocular system with telescope recoil damping reduces the danger of injury, especially with shots aimed in an upward direction. The main tube is selectable in steel or light metal construction. Because of Nova's centered reticle, the aiming mark remains in the center of the field of view regardless of corrections of the impact point. See **Specifications** table on the following page.

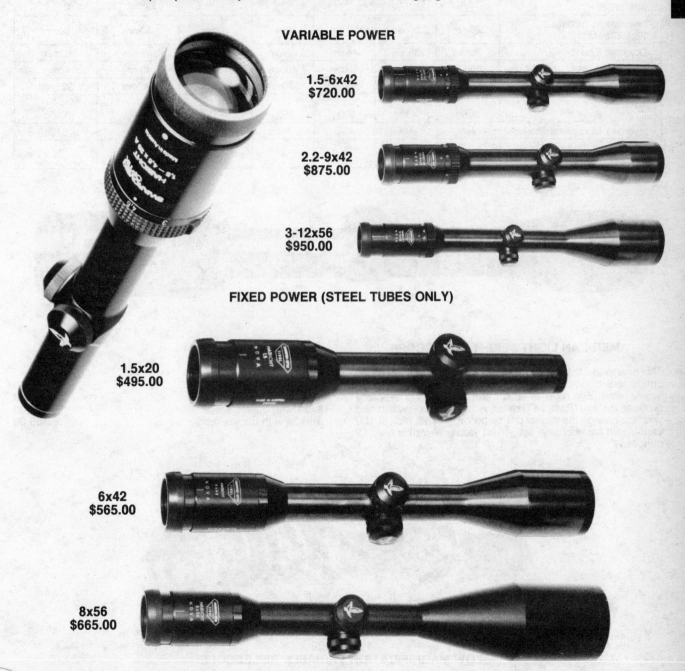

VARIABLE POWER

1.5-6x42
$720.00

2.2-9x42
$875.00

3-12x56
$950.00

FIXED POWER (STEEL TUBES ONLY)

1.5x20
$495.00

6x42
$565.00

8x56
$665.00

SWAROVSKI

SPECIFICATIONS

Telescopic Sights	1.5x20	4x32	6x42	8x56	1.5-6x42	2.2-9x42	3-12x56
Magnification	1.5x	4x	6x	8x	1.5-6x	2.2-9x	3-12x
Max. effective objective dia.	20mm	32mm	42mm	56mm	42mm	42mm	56mm
Exit pupil dia.	12.7mm	8mm	7mm	7mm	14.3-7mm	14.3-4.7mm	14.3-4.7mm
Field of view at 100m	18.5m	10m	7m	5.2m	18.5-6.5m	12-4.5m	9-3.3m
Twilight effective factor (DIN 58388)	4.2	11.3	15.9	21.1	4.2-15.9	6.2-19.4	8.5-25.9
Intermediary tube dia. Steel-Standard	26mm	26mm	26mm	26mm	30mm	30mm	30mm
Objective tube dia.	26mm	38mm	48mm	62mm	48mm	48mm	62mm
Ocular tube dia.	40mm	40mm	40mm	40mm	40mm	40mm	40mm
Scope length	247mm	290mm	322mm	370mm	322mm	342mm	391mm
Weight　　　　Steel	360g	430g	500g	660g	570g	580g	710g
(approx.)　Light metal with rail	NA	NA	NA	NA	480g	470g	540g
A change of the impact point per click in mm/100m	12	7	6	4	9	6	4

AMERICAN LIGHTWEIGHT RIFLESCOPE

This new model features precision ground, coated and aligned optics sealed in a special aluminum alloy tube to withstand heavy recoil. Eye relief is 85mm and the recoiling eyepiece protects the eye. Positive click adjustments for elevation and windage change the impact point (approx. 1/4") per click at 100 yards, with parallax also set at 100 yards. Weight is only 13 ounces.

Prices:
1.5-4.5x20 . . . . **$525.00**
4x32 with duplex reticle **420.00**
6x36 with duplex reticle **450.00**
3-9x36 with duplex reticle **565.00**

1.5-4.5x20
LOW MAGNIFICATION VARIABLE RIFLESCOPE

TASCO SCOPES

MODEL WA1.35×20

WORLD CLASS WIDE ANGLE® RIFLESCOPES

Features:
- 25% larger field of view
- Exceptional optics
- Fully coated for maximum light transmission
- Waterproof, shockproof, fog-proof
- Non-removable eye bell
- Free haze filter lens caps
- TASCO's unique World Class Lifetime Warranty

This member of Tasco's World Class Wide Angle line offers a wide field of view—115 feet at 1X and 31 feet at 3.5X—and quick sighting without depending on a critical view. The scope is ideal for hunting deer and dangerous game, especially in close quarters or in heavily wooded and poorly lit areas. Other features include 1/2-minute positive click stops, fully coated lenses (including Supercon process), nonremovable eyebell and windage/elevation screws. Length is 9³⁄₄″, with 1″ diameter tube. Weight is 10.5 ounces.

MODEL WA39×40

WIDE ANGLE VARIABLE ZOOM RIFLESCOPES (ALL WATERPROOF)

MODEL NO.	DESCRIPTION	RETICLE	PRICE
WA13.5×20	1X-3.5X Zoom (20mm)	Wide Angle 30/30	$196.00
WA39X40TV	3X-9X (40mm)	Wide Angle 30/30	176.00
WA4×40	4X (40mm)	Wide Angle 30/30	144.00
WA6×40	6X (40mm)	Wide Angle 30/30	152.00
WA1.755×20	1.75X-5X Zoom (20mm)	Wide Angle 30/30	205.00
WA27×32	2X-7X Zoom (32mm)	Wide Angle 30/30	188.00
WA39×32	3X-9X Zoom (32mm)	Wide Angle 30/30	168.00
WA39×40	3X-9X Zoom (40mm)	Wide Angle 30/30	176.00
CW28×32	2X-8X (32mm)	Wide Angle 30/30	188.00
CW4×32	4X (32mm)	Wide Angle 30/30	148.00
ER39×40WA	3X-9X 40m Electronic Reticle	Wide Angle 30/30 Electronic Red	344.00

TASCO SCOPES

**RIMFIRE RIFLESCOPE
FOR 22's WITH 22 RING MOUNTS**

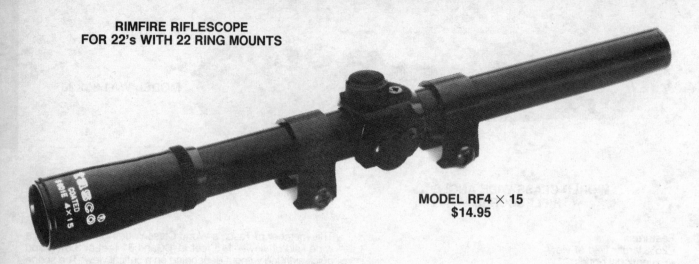

**MODEL RF4 × 15
$14.95**

SPECIFICATIONS

Model	Power	Objective Diameter	Finish	Reticle	Field of View @ 100 yards	Eye Relief	Tube Diam.	Scope Length	Scope Weight	Price
RF4X15	4	15mm	Black	Cross Hair	21'	2½"	¾"	11"	4 oz.	**$14.80**
RF4X32V	4	32mm	Black	30/30	31'	3"	1"	12¼"	12.6 oz.	76.80
RF4X20DS	4	20mm	Dull Satin	Cross Hair	20'	2½"	¾"	10½"	3.8 oz.	23.20
RF37X20	3-7	20mm	Black	30/30	24'-11'	2½"	¾"	11½"	5.7 oz.	39.20
P1.5X15	1.5	15mm	Black	Cross Hair	22½'	9½"-20¾"	¾"	8¾"	3.25 oz.	29.60

TRAJECTORY-RANGE FINDING RIFLESCOPE

All Tasco TR Scopes have fully coated optics, Opti-Centered® stadia reticle, ¼-minute positive click stops and haze filter caps. All are fog-proof, shockproof, waterproof and anodized.

MODEL NO.	DESCRIPTION	RETICLE	PRICE
TR39X40WA	3X-9X Zoom (40mm) Wide Angle	30/30 RF	**$208.00**
TR416X40	4X-16X Zoom (40mm)	30/30 RF	224.00
TR624X40	6X-24X Zoom (40mm)	30/30 RF	256.00

TASCO SCOPES

PRO-POINT MULTI-PURPOSE SCOPES

Tasco's Pro-Point is a true 1X-30 mm scope with electronic red dot reticle that features unlimited eye relief, enabling shooters to shoot with both eyes open. It is now available with a 3X booster, plus a special, open T-shaped electronic reticle with a dot in the center, making it ideal for fast-action pistol competition and bull's eye marksmanship. It also has application for rifle, shotgun, bow and black powder. The new compact version (PDP2) houses a lithium battery pack, making it 1¼ inches narrower than previous models and lighter as well (5.5 oz.). A mercury battery converter is provided for those who prefer standard batteries.

Tasco's new 3X booster with crosshair reticle weighs 6.1 oz. and is 5½ inches long. Model PB2 fits the new PDP2/ PDP2MA, and because both units include separate windage and elevation systems the electronic red dot is movable within the crosshair. That means it can be set for two different distances, making it the ultimate rangefinder. Another 3X booster—the PB1—has no crosshairs and fits all other Pro-Point models. Specifications and prices are listed below.

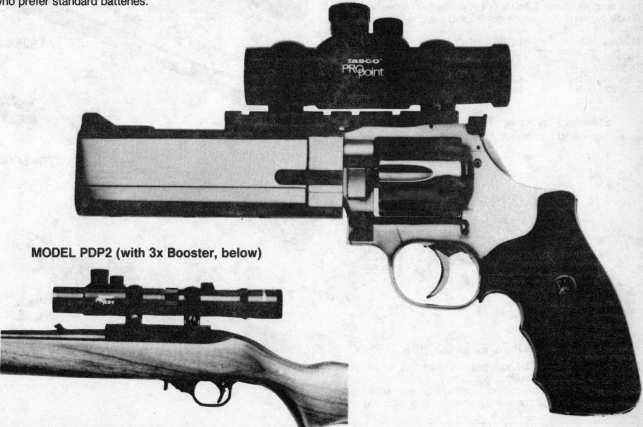

MODEL PDP2 (with 3x Booster, below)

SPECIFICATIONS PROPOINT SCOPES

Model	Power	Objective Diameter	Finish	Reticle	Field of View @ 100 Yds.	Eye Relief	Tube Diam.	Scope Length	Scope Weight	Prices
PDP2	1X	25mm	Matte Black	Illum. Red Dot	40'	Unltd.	30mm	5"	5.5 oz.	$280.00
PDP2MA	1X	25mm	Matte Alum.	Illum. Red Dot	40'	Unltd.	30mm	5"	5.5 oz.	280.00
PDP2T3	1X	25mm	Matte Black	Illum. T-3 Red Dot	40'	Unltd.	30mm	5"	5.5 oz.	280.00
PB1	3X Power Booster	13mm	Matte Black	No reticle	For use with all models of ProPoint			5.5"	6.3 oz.	160.00
PB2	3X Power Booster	13mm	Matte Black	Cross Hair	For use with PDP2 only			5.5"	6.1 oz.	160.00

TASCO TS® SCOPES

For silhouette and target shooting, Tasco's TS® scopes adjust for varying long-range targets, with 1/8-minute Positrac® micrometer windage and elevation adjustments. All TS® scopes are waterproof, fog-proof, shockproof, fully Supercon-coated, and include screw-in metal lens protectors. All include two metal mirage deflection and sunshade hoods, five and eight inches in length, which can be used separately or together to eliminate image distortion resulting from excessive barrel temperatures or to shade the objective lens from direct sunlight. All include a focusing objective for precise parallax correction and extra-large 44mm objective lenses for extra brightness at high magnifications. Each scope is available in a choice of two reticle patterns: 3/4-minute dot (A) and fine crosshair (B).

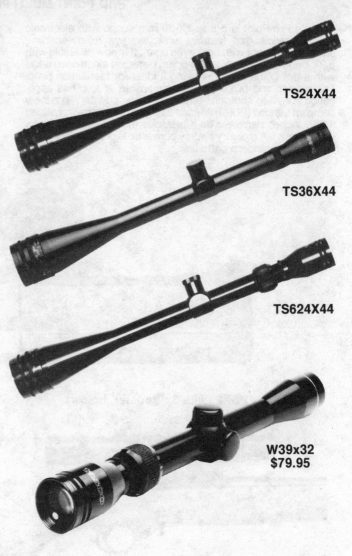

TS24X44

TS36X44

TS624X44

MODEL NO.	DESCRIPTION	PRICE
TS24X44A,B	24X (44mm)	$320.00
TS36X44A,B	36X (44mm)	352.00
TS624X44A,B	6X-24X Zoom (44mm)	392.00
TS832X44A,B	8X-32X (44 mm)	432.00

Standard features: Two mirage deflection and sunshine hoods (3″ and 5″)

W4x32
$59.95

W39x32
$79.95

TRADITIONAL RIFLESCOPES

Tasco's waterproof riflescopes can endure rain, snow, heat, dust, sand and altitude changes. They feature fully coated optics, non-removable eye bell, 1/4 minute positive click stops, Opti-Centered 30/30 rangefinding reticle, haze filter caps.

Model	Power	Objective Diameter	Finish	Reticle	Field of View @ 100 yards	Eye Relief	Tube Diam.	Scope Length	Scope Weight	Prices
W4X32V	4X	32mm	Black	30/30	32′	3″	1″	12″	12.5 oz.	$ 67.20
*W4X32TV	4X	32mm	Black	30/30TV	35′	3″	1″	13″	12.7 oz.	67.20
W4X40V	4X	40mm	Black	30/30	32′	3″	1″	12″	12.5 oz.	92.00
W6X40V	6X	40mm	Black	30/30	30′	3″	1″	12.5″	11.5 oz.	100.00
W39X32V	3X-9X	32mm	Black	30/30	39′-13′	3″	1″	13.25″	12.2 oz.	86.40
W39X32TV	3X-9X	32mm	Black	30/30TV	39-13′	3″	1″	13.25″	12.2 oz.	86.40
W39X40V	3X-9X	40mm	Black	30/30	29′-13′	3″	1″	12.5″	13 oz.	112.00

* New for 1990

TASCO PISTOL SCOPES

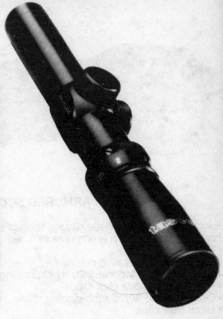

PRO-CLASS PISTOL SCOPES

Model	Power	Objective Diameter	Finish	Reticle	Field of View @ 100 Yds.	Eye Relief	Tube Diam.	Scope Length	Scope Weight	Price
P1X22S	1X	22mm	Dull Satin	GTD	43'-22'	8-28"	30mm	6.5"	7.7 oz.	$160.00
P1X22S/A	1X	22mm	Dull Satin	30/30	43'-22'	8-28"	30mm	6.5"	7.7 oz.	160.00
P1.254X22	1.25X-4X	22mm	Dull Satin	30/30	23'-9'	12-28"	30mm	9.25"	9.5 oz.	256.00
P2X22S	2X	22mm	Dull Satin	GTD	23'-18'	10-24"	30mm	6.5"	7.7 oz.	160.00
P2X22S/A	2X	22mm	Dull Satin	30/30	23'-18'	10-24"	30mm	6.5"	7.7 oz.	160.00
P3X22	3X	22mm	Dull Satin	GTD	13'-6'	12-24"	30mm	8.25"	8.5 oz.	160.00
P3X22S/A	3X	22mm	Dull Satin	30/30	13'-6'	12-24"	30mm	8.25"	8.5 oz.	160.00
P3X22SMA	3X	22mm	Matte Alum.	GTD	13'-6'	12-24"	30mm	8.25"	8.5 oz.	160.00
P3X22SMA/A	3X	22mm	Matte Alum.	30/30	13'-6'	12-24"	30mm	8.25"	8.5 oz.	160.00
P4X30	4X	30mm	Dull Satin	GTD	7'-6'	12-24"	30mm	9.75"	12.1 oz.	216.00
P4X30/A	4X	30mm	Dull Satin	30/30	7'-6'	12-24"	30mm	9.75"	12.1 oz.	216.00
P4X30MA	4X	30mm	Matte Alum.	GTD	7'-6'	12-24"	30mm	9.75"	12.1 oz.	216.00
P4X30MA/A	4X	30mm	Matte Alum.	30/30	7'-6'	12-24"	30mm	9.75"	12.1 oz.	216.00
P6X40	6X	40mm	Dull Satin	GTD	5.2'-5.5'	12-23"	30mm	11"	14.5 oz.	216.00
P6X40/A	6X	40mm	Dull Satin	30/30	5.2'-5.5'	12-23"	30mm	11"	14.5 oz.	216.00
ER2X22P	2X	22mm	Dull Satin	30/30ER	25'-15'	8-20"	30mm	8.75"	9.4 oz.	304.00
ER4X30	4X	30mm	Dull Satin	30/30ER	7'-6'	12-24"	30mm	9.75"	12 oz.	344.00

TASCO PISTOL SCOPES

RUBBER ARMORED SCOPES

Extra padding helps these rugged scopes stand up to rough handling. Custom-fitting rings are included. Scopes feature:
- Fully coated optics
- Windage and elevation controls
- Waterproofing, fogproofing, shockproofing
- 1/4-minute positive click stops
- Opti-centered 30/30 rangefinding reticle
- Haze filter caps

Model	Power	Objective Diameter	Finish	Reticle	Field of View @ 100 Yards	Eye Relief	Tube Diam.	Scope Length	Scope Weight	Price
RC4X40A,B	4	40mm	Green Rubber	30/30	27'	3 1/4"	1"	12 1/2"	14.2 oz.	**136.00**
RC39X40A,B	3-9	40mm	Green Rubber	30/30	35'-14'	3 1/4"	1"	12 5/8"	14.3 oz.	**164.00**

"A" fits standard dove tail base.
"B" fits 3/8" grooved receivers—most 22 cal. and airguns.

MAG IV RIFLESCOPES

MAG IV scopes yield four times magnification range in a standard size riflescope and one-third more zooming range than most variable scopes. Features include: Fully coated optics and large objective lens to keep target in low light . . . Nonremovable eye bell. . . 1/4-minute positive click stops . . . Nonremovable windage and elevation screws. . . Opti-centered 30/30 rangefinding reticle . . . Waterproof, fogproof, shockproof.

SPECIFICATIONS

Model	Power	Objective Diameter	Finish	Reticle	Field of View @ 100 Yds.	Eye Relief	Tube Diam.	Scope Length	Scope Weight	Price
W312X40	3-12	40mm	Black	30/30	35'-9'	3 1/8"	1"	12 3/16"	12 oz.	$136.00
W416X40†	4-16	40mm	Black	30/30	26'-6'	3 1/8"	1"	14 1/8"	15.6 oz.	176.00
W624X40†	6-24	40mm	Black	30/30	17'-4'	3"	1"	15 3/8"	16.75 oz.	232.00

† Indicates focusing objective.

TASCO

TASCO TITAN RIFLESCOPES

Tasco's new Titan riflescope features image brightness and clarity, true multi-coating, strength and rigidity, lightweight aluminum with the strength of steel, and a 30mm tube diameter. It also includes fast focus, reticle center indicator, finger adjustable windage and elevation, titanium parts, special reticle design (located in the first image plane), and a 42mm objective lens. In addition, it offers one-piece body construction, individual serial number, special lubrication, extra wide field of view and maximum eye relief. Specifications and prices are listed below.

Model	Power	Objective Diameter	Finish	Reticle	Field of View @ 100 Yds.	Eye Relief	Tube Diam.	Scope Length	Scope Weight	Price
TT1.56X42	1.5X-6X	42mm	Black	Titan Quad	59'-20'	3.5"	30mm	12"	16.4 oz.	$528.00
TT156X42DS	1.5X-6X	42mm	Dull Satin	Titan Quad	59'-20'	3.5"	30mm	12"	16.4 oz.	528.00
TT39X42DS	3X-9X	42mm	Dull Satin	Titan Quad	37'-13'	5-4"	30mm	12.5"	16.8 oz.	480.00
TT39X42	3X-9X	42mm	Black	Titan Quad	37'-13'	5-4"	30mm	12.5"	16.8 oz.	480.00

TASCO

SHOTGUN SCOPES & MOUNTS

For shotgun slug or buckshot shooters, Tasco offers a combination of scopes and mounts engineered to fit Remington, Mossberg and other popular shotguns. These scopes emphasize low magnification power and the widest possible field of view. The SG2.5X32, for example, offers a generous 42' wide field of view at 100 yards for spotting game easily in dense cover. This scope also features its own built-in precision mount designed to fit any shotgun without drilling. Specifications and prices are listed in the table below.

Model	Power	Objective Diameter	Finish	Reticle	Field of View @ 100 Yds.	Eye Relief	Tube Diam.	Scope Length	Scope Weight	Prices
WA1.755X20	1.75X-5X	20mm	Black	30/30	72'-24'	3"	1"	10.5"	10 oz.	$205.60
WA13.5X20	1X-3.5X	20mm	Black	30/30	103'-31'	3"	1"	9"	12 oz.	196.00
*SG2.5X32	2.5X	32mm	Black	30/30	42'	3"	1"	12.25"	12 oz.	104.00
SGPD1	1X	25mm	Black Matte	Red Dot	40'	UNLTD.	30mm	5"	8.75 oz.	304.00
SGPD2	1X	25mm	Black Matte	Red Dot	40'	UNLTD.	30mm	5"	8.75 oz.	304.00

* SG2.5X32 is WS2.5X32 with 885SGM. SGPD1 fits Remington 870, 1100, 1187, SGPD2 fits Mossberg 500.

Model	Application	Model	Application	Prices
885SGMC	Remington 870/1100/1187	888SGMC	Mossberg 500	$32.00
886SGMC	Browning A5	889SGMC	Savage 67	32.00
887SGMC	Winchester Ranger			32.00

MAG IV-44
$224.00

MAG IV-44 (2.5X-10X44mm)

The 44mm objective lens in this scope lets in 10% more light than standard 40mm lenses. Tasco's "Supercon" multi-layered lens coating and fully coated optics provide additional brightness and clarity.

THOMPSON/CENTER

T/C RECOIL PROOF SCOPES

Thompson/Center's new line of Recoil Proof Pistol and Rifle Scopes features lighted duplex reticles, including 9 models for pistols and 4 for rifles. The lighted duplex reticles include an off-on switch which acts as a rheostat, allowing the shooter to control the intensity of the lighted reticle. These help shooters achieve precise crosshair placement on game during prime hunting hours at dusk or dawn.

STANDARD RETICLES

2.5x Pistol Scope w/Rail Mount
$146.25

2.5X-7X Pistol Scope (Black)
$227.60

2.5X-7X Pistol Scope (Silver)
$238.50 ($227.60 Black)

LIGHTED RETICLES

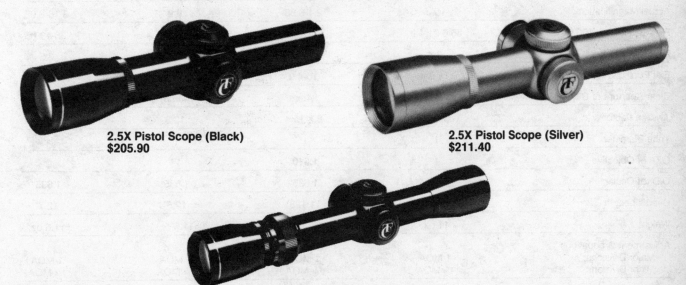

2.5X Pistol Scope (Black)
$205.90

2.5X Pistol Scope (Silver)
$211.40

2.5X-7X Pistol Scope (Black)
$265.50

WEATHERBY SUPREME SCOPES

WEATHERBY SUPREME SCOPES

As every hunter knows, one of the most difficult problems is keeping running game in the field of view of the scope. Once lost, precious seconds fade away trying to find the animal in the scope again. Too much time wasted means the ultimate frustration. No second shot. Or no shot at all. The Weatherby Wide Field helps you surmount the problem by increasing your field of view.

FEATURES:

Optical excellence—now protected with multicoated anti-glare coating. • Fog-free and waterproof construction. • Constantly self-centered reticles. • Non-magnifying reticle. • 1/4" adjustments. • Quick variable power change. • Unique luminous reticle. • Neoprene eyepiece. • Binocular-type speed focusing. • Rugged score tube construction. Autocom point-blank system.

4 POWER

These are fixed-power scopes for big game and varmint hunting. Bright, clear image. Multicoated lenses for maximum luminosity under adverse conditions. 32-foot field of view at 100 yards.

3 TO 9 POWER

The most desirable variable for every kind of shooting from target to long-range big game. Outstanding light-gathering power. Fast, convenient focusing adjustment.

1 3/4 TO 5 POWER

A popular model for close-range hunting with large-bore rifles. Includes the Autocom system, which automatically compensates for trajectory and eliminates the need for range-finding without making elevation adjustments. Just aim and shoot!

Fixed Power:	PRICES
4 × 44	$300.00

Variable Power:	
1.75-5 × 20	290.00
2-7 × 34	300.00
3-9 × 44	350.00

SUPREME RIFLESCOPES SPECIFICATIONS

Item	1.75-5X20	2-7X34	4X44	3-9X44
Actual Magnification	1.7-5	2.1-6.83	3.9	3.15-8.98
Field of View @ 100 yards	66.6-21.4 ft.	59-16 ft.	32 ft.	36-13 ft.
Eye Relief (inches)	3.4	3.4	3.0	3.5
Exit Pupil dia. in mm	11.9-4	10-4.9	10	10-4.9
Clear Aperture of Objective	20mm	34mm	44mm	44mm
Twilight Factor	5.9-10	8.2-15.4	13.3	11.5-19.9
Tube Diameter	1″	1″	1″	1″
O.D. of Objective	1″	1.610″	2″	2″
O.D. of Ocular	1.635″	1.635″	1.635″	1.635″
Overall Length	10.7″	11.125″	12.5″	12.7″
Weight	11 oz.	10.4 oz.	11.6 oz.	11.6 oz.
Adjustment Graduations Major Divisions: Minor Divisions:	1 MOA 1/4 MOA	1 MOA 1/4 MOA	1 MOA 1/4 MOA	1 MOA 1/4 MOA
Maximum Adjustment (W&E)	60″	60″	60″	60″
Reticles Available	LUMIPLEX	LUMIPLEX	LUMIPLEX	LUMIPLEX

WEAVER SCOPES

MODEL V9
3x-9x38 Variable Hunting Scope
$167.42

MODEL K4
4x38 Fixed Power Hunting Scope
$128.33

MODEL V3
1x-3x20 Variable Hunting Scope
$155.17

MODEL K2.5
2.5x20 Fixed Power Hunting Scope
$118.31

MODEL K6
6x38 Fixed Power Hunting Scope
$139.77

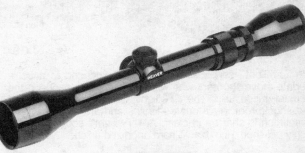

MODEL RV7
2x-7x32 Rimfire Variable Scope
$131.95

MODEL V10
2x-10x38 Variable All-Purpose Scope
$177.80

MODEL RK4
4x32 Rimfire Fixed Power Scope
$108.62

Also available:
MODEL KT 15. 15x42 Target Silhouette Scope. **$280.00**

WILLIAMS TWILIGHT SCOPES

1.5x-5x (and 2x-6x): $196.30

2¹/₂x: $138.95

4x: $145.25

3x-9x: $206.30

The "Twilight" series of scopes was introduced to accommodate those shooters who want a high-quality scope in the medium-priced field. The "Twilight" scopes are waterproof and shockproof, have coated lenses and are nitrogen-filled. Resolution is sharp and clear. All "Twilight" scopes have a highly polished, rich, black, hard anodized finish.

There are five models available: the 2¹/₂x, the 4x, the 1.5x-5x, the 2x-6x, and the 3x-9x. They are available in T-N-T reticle only (which stands for "thick and thin").

OPTICAL SPECIFICATIONS	2.5X	4X	1.5X-5X		2X-6X		3X-9X	
			At 1.5X	At 5X	At 2X	At 6X	At 3X	At 9X
Clear aperture of objective lens	20mm	32mm	20mm	Same	32mm	Same	40mm	Same
Clear aperture of ocular lens	32mm	32mm	32mm	Same	32mm	Same	32mm	Same
Exit Pupil	8mm	8mm	13.3mm	4mm	16mm	5.3mm	13.3mm	44.4mm
Relative Brightness	64	64	177	16	256	28	161.2	17.6
Field of view (degree of angle)	6°10′	5°30′	11°	4°	8°30′	3°10′	7°	2°20′
Field of view at 100 yards	32′	29′	57³/₄′	21′	45¹/₂′	16³/₄′	36¹/₂′	12³/₄′
Eye Relief	3.7″	3.6″	3.5″	3.5″	3″	3″	3.1″	2.9″
Parallax Correction (at)	50 yds.	100 yds.	100 yds.	Same	100 yds.	Same	100 yds.	Same
Lens Construction	9	9	10	Same	11	Same	11	Same
MECHANICAL SPECIFICATIONS								
Outside diameter of objective end . .	1.00″	1.525″	1.00″	Same	1.525″	Same	1.850″	1.850″
Outside diameter of ocular end	1.455″	1.455″	1.455″	Same	1.455″	Same	1.455″	Same
Ouside diameter of tube	1″	1″	1″	Same	1″	Same	1″	Same
Internal adjustment graduation	¹/₄ min.	¹/₄ min.	¹/₄ min.	Same	¹/₄ min.	Same	¹/₄ min.	Same
Minimum internal adjustment	75 min.	75 min.	75 min.	Same	75 min.	Same	60 min.	Same
Finish			Glossy Hard Black Anodized					
Length	10″	11³/₄″	10³/₄″	Same	11¹/₂″	11¹/₂″	12³/₄″	12³/₄″
Weight	8¹/₂ oz.	9¹/₂ oz.	10 oz.	Same	11¹/₂ oz.	Same	13¹/₂ oz.	Same

WILLIAMS SIGHT-OVER-SCOPE

**S-O-S
(SIGHT-OVER-SCOPE)
MOUNTING SYSTEMS
Shown on a Marlin Model 336**

MODELS	S-O-S FRONT	S-O-S REAR
Remington Models 760-740-742, and Savage Model 170	1	2
Browning A-Bolt	3	3
Winchester Models 70 Standard, 670 & 770	4***	3
*1917 Enfield and Sauer 200	4***	4***
Remington Models 700-721-722-725-700, L.H. and 40X; Weatherby MK-V and Vanguard; Ruger 77ST; and Howa 1500	4***	5
Savage Models 110, 111 and 112V	4***	16
Winchester Models 88 and 100	6	6
Browning BAR Auto and BLR Lever	7	7
Marlin Models 336, 1894 & 1894C	8	8
Remington Model 788	9	9
Thompson/Center 45 & 50 Cal. Hawken and 54 Cal. Renegade	10**	10**
Remington 541-S. Also, Remington Models 580-581-582 (require drilling & tapping)	11	11
Ruger Model 44	11	12
Ruger Model 10/22	13	12
Browning Safari Bolt and Mark X	14	15
Ithaca LSA-55 and LSA-65 Bolt	16	16
Rem. Models Four, Six, 7400 and 7600	17	18
Savage Model 99	19	20**
Winchester Model 94 Angle Eject	21	22**

*With the rear receiver radiused the same diameter as the front receiver ring.
**Requires sub-block
***New long extension-style Streamline top mount base No. 4 for use when installing many of the newer variable scopes with shorter 1″ tubes on rifles with long actions for proper fit and eye relief.

The S-O-S System (on a Ruger 10/22)

S-O-S Kit Complete for Williams Rings	**$47.00**
S-O-S Streamline Set (except w/sub-block)	**54.15**
S-O-S Streamline Set 10 & 10	**61.75**
S-O-S Streamline Set 19 & 20, 21 & 22	**56.55**

This concept in sighting known as the S-O-S (Sight-Over-Scope) allows the scope to be mounted low and permits instant use of open sight for quick, fast action shots at close range. The compact S-O-S has both elevation and windage in the rear sight, and the front sight has additional windage.

The "Guide-Line" S-O-S ring top kit will work with all Williams mounts having the two-piece 1-inch rings. The sights are made from an aluminum alloy. They are rustproof and attractively anodized.

The S-O-S front sight is furnished with a fluorescent orange 3/32-inch bead (white or gold is optional.) The S-O-S rear sight is furnished with the WGRS-M/L Guide Receiver Sight with the regular 3/8 X .125 Buckbuster long shank aperture. (Twilight or Regular apertures in the 3/8 X .093 and 3/8 X .050 are optional.) Specify the long shank aperture to fit the WGRS receiver sight.

WILLIAMS

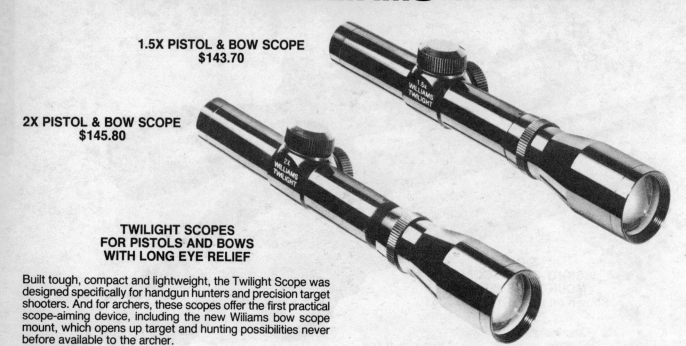

1.5X PISTOL & BOW SCOPE
$143.70

2X PISTOL & BOW SCOPE
$145.80

TWILIGHT SCOPES
FOR PISTOLS AND BOWS
WITH LONG EYE RELIEF

Built tough, compact and lightweight, the Twilight Scope was designed specifically for handgun hunters and precision target shooters. And for archers, these scopes offer the first practical scope-aiming device, including the new Wiliams bow scope mount, which opens up target and hunting possibilities never before available to the archer.

OPTICAL SPECIFICATIONS	1.5X20	2X20
Clear Aperture of Objective Lens	20mm	20mm
Clear Aperture of Ocular Lens	30mm	30mm
Exit Pupil	13.3mm	10mm
Relative Brightness	177	100
Field of View (Degree of Angle)	3°4′	3°20′
Field of View at 100 Yards	19 ft.	17½ ft.
Eye Relief	18″-25″	18″-25″
Parallax Correciton (at)	50 yds.	50 yds.
Lens Construction	6	6

MECHANICAL SPECIFICATIONS	1.5X20	2.20
Outside Diameter of Objective End	1″	1″
Outside Diameter of Ocular End	36.5mm	36.5mm
Outside Diameter of Tube	1″	1″
Internal Adjustment Graduation	1/4″	1/4″
Minimum Internal Adjustment	170″	162″
Finish	Glossy Hard Black Anodized	
Length	209mm	216mm
Weight	6.4 oz.	6.6 oz.

QUICK CONVERTIBLE SIDE MOUNTS

The Williams QC Side Mount permits the shooter to have both scope and iron sight always available for instant use. From the same base, shooter has his choice of rings that place scope directly over the bore or in the offset position.

MOUNTING PLATES:

FOR 30-M1 CARBINE
(Attach with 8-40 fillister screws.) Use the Williams SM-740 side mount base with this mounting plate. Scope can be offset or high over bore. **Price: $12.10**

FOR SMLE NO. 1
(Attach with 8-40 fillister head mounting screws.) This mounting plate is supplied with long 8-40 fillister head screws to replace SM-70 short screws. Use the SM-70 base. Mount can be installed offset or central over bore. **Price: $7.80**

FOR M1 GARAND RIFLE
The mounting screws for this mounting plate are 8-40 × .475 fillister head. Use the Williams SM-740 (4 holes) side mount with this mounting plate. **Price: $12.10**

SM94/36 QUICK CONVERTIBLE
SIDE MOUNT ON 94 WINCHESTER
$51.40

WILLIAMS RECEIVER SIGHTS

TARGET FP RECEIVER SIGHT (HIGH)

TARGET FP RECEIVER SIGHT (LOW)

FP RECEIVER SIGHT MODEL FP-RU77
(Ruger Model 77)

GUIDE RECEIVER SIGHT
(on Ruger Mini-30)

TARGET FP RECEIVER SIGHTS

Available in High or Low sight line models, Target FP receiver sights with proper attaching bases can be attached to most 22-caliber target rifles and many sporter-type rifles as well. In most cases, the High models are recommended on target-type rifles with globe front sights. The Low models are for sporter-type rifles and are compatible with standard sights or the lowest globe-type front sights. **Price: $64.85 (Base only: $10.90).**

FP RECEIVER SIGHTS

Internal micrometer adjustments have positive internal locks. The FP model is made of an alloy with a tensile strength of 85,000 lbs., yet it weighs only 1½ oz. Target knobs are available on all models if desired. FP sights fit more than 100 different guns.

Prices:
FP RECEIVER SIGHT **$47.00**
    With "Twilight" Aperture 49.37
    With Target Knobs 56.90
    With Target Knobs & "Twilight" Aperture 58.37

GUIDE RECEIVER SIGHTS

Features compact, low profile and positive windage and elevation locks. Lightweight, strong, and rustproof. These sights utilize dovetail or existing screws on top of receiver for installation. Made from an aluminum alloy that is stronger than many steels.

Prices:
GUIDE RECEIVER SIGHT **$25.79**
    With Twilight Aperture 27.26
    With ¼" "U" blade 23.69

ZEISS RIFLESCOPES

THE C-SERIES

The C-Series was designed by Zeiss specifically for the American hunter. It is based on space-age alloy tubes with integral objective and ocular bells, and an integral adjustment turret. This strong, rigid one-piece construction allows perfect lens alignment, micro-precise adjustments and structural integrity. Other features include quick focusing, a generous 3½″ of eye relief, rubber armoring, T-Star multi-layer coating, and parallax setting (free at 100 yards).

DIATAL-C 10x36T*
$675.00

DIAVARI-C 3-9x36T*
$755.00

DIATAL-C 6x32T*
$565.00

DIATAL-C 4x32T*
$525.00

DIAVARI-C 1.5-4.5x18T*
$725.00

PRODUCT SPECIFICATIONS	4×32	6×32	10×36	3-9×36		C1.5-4.5×18	
Magnification	4X	6X	10X	3X	9X	1.5X	4.5X
Objective Diameter (mm)/(inch)	1.26″	1.26″	1.42″	1.42″		15.0/0.6	18.0/0.7
Exit Pupil	0.32″	0.21″	0.14″	0.39″	0.16″	10.0	4.0
Twilight Performance	11.3	13.9	19.0	8.5	18.0	4.2	9.0
Field of View at 100 yds.	30′	20′	12′	36′	13′	72′	27′
Eye Relief	3.5″	3.5″	3.5″	3.5″	3.5″	3.5″	
Maximum Interval Adjustment (elevation and windage (MOA)	80	80	50	50		10.5′ @ 100 yds.	
Click-Stop Adjustment 1 click = 1 interval (MOA)	¼	¼	¼	¼		.36″ @ 100 yds.	
Length	10.6″	10.6″	12.7″	11.2″		11.8″	
Weight approx. (ounces)	11.3	11.3	14.1	15.2		13.4	
Tube Diameter	1″	1″	1″	1″		1″	
Objective Tube Diameter	1.65″	1.65″	1.89″	1.73″		1″	
Eyepiece O.D.	1.67″	1.67″	1.67″	1.67″		1.8″	

CENTERFIRE PISTOL & REVOLVER AMMUNITION

CENTERFIRE RIFLE AMMUNITION

22 RIMFIRE AMMUNITION

SHOTSHELL AMMUNITION

Ammunition

FOR ADDRESSES AND PHONE NUMBERS OF MANUFACTURERS AND DISTRIBUTORS INCLUDED IN THIS SECTION, SEE *DIRECTORY OF MANUFACTURERS AND SUPPLIERS*

ACTIV AMMUNITION

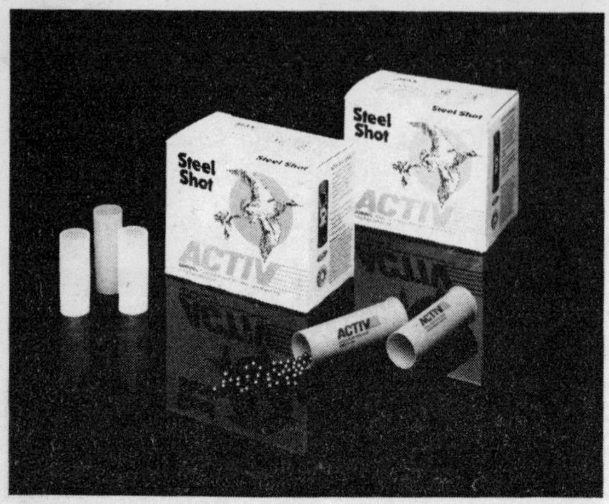

Buckshot Specifications

Model	Gauge	Length (in.)	Ounces Shot	Shot Size	Rnds./ Box	Rnds./ Case
BK12XL	12	3	15 Pellets	#00	5	250
BK12XL	12	3	24 Pellets	#1	5	250
BK12XL	12	3	41 Pellets	#4	5	250
BK12YL	12	2¾	12 Pellets	#00	5	250
BK12YL	12	2¾	20 Pellets	#1	5	250
BK12YL	12	2¾	34 Pellets	#4	5	250
BK12ZL	12	2¾	9 Pellets	#00	5	250
BK12ZL	12	2¾	16 Pellets	#1	5	250
BK12ZL	12	2¾	27 Pellets	#4	5	250

Steel Shot Specifications

Model	Gauge	Length (inch)	Dram Equiv.	Ounces Shot	Standard Shot Sizes	Rnds/ box	Rnds/ case
ST123E	12	3	Max	1⅜	BB, 1, 2, 3, 4	20	200
ST123F	12	3	Max	1¼	BB, 1, 2, 3, 4	20	200
ST12F	12	2¾	Max	1¼	BB, 1, 2, 3, 4	20	200
ST12G	12	2¾	Max	1⅛	BB, 1, 2, 3, 4	20	200
ST20J	20	2¾	Max	¾	3, 4	20	480

Target Load Specifications

Model	Gauge	Length (inch)	Dram Equiv.	Ounces Shot	Standard Shot Sizes	Rnds/ box	Rnds/ case
Tournament Grade: High Quality Target Loads Trap and Skeet							
TG12G	12	2¾	3	1⅛	7½, 8, 9	25	500
TG12GL	12	2¾	2¾	1⅛	7½, 8, 9	25	500
TG12UL	12	Ultra Lite		1⅛	7½, 8, 9	25	500
TG12H	12	2¾	2¾	1	7½, 8, 9	25	500
A20I	20	2¾	2½	⅞	7½, 8, 9	25	500
International Trap Loads. Nickel Plated Shot							
A12GH	12	2¾	3¼	1⅛	7½, 8, 9	25	500
A12HH	12	2¾	3¼	1	7½, 8, 9	25	500
A12TH	12	2¾	3	1 (28 gr)	7½, 8, 9	25	500
Nickel Plated Pigeon Loads							
A12FH	12	2¾	3¼	1¼	7½, 8, 9	25	500

Steel Shot Information

Shot Size	Average Pellet Count Per Given Weight (Approx.)		
	1⅛ oz.	1¼ oz.	1⅜ oz.
BB	81	89	98
1	114	127	139
2	137	151	166
3	164	182	200
4	205	227	250

Steel Shot Ballistics

Model	Average Pressure (psi)	Average Velocity (fps)
ST12G	11000	1365
ST12F	11000	1275
ST123F	10500	1375
ST123E	11000	1280
ST20J	11000	1400

Red Hornet Series Specifications

Model	Gauge	Length (inch)	Dram Equiv.	Ounces Shot	Standard Shot Sizes	Rnds/ box	Rnds/ case
Duck & Pheasant Promotional Loads							
H12FH	12	2¾	3¾	1¼	4, 5, 6, 7½, 8, 9	25	500
H16GX	16	2¾	3¼	1	4, 5, 6, 7½	25	500
H20HH	20	2¾	2¾	1	4, 5, 6, 7½	25	500
Dove & Target Promotional Loads							
H12H	12	2¾	3	1	7½, 8	25	500
Dove & Quail Promotional Loads							
H12HH	12	2¾	3¼	1	6, 7½, 8	25	500
H16H	16	2¾	2½	1	6, 7½, 8	25	500
H20I	20	2¾	2½	⅞	6, 7½, 8	25	500

Slugs Specifications

Model	Gauge	Length (in.)	Dram Equiv.	Weight	Rnds./ Box	Rnds./ Case
SL123F	12	3	Max	1¼	5	250
SL12F	12	2¾	Max	1¼	5	250
SL12H	12	2¾	Max	1	5	250
SL16H	16	2¾	Max	1	5	250
SL20I	20	2¾	Max	⅞	5	250

ACTIV AMMUNITION

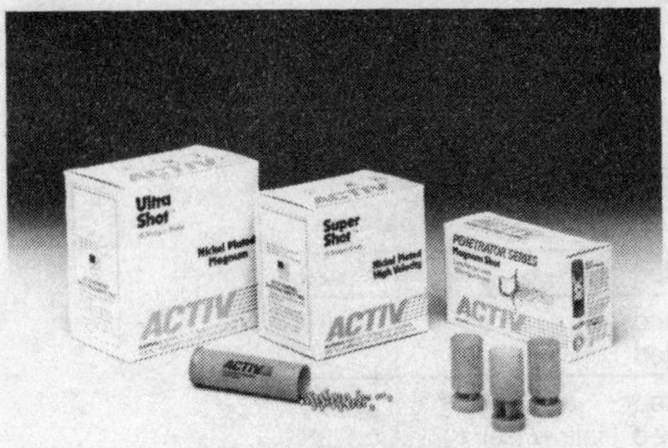

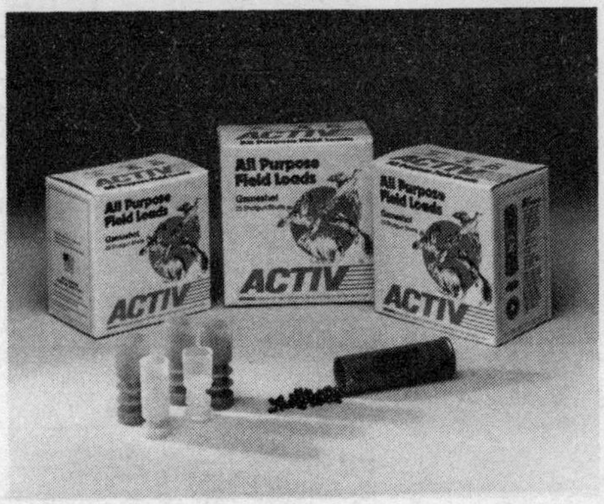

Ultrashot Nickel Magnum Loads Specifications

Model	Gauge	Length (inch)	Dram Equiv.	Ounces Shot	Standard Shot Sizes	Rnds/ box	Rnds/ case
N12A	12	3	4	2	4, 6	25	250
N12B	12	3	4	1⅞	BB, 2, 4, 6	25	250
N12C	12	3	4	1⅝	2, 4, 6	25	250
N12D	12	2¾	4½	1½	BB, 2, 4, 6	25	250
N20F	20	3	3	1¼	2, 4, 6, 7½	25	500
N20GL	20	2¾	2¾	1⅛	4, 6, 7½	25	500

Penetrator Series Nickel Turkey Loads Specifications

Model	Gauge	Length (inch)	Dram Equiv.	Ounces Shot	Standard Shot Sizes	Rnds/ box	Rnds/ case
P123A	12	3	4	2	4, 6	10	100
P12A	12	2¾	4	1¾	4, 6, 7½	10	100
P12D	12	2¾	4½	1½	4, 6	10	100
P12DL	12	2¾	4	1½	4, 6	10	100

Super Shot Nickel High Velocity Loads Specifications

Model	Gauge	Length (inch)	Dram Equiv.	Ounces Shot	Standard Shot Sizes	Rnds/ box	Rnds/ case
N12E	12	2¾	4	1⅜	4, 6	25	250
N12FH	12	2¾	3¾	1¼	4, 6, 7½	25	250
N16GX	16	2¾	3¼	1	4, 6, 7½	25	250
N20HH	20	2¾	2¾	1	4, 6, 7½	25	500

All Purpose Field Loads Specifications

Model	Gauge	Length (inch)	Dram Equiv.	Ounces Shot	Standard Shot Sizes	Rnds/ box	Rnds/ case
G12FH	12	2¾	3¾	1¼	4, 5, 6, 7½	25	500
G12F	12	2¾	3¼	1¼	6, 7½, 8, 9	25	500
G12GL	12	2¾	3¼	1⅛	6, 7½, 8, 9	25	500
G12HH	12	2¾	3¼	1	6, 7½, 8, 9	25	500
G16GX	16	2¾	3¼	1	4, 5, 6, 7½	25	500
G16GLX	16	2¾	2¾	1	6, 7½, 8, 9	25	500
G16H	16	2¾	2½	1	6, 7½, 8, 9	25	500
G20HH	20	2¾	2¾	1	4, 5, 6, 7½	25	500
G20H	20	2⅔	2½	1	6, 7½, 8, 9	25	500
G20I	20	2¾	2½	⅞	6, 7½, 8, 9	25	500

FEDERAL AMMUNITION

22 RIMFIRE CARTRIDGES

LOAD NO.	CARTRIDGES	BULLET TYPE	BULLET WEIGHT GRAINS

HI-POWER® 22'S — 50 rounds per box, 100 boxes per case. 5000 rounds per case.

LOAD NO.	CARTRIDGES	BULLET TYPE	BULLET WEIGHT GRAINS
701	22 Short	Copper Plated	29
706	22 Long	Copper Plated	29
700CB	22 Long	Copper Plated	29
710	22 Long Rifle	Copper Plated	40
712	22 Long Rifle	Copper Plated, Hollow Point	38

HI-POWER® 22'S — 100 PACK — 50 boxes per case. 5000 rounds per case.

LOAD NO.	CARTRIDGES	BULLET TYPE	BULLET WEIGHT GRAINS
810	22 Long Rifle	Copper Plated	40
812	22 Long Rifle	Copper Plated, Hollow Point	38

MAGNUM 22'S — 50 rounds per box, 50 boxes per case. 2500 rounds per case.

LOAD NO.	CARTRIDGES	BULLET TYPE	BULLET WEIGHT GRAINS
757	22 Win Mag	Jacketed Hollow Point	50

22 SHOT — 50 rounds per box, 50 boxes per case. 2500 rounds per case.

LOAD NO.	CARTRIDGES	BULLET TYPE	BULLET WEIGHT GRAINS
716	22 Long Rifle	#12 Shot	—

FEDERAL CENTERFIRE RIFLE CARTRIDGES

LOAD NO.	CARTRIDGES	BULLET TYPE	BULLET WEIGHT GRAINS
222A	222 Rem	Soft Point	50
222B	222 Rem	Metal Case Boat Tail	55
22250A	22-250 Rem	Soft Point	55
22250C	22-250 Rem	Varmint, Hollow Point	40
223A	223 Rem (5.56 mm)	Soft Point	55
223B	223 Rem (5.56 mm)	Metal Case Boat Tail	55
223C	223 Rem (5.56 mm)	Hollow Point Boat Tail	55
223D	223 Rem (5.56 mm)	Varmint, Hollow Point	40
223M	223 Rem (5.56 mm)	Boat Tail, Hollow Point Match	69
6A	6MM Rem	Soft Point	80
6B	6MM Rem	Hi-Shok Soft Point	100
243A	243 Win	Soft Point	80
243B	243 Win	Hi-Shok Soft Point	100
243V	243 Win	Varmint, Hollow Point	60
257A	257 Roberts (High Vel + P)	Hi-Shok Soft Point	117
2506A	25-06 Rem	Hollow Point	90
2506B	25-06 Rem	Hi-Shok Soft Point	117
270A	270 Win	Hi-Shok Soft Point	130
270B	270 Win	Hi-Shok Soft Point	150
NEW 280B	280 Rem	Hi-Shok Soft Point	180
7A	7MM Mauser	Hi-Shok Soft Point	175
7B	7MM Mauser	Hi-Shok Soft Point	140
7RA	7MM Rem Magnum	Hi-Shok Soft Point	150
7RB	7MM Rem Magnum	Hi-Shok Soft Point	175
30CA	30 Carbine	Soft Point	110
76239B	7.62x39 Soviet	Soft Point	123
730A	7-30 Waters	Boat Tail Soft Point	120
3030A	30-30 Win	Hi-Shok Soft Point	150
3030B	30-30 Win	Hi-Shok Soft Point	170
3030C	30-30 Win	Hollow Point	125

20 rds per box, 25 boxes per case; 500 rds per case.

FEDERAL AMMUNITION

LOAD NO.	CARTRIDGES	BULLET TYPE	BULLET WEIGHT GRAINS

CENTERFIRE RIFLE CARTRIDGES

LOAD NO.	CARTRIDGES	BULLET TYPE	BULLET WEIGHT GRAINS
3006A	30-06 Springfield	Hi-Shok Soft Point	150
3006B	30-06 Springfield	Hi-Shok Soft Point	180
3006C	30-06 Springfield	Soft Point	125
3006D	30-06 Springfield	Boat Tail Soft Point	165
3006H	30-06 Springfield	Hi-Shok Soft Point	220
3006J	30-06 Springfield	Round Nose	180
300A	300 Savage	Hi-Shok Soft Point	150
300B	300 Savage	Hi-Shok Soft Point	180
300WB	300 Win Magnum	Hi-Shok Soft Point	180
303A	303 British	Hi-Shok Soft Point	180
303B	303 British	Hi-Shok Soft Point	150
308A	308 Win	Hi-Shok Soft Point	150
308B	308 Win	Hi-Shok Soft Point	180
308M	308 Win (Match)	Boat Tail Hollow Point Match	168
8A	8MM Mauser	Hi-Shok Soft Point	170
32A	32 Win Special	Hi-Shok Soft Point	170
338C	338 Win Magnum	Soft Point	225
35A	35 Rem	Hi-Shok Soft Point	200
375A	375 H&H Magnum	Hi-Shok Soft Point	270
375B	375 H&H Magnum	Hi-Shok Soft Point	300
+44A	44 Rem Magnum	Hollow Soft Point	240
4570A	45-70 Government	Hollow Soft Point	300

NEW is marked at the 303A/303B rows.

+ For Rifle or Pistol. 20 rds per box, 25 boxes per case; 500 rounds per case.

FEDERAL AMMUNITION

LOAD NO.	CARTRIDGES	BULLET TYPE	BULLET WEIGHT GRAINS

CENTERFIRE PISTOL CARTRIDGES

LOAD NO.	CARTRIDGES	BULLET TYPE	BULLET WEIGHT GRAINS
*25AP	25 Auto Pistol (6.35mm)	Metal Case	50
32AP	32 Auto Pistol (7.65mm)	Metal Case	71
32LA	32 S&W Long	Lead Wadcutter	98
32LB	32 S&W Long	Lead Round Nose	98
32HRA	32 H&R Magnum	Lead Semi-Wadcutter	95
32HRB	32 H&R Magnum	Jacketed Hollow Point	85
380AP	380 Auto Pistol	Metal Case	95
380BP	380 Auto Pistol	Jacketed Hollow Point	90
9AP	9MM Luger Auto Pistol	Metal Case	124
9BP	9MM Luger Auto Pistol	Jacketed Hollow Point	115
9MP	9MM Luger (Match)	Metal Case, S.W.C.	124
9FA	9MM Federal	Jacketed Hollow Point	115
38A	38 Special (Match)	Lead Wadcutter	148
38B	38 Special	Lead Round Nose	158
38C	38 Special	Lead Semi-Wadcutter	158
38E	38 Special (High Vel + P)	Jacketed Hollow Point	125
38F	38 Special (High Vel + P)	Jacketed Hollow Point	110
38G	38 Special (High Vel + P)	Lead SW Hollow Point	158
38H	38 Special (High Vel + P)	Lead Semi-Wadcutter	158
38J	38 Special (High Vel + P)	Jacketed Soft Point	125
357A	357 Magnum	Jacketed Soft Point	158
357B	357 Magnum	Jacketed Hollow Point	125
357C	357 Magnum	Lead Semi-Wadcutter	158
357D	357 Magnum	Jacketed Hollow Point	110
357E	357 Magnum	Jacketed Hollow Point	158
357G	357 Magnum	Jacketed Hollow Point	180
41A	41 Rem Magnum	Jacketed Hollow Point	210
***+44A	44 Rem Magnum	Hollow Soft Point	240
44B	44 Rem Magnum	Jacketed Hollow Point	180
**A44B20	44 Rem Magnum	Jacketed Hollow Point	180
+44D	44 Rem Magnum	Metal Case Profile	250
44SA	44 S&W Special	Lead SW Hollow Point	200
45LCA	44 Colt	Lead SW Hollow Point	225
45A	45 Automatic (Match)	Metal Case	230
45B	45 Automatic (Match)	Metal Case, S.W.C.	185
45C	45 Automatic	Jacketed Hollow Point	185

50 rds per box, 20 boxes per case; 1000 rds per case.

+   For Rifle or Pistol.
*   25AP packed 25 rounds per box, 40 boxes per case.
**   A44B20 packed 20 rounds per box, 50 boxes per case.
***   44A packed 20 rounds per box, 25 boxes per case. 500 rounds per case.

FEDERAL AMMUNITION

LOAD NO.	CALIBER	BULLET TYPE	BULLET WEIGHT GRAMS

NORMA CENTERFIRE RIFLE CARTRIDGES–Specialty Calibers
20 rounds per box, 10 boxes per case. 200 rounds per case.

LOAD NO.	CALIBER	BULLET TYPE	BULLET WEIGHT GRAMS
15701	220 Swift	Soft Point	50
15604	22 Savage H.P.	Soft Point	71
16531	6.5x50 Japanese	Soft Point Boat Tail	139
16532	6.5x50 Japanese	Soft Point	156
16535	6.5x52 Carcano	Soft Point	156
16537	6.5x52 Carcano	Soft Point	139
16558	6.5x55 Swedish	Protected Power Cavity	139
16552	6.5x55 Swedish	Soft Point	156
17002	7x57 Mauser	Soft Point	154
17005	7x57 R	Soft Point	154
17011	7x61 Sharpe & Hart Super	Soft Point	154
17013	7x64 Brenneke	Soft Point	154
17511	7.5x55 Swiss	Soft Point Boat Tail	180
17634	7.62x54R Russian	Soft Point Boat Tail	180
17637	7.62x54R Russian	Soft Point	150
17638	308 Norma Magnum	Dual Core	180
17701	7.65x53 Argentine	Soft Point	150
17702	7.65x53 Argentine	Soft Point	180
17712	.303 British	Soft Point	150
11721	7.7x58 Japanese	Soft Point	130
17722	7.7x58 Japanese	Soft Point Boat Tail	180
18017	8x57 JS Mauser	Protected Power Cavity	165
18003	8x57 JS Mauser	Soft Point	196
19303	9.3x57 Mauser	Soft Point	286
19315	9.3x62 Mauser	Soft Point	286
19004	358 Norma Magnum	Soft Point	250

NORMA CENTERFIRE PISTOL CARTRIDGES
20 rounds per box, 25 boxes per case. 500 rounds per case.

LOAD NO.	CALIBER	BULLET TYPE	BULLET WEIGHT GRAMS
11002	10mm Auto	Jacketed Hollow Point	170
11001	10mm Auto	Full Metal Jacket	200

FEDERAL AMMUNITION

LOAD NO.	CARTRIDGES	BULLET TYPE	BULLET WEIGHT GRAINS

PREMIUM® HYDRA-SHOK™ PISTOL & REVOLVER CARTRIDGES
20 rounds per box, 25 boxes per case. 500 rounds per case.

	LOAD NO.	CARTRIDGES	BULLET TYPE	BULLET WEIGHT GRAINS
NEW	P380HS1	380 Automatic	Hydra-Shok	90
	P38HS1	38 Special (+P)	Hydra-Shok	129
	P357HS1	357 Magnum	Hydra-Shok	158
	P9HS1	9MM Luger	Hydra-Shok	124
	P9HS2	9MM Luger	Hydra-Shok	147
NEW	P10HS1	10MM Automatic	Hydra-Shok	180
NEW	P44HS1	44 Rem Magnum	Hydra-Shok	240
	P45HS1	45 Automatic	Hydra-Shok	230

PREMIUM® NYCLAD® PISTOL & REVOLVER CARTRIDGES
50 rounds per box, 20 boxes per case. 1000 rounds per case.

LOAD NO.	CARTRIDGES	BULLET TYPE	BULLET WEIGHT GRAINS
P9BP	9MM Luger Auto Pistol	Hollow Point	124
P38B	38 Special	Round Nose	158
P38G	38 Special (High Vel + P)	SW Hollow Point	158
P38M	38 Special	Hollow Point	125
P38N	38 Special (High Vel + P)	Hollow Point	125
P357E	357 Magnum	SW Hollow Point	158

PREMIUM® CENTERFIRE RIFLE CARTRIDGES
20 rounds per box, 25 boxes per case. 500 rounds per case.

	LOAD NO.	CARTRIDGES	BULLET TYPE	BULLET WEIGHT GRAINS
	P223E	223 Rem	Boat Tail Hollow Point	55
	P22250B	22-250 Rem	Boat Tail Hollow Point	55
	P2506C	25-06 Rem	Boat Tail Soft Point	117
	P6C	6MM Rem	Nosler Partition	100
	P243C	243 Win	Boat Tail Soft Point	100
	P243D	243 Win	Boat Tail Hollow Point	85
NEW	P243E	243 Win	Nosler Partition	100
	P257B	257 Roberts (High Vel + P)	Nosler Partition	120
	P270C	270 Win	Boat Tail Soft Point	150
	P270D	270 Win	Boat Tail Soft Point	130
	P270E	270 Win	Nosler Partition	150
	P280A	280 Rem	Nosler Partition	150
	P7C	7MM Mauser	Nosler Partition	140
	P7RD	7MM Rem Magnum	Boat Tail Soft Point	150
	P7RE	7MM Rem Magnum	Boat Tail Soft Point	165
	P7RF	7MM Rem Magnum	Nosler Partition	160
	P7RG	7MM Rem Magnum	Nosler Partition	140
	P3030D	30-30 Win	Nosler Partition	170
	P3006D	30-06 Springfield	Boat Tail Soft Point	165
	P3006F	30-06 Springfield	Nosler Partition	180
	P3006G	30-06 Springfield	Boat Tail Soft Point	150
	P3006L	30-06 Springfield	Boat Tail Soft Point	180
	P300WC	300 Win Magnum	Boat Tail Soft Point	200
	P308C	308 Win	Boat Tail Soft Point	165
NEW	P308E	308 Win	Nosler Partition	180

FEDERAL AMMUNITION

LOAD NO.	CARTRIDGES	BULLET TYPE	BULLET WEIGHT GRAINS

PREMIUM® SAFARI™ RIFLE CARTRIDGES — 20 rounds per box, 20 boxes per case. 400 rounds per case.

	LOAD NO.	CARTRIDGES	BULLET TYPE	BULLET WEIGHT GRAINS
	P300WD2	300 Win Magnum	Nosler Partition	180
NEW	P300HA	300 H&H Magnum	Nosler Partition	180
	P338A2	338 Win Magnum	Nosler Partition	210
	P338B2	338 Win Magnum	Nosler Partition	250
	P375C	375 H&H Magnum	Boat Tail Soft Point	250
	P375D	375 H&H Magnum	Solid	300
NEW	P375F	375 H&H Magnum	Nosler Partition	300
	P458A	458 Win Magnum	Soft Point	350
	P458B	458 Win Magnum	Soft Point	510
	P458C	458 Win Magnum	Solid	500
	P416A	416 Rigby	Soft Point	410
	P416B	416 Rigby	Solid	410
	P470A	470 Nitro Express	Soft Point	500
	P470B	470 Nitro Express	Solid	500

PREMIUM® SHOTSHELLS

LOAD NO.	GAUGE	SHELL LENGTH (INCHES)	POWDER DRAMS EQUIV.	OUNCES SHOT	SHOT SIZES

MAGNUM LOADS — 25 rounds per box, 10 boxes per case. 250 rounds per case.

	LOAD NO.	GAUGE	SHELL LENGTH (INCHES)	POWDER DRAMS EQUIV.	OUNCES SHOT	SHOT SIZES
	P109	10	3½	4½	2¼	BB, [2,] 4, 6
	P159	12	3	4	2	BB, 2, 4, 6
	P158	12	3	4	1⅞	BB, 2, 4, 6
	P156	12	2¾	4	1½	BB, 2, 4, 6
NEW	P165	16	2¾	3¼	1¼	4, 6
	P258	20	3	3	1¼	4, 6
	P256	20	2¾	2¾	1⅛	4, 6

MAGNUM LOADS — 10 rounds per box, 25 boxes per case. 250 rounds per case.

	LOAD NO.	GAUGE	SHELL LENGTH (INCHES)	POWDER DRAMS EQUIV.	OUNCES SHOT	SHOT SIZES
NEW	ST135	12	3½	Max.	2¼	4, 6
	ST159*	12	3	4	2	4, 6

*Seasonal availability.

HI-POWER LOADS — 25 rounds per box, 10 boxes per case. 250 rounds per case.

LOAD NO.	GAUGE	SHELL LENGTH (INCHES)	POWDER DRAMS EQUIV.	OUNCES SHOT	SHOT SIZES
P154	12	2¾	3¾	1¼	4, 6, 7½
P254	20	2¾	2¾	1	6
P283	28	2¾	2¼	¾	6, 7½, 8

FIELD LOADS — 25 rounds per box, 10 boxes per case. 250 rounds per case.

LOAD NO.	GAUGE	SHELL LENGTH (INCHES)	POWDER DRAMS EQUIV.	OUNCES SHOT	SHOT SIZES
P153	12	2¾	3¼	1¼	7½, 8
P152	12	2¾	3¼	1⅛	[7½]
P252	20	2¾	2½	1	7½, 8

BUCKSHOT — 5 rounds per box, 50 boxes per case. 250 rounds per case.

LOAD NO.	GAUGE	SHELL LENGTH (INCHES)		SHOT SIZES	
P108	10	3½	Magnum	00 Buck	18 Pellets
P108	10	3½	Magnum	[4 Buck]	54 Pellets
P158	12	3	Magnum	000 Buck	10 Pellets
P158	12	3	Magnum	00 Buck	15 Pellets
P158	12	3	Magnum	4 Buck	41 Pellets
P158	12	3	Magnum	1 Buck	24 Pellets
P156	12	2¾	Magnum	00 Buck	12 Pellets
P156	12	2¾	Magnum	4 Buck	34 Pellets
P154	12	2¾	Max.	00 Buck	9 Pellets
P154	12	2¾	Max.	[4 Buck]	27 Pellets

□ Discontinued item, subject to stock on hand

FEDERAL SHOTSHELLS

LOAD NO.	GAUGE	SHELL LENGTH (INCHES)	POWDER DRAMS EQUIV.	SHOT SIZES	

MAGNUM BUCKSHOT — 5 rounds per box, 50 boxes per case. 250 rounds per case.

LOAD NO.	GAUGE	SHELL LENGTH (INCHES)	POWDER DRAMS EQUIV.	SHOT SIZES	
F131	12	3	Mag.	000 Buck	10 Pellets
F131	12	3	Mag.	00 Buck	15 Pellets
F131	12	3	Mag.	1 Buck	24 Pellets
F131	12	3	Mag.	4 Buck	41 Pellets
F130	12	2¾	Mag.	00 Buck	12 Pellets
F130	12	2¾	Mag.	1 Buck	20 Pellets
F130	12	2¾	Mag.	4 Buck	34 Pellets
F207	20	3	Mag.	2 Buck	18 Pellets

HI-POWER® BUCKSHOT — 5 rounds per box, 50 boxes per case. 250 rounds per case.

LOAD NO.	GAUGE	SHELL LENGTH (INCHES)	POWDER DRAMS EQUIV.	SHOT SIZES	
F127	12	2¾	Max.	000 Buck	8 Pellets
F127	12	2¾	Max.	00 Buck	9 Pellets
F127	12	2¾	Max.	0 Buck	12 Pellets
F127	12	2¾	Max.	1 Buck	16 Pellets
F127	12	2¾	Max.	4 Buck	27 Pellets
F164	16	2¾	Max.	1 Buck	12 Pellets
F203	20	2¾	Max.	3 Buck	20 Pellets

LOAD NO.	GAUGE	SHELL LENGTH (INCHES)	POWDER DRAMS EQUIV.	OUNCES SHOT	SHOT SIZES

TRAP LOADS — 25 rounds per box, 10 boxes per case, 250 rounds per case.

LOAD NO.	GAUGE	SHELL LENGTH (INCHES)	POWDER DRAMS EQUIV.	OUNCES SHOT	SHOT SIZES
H114	12	2¾	**E.L.	1⅛	7½, 8, 8½
H115	12	2¾	2¾	1⅛	7½, 8
H116	12	2¾	3	1⅛	7½, 8
H117	12	2¾	2¾	1⅛	7½, 8
H118	12	2¾	3	1⅛	7½, 8
H113	12	2¾	2¾	1	8½

SKEET LOADS — 25 rounds per box, 10 boxes per case. 250 rounds per case.

LOAD NO.	GAUGE	SHELL LENGTH (INCHES)	POWDER DRAMS EQUIV.	OUNCES SHOT	SHOT SIZES
H114	12	2¾	**E.L.	1⅛	9
H115	12	2¾	2¾	1⅛	9
H116	12	2¾	3	1⅛	9
H117	12	2¾	2¾	1⅛	9
H118	12	2¾	3	1⅛	9
H206	20	2¾	2½	⅞	9
H280	28	2¾	2	¾	9
H412	410	2½	Max.	½	9

SPORTING CLAY LOADS — 25 rounds per box, 10 boxes per case. 250 rounds per case.

LOAD NO.	GAUGE	SHELL LENGTH (INCHES)	POWDER DRAMS EQUIV.	OUNCES SHOT	SHOT SIZES
H122	12	2¾	3	1⅛	8, 9
NEW H222	20	2¾	2½	⅞	7½, 8

INTERNATIONAL LOADS — 25 rounds per box, 10 boxes per case. 250 rounds per case.

LOAD NO.	GAUGE	SHELL LENGTH (INCHES)	POWDER DRAMS EQUIV.	OUNCES SHOT	SHOT SIZES
NEW H110	12	2¾	3¼	1	8, 9
NEW H119	12	2¾	3¼	1	7½ Copper Plated
NEW H128	12	2¾	3½	1	10

FEDERAL SHOTSHELLS

LOAD NO.	GAUGE	SHELL LENGTH (INCHES)	POWDER DRAMS EQUIV.	OUNCES SHOT	SHOT SIZES	APPROX. CASE WT. (LBS.)

POWER MAGNUM — 25 rounds per box, 10 boxes per case. 250 rounds per case.

LOAD NO.	GAUGE	SHELL LENGTH	POWDER DRAMS	OUNCES SHOT	SHOT SIZES	CASE WT.
F103	10	3½	4¼	2	BB, 2, 4,	44
F131	12	3	4	1⅞	BB, 2, 4	39
F129	12	3	4	1⅝	2, 4, 6	36
F130	12	2¾	3¾	1½	BB, 2, 4, 5, 6	33
F165	16	2¾	3¼	1¼	2, 4, 6	28
F207	20	3	3	1¼	2, 4, 6, 7½	27
F205	20	2¾	2¾	1⅛	4, 6, 7½	25

POWER MAGNUM — 10 rounds per box, 25 boxes per case. 250 rounds per case.

LOAD NO.	GAUGE	SHELL LENGTH	POWDER DRAMS	OUNCES SHOT	SHOT SIZES	CASE WT.
ST131*	12	3	4	1⅞	6	40

*Seasonal availability.

CLASSIC™ HI-BRASS™ — 25 rounds per box, 10 boxes per case. 250 rounds per case.

LOAD NO.	GAUGE	SHELL LENGTH	POWDER DRAMS	OUNCES SHOT	SHOT SIZES	CASE WT.
H126	12	2¾	3¾	1¼	2, 4, 5, 6, 7½, 8, 9	28
H163	16	2¾	3¼	1⅛	4, 6, 7½	25
H204	20	2¾	2¾	1	4, 5, 6, 7½, 8	21
H413	410	3	Max.	11/16	4, 5, 6, 7½, 8	14
H412	410	2½	Max.	½	6, 7½	12

STEEL SHOT MAGNUM — 25 rounds per box, 10 boxes per case. 250 rounds per case.

LOAD NO.	GAUGE	SHELL LENGTH	POWDER DRAMS	OUNCES SHOT	SHOT SIZES	CASE WT.
W104	10	3½	Max.	1⅝	F,T,BBB,BB	38
W135	12	3½	Max.	1 9/16	F,T, BB, 2	35
W149	12	3	Max.	1⅜	F,T,BBB,BB,1,2,3,4	32
W140	12	3	Max.	1¼	BB,1,2,3,4	28
W148	12	2¾	Max.	1¼	T,BBB,BB,1,2,3,4	28
W168	16	2¾	Max.	15/16	2, 4	22
W209	20	3	3¼	1	2,3,4, 6	22

STEEL SHOT HI-POWER® — 25 rounds per box, 10 boxes per case. 250 rounds per case.

LOAD NO.	GAUGE	SHELL LENGTH	POWDER DRAMS	OUNCES SHOT	SHOT SIZES	CASE WT.
W147	12	2¾	3¾	1⅛	BB, 2, 3, 4, 5, 6	27
W208	20	2¾	3	¾	3, 4, 6	20

STEEL SHOT TRI-POWER™ — 10 rounds per box, 25 boxes per case. 250 rounds per case.

LOAD NO.	GAUGE	SHELL LENGTH	POWDER DRAMS	OUNCES SHOT	SHOT SIZES	CASE WT.
W348	12	2¾	3½	1¼	(BB, 1, 4)	29
W349	12	3	Max.	1⅜	(T, BB, 2)	32

FIELD — 25 rounds per box, 10 boxes per case. 250 rounds per case.

LOAD NO.	GAUGE	SHELL LENGTH	POWDER DRAMS	OUNCES SHOT	SHOT SIZES	CASE WT.
H125	12	2¾	3¼	1¼	7½, 8, 9	28
H123	12	2¾	3¼	1⅛	4, 6, 7½, 8, 9	26
H162	16	2¾	2¾	1⅛	6, 7½, 8	26
H202	20	2¾	2½	1	6, 7½, 8	23

HI-SHOK® RIFLED SLUGS — 5 rounds per box, 50 boxes per case. 250 rounds per case.

LOAD NO.	GAUGE	SHELL LENGTH	POWDER DRAMS	OUNCES SHOT	SHOT SIZES	CASE WT.
F103	10	3½	Mag.	1¾	Rifled Slug	40
F131	12	3	Mag.	1¼	Rifled Slug	31
F130	12	2¾	Mag.	1¼	Rifled Slug	30
F127	12	2¾	Max.	1	Rifled Slug	26
F164	16	2¾	Max.	⅘	Rifled Slug	22
F203	20	2¾	Max.	¾	Rifled Slug	19
F412	410	2½	Max.	⅕	Rifled Slug	9

No split case orders accepted for shotshells.

☐ Discontinued — subject to stock on hand.

AMMUNITION 463

FEDERAL AMMUNITION

SPECIAL LOADS

	LOAD NO.	GAUGE	SHELL LENGTH	DRAM EQUIV.	OUNCES SHOT	SHOT SIZES

GAME LOADS — 25 rounds per box, 10 boxes per case. 250 rounds per case.

	LOAD NO.	GAUGE	SHELL LENGTH	DRAM EQUIV.	OUNCES SHOT	SHOT SIZES
	H121	12	2¾	3¼	1	6, 7½, 8
	H160	16	2¾	2½	1	6, 7½, 8
	H200	20	2¾	2½	⅞	6, 7½, 8

DOVE LOADS — 20 rounds per box, 10 boxes per case. 200 rounds per case.

	LOAD NO.	GAUGE	SHELL LENGTH	DRAM EQUIV.	OUNCES SHOT	SHOT SIZES
NEW	FD12	12	2¾	3¼	1	8
NEW	FD20	20	2¾	2½	⅞	8

STEEL SHOT — 25 rounds per box, 10 boxes per case. 250 rounds per case.

	LOAD NO.	GAUGE	SHELL LENGTH	DRAM EQUIV.	OUNCES SHOT	SHOT SIZES
	W146	12	2¾	Max.	1	2, 3, 4

HI-POWER LOADS — 25 rounds per box, 10 boxes per case. 250 rounds per case.

	LOAD NO.	GAUGE	SHELL LENGTH	DRAM EQUIV.	OUNCES SHOT	SHOT SIZES
	H127	12	2¾	3¾	1¼	4, 6, 7½
	H164	16	2¾	3¼	1⅛	6
	H203	20	2¾	2¾	1	6, 7½
NEW	H415	410	3	Max.	11/16	4, 6, 7½
NEW	H414	410	2½	Max.	½	6

LIGHTNING 22'S — 50 rounds per box, 100 boxes per case. 5000 rounds per case.

510	40-grain solid bullet

HORNADY AMMUNITION

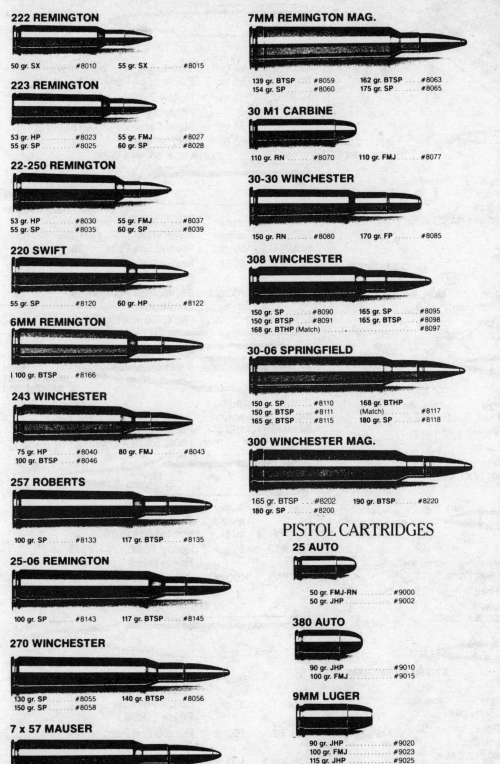

222 REMINGTON

50 gr. SX .... #8010   55 gr. SX .... #8015

223 REMINGTON

53 gr. HP .... #8023   55 gr. FMJ ...... #8027
55 gr. SP .... #8025   60 gr. SP .... #8028

22-250 REMINGTON

53 gr. HP .... #8030   55 gr. FMJ ...... #8037
55 gr. SP .... #8035   60 gr. SP .... #8039

220 SWIFT

55 gr. SP .... #8120   60 gr. HP .... #8122

6MM REMINGTON

I 100 gr. BTSP ..... #8166

243 WINCHESTER

75 gr. HP .... #8040   80 gr. FMJ ...... #8043
100 gr. BTSP .... #8046

257 ROBERTS

100 gr. SP ...... #8133   117 gr. BTSP ..... #8135

25-06 REMINGTON

100 gr. SP ...... #8143   117 gr. BTSP ..... #8145

270 WINCHESTER

130 gr. SP ...... #8055   140 gr. BTSP .... #8056
150 gr. SP ...... #8058

7 x 57 MAUSER

139 gr. BTSP ..... #8155   154 gr. SP ...... #8156

7MM REMINGTON MAG.

139 gr. BTSP .... #8059   162 gr. BTSP .... #8063
154 gr. SP ...... #8060   175 gr. SP ...... #8065

30 M1 CARBINE

110 gr. RN ...... #8070   110 gr. FMJ ..... #8077

30-30 WINCHESTER

150 gr. RN ...... #8080   170 gr. FP ...... #8085

308 WINCHESTER

150 gr. SP ...... #8090   165 gr. SP ...... #8095
150 gr. BTSP .... #8091   165 gr. BTSP .... #8098
168 gr. BTHP (Match) .... #8097

30-06 SPRINGFIELD

150 gr. SP ...... #8110   168 gr. BTHP
150 gr. BTSP .... #8111   (Match) .... #8117
165 gr. BTSP .... #8115   180 gr. SP ...... #8118

300 WINCHESTER MAG.

165 gr. BTSP ... #8202   190 gr. BTSP ..... #8220
180 gr. SP ..... #8200

PISTOL CARTRIDGES

25 AUTO

50 gr. FMJ-RN .... #9000
50 gr. JHP .... #9002

380 AUTO

90 gr. JHP ...... #9010
100 gr. FMJ ..... #9015

9MM LUGER

90 gr. JHP ...... #9020
100 gr. FMJ ..... #9023
115 gr. JHP ..... #9025
115 gr. FMJ ..... #9026
124 gr. FMJ-FP .. #9027
124 gr. FMJ-RN .. #9029
147 gr. HP ...... #9028

38 SPECIAL

125 gr. JHP .... #9032
140 gr. JHP .... #9035
148 gr. HBWC (Match) ... #9043
158 gr. JHP .... #9036
L 158 gr. LRN .... #9045
L 158 gr. SWC .... #9046
L 158 gr. SWC/HP ...... #9047

357 MAG.

125 gr. JHP .... #9050
125 gr. JFP .... #9053
140 gr. JHP .... #9055
158 gr. JHP .... #9056
158 gr. JFP .... #9058
L 158 gr. SWC .... #9065
L 158 gr. SWC/HP ...... #9066

10MM

155 gr. JHP .... #9122
170 gr. JHP .... #9125
200 gr. FMJ-FP .... #9128
200 gr. HP .... #9129

44 REM. MAG.

180 gr. JHP .... #9081
200 gr. JHP .... #9080
240 gr. JHP .... #9085
L 240 gr. SWC .... #9087
L 240 gr. SWC/HP ...... #9086

45 ACP

185 gr. JHP .... #9090
200 gr. SWC .... #9110
200 gr. FMJ-C/T (Match) .. #9111
230 gr. FMJ-RN .... #9097
230 gr. FMJ-FP .... #9098

REMINGTON CENTERFIRE RIFLE CARTRIDGES

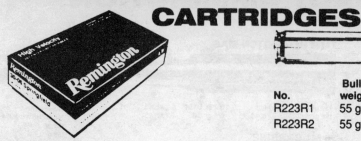

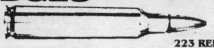

223 REMINGTON (5.56MM)

No.	Bullet weight	Bullet style	Wt. case, lbs.
R223R1	55 gr.	Pointed Soft Point	15
R223R2	55 gr.	Hollow Point Power-Lokt®	15
R223R3	55 gr.	Metal Case	15
R223R4†	60 gr.	Hollow Point	14

20 IN A BOX, 500 IN A CASE.

17 REMINGTON

No.	Bullet weight	Bullet style	Wt. case, lbs.
R17REM	25 gr.	Hollow Point Power-Lokt®	12

20 IN A BOX, 500 IN A CASE.

6MM REMINGTON

No.	Bullet weight	Bullet style	Wt. case, lbs.
R6MM1*	80 gr.	Pointed Soft Point	26
R6MM2*	80 gr.	Hollow Point Power-Lokt®	26
R6MM4	100 gr.	Pointed Soft Point Core-Lokt®	26

20 IN A BOX, 500 IN A CASE.

* May be used in rifles chambered for .244 Remington.

22 HORNET

No.	Bullet weight	Bullet style	Wt. case, lbs.
R22HN1	45 gr.	Pointed Soft Point	9
R22HN2	45 gr.	Hollow Point	9

20 IN A BOX, 500 IN A CASE.

222 REMINGTON

No.	Bullet weight	Bullet style	Wt. case, lbs.
R222R1	50 gr.	Pointed Soft Point	14
R222R4	50 gr.	Hollow Point Power-Lokt®	14
R222R4	55 gr.	Metal Case	14

20 IN A BOX, 500 IN A CASE.

6MM BENCH REST REMINGTON

No.	Bullet weight	Bullet style	Wt. case, lbs.
R6MMBR†	100 gr.	Pointed Soft Point	21

20 IN A BOX, 500 IN A CASE.

243 WIN.

No.	Bullet weight	Bullet style	Wt. case, lbs.
R243W1	80 gr.	Pointed Soft Point	25
R243W2	80 gr.	Hollow Point Power-Lokt®	25
R243W3	100 gr.	Pointed Soft Point Core-Lokt®	25

20 IN A BOX, 500 IN A CASE.

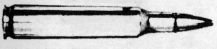

222 REMINGTON MAGNUM

No.	Bullet weight	Bullet style	Wt. case, lbs.
R222M1	55 gr.	Pointed Soft Point	15
R222M2	55 gr.	Hollow Point Power-Lokt®	15

20 IN A BOX, 500 IN A CASE.

25-06 REMINGTON

No.	Bullet weight	Bullet style	Wt. case, lbs.
R25061	87 gr.	Hollow Point Power-Lokt®	27
R25062	100 gr.	Pointed Soft Point Core-Lokt®	27
R25063	120 gr.	Pointed Soft Point Core-Lokt®	27

20 IN A BOX, 500 IN A CASE.

22-250 REMINGTON

No.	Bullet weight	Bullet style	Wt. case, lbs.
R22501	55 gr.	Pointed Soft Point	21
R22502	55 gr.	Hollow Point Power-Lokt®	21

20 IN A BOX, 500 IN A CASE.

REMINGTON CENTERFIRE RIFLE CARTRIDGES

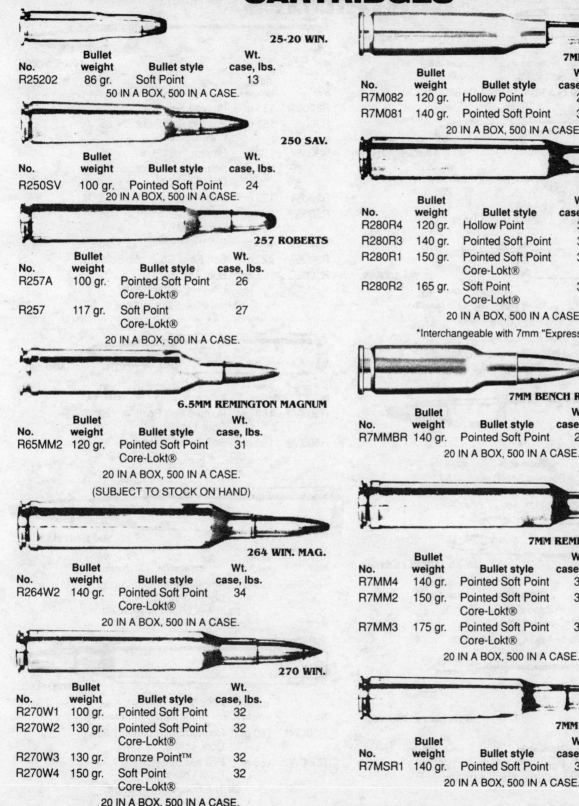
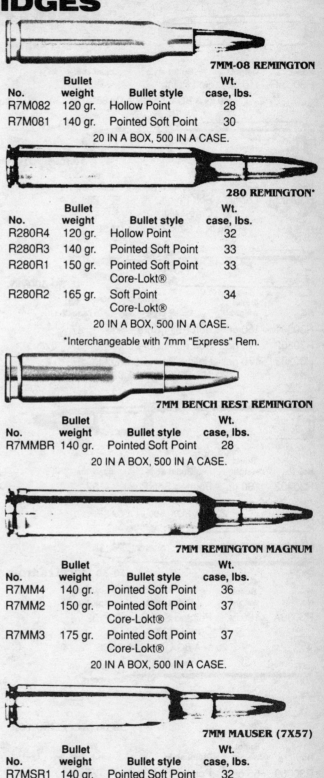

25-20 WIN.

No.	Bullet weight	Bullet style	Wt. case, lbs.
R25202	86 gr.	Soft Point	13

50 IN A BOX, 500 IN A CASE.

250 SAV.

No.	Bullet weight	Bullet style	Wt. case, lbs.
R250SV	100 gr.	Pointed Soft Point	24

20 IN A BOX, 500 IN A CASE.

257 ROBERTS

No.	Bullet weight	Bullet style	Wt. case, lbs.
R257A	100 gr.	Pointed Soft Point Core-Lokt®	26
R257	117 gr.	Soft Point Core-Lokt®	27

20 IN A BOX, 500 IN A CASE.

6.5MM REMINGTON MAGNUM

No.	Bullet weight	Bullet style	Wt. case, lbs.
R65MM2	120 gr.	Pointed Soft Point Core-Lokt®	31

20 IN A BOX, 500 IN A CASE.

(SUBJECT TO STOCK ON HAND)

264 WIN. MAG.

No.	Bullet weight	Bullet style	Wt. case, lbs.
R264W2	140 gr.	Pointed Soft Point Core-Lokt®	34

20 IN A BOX, 500 IN A CASE.

270 WIN.

No.	Bullet weight	Bullet style	Wt. case, lbs.
R270W1	100 gr.	Pointed Soft Point	32
R270W2	130 gr.	Pointed Soft Point Core-Lokt®	32
R270W3	130 gr.	Bronze Point™	32
R270W4	150 gr.	Soft Point Core-Lokt®	32

20 IN A BOX, 500 IN A CASE.

7MM-08 REMINGTON

No.	Bullet weight	Bullet style	Wt. case, lbs.
R7M082	120 gr.	Hollow Point	28
R7M081	140 gr.	Pointed Soft Point	30

20 IN A BOX, 500 IN A CASE.

280 REMINGTON*

No.	Bullet weight	Bullet style	Wt. case, lbs.
R280R4	120 gr.	Hollow Point	32
R280R3	140 gr.	Pointed Soft Point	33
R280R1	150 gr.	Pointed Soft Point Core-Lokt®	33
R280R2	165 gr.	Soft Point Core-Lokt®	34

20 IN A BOX, 500 IN A CASE.

*Interchangeable with 7mm "Express" Rem.

7MM BENCH REST REMINGTON

No.	Bullet weight	Bullet style	Wt. case, lbs.
R7MMBR	140 gr.	Pointed Soft Point	28

20 IN A BOX, 500 IN A CASE.

7MM REMINGTON MAGNUM

No.	Bullet weight	Bullet style	Wt. case, lbs.
R7MM4	140 gr.	Pointed Soft Point	36
R7MM2	150 gr.	Pointed Soft Point Core-Lokt®	37
R7MM3	175 gr.	Pointed Soft Point Core-Lokt®	37

20 IN A BOX, 500 IN A CASE.

7MM MAUSER (7X57)

No.	Bullet weight	Bullet style	Wt. case, lbs.
R7MSR1	140 gr.	Pointed Soft Point	32

20 IN A BOX, 500 IN A CASE.

REMINGTON CENTERFIRE RIFLE CARTRIDGES

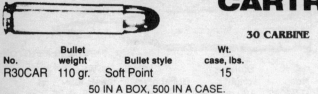

30 CARBINE

No.	Bullet weight	Bullet style	Wt. case, lbs.
R30CAR	110 gr.	Soft Point	15

50 IN A BOX, 500 IN A CASE.

30 REMINGTON

No.	Bullet weight	Bullet style	Wt. case, lbs.
R30REM	170 gr.	Soft Point Core-Lokt®	26

20 IN A BOX, 500 IN A CASE.

30-30 WIN.

No.	Bullet weight	Bullet style	Wt. case, lbs.
R30301	150 gr.	Soft Point,Core-Lokt®	27
R30302	170 gr.	Soft Point,Core-Lokt®	27
R30303	170 gr.	Hollow Point,Core-Lokt®	27

20 IN A BOX, 500 IN A CASE.

30-40 KRAG

No.	Bullet weight	Bullet style	Wt. case, lbs.
R30402	180 gr.	Pointed Soft Point Core-Lokt®	32

20 IN A BOX, 500 IN A CASE.

30-30 "ACCELERATOR"

No.	Bullet weight	Bullet style	Wt. case, lbs.
R3030A	180 gr.	Pointed Soft Point Core-Lokt®	32

20 IN A BOX, 500 IN A CASE.

30-06 "ACCELERATOR"

No.	Bullet weight	Bullet style	Wt. case, lbs.
R30069	55 gr.	Pointed Soft Point	26

20 IN A BOX, 500 IN A CASE.

30-06 SPFD.

No.	Bullet weight	Bullet style	Wt. case, lbs.
R30061	125 gr.	Pointed Soft Point	35
R30062	150 gr.	Pointed Soft Point Core-Lokt®	35
R30063	150 gr.	Bronze Point™	35
R3006B	165 gr.	Pointed Soft Point Core-Lokt®	35
R30064	180 gr.	Soft Point Core-Lokt®	35
R30065	180 gr.	Pointed Soft Point Core-Lokt®	35
R30066	180 gr.	Bronze Point™	35
R30067	220 gr.	Soft Point Core-Lokt®	35
R3006C	168 gr.	Boat Tail Hollow Point (Match)	31

20 IN A BOX, 500 IN A CASE.

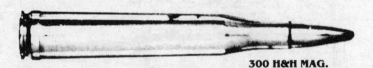

300 SAV.

No.	Bullet weight	Bullet style	Wt. case, lbs.
R30SV2	150 gr.	Pointed Soft Point Core-Lokt®	29
R30SV3	180 gr.	Soft Point Core-Lokt®	29

20 IN A BOX, 500 IN A CASE.

300 H&H MAG.

No.	Bullet weight	Bullet style	Wt. case, lbs.
R300HH	180 gr.	Pointed Soft Point Core-Lokt®	39

20 IN A BOX, 500 IN A CASE.

300 WIN. MAG.

No.	Bullet weight	Bullet style	Wt. case, lbs.
R300W1	150 gr.	Pointed Soft Point Core-Lokt®	39
R300W2	180 gr.	Pointed Soft Point Core-Lokt®	39

20 IN A BOX, 500 IN A CASE.

REMINGTON CENTERFIRE RIFLE CARTRIDGES

WITH KLEANBORE® PRIMING

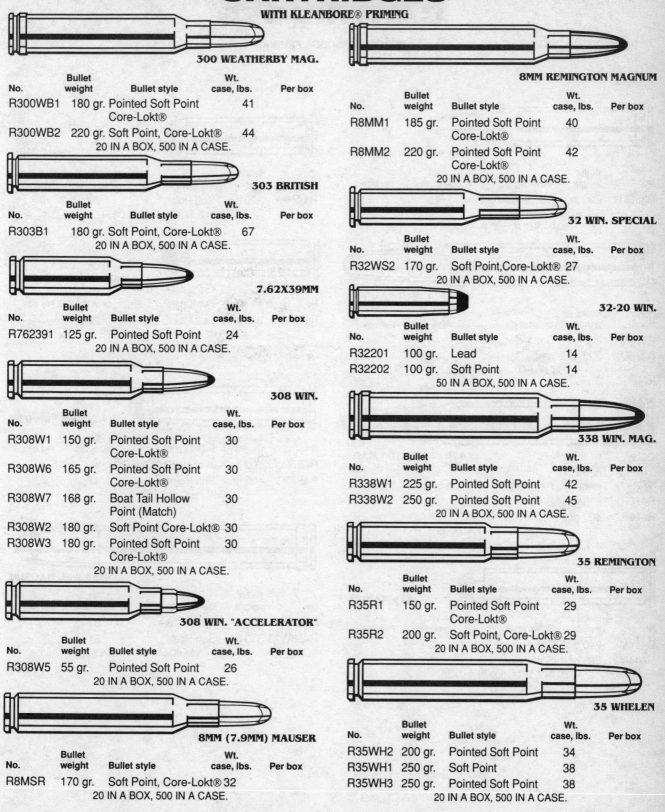

300 WEATHERBY MAG.

No.	Bullet weight	Bullet style	Wt. case, lbs.	Per box
R300WB1	180 gr.	Pointed Soft Point Core-Lokt®	41	
R300WB2	220 gr.	Soft Point, Core-Lokt®	44	

20 IN A BOX, 500 IN A CASE.

303 BRITISH

No.	Bullet weight	Bullet style	Wt. case, lbs.	Per box
R303B1	180 gr.	Soft Point, Core-Lokt®	67	

20 IN A BOX, 500 IN A CASE.

7.62X39MM

No.	Bullet weight	Bullet style	Wt. case, lbs.	Per box
R762391	125 gr.	Pointed Soft Point	24	

20 IN A BOX, 500 IN A CASE.

308 WIN.

No.	Bullet weight	Bullet style	Wt. case, lbs.	Per box
R308W1	150 gr.	Pointed Soft Point Core-Lokt®	30	
R308W6	165 gr.	Pointed Soft Point Core-Lokt®	30	
R308W7	168 gr.	Boat Tail Hollow Point (Match)	30	
R308W2	180 gr.	Soft Point Core-Lokt®	30	
R308W3	180 gr.	Pointed Soft Point Core-Lokt®	30	

20 IN A BOX, 500 IN A CASE.

308 WIN. "ACCELERATOR"

No.	Bullet weight	Bullet style	Wt. case, lbs.	Per box
R308W5	55 gr.	Pointed Soft Point	26	

20 IN A BOX, 500 IN A CASE.

8MM (7.9MM) MAUSER

No.	Bullet weight	Bullet style	Wt. case, lbs.	Per box
R8MSR	170 gr.	Soft Point, Core-Lokt®	32	

20 IN A BOX, 500 IN A CASE.

8MM REMINGTON MAGNUM

No.	Bullet weight	Bullet style	Wt. case, lbs.	Per box
R8MM1	185 gr.	Pointed Soft Point Core-Lokt®	40	
R8MM2	220 gr.	Pointed Soft Point Core-Lokt®	42	

20 IN A BOX, 500 IN A CASE.

32 WIN. SPECIAL

No.	Bullet weight	Bullet style	Wt. case, lbs.	Per box
R32WS2	170 gr.	Soft Point, Core-Lokt®	27	

20 IN A BOX, 500 IN A CASE.

32-20 WIN.

No.	Bullet weight	Bullet style	Wt. case, lbs.	Per box
R32201	100 gr.	Lead	14	
R32202	100 gr.	Soft Point	14	

50 IN A BOX, 500 IN A CASE.

338 WIN. MAG.

No.	Bullet weight	Bullet style	Wt. case, lbs.	Per box
R338W1	225 gr.	Pointed Soft Point	42	
R338W2	250 gr.	Pointed Soft Point	45	

20 IN A BOX, 500 IN A CASE.

35 REMINGTON

No.	Bullet weight	Bullet style	Wt. case, lbs.	Per box
R35R1	150 gr.	Pointed Soft Point Core-Lokt®	29	
R35R2	200 gr.	Soft Point, Core-Lokt®	29	

20 IN A BOX, 500 IN A CASE.

35 WHELEN

No.	Bullet weight	Bullet style	Wt. case, lbs.	Per box
R35WH2	200 gr.	Pointed Soft Point	34	
R35WH1	250 gr.	Soft Point	38	
R35WH3	250 gr.	Pointed Soft Point	38	

20 IN A BOX, 500 IN A CASE.

REMINGTON CENTERFIRE RIFLE CARTRIDGES

WITH KLEANBORE® PRIMING

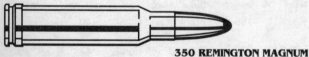

350 REMINGTON MAGNUM

No.	Bullet weight	Bullet style	Wt. case, lbs.	Per box
R350M1	200 gr.	Pointed Soft Point Core-Lokt®	40	
		20 IN A BOX, 500 IN A CASE.		

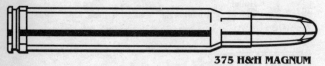

375 H&H MAGNUM

No.	Bullet weight	Bullet style	Wt. case, lbs.	Per box
R375M1	270 gr.	Soft Point	48	
R375M2	300 gr.	Metal Case	48	
		20 IN A BOX, 500 IN A CASE.		

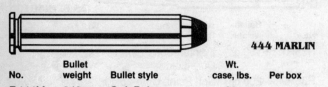

416 REMINGTON MAG.

No.	Bullet weight	Bullet style	Wt. case, lbs.	Per box
R416R1	400 gr.	Solid	56	
R416R2	400 gr.	Pointed Soft Point	56	
		20 IN A BOX, 500 IN A CASE.		

444 MARLIN

No.	Bullet weight	Bullet style	Wt. case, lbs.	Per box
R444M	240 gr.	Soft Point	38	
R444M2	265 gr.	Soft Point	40	
		20 IN A BOX, 500 IN A CASE.		

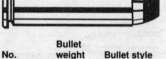

44-40 WIN.

No.	Bullet weight	Bullet style	Wt. case, lbs.	Per box
R4440W	200 gr.	Soft Point	23	
		50 IN A BOX, 500 IN A CASE.		

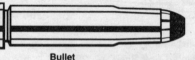

44 REMINGTON MAGNUM

No.	Bullet weight	Bullet style	Wt. case, lbs.	Per box
R44MG2	240 gr.	Soft Point	29	
		20 IN A BOX, 500 IN A CASE.		

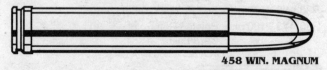

45-70 GOVERNMENT

No.	Bullet weight	Bullet style	Wt. case, lbs.	Per box
R4570L	300 gr.	Jacketed Hollow Point	45	
R4570G	405 gr.	Soft Point	47	
		20 IN A BOX, 500 IN A CASE.		

458 WIN. MAGNUM

No.	Bullet weight	Bullet style	Wt. case, lbs.	Per box
R458W1	500 gr.	Metal Case	61	
R458W2	510 gr.	Soft Point	61	
		20 IN A BOX, 500 IN A CASE.		

REMINGTON CENTERFIRE PISTOL AND REVOLVER CARTRIDGES

WITH KLEANBORE® PRIMING

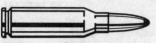

221 REMINGTON "FIRE BALL"

No.	Bullet weight	Bullet style	Wt. case, lbs.	Per box
R221F	50 gr.	Pointed Soft Point	12	

20 IN A BOX, 500 IN A CASE.

25 (6.35MM) AUTO. PISTOL

No.	Bullet weight	Bullet style	Wt. case, lbs.	Per box
R25AP	50 gr.	Metal Case	7	

50 IN A BOX, 500 IN A CASE.

32 S&W

No.	Bullet weight	Bullet style	Wt. case, lbs.	Per box
R32SW	88 gr.	Lead	11	

50 IN A BOX, 500 IN A CASE.

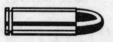

32 S&W LONG

No.	Bullet weight	Bullet style	Wt. case, lbs.	Per box
R32SWL	98 gr.	Lead	12	

50 IN A BOX, 500 IN A CASE.

32 (7.65MM) AUTO. PISTOL

No.	Bullet weight	Bullet style	Wt. case, lbs.	Per box
R32AP	71 gr.	Metal Case	9	

50 IN A BOX, 500 IN A CASE.

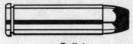

357 MAGNUM

No.	Bullet weight	Bullet style	Wt. case, lbs.	Per box
R357M7	110 gr.	Semi-Jacketed Hollow Point	16	
R357M1	125 gr.	Semi-Jacketed Hollow Point	17	
R357M8	125 gr.	Semi-Jacketed Soft Point	17	
R357M9	140 gr.	Semi-Jacketed Hollow Point	18	
R357M2	158 gr.	Semi-Jacketed Hollow Point	19	
R357M3	158 gr.	Soft Point	19	
R357M5	158 gr.	Lead	19	
R357M6	158 gr.	Lead (Brass Case)	20	
R357M10	180 gr.	Semi-Jacketed Hollow Point	22	
R357M11	140 gr.	Semi-Jacketed Hollow Point (Med. Vel.)	16	
R357MB	140 gr.	Multi-Ball	18	

50 IN A BOX, 500 IN A CASE.

357 REMINGTON MAXIMUM

No.	Bullet weight	Bullet style	Wt. case, lbs.	Per box
357MX1	158 gr.	Semi-Jacketed Hollow Point	29	

20 IN A BOX, 500 IN A CASE.

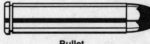

9MM LUGER AUTO. PISTOL

No.	Bullet weight	Bullet style	Wt. case, lbs.	Per box
R9MM5	88 gr.	Jacketed Hollow Point	20	
R9MM1	115 gr.	Jacketed Hollow Point	22	
R9MM3	115 gr.	Metal Case	22	
R9MM2	124 gr.	Metal Case	23	
R9MM6	115 gr.	Jacketed Hollow Point (+P)	13	
R9MM7	140 gr.	JHP (Practice)	15	
R9MM8†	147 gr.	JHP	16	

50 IN A BOX, 500 IN A CASE.

> (+P) Ammunition with (+P) on the case headstamp is loaded to higher pressure. Use only in firearms designated for this cartridge and so recommended by the gun manufacturer.

†New for 1990

REMINGTON CENTERFIRE PISTOL AND REVOLVER CARTRIDGES

380 AUTO. PISTOL

No.	Bullet weight	Bullet style	Wt. case, lbs.
R380A1	88 gr.	Jacketed Hollow Point	12
R380AP	95 gr.	Metal Case	12

50 IN A BOX, 500 IN A CASE.

38 AUTO. COLT PISTOL

Adapted only for 38 Colt Sporting, Military and Pocket Model Automatic Pistols.

No.	Bullet weight	Bullet style	Wt. case, lbs.
R38ACP	130 gr.	Metal Case	16

50 IN A BOX, 500 IN A CASE.
(Subject to stock on hand)

38 SUPER AUTO. COLT PISTOL

Adapted only for 38 Colt Super and Colt Commander Automatic Pistols.

No.	Bullet weight	Bullet style	Wt. case, lbs.
R38SU1	115 gr.	Jacketed Hollow Point (+P)	14
R38SUP	130 gr.	Metal Case (+P)	16

50 IN A BOX, 500 IN A CASE.

38 S&W

No.	Bullet weight	Bullet style	Wt. case, lbs.
R38SW	146 gr.	Lead	16

50 IN A BOX, 500 IN A CASE.

38 SPECIAL

No.	Bullet weight	Bullet style	Wt. case, lbs.
R38S1	95 gr.	Semi-Jacketed Hollow Point (+P)	13
R38S10	110 gr.	Semi-Jacketed Hollow Point (+P)	13
R38S2	125 gr.	Semi-Jacketed Hollow Point (+P)	17
R38S13	125 gr.	Semi-Jacket Soft Point (+P)	17
R38S3	148 gr.	Targetmaster Lead Wadcutter, brass case	17
R38S4	158 gr.	Targetmaster Lead Round Nose	18
R38S5	158 gr.	Lead	18
R38S6	158 gr.	Lead Semi-Wadcutter	18
R38S14	158 gr.	Lead Semi-Wadcutter (+P)	18
R38S7	158 gr.	Metal Point	18
R38S12	158 gr.	Lead Hollow Point (+P)	18
R38SMB	140 gr.	Multi-Ball	17

50 IN A BOX, 500 IN A CASE.

38 SHORT COLT

No.	Bullet weight	Bullet style	Wt. case, lbs.
R38SC	125 gr.	Lead	14

50 IN A BOX, 500 IN A CASE.

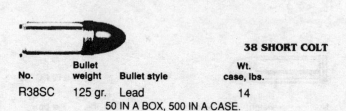

10MM AUTO.

No.	Bullet weight	Bullet style	Wt. case, lbs.
R10MM1†	170 gr.	Hollow Point	21
R10MM2†	200 gr.	Metal Case	24

50 IN A BOX, 500 IN A CASE.

(+P) Ammunition with (+P) on the case headstamp is loaded to higher pressure. Use only in firearms designated for this cartridge and so recommended by the gun manufacturer.

REMINGTON CENTERFIRE PISTOL AND REVOLVER CARTRIDGES

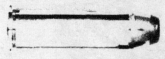

41 REMINGTON MAGNUM

No.	Bullet weight	Bullet style	Wt. case, lbs.
R41MG3†	170 gr.	Semi-Jacketed Hollow Point	24
R41MG1	210 gr.	Soft Point	26
R41MG2	210 gr.	Lead	26

50 IN A BOX, 500 IN A CASE.

44 REMINGTON MAGNUM

No.	Bullet weight	Bullet style	Wt. case, lbs.
R44MG5	180 gr.	Semi-Jacketed Hollow Point	29
R44MG1	310 gr.	Semi-Jacketed Hollow Point	27
R44MG1	240 gr.	Lead, Gas-Check	29
R44MG4	240 gr.	Lead	29
R44MG2	240 gr.	Soft Point	29
R44MG3	240 gr.	Semi-Jacketed Hollow Point	29

20 IN A BOX, 500 IN A CASE.

44 S&W SPECIAL

No.	Bullet weight	Bullet style	Wt. case, lbs.
R44SW1	200 gr.	Lead Semi-Wadcutter	22
R44SW	246 gr.	Lead	25

50 IN A BOX, 500 IN A CASE.

45 COLT

No.	Bullet weight	Bullet style	Wt. case, lbs.
R45C1	225 gr.	Lead Semi-Wadcutter	24
R45C	250 gr.	Lead	26

50 IN A BOX, 500 IN A CASE.

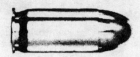

45 AUTO.

No.	Bullet weight	Bullet style	Wt. case, lbs.
R45AP1	185 gr.	Targetmaster Metal Case Wadcutter	11
R45AP2	185 gr.	Jacketed Hollow Point	11
R45AP4	230 gr.	Metal Case	13
R45AP6†	185 gr.	Jacketed Hollow Point (+P)	21

50 IN A BOX, 500 IN A CASE.

.45 AUTO. SHOT CARTRIDGE

No.	Bullet style	Wt. case, lbs.
R45AP5	650 Pellets — No. 12 Shot	18

20 IN A BOX, 500 IN A CASE.

REMINGTON CENTERFIRE BLANK

No.	Caliber	No. in case	Wt. case, lbs.
R32BLNK	32 S&W	500	4
R38SWBL	38 S&W	500	7
R38BLNK	38 Special	500	7

50 IN A BOX.

(+P) Ammunition with (+P) on the case headstamp is loaded to higher pressure. Use only in firearms designated for this cartridge and so recommended by the gun manufacturer.

REMINGTON RIMFIRE CARTRIDGES

"HIGH VELOCITY" CARTRIDGES WITH "GOLDEN" BULLETS

22 SHORT

No.	Bullet weight and style	Wt. case, lbs.
1022	29 gr., Lead	29
1122	27 gr., Lead, Hollow Point	28

50 IN A BOX, 5,000 IN A CASE.

22 LONG

No.	Bullet weight and style	Wt. case, lbs.
1322	29 gr., Lead	31

50 IN A BOX, 5,000 IN A CASE.

22 LONG RIFLE

No.	Bullet weight and style	Wt. case, lbs.
1522	40 gr., Lead	40
1622	36 gr., Lead, Hollow Point	38

50 IN A BOX, 5,000 IN A CASE.

100 PACK

No.	Bullet weight and style	Wt. case, lbs.
1500	40 gr., Lead	40
1600	36 gr., Lead, Hollow Point	38

100 IN A BOX, 5,000 IN A CASE.

"TARGET" STANDARD VELOCITY CARTRIDGES

22 SHORT

No.	Bullet weight and style	Wt. case, lbs.
5522	29 gr., Lead	29

50 IN A BOX, 5,000 IN A CASE.

22 LONG RIFLE

No.	Bullet weight and style	Wt. case, lbs.
6122	40 gr., Lead	40

50 IN A BOX, 5,000 IN A CASE.

100 PACK

No.	Bullet weight and style	Wt. case, lbs.
6100	40 gr., Lead	40

100 IN A BOX, 5,000 IN A CASE.

CB22™ CARTRIDGES LOW NOISE LEVEL

Velocity of 720 f.p.s.; the quietness of an airgun, the impact of a .22 bullet.

22 SHORT

22 LONG

No.	Bullet weight and style	Wt. case, lbs.
CB-22S Short	30 gr., Lead	29
CB-22L Long	20 gr., Lead	30

50 IN A BOX, 5,000 IN A CASE.

YELLOW JACKET® CARTRIDGES HYPER-VELOCITY

22 LONG RIFLE

No.	Bullet weight and style	Wt. case, lbs.
1722	33 gr., Truncated Cone, Hollow Point	36

50 IN A BOX, 5,000 IN A CASE.

"VIPER" CARTRIDGES HYPER-VELOCITY

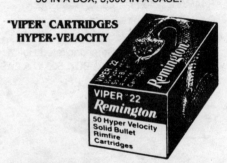

22 LONG RIFLE

No.	Bullet weight and style	Wt. case, lbs.
1922	36 gr., Truncated Cone, Solid Point, Copper Plated	38

50 IN A BOX, 5,000 IN A CASE.

"THUNDERBOLT" CARTRIDGES HI-SPEED

22 LONG RIFLE

No.	Bullet weight and style	Wt. case, lbs.
TB22A	36 gr., Truncated Cone, Solid Point	40

50 IN A BOX, 5,000 IN A CASE.

REMINGTON SHOTGUN SHELLS

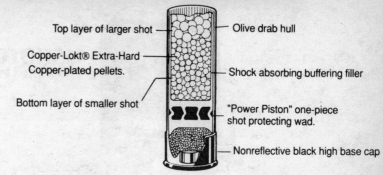

Top layer of larger shot
Copper-Lokt® Extra-Hard Copper-plated pellets.
Bottom layer of smaller shot

Olive drab hull
Shock absorbing buffering filler
"Power Piston" one-piece shot protecting wad.
Nonreflective black high base cap

- Combined large and smaller shot sizes.
- Available in lead or steel shot magnum loads.

Patented Remington Duplex® Shotgun Shell

	No.	Gauge	Length shell, in.	Powder equiv. drams	Shot, oz.	Size shot	Wt. case, lbs.
MULTIRANGE	MRP12S	12	2 3/4	Max.	1 1/2	BBx4,2x4,,2x6, 4x6	35
DUPLEX®	MRP12H	12	3	Max.	1 7/8	BBx4, 2x4, 2x6, 4x6	41
MAGNUM							
COPPER PLATED							
LEAD SHOT							
MULTIRANGE	MRS10M	10	3 1/2	Max.	1 3/4	TxBB†,BBBx1†	48
DUPLEX®	MRS12	12	2 3/4	Max.	1 1/8	BBx1,BBx2,BBx4,2x6,1x3	29
MAGNUM	MRS12SM	12	2 3/4	Max.	1 1/4	BBx2†,1x3†	31
STEEL SHOT	MRS12H	12	3	Max.	1 1/4	BBx1, BBx2, BBx4, 2x6,1x3	29
	MRS12HM	12	3	Max.	1 3/8	BBBx1†, BBx2†, 1x3†	35

10 IN A BOX, 250 IN A CASE.

REMINGTON "PREMIER" HIGHEST GRADE SHOTSHELLS
WITH "COPPER-LOKT" EXTRA HARD PLATED SHOT AND "POWER-PISTON" WADS

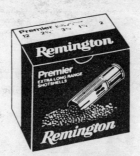

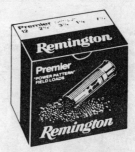

	No.	Gauge	Length shell, in.	Powder equiv. drams	Shot, oz.	Size shot	Wt. case, lbs.
PREMIER™	PR10H Mag.†	10	3 1/2	4 1/2	2 1/4	2, 4, 6	49
EXTENDED	PR12S Mag.	12	2 3/4	Max.	1 1/2	BB, 2,4, 6	34
RANGE	PR12 Mag.	12	3	4	1 5/8	4, 6	37
BUFFERD	PR12H Mag.	12	3	Max.	1 7/8	BB, 2, 4, 6†	41
MAGNUM	PR20S Mag.	20	2 3/4	Max.	1 1/8	4, 6	26
LOADS	PR20H Mag.	20	3	Max.	1 1/4	2, 4, 6	30
PREMIER™	PR12	12	2 3/4	2 3/4	1 1/4	2, 4, 6, 7 1/2	29
EXTRA LONG	PR20	20	2 3/4	2 3/4	1	4, 6	24
RANGE LOADS							
PREMIER™	PR12F	12	2 3/4	3 1/4	1 1/8	7 1/2, 8	29
"POWER-PATTERN"	PR12HF	12	2 3/4	3 1/4	1 1/4	7 1/2, 8	29
	PR20F	20	2 3/4	2 1/2	1	7 1/2, 8	23

25 IN A BOX, 250 IN A CASE.

SHOTGUN SHELLS
REMINGTON PREMIER™ TARGET LOADS

	No.	Gauge	Length shell, in.	Powder equiv. drams	Size, oz.	Size shot	Wt. case, lbs.
PREMIER™ TARGET LOADS	RTL12L•	12	2 3/4	2 3/4	1 1/8	7 1/2, 8, 8 1/2, 9	27
	RTL12M•	12	2 3/4	3	1 1/8	7 1/2, 8, 9	27
	RTL20	20	2 3/4	2 1/2	7/8	9	41
"REMLITE" PREMIER™ TARGET LOAD	LRTL12†•	12	2 3/4	—	1 1/8	7 1/2, 8, 9	27
DUPLEX® PREMIER™ TARGET LOAD	MRTL12L†•	12	2 3/4	2 3/4	1 1/8	7 1/2X8	27
	MRTL12M†•			3	1 1/8	7 1/2X8	27
SKEET LOADS	SP28	28	2 3/4	2	3/4	9	37
	SP410	.410	2 1/2	Max.	1/2	9	22
PREMIER™ PIGEON LOADS	RTL12P•	12	2 3/4	3 1/4	1 1/4	7 1/2, 8	27
	RTL12PN•	12	2 3/4	3 1/4	1 1/4	7 1/2, 8 (nickel)	27
PREMIER™ INTERNATIONAL TARGET LOADS	IRT12•	12	2 3/4	3 1/4	1 1/8	7 1/2, 8	54
	NIRT12•	12	2 3/4	3 1/4	1 1/8	7 1/2, 8 (nickel)	54

25 IN A BOX, 500 IN A CASE • 25 IN A BOX, 250 IN A CASE

REMINGTON PROMOTIONAL SHOTSHELLS

	No.	Gauge	Length shell, in.	Powder equiv. drams	Size, oz.	Size shot	Wt. case, lbs.
DOVE/QUAIL FIELD LOADS	DQ12W•	12	2 3/4	3 1/4	1	7 1/2, 8	24
	DQ16W•	16	2 3/4	2 1/2	1	7 1/2, 8	24
	DQ20W•	20	2 3/4	2 1/2	7/8	7 1/2, 8	20
RABBIT/SQUIRREL FIELD LOADS	RS12W•	12	2 3/4	3 1/4	1	6	24
	RS16W•	16	2 3/4	2 1/2	1	6	24
	RS20W•	20	2 3/4	2 1/2	1	6	20
DUCK/PHEASANT FIELD LOADS	DP12	12	2 3/4	3 3/4	1 1/4	4, 5, 6, 7 1/2	58
	DP16	16	2 3/4	3 1/4	1 1/8	4, 6, 7 1/2	52
	SP20	20	2 3/4	2 2/3	1	4, 6, 7 1/2	46
SPORT LOADS	SL12•	12	2 3/4	3 1/4	1	8	24
	SL20•	20	2 3/4	2 1/2	7/8	8	20

25 IN A BOX, 500 IN A CASE • 25 IN A BOX, 250 PER CASE

REMINGTON SHOTGUN SHELLS

REMINGTON NITRO MAGNUM®, EXPRESS™, AND SHUR SHOT® SHOTSHELLS

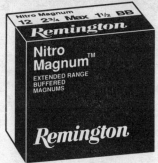  

	No.	Gauge	Length shell, in.	Powder equiv. drams	Shot, oz.	Size shot	Wt. case, lbs.
NITRO	SP10HNM•†	10	3 1/2	4 1/2	2 1/4	2, 4, 6	49
MAG®	SP12SNM•	12	2 3/4	Max.	1 1/2	2, 4, 6	34
EXTENDED	SP12NM•	12	3	4	1 5/8	2, 4, 6	35
RANGE	SP12HNM•	12	3	Max.	1 7/8	2, 4, 6†	35
BUFFERED	SP20SNM•	20	2 3/4	Max.	1 1/8	4, 6	26
MAGNUMS	SP20HNM•	20	3	Max.	1 1/4	2, 4, 6, 7 1/2	30
EXPRESS™	SP10MAG•	10	3 1/2	Max.	2	BB, 2, 4	45
EXTRA LONG RANGE	SP12	12	2 3/4	3 3/4	1 1/4	BB, 2, 4, 5, 6, 7 1/2, 9	58
LOADS	SP16	16	2 3/4	3 1/4	1 1/8	4, 5, 6, 7 1/2, 9	52
	SP16CMAG	16	2 3/4	Max.	1 1/4	2, 4, 6	58
	SP20	20	2 3/4	2 3/4	1	4, 5, 6, 7 1/2, 9	47
	SP28	28	2 3/4	2 1/4	3/4	6, 7 1/2	36
	SP410	410	2 1/2	Max.	1/2	4, 6, 7 1/2	23
	SP4103	410	3	Max.	11/16	4, 5, 6, 7 1/2, 9	31
SHUR SHOT®	R12H	12	2 3/4	3 1/4	1 1/8	4, 5, 6, 9	51
FIELD	R12H250CS•	12	2 3/4	3 1/4	1 1/8	7 1/2, 8	29
LOADS	RP12H250CS•	12	2 3/4	3 1/4	1 1/4	7 1/2, 8	30
	R16H	16	2 3/4	2 3/4	1 1/8	4, 6, 7 1/2, 8, 9	51
	R20M	20	2 3/4	2 1/2	1	4, 5, 6, 9	45
	R20M250CS•	20	2 3/4	2 1/2	1	7 1/2, 8	23

25 IN A BOX, 500 IN A CASE. • 25 IN A BOX, 250 PER CASE

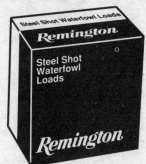

REMINGTON STEEL SHOT WATERFOWL LOADS

	No.	Gauge	Length shell, in.	Powder equiv. drams	Shot, oz.	Size shot	Wt. case, lbs.
STEEL SHOT	STL10MAG	10	3 1/2	Max.	1 3/4	T, BBB, BB, 1, 2, 3	48
WATERFOWL	STL12	12	2 3/4	Max.	1 1/8	BB, 1, 2, 3, 4, 6	28
LOADS	STL12SMAG	12	2 3/4	Max.	1 1/4	T†, BBB†, BB†, 1, 2, 3, 4	30
	STL12MAG	12	3	Max.	1 1/4	BB, 1, 2, 3, 4, 6	30
	STL12HMAG	12	3	Max.	1 3/8	T†, BBB†, BB, 1, 2, 3, 4	32
	STL20HMAG	20	3	Max.	1	2, 3, 4, 6	23

25 IN A BOX, 250 PER CASE.

†New for 1990

REMINGTON SHOTGUN SHELLS

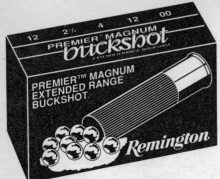

REMINGTON PREMIER™ MAGNUM BUCKSHOT
WITH EXTRA HARD NICKEL PLATED SHOT

Nickel plated extra-hard buckshot and granulated polyethylene filler for reduced deformation and improved pattern.

	No.	Gauge	Length shell, in.	Powder equiv. drams	Size Shot	Pellets	Wt. case, lbs.	Per box
PREMIER™	PR12SNBK	12	2 3/4	4	00	12	29	
MAGNUM	PR12SNBK	12	2 3/4	4	4	34	31	
EXTENDED	PR12HNBK	12	3	4	000	10	40	
RANGE	PR12HNBK	12	3	4	00	15	40	
BUCKSHOT	PR12HNBK	12	3	Max.	1	24	40	
WITH NICKEL	PR12HNBK	12	3	4	4	41	42	
PLATED SHOT								

10 IN A BOX, 250 RDS. PER CASE.

REMINGTON "EXPRESS" BUCKSHOT LOADS AND "SLUGGER" RIFLED SLUGS

	No.	Gauge	Length shell, in.	Powder equiv. drams	Size, oz.	Size shot	Wt. case, lbs.	Per box
"POWER PAKT"	SP12BK	12	2 3/4	3 3/4	—	000 Buck—8 Pellets	31	
EXPRESS™	SP12BK	12	2 3/4	3 3/4	—	00 Buck—9 Pellets	29	
BUCKSHOT	SP12BK	12	2 3/4	3 3/4	—	0 Buck—12 Pellets	32	
LOADS	SP12BK	12	2 3/4	3 3/4	—	1 Buck—16 Pellets	32	
	SP12BK	12	2 3/4	3 3/4	—	4 Buck—27 Pellets	31	
	SP16BK	16	2 3/4	3	—	1 Buck—12 Pellets	26	
	SP20BK	20	2 3/4	2 3/4	—	3 Buck—20 Pellets	24	
"POWER PAKT"	SP12SMagBK	12	2 3/4	4	—	00 Buck—12 Pellets	34	
EXPRESS™	SP12SMagBK	12	2 3/4	4	—	1 Buck—20 Pellets	34	
MAGNUM	SP12HMagBK	12	3	4	—	000 Buck—10 Pellets	40	
BUCKSHOT	SP12HMagBK	12	3	4	—	00 Buck—15 Pellets	40	
LOADS	SP12HMagBK	12	3	4	—	1 Buck—24 Pellets	40	
	SP12HMagBK	12	3	4	—	4 Buck—41 Pellets	42	
SLUGGER®	SP12SMagRS	12	2 3/4	Max.	1	Rifled Slug	26	
MAGNUM	SP12MagRS	12	3	Max.	1	Rifled Slug	26	
RIFLED SLUG								
LOADS								
SLUGGER®	SP12RS	12	2 3/4	Max.	1	Rifled Slug H.P.	26	
RIFLED SLUG	SP16RS	16	2 3/4	3	4/5	Rifled Slug H.P.	24	
LOADS	SP20RS	20	2 3/4	2 3/4	5/8	Rifled Slug H.P.	19	
	SP410RS	.410	2 1/2	Max.	1/5	Rifled Slug	8	

5 IN A BOX, 250 PER CASE

WINCHESTER SHOTSHELLS

SUPER-X GAME LOADS

Gauge	Symbol	Length of Shell In.	Powder Dram Equivalent	Velocity fps @ 3 ft.	Oz. Shot	Standard Shot Sizes
12	X12	2¾	3¾	1330	1¼	2, 4, 5, 6, 7½, 9
16	X16H	2¾	3¼	1295	1⅛	4, 6, 7½
20	X20	2¾	2¾	1220	1	4, 5, 6, 7½, 9
28	X28H	2¾	MAX	1125	1	6, 7½, 8
28	X28	2¾	2¼	1295	¾	6, 7½
410	X41	2½	MAX	1245	½	4, 6, 7½
410	X413	3	MAX	1135	11/16	4, 6, 7½

SUPER-X BUCKSHOT LOADS WITH BUFFERED SHOT

Gauge	Symbol	Length of Shell In.	Powder Dram Equivalent	Velocity fps @ 3 ft.	Total Pellets	Standard Shot Sizes
12	X12000B5	2¾	N/A	1325	8	000 Buck
12	X12RB5	2¾	N/A	1325	9	00 Buck
12	X120B5	2¾	N/A	1275	12	0 Buck
12	X121B5	2¾	N/A	1250	16	1 Buck
12	X124B5	2¾	N/A	1325	27	4 Buck
16	X16B5	2¾	N/A	1225	12	1 Buck
20	X20B5	2¾	N/A	1200	20	3 Buck

SUPER STEEL NON-TOXIC GAME LOADS

Gauge	Symbol	Length of Shell In.	Powder Dram Equivalent	Velocity fps @ 3 ft.	Oz. Shot	Standard Shot Sizes
12	W12SD	2¾	MAX	1375	1	2, 4, 6
12	X12SSL	2¾	MAX	1365	1⅛	1, 2, 3, 4, 5, 6
New 16	X16SS	2¾	MAX	1300	⅞	2, 4
20	X20SSL	2¾	MAX	1425	¾	4, 6

SUPER STEEL NON-TOXIC MAGNUM LOADS

10	X10SSM	3½	MAX	1260	1¾	BB, 1, 2
12	X12SSM	3	MAX	1265	1⅜	BB, 1, 2, 3, 4
12	X123SSM	3	MAX	1375	1¼	BB, 1, 2, 3, 4, 5
12	X12SSF	2¾	MAX	1275	1¼	BB, 1, 2, 3, 4, 5, 6
20	X20SSM	3	MAX	1330	1	2, 3, 4, 5, 6

SUPER STEEL NON-TOXIC COPPERPLATED MAGNUM LOADS

10	XS10C	3½	MAX	1350	1⅝	F, T, BBB
12	XS123	3	MAX	1375	1¼	F, T, BBB
New 12	XS12	2¾	MAX	1300	1⅛	T, BBB

XPERT FIELD LOADS — IMPROVED UPLAND GAME LOAD

Gauge	Symbol	Length of Shell In.	Powder Dram Equivalent	Velocity fps @ 3 ft.	Oz. Shot	Standard Shot Sizes
12	WW12SP	2¾	3¼	1220	1¼	6, 7½, 8
12	UWH12	2¾	3¼	1255	1⅛	6, 7½, 8, 9
12	UWL12	2¾	3¼	1290	1	6, 7½, 8
16	UWH16	2¾	2¾	1185	1⅛	6, 7½, 8
20	UWH20	2¾	2½	1165	1	6, 7½, 8, 9
20	UWL20	2¾	2½	1210	⅞	6, 7½, 8

WINCHESTER AA® TARGET LOADS

Gauge	Symbol	Length of Shell In.	Powder Dram Equivalent	Velocity fps @ 3 ft.	Oz. Shot	Standard Shot Sizes
New 12	W12AAHANV	2¾	3	1200	1⅛	7½, 8, 9
12	WW12MAAP	2¾	3	1200	1⅛	7½, 8, 9
12	W12SLAA	2¾	2¾	1125	1⅛	7½, 8, 8½, 9
12	WW12AAP	2¾	2¾	1145	1⅛	7½, 8, 9
12	WW12LAAP	2¾	2¾	1180	1	7½, 8, 9
20	WW20AAP	2¾	2½	1200	⅞	8, 9
28	WW28AAP	2¾	2	1200	¾	9
410	WW41AAP	2½	MAX	1200	½	9

DOUBLE X MAGNUM GAME LOADS — COPPERPLATED, BUFFERED SHOT

Gauge	Symbol	Length of Shell In.	Powder Dram Equivalent	Velocity fps @ 3 ft.	Oz. Shot	Standard Shot Sizes
10	X103XC	3½	4½	1210	2¼	BB, 2, 4
New 10	X103XCT	3½	4½	1210	2¼	6
12	X123XC	3	4	1210	1⅞	BB, 2, 4, 6
12	X12MXC	3	4	1280	1⅝	2, 4, 5, 6
12	X123MXCT	3	MAX	1125	2	4, 5, 6
12	X12XC	2¾	MAX	1260	1½	BB, 2, 4, 5, 6
New 12	X12HXCT	2¾	MAX	1250	1⅝	4, 5, 6
16	X16XC	2¾	3¼	1260	1¼	4, 6
20	X203XC	3	3	1185	1¼	2, 4, 6
20	X20XC	2¾	2¾	1175	1⅛	4, 6, 7½

DOUBLE X MAGNUM BUCKSHOT LOADS — COPPERPLATED, BUFFERED SHOT

Gauge	Symbol	Length of Shell In.	Powder Dram Equivalent	Velocity fps @ 3 ft.	Total Pellets	Standard Shot Sizes
10	X10C4B	3½	N/A	1100	54	4 Buck
12	X123C000B	3	N/A	1225	10	000 Buck
12	X12XC3B5	3	N/A	1210	15	00 Buck
12	X12XC0B5	2¾	N/A	1290	12	00 Buck
12	X12C1B	2¾	N/A	1075	20	1 Buck
•12	X1231B5	3	N/A	1040	24	1 Buck
12	X12XCMB5	3	N/A	1210	41	4 Buck
12	X12XC4B5	2¾	N/A	1250	34	4 Buck
New 20	X203C3B	3	N/A	1150	24	3 Buck

(• Not Copperplated)

SUPER-X HOLLOW POINT RIFLE SLUG LOADS

Gauge	Symbol	Length of Shell In.	Powder Dram Equivalent	Velocity fps @ 3 ft.	Oz.	Standard Shot Sizes
12	X12RS15	2¾	MAX	1600	1	Rifled Slug
16	X16RS5	2¾	MAX	1570	⅘	Rifled Slug
20	X20RSM5	2¾	MAX	1570	¾	Rifled Slug
410	X41RS5	2½	MAX	1815	⅕	Rifled Slug

HOLLOW POINT RIFLE SLUG TRAJECTORY

25 yds.	50 yds.	75 yds.	100 yds.
+.2"	0"	−1.8"	−5.5"

See illustration on preceeding page for graphic representation of trajectory.

FIELD TRIAL AND BLANK LOADS WESTERN® FIELD TRIAL POPPER-LOAD

12	XP12FBL	2¾	—	—	—	Blank

BLANK LOADS

10	UW10BL	2⅞	8	Black Powder	—	Blank
12	UW12BL	2¾	6	Black Powder	—	Blank

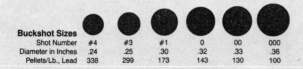

Buckshot Sizes						
Shot Number	#4	#3	#1	0	00	000
Diameter in Inches	.24	.25	.30	.32	.33	.36
Pellets/Lb., Lead	338	299	173	143	130	100

Shot Sizes													
Shot Number	9	8	7½	6	5	4	3	2	1	BB	BBB	T	F
Diameter in Inches	.08	.09	.095	.11	.12	.13	.14	.15	.16	.18	.19	.20	.22
Pellets/Oz., Lead:	585	410	350	225	170	135	—	87	—	50	—	—	—
Steel:	—	—	—	316	243	191	153	125	103	72	61	53	39

Ballistics

FEDERAL BALLISTICS

Hi-Power® Centerfire Rifle Ballistics [Approximate] Usage Key: ①=Varmints, predators, small game ②=Medium game ③=Large, heavy game ④=Dangerous game ⑤=Target shooting, training, practice

USAGE	FEDERAL LOAD NO.	CALIBER	BULLET WGT. IN GRAINS	GRAMS	BULLET STYLE**	FACTORY PRIMER NO.	VELOCITY IN FEET PER SECOND (TO NEAREST 10 FEET) MUZZLE	100 YDS.	200 YDS.	300 YDS.	400 YDS.	500 YDS.	ENERGY IN FOOT/POUNDS (TO NEAREST 5 FOOT/POUNDS) MUZZLE	100 YDS.	200 YDS.	300 YDS.	400 YDS.	500 YDS.
①	222A	222 Rem. (5.56x43mm)	50	3.24	Soft Point	205	3140	2600	2120	1700	1350	1110	1095	750	500	320	200	135
⑤	222B		55	3.56	FMJ Boat-tail	205	3020	2740	2480	2230	1990	1780	1115	915	750	610	485	385
①	22250A	22-250 Rem.	55	3.56	Soft Point	210	3680	3140	2660	2220	1830	1490	1655	1200	860	605	410	270
①	22250C		40	2.59	Hollow Point Varmint	210	4000	3320	2720	2200	1740	1360	1420	980	660	430	265	165
①	223A	223 Rem. (5.56x45mm)	55	3.56	Soft Point	205	3240	2750	2300	1910	1550	1270	1280	920	650	445	295	195
⑤	223B		55	3.56	FMJ Boat-tail	205	3240	2950	2670	2410	2170	1940	1280	1060	875	710	575	460
①	223C		55	3.56	Hollow Point Boat-tail	205	3240	2770	2340	1950	1610	1330	1280	935	670	465	315	215
①	223D		40	2.59	Hollow Point Varmint	205	3650	3010	2450	1950	1530	1330	1185	805	535	340	205	130
①	6A	6mm Rem.	80	5.18	Soft Point	210	3470	3060	2690	2350	2040	1750	2140	1665	1290	980	735	540
②	6B		100	6.48	Hi-Shok Soft Point	210	3100	2830	2570	2330	2100	1890	2135	1775	1470	1205	985	790
①	243A	243 Win. (6.16x51mm)	80	5.18	Soft Point	210	3350	2960	2590	2260	1950	1670	1995	1550	1195	905	675	495
②	243B		100	6.48	Hi-Shok Soft Point	210	2960	2700	2450	2220	1990	1790	1945	1615	1330	1090	880	710
①	243V		60	3.89	Hollow Point Varmint	210	3600	3110	2660	2260	1890	1560	1725	1285	945	680	475	325
②	257A	257 Roberts (Hi-Vel. +P)	117	7.58	Hi-Shok Soft Point	210	2780	2560	2360	2160	1970	1790	2010	1710	1445	1210	1010	835
①	2506A	25-06 Rem.	90	5.83	Hollow Point Varmint	210	3440	3040	2680	2340	2030	1750	2365	1850	1435	1100	825	610
②	2506B		117	7.58	Hi-Shok Soft Point	210	2990	2730	2480	2250	2030	1830	2320	1985	1645	1350	1100	885
②	270A	270 Win.	130	8.42	Hi-Shok Soft Point	210	3060	2800	2560	2330	2110	1900	2700	2265	1890	1565	1285	1045
②	270B		150	9.72	Hi-Shok Soft Point RN	210	2850	2500	2180	1890	1620	1390	2705	2085	1585	1185	870	640
②	7A	7mm Mauser	175	11.34	Hi-Shok Soft Point RN	210	2440	2140	1860	1600	1380	1200	2315	1775	1340	1000	740	565
②	7B	(7x57mm Mauser)	140	9.07	Hi-Shok Soft Point	210	2660	2450	2260	2070	1890	1730	2200	1865	1585	1330	1110	930
② NEW	280B	280 Rem.	150	9.72	Soft Point	210	2890	2670	2460	2260	2060	1880	2780	2370	2015	1695	1420	1180
②	7RA	7mm Rem. Magnum	150	9.72	Hi-Shok Soft Point	215	3110	2830	2570	2320	2090	1870	3220	2670	2200	1790	1450	1160
③	7RB		175	11.34	Hi-Shok Soft Point	215	2860	2650	2440	2240	2060	1880	3180	2720	2310	1960	1640	1370
②	730A	7-30 Waters	120	7.77	Boat-tail Soft Point	210	2700	2300	1930	1600	1330	1140	1940	1405	990	685	470	345
①	30CA	30 Carbine	110	7.13	Hi-Shok Soft Point RN	205	1990	1570	1240	1040	920	840	965	600	375	260	210	175
②	76239B	7.62x39mm Soviet	123	7.97	Hi-Shok Soft Point	210	2300	2030	1780	1550	1350	1200	1445	1125	860	655	500	395
②	3030A	30-30 Win.	150	9.72	Hi-Shok Soft Point FN	210	2390	2020	1680	1400	1180	1040	1900	1355	945	650	460	355
②	3030B		170	11.01	Hi-Shok Soft Point FN	210	2200	1900	1620	1380	1190	1060	1830	1355	990	720	535	425
①	3030C		125	8.10	Hollow Point Varmint	210	2570	2090	1660	1320	1080	960	1830	1210	770	480	320	260
②	3006A	30-06 Springfield	150	9.72	Hi-Shok Soft Point	210	2910	2620	2340	2080	1840	1620	2820	2280	1825	1445	1130	875
③	3006B	(7.62x63mm)	180	11.66	Hi-Shok Soft Point	210	2700	2470	2250	2040	1850	1660	2915	2435	2025	1665	1360	1105
①	3006C		125	8.10	Hi-Shok Soft Point	210	3140	2780	2450	2140	1850	1600	2735	2145	1660	1270	955	705
②	3006D		165	10.69	Boat-tail Soft Point	210	2800	2610	2420	2240	2070	1910	2870	2490	2150	1840	1580	1340
③	3006H		220	14.25	Hi-Shok Soft Point RN	210	2410	2130	1870	1630	1420	1250	2835	2215	1705	1300	985	760
③	3006J		180	11.66	Hi-Shok Soft Point RN	210	2700	2350	2020	1730	1470	1250	2915	2200	1630	1190	860	620
②	300A	300 Savage	150	9.72	Hi-Shok Soft Point	210	2630	2350	2100	1850	1630	1430	2305	1845	1460	1145	885	685
②	300B		180	11.66	Hi-Shok Soft Point	210	2350	2140	1940	1750	1570	1410	2205	1825	1495	1215	985	800
②	308A	308 Win. (7.62x51mm)	150	9.72	Hi-Shok Soft Point	210	2820	2530	2260	2010	1770	1560	2650	2140	1705	1345	1050	810
②	308B		180	11.66	Hi-Shok Soft Point	210	2620	2390	2180	1970	1780	1600	2745	2290	1895	1555	1270	1030
③	300WB	300 Win. Magnum	180	11.66	Hi-Shok Soft Point	215	2960	2750	2540	2340	2160	1980	3500	3010	2580	2195	1860	1565
②	303A	303 British	180	11.66	Hi-Shok Soft Point	210	2460	2230	2020	1820	1630	1460	2420	1995	1625	1315	1060	850
② NEW	303B		150	9.72	Hi-Shok Soft Point	210	2690	2440	2210	1980	1780	1590	2400	1980	1620	1310	1055	840
②	*8A	8mm Mauser (8x57mm JS Mauser)	170	11.01	Hi-Shok Soft Point	210	2360	1970	1620	1330	1120	1000	2100	1465	995	670	475	375
②	32A	32 Win. Special	170	11.01	Hi-Shok Soft Point	210	2250	1920	1630	1370	1180	1040	1910	1395	1000	710	520	410
③	338C	338 Win. Magnum	225	14.58	Soft Point	215	2780	2570	2370	2180	2000	1830	3860	3305	2815	2380	2000	1670
②	35A	35 Rem.	200	12.96	Hi-Shok Soft Point	210	2080	1700	1380	1140	1000	910	1920	1280	840	575	445	370
②	357G	357 Magnum	180	11.66	Hollow Point	100	1550	1160	980	860	770	680	960	535	385	295	235	185
③	375A	375 H&H Magnum	270	17.50	Hi-Shok Soft Point	215	2690	2420	2170	1920	1700	1500	4340	3510	2810	2220	1740	1355
④	375B		300	19.44	Hi-Shok Soft Point	215	2530	2270	2020	1790	1580	1400	4265	3425	2720	2135	1665	1295
②	44A	44 Rem. Magnum	240	15.55	Hollow Point	150	1760	1380	1090	950	860	790	1650	1015	640	485	395	330
②	4570A	45-70 Government	300	19.44	Hollow Point	210	1880	1650	1430	1240	1110	1010	2355	1815	1355	1015	810	680

* Only for use in barrels intended for .323 inch diameter bullets. Do not use in 8x57mm J Commission Rifles (M1888) or in sporting or other military arms of .318 inch bore diameter.
**RN=Round Nose FN=Flat Nose FMJ=Full Metal Jacket HP=Hollow Point

Match Rifle Ballistics [Approximate]

USAGE	FEDERAL LOAD NO.	CALIBER	BULLET WGT. IN GRAINS	GRAMS	BULLET STYLE	FACTORY PRIMER NO.	VELOCITY IN FEET PER SECOND (TO NEAREST 10 FEET) MUZZLE	100 YDS.	200YDS.	300YDS.	400YDS.	500YDS.	600YDS.	700YDS.	800YDS.	900YDS.	1000YDS.	ENERGY IN FOOT/POUNDS MUZZLE	100YDS.
⑤	223M	223 Rem. (5.56 x 45mm)	69	4.47	Boat-tail HP Match	205M	3000	2720	2460	2210	1980	1760	1560	1390	1240	1130	1060	1380	1135
⑤	308M	308 Win. (7.62 x 51mm)	168	10.88	Boat-tail HP Match	210M	2600	2420	2240	2070	1910	1760	1610	1480	1360	1260	1170	2520	2180

FEDERAL BALLISTICS

WIND DRIFT IN INCHES 10 MPH CROSSWIND					HEIGHT OF BULLET TRAJECTORY IN INCHES ABOVE OR BELOW LINE OF SIGHT IF ZEROED AT ⊕ YARDS. SIGHTS 1.5 INCHES ABOVE BORE LINE. AVERAGE RANGE				LONG RANGE						TEST BARREL LENGTH INCHES	FEDERAL LOAD NO.
100 YDS.	200 YDS.	300 YDS.	400 YDS.	500 YDS.	50 YDS.	100 YDS.	200 YDS.	300 YDS.	50 YDS.	100 YDS.	200 YDS.	300 YDS.	400 YDS.	500 YDS.		
1.7	7.3	18.3	36.4	63.1	-0.2	⊕	-3.7	-15.3	+0.7	+1.9	⊕	-9.7	-31.6	-71.3	24	222A
0.9	3.4	8.5	16.8	26.3	-0.2	⊕	-3.1	-12.0	+0.6	+1.6	⊕	-7.3	-21.5	-44.6	24	222B
1.2	5.2	12.5	24.4	42.0	-0.4	⊕	-2.1	-9.1	+0.1	+1.0	⊕	-6.0	-19.1	-42.6	24	22250A
1.3	5.7	14.0	27.9	49.2	-0.4	⊕	-1.7	-8.1	0	+0.8	⊕	-5.6	-18.4	-42.8	24	22250C
1.4	6.1	15.0	29.4	50.8	-0.3	⊕	-3.2	-12.9	+0.5	+1.6	⊕	-8.2	-26.1	-58.3	24	223A
0.8	3.3	7.8	14.5	24.0	-0.3	⊕	-2.5	-9.9	+0.3	+1.3	⊕	-6.1	-18.3	-37.8	24	223B
1.3	5.8	14.2	27.7	47.6	-0.3	⊕	-2.7	-10.8	+0.4	+1.4	⊕	-6.7	-20.5	-43.4	24	223C
1.5	6.5	16.1	32.3	56.9	-0.4	⊕	-2.4	-10.7	+0.2	+1.2	⊕	-7.1	-23.4	-54.2	24	223D
1.0	4.1	9.9	18.8	31.6	-0.3	⊕	-2.2	-9.3	+0.2	+1.1	⊕	-5.9	-18.2	-39.0	24	6A
0.8	3.3	7.9	14.7	24.1	-0.3	⊕	-2.9	-11.0	+0.5	+1.4	⊕	-6.7	-19.8	-40.6	24	6B
1.0	4.3	10.4	19.8	33.3	-0.3	⊕	-2.5	-10.2	+0.3	+1.3	⊕	-6.4	-19.7	-42.2	24	243A
0.9	3.6	8.4	15.7	25.8	-0.2	⊕	-3.3	-12.4	+0.6	+1.6	⊕	-7.5	-22.0	-45.4	24	243B
1.1	4.8	11.7	22.6	38.7	-0.4	⊕	-2.1	-9.2	+0.2	+1.1	⊕	-6.0	-18.9	-41.6	24	243V
0.8	3.3	7.7	14.3	23.4	-0.1	⊕	-3.8	-14.0	+0.8	+1.9	⊕	-8.2	-24.0	-48.9	24	257A
1.0	4.1	9.8	18.7	31.3	-0.3	⊕	-2.3	-9.4	+0.2	+1.1	⊕	-6.0	-18.3	-39.2	24	2506A
0.8	3.4	8.1	15.1	24.9	-0.2	⊕	-3.2	-12.0	+0.6	+1.6	⊕	-7.2	-21.4	-44.0	24	2506B
0.8	3.2	7.6	14.2	23.3	-0.2	⊕	-2.9	-11.2	+0.5	+1.5	⊕	-6.8	-20.0	-41.1	24	270A
1.2	5.3	12.8	24.5	41.3	-0.1	⊕	-4.1	-15.5	+0.9	+2.0	⊕	-9.4	-28.6	-61.0	24	270B
1.5	6.2	15.0	28.7	47.8	-0.1	⊕	-6.2	-22.6	+1.6	+3.1	⊕	-13.3	-40.1	-84.6	24	7A
1.3	3.2	8.2	15.4	23.4	-0.1	⊕	-4.3	-15.4	+1.0	+2.1	⊕	-9.0	-26.1	-52.9	24	7B
0.7	3.1	7.2	13.4	21.9	-0.2	⊕	-3.4	-12.6	+0.7	+1.7	⊕	-7.5	-21.8	-44.3	24	280B
0.8	3.4	8.1	15.1	24.9	-0.3	⊕	-2.9	-11.0	+0.5	+1.4	⊕	-6.7	-19.9	-41.0	24	7RA
0.7	3.1	7.2	13.3	21.7	-0.2	⊕	-3.5	-12.8	+0.7	+1.7	⊕	-7.6	-22.1	-44.9	24	7RB
1.6	7.2	17.7	34.5	58.1	0	⊕	-5.2	-19.8	+1.2	+2.6	⊕	-12.0	-37.6	-81.7	24	730A
3.4	15.0	35.5	63.2	96.7	+0.6	⊕	-12.8	-46.9	+3.9	+6.4	⊕	-27.7	-81.8	-167.8	18	30CA
1.5	6.4	15.2	28.7	47.3	+0.2	⊕	-7.0	-25.1	+1.9	+3.5	⊕	-14.5	-43.4	-90.6	20	76239B
2.0	8.5	20.9	40.1	66.1	+0.2	⊕	-7.2	-26.7	+1.9	+3.6	⊕	-15.9	-49.1	-104.5	24	3030A
1.9	8.0	19.4	36.7	59.8	+0.3	⊕	-8.3	-29.8	+2.4	+4.1	⊕	-17.4	-52.4	-109.4	24	3030B
2.2	10.1	25.4	49.4	81.6	+0.1	⊕	-6.6	-26.0	+1.7	+3.3	⊕	-16.0	-50.9	-109.5	24	3030C
1.0	4.2	9.9	18.7	31.2	-0.2	⊕	-3.6	-13.6	+0.7	+1.8	⊕	-8.2	-24.4	-50.9	24	3006A
0.9	3.7	8.8	16.5	27.1	-0.1	⊕	-4.2	-15.3	+1.0	+2.1	⊕	-9.0	-26.4	-54.0	24	3006B
1.1	4.5	10.8	20.5	34.4	-0.3	⊕	-3.0	-11.9	+0.5	+1.5	⊕	-7.3	-22.3	-47.5	24	3006C
0.7	2.8	6.6	12.3	19.9	-0.2	⊕	-3.6	-13.2	+0.8	+1.8	⊕	-7.8	-22.4	-45.2	24	3006D
1.4	6.0	14.3	27.2	45.0	-0.1	⊕	-6.2	-22.4	+1.7	+3.1	⊕	-13.1	-39.3	-82.2	24	3006H
1.5	6.4	15.7	30.4	51.2	-0.1	⊕	-4.9	-18.3	+1.1	+2.4	⊕	-11.0	-33.6	-71.9	24	3006J
1.1	4.8	11.6	21.9	36.3	0	⊕	-4.8	-17.6	+1.2	+2.4	⊕	-10.4	-30.9	-64.4	24	300A
1.1	4.6	10.9	20.3	33.3	+0.1	⊕	-6.1	-21.6	+1.7	+3.1	⊕	-12.4	-36.1	-73.8	24	300B
1.0	4.4	10.4	19.7	32.7	-0.1	⊕	-3.9	-14.7	+0.8	+2.0	⊕	-8.8	-26.3	-54.8	24	308A
0.9	3.9	9.2	17.2	28.3	-0.1	⊕	-4.6	-16.5	+1.1	+2.3	⊕	-9.7	-28.3	-57.8	24	308B
0.7	2.8	6.6	12.3	20.0	-0.2	⊕	-3.1	-11.7	+0.6	+1.6	⊕	-7.0	-20.3	-41.1	24	300WB
1.1	4.5	10.6	19.9	32.7	0	⊕	-5.5	-19.6	+1.4	+2.8	⊕	-11.3	-33.2	-68.1	24	303A
1.0	4.1	9.6	18.1	29.9	-0.1	⊕	-4.4	-15.9	+1.0	+2.2	⊕	-9.4	-27.6	-56.8	24	303B
2.1	9.3	22.9	43.9	71.7	+0.2	⊕	-7.6	-28.5	+2.1	+3.8	⊕	-17.1	-52.9	-111.9	24	8A
1.9	8.4	20.3	38.6	63.0	+0.3	⊕	-8.0	-29.2	+2.3	+4.0	⊕	-17.2	-52.3	-109.8	24	32A
0.8	3.1	7.3	13.6	22.2	-0.1	⊕	-3.8	-13.7	+0.8	+1.9	⊕	-8.1	-23.5	-47.5	24	338C
2.7	12.0	29.0	53.3	83.3	+0.5	⊕	-10.7	-39.3	+3.2	+5.4	⊕	-23.3	-70.0	-144.0	24	35A
5.8	21.7	45.2	76.1	NA	⊕	-3.4	-29.7	-88.2	+1.7	⊕	-22.8	-77.9	-173.8	-321.4	18	357G
1.1	4.5	10.8	20.3	33.7	-0.4	⊕	-5.5	-18.4	+1.0	+2.2	⊕	-9.7	-28.8	-59.9	24	375A
1.2	5.0	11.9	22.4	37.1	+0.5	⊕	-6.3	-21.2	+1.3	+2.6	⊕	-11.2	-33.3	-69.1	24	375B
4.2	17.8	39.8	68.3	102.5	⊕	-2.2	-21.7	-67.2	+1.1	⊕	-17.4	-60.7	-136.0	-250.2	20	44A
1.7	7.6	18.6	35.7	NA	⊕	-1.3	-14.1	-43.7	+0.7	⊕	-11.5	-39.7	-89.1	-163.1	24	4570A

These trajectory tables were calculated by computer using the best available data for each load. Trajectories are representative of the nominal behavior of each load at standard conditions (59°F temperature; barometric pressure of 29.53 inches; altitude at sea level). Shooters are cautioned that actual trajectories may differ due to variations in altitude, atmospheric conditions, guns, sights, and ammunition.

ENERGY IN FOOT/POUNDS (TO NEAREST 5 FOOT/POUNDS)									WIND DRIFT IN INCHES 10 MPH CROSSWIND										HEIGHT OF BULLET TRAJECTORY IN INCHES ABOVE OR BELOW LINE OF SIGHT IF ZEROED AT ⊕ YARDS. SIGHTS 1.5 INCHES ABOVE BORE LINE.									
200 YDS.	300 YDS.	400 YDS.	500 YDS.	600 YDS.	700 YDS.	800 YDS.	900 YDS.	1000 YDS.	100 YDS.	200 YDS.	300 YDS.	400 YDS.	500 YDS.	600 YDS.	700 YDS.	800 YDS.	900 YDS.	1000 YDS.	100 YDS.	200 YDS.	300 YDS.	400 YDS.	500 YDS.	600 YDS.	700 YDS.	800 YDS.	900 YDS.	1000 YDS.
925	750	600	475	375	295	235	195	170	0.9	3.7	8.7	16.3	27.0	41.3	59.5	82.2	109.2	140.0	+1.6	⊕	-7.4	-21.9	-45.3	-79.8	-128.7	-194.1	-280.2	-388.7
1870	1600	1355	1150	970	815	690	590	510	0.8	3.1	7.4	13.6	22.2	33.3	47.1	64.1	84.2	107.5	+17.5	+30.5	+36.6	+34.5	+22.9	⊕	-36.1	-87.8	-157.5	-247.4

FEDERAL BALLISTICS

Premium Safari Rifle Ballistics (Approximate)

Usage Key: [1] =Varmints, predators, small game [2] =Medium game [3] =Large, heavy game [4] =Dangerous game

USAGE	FEDERAL LOAD NO.	CALIBER	BULLET WGT. IN GRAINS	GRAMS	BULLET STYLE	FACTORY PRIMER NO.	VELOCITY IN FEET PER SECOND (TO NEAREST 10 FEET) MUZZLE	100 YDS.	200 YDS.	300 YDS.	400 YDS.	500 YDS.	ENERGY IN FOOT-POUNDS (TO NEAREST 5 FOOT/POUNDS) MUZZLE	100 YDS.	200 YDS.	300 YDS.	400 YDS.	500 YDS.
[3] NEW	P300HA	300 H&H Magnum	180	11.66	Nosler Partition	215	2880	2680	2480	2290	2110	1940	3315	2860	2455	2100	1780	1500
[3]	P300WD2	300 Win. Magnum	180	11.66	Nosler Partition	215	2960	2750	2540	2340	2160	1980	3500	3010	2580	2195	1860	1565
[3]	P338A2	338 Win. Magnum	210	13.60	Nosler Partition	215	2830	2590	2370	2150	1940	1750	3735	3130	2610	2155	1760	1435
[3]	P338B2	338 Win. Magnum	250	16.20	Nosler Partition	215	2660	2400	2150	1910	1690	1500	3925	3185	2555	2055	1590	1245
[3]	P375C	375 H&H Magnum	250	16.20	Boat-tail SP	215	2670	2450	2240	2040	1850	1680	3955	3335	2790	2315	1905	1565
[4]	P375D	375 H&H Magnum	300	19.44	Solid	215	2530	2170	1840	1550	1310	1140	4265	3140	2260	1605	1140	860
[4] NEW	P375F	375 H&H Magnum	300	19.44	Nosler Partition	215	2530	2320	2120	1930	1750	1590	4265	3585	2995	2475	2040	1675
[3]	P458A	458 Win. Magnum	350	22.68	Soft Point	215	2470	1990	1570	1250	1060	950	4740	3065	1915	1205	870	705
[4]	P458B	458 Win. Magnum	510	33.04	Soft Point	215	2090	1820	1570	1360	1190	1080	4945	3730	2790	2080	1605	1320
[4]	P458C	458 Win. Magnum	500	32.40	Solid	215	2090	1870	1670	1480	1320	1190	4850	3880	3085	2440	1945	1585
[4]	P416A	416 Rigby	410	26.57	Soft Point	215	2370	2110	1870	1640	1440	1280	5115	4050	3165	2455	1895	1485
[4]	P416B	416 Rigby	410	26.57	Solid	215	2370	2110	1870	1640	1440	1280	5115	4050	3165	2455	1895	1485
[4]	P470A	470 Nitro Express	500	32.40	Soft Point	215	2150	1890	1650	1440	1270	1140	5130	3965	3040	2310	1790	1435
[4]	P470B	470 Nitro Express	500	32.40	Solid	215	2150	1890	1650	1440	1270	1140	5130	3965	3040	2310	1790	1435

Premium Rifle Sierra Boat-tail Ballistics (Approximate)

USAGE	FEDERAL LOAD NO.	CALIBER	BULLET WGT. IN GRAINS	GRAMS	BULLET STYLE	FACTORY PRIMER NO.	VELOCITY IN FEET PER SECOND MUZZLE	100 YDS.	200 YDS.	300 YDS.	400 YDS.	500 YDS.	ENERGY IN FOOT/POUNDS (TO NEAREST 5 FOOT/POUNDS) MUZZLE	100 YDS.	200 YDS.	300 YDS.	400 YDS.	500 YDS.
[1]	P223E	223 Rem. (5.56x45mm)	55	3.56	Boat-tail H.P.	205	3240	2770	2340	1950	1610	1330	1280	935	670	465	315	215
[1]	P22250B	22-250 Rem.	55	3.56	Boat-tail H.P.	210	3680	3280	2920	2590	2280	1990	1655	1315	1040	815	630	480
[2]	P243C	243 Win. (6.16x51mm)	100	6.48	Boat-tail S.P.	210	2960	2760	2570	2380	2210	2040	1950	1690	1460	1260	1080	925
[1]	P243D	243 Win. (6.16x51mm)	85	5.50	Boat-tail H.P.	210	3320	3070	2830	2600	2380	2180	2080	1770	1510	1280	1070	890
[2]	P2506C	25-06 Rem.	117	7.58	Boat-tail S.P.	210	2990	2770	2570	2370	2190	2000	2320	2000	1715	1465	1240	1045
[2]	P270C	270 Win.	150	9.72	Boat-tail S.P.	210	2850	2660	2480	2300	2130	1970	2705	2355	2040	1760	1510	1290
[2]	P270D	270 Win.	130	8.42	Boat-tail S.P.	210	3060	2830	2620	2410	2220	2030	2700	2320	1980	1680	1420	1190
[2]	P7RD	7mm Rem. Magnum	150	9.72	Boat-tail S.P.	215	3110	2920	2750	2580	2410	2250	3220	2850	2510	2210	1930	1690
[3]	P7RE	7mm Rem. Magnum	165	10.69	Boat-tail S.P.	215	2950	2800	2650	2510	2370	2230	3190	2865	2570	2300	2050	1825
[2]	P3006D	30-06 Spring. (7.62x63mm)	165	10.69	Boat-tail S.P.	210	2800	2610	2420	2240	2070	1910	2870	2490	2150	1840	1580	1340
[2]	P3006G	30-06 Spring. (7.62x63mm)	150	9.72	Boat-tail S.P.	210	2910	2690	2480	2270	2070	1880	2820	2420	2040	1710	1430	1180
[3]	P3006L	30-06 Spring. (7.62x63mm)	180	11.66	Boat-tail S.P.	210	2700	2540	2380	2220	2080	1930	2915	2570	2260	1975	1720	1495
[2]	P308C	308 Win. (7.62x51mm)	165	10.69	Boat-tail S.P.	210	2700	2520	2330	2160	1990	1830	2670	2310	1990	1700	1450	1230
[3]	P300WC	300 Win. Magnum	200	12.96	Boat-tail S.P.	215	2830	2680	2530	2380	2240	2110	3560	3180	2830	2520	2230	1970

Premium Rifle Nosler Partition Ballistics (Approximate)

USAGE	FEDERAL LOAD NO.	CALIBER	BULLET WGT. IN GRAINS	GRAMS	BULLET STYLE	FACTORY PRIMER NO.	VELOCITY IN FEET PER SECOND (TO NEAREST 10 FEET) MUZZLE	100 YDS.	200 YDS.	300 YDS.	400 YDS.	500 YDS.	ENERGY IN FOOT/POUNDS (TO NEAREST 5 FOOT/POUNDS) MUZZLE	100 YDS.	200 YDS.	300 YDS.	400 YDS.	500 YDS.
[2]	P6C	6mm Rem.	100	6.48	Nosler Partition	210	3100	2830	2570	2330	2100	1890	2135	1775	1470	1205	985	790
[2] NEW	P243E	243 Win.	100	6.48	Nosler Partition	210	2960	2730	2510	2300	2100	1910	1945	1650	1395	1170	975	805
[2]	P257B	257 Roberts (Hi-Vel.+P)	120	7.77	Nosler Partition	210	2780	2560	2360	2160	1970	1790	2060	1750	1480	1240	1030	855
[2]	P270E	270 Win.	150	9.72	Nosler Partition	210	2850	2590	2340	2100	1880	1670	2705	2225	1815	1470	1175	930
[2]	P7C	7mm Mauser (7x57mm Mauser)	140	9.07	Nosler Partition	210	2660	2450	2260	2070	1890	1730	2200	1865	1585	1330	1110	930
[2]	P280A	280 Rem.	150	9.72	Nosler Partition	210	2890	2620	2370	2140	1910	1710	2780	2295	1875	1520	1215	970
[3]	P7RF	7mm Rem. Magnum	160	10.37	Nosler Partition	215	2950	2730	2520	2320	2120	1940	3090	2650	2250	1910	1600	1340
[2]	P7RG	7mm Rem. Magnum	140	9.07	Nosler Partition	215	3150	2920	2700	2500	2300	2110	3085	2650	2270	1940	1640	1380
[2]	P3030D	30-30 Win.	170	11.01	Nosler Partition	210	2200	1900	1620	1380	1190	1060	1830	1355	990	720	535	425
[3]	P3006F	30-06 Spring. (7.62x63mm)	180	11.66	Nosler Partition	210	2700	2470	2250	2040	1850	1660	2910	2440	2020	1670	1360	1110
[3] NEW	P308E	308 Win. (7.62x51mm)	180	11.66	Nosler Partition	210	2620	2430	2240	2060	1890	1730	2745	2355	2005	1700	1430	1200

+P ammunition is loaded to a higher pressure. Use only in firearms so recommended by the gun manufacturer.

WIND DRIFT IN INCHES 10 MPH CROSSWIND					HEIGHT OF BULLET TRAJECTORY IN INCHES ABOVE OR BELOW LINE OF SIGHT IF ZEROED AT ⊕ YARDS. SIGHTS 1.5 INCHES ABOVE BORE LINE. AVERAGE RANGE				LONG RANGE						TEST BARREL LENGTH INCHES	FEDERAL LOAD NO.
100 YDS.	200 YDS.	300 YDS.	400 YDS.	500 YDS.	50 YDS.	100 YDS.	200 YDS.	300 YDS.	50 YDS.	100 YDS.	200 YDS.	300 YDS.	400 YDS.	500 YDS.		
0.7	2.9	6.7	12.4	20.1	-0.2	⊕	-3.4	-12.4	+0.7	+1.7	⊕	-7.4	-21.3	-43.2	24	P300HA
0.7	2.8	6.6	12.3	20.0	-0.2	⊕	-3.1	-11.7	+0.6	+1.6	⊕	-7.0	-20.3	-41.1	24	P300WD2
0.8	3.5	8.3	15.4	25.4	-0.2	⊕	-3.7	-13.6	+0.8	+1.8	⊕	-8.1	-23.7	-48.6	24	P338A2
1.1	4.5	10.8	20.3	33.6	-0.1	⊕	-4.6	-16.7	+1.1	+2.3	⊕	-9.8	-29.1	-60.2	24	P338B2
0.9	3.6	8.5	15.9	26.1	+0.4	⊕	-5.3	-17.6	+1.7	+2.7	⊕	-9.6	-27.6	-55.6	24	P375C
1.7	7.2	17.6	33.9	56.5	⊕	-1.1	-9.1	-27.5	+0.5	⊕	-7.0	-24.2	-55.8	-106.5	24	P375D
0.9	3.9	9.1	17.0	27.8	0	⊕	-5.0	-17.7	+1.2	+2.5	⊕	-10.3	-29.9	-60.8	24	P375F
2.5	11.0	27.6	52.6	83.9	⊕	-1.5	-11.0	-34.9	+0.1	⊕	-7.5	-29.1	-71.1	-138.0	24	P458A
1.9	7.9	18.9	35.3	56.8	⊕	-1.8	-13.7	-39.7	+0.4	⊕	-9.1	-32.3	-73.9	-138.0	24	P458B
1.5	6.1	14.5	26.9	43.7	⊕	-1.7	-12.9	-36.7	+0.4	⊕	-8.5	-29.5	-66.2	-122.0	24	P458C
1.3	5.7	13.6	25.6	42.3	⊕	-1.2	-9.8	-28.5	+0.6	⊕	-7.4	-24.8	-55.0	-101.6	24	P416A
1.3	5.7	13.6	25.6	42.3	⊕	-1.2	-9.8	-28.5	+0.6	⊕	-7.4	-24.8	-55.0	-101.6	24	P416B
1.6	7.0	16.6	31.1	50.6	⊕	-1.6	-12.6	-36.2	+0.8	⊕	-9.3	-31.3	-69.7	-128.6	24	P470A
1.6	7.0	16.6	31.1	50.6	⊕	-1.6	-12.6	-36.2	+0.8	⊕	-9.3	-31.3	-69.7	-128.6	24	P470B

WIND DRIFT IN INCHES 10 MPH CROSSWIND					HEIGHT OF BULLET TRAJECTORY IN INCHES ABOVE OR BELOW LINE OF SIGHT IF ZEROED AT ⊕ YARDS. SIGHTS 1.5 INCHES ABOVE BORE LINE. AVERAGE RANGE				LONG RANGE						TEST BARREL LENGTH INCHES	FEDERAL LOAD NO.
100 YDS.	200 YDS.	300 YDS.	400 YDS.	500 YDS.	50 YDS.	100 YDS.	200 YDS.	300 YDS.	50 YDS.	100 YDS.	200 YDS.	300 YDS.	400 YDS.	500 YDS.		
1.3	5.8	14.2	27.7	47.6	-0.3	⊕	-2.7	-10.8	+0.4	+1.4	⊕	-6.7	-20.5	-43.4	24	P223E
0.8	3.6	8.4	15.8	26.3	-0.4	⊕	-1.7	-7.6	0	+0.9	⊕	-5.0	-15.1	-32.0	24	P22250B
0.6	2.6	6.1	11.3	18.4	-0.2	⊕	-3.1	-11.4	+0.6	+1.5	⊕	-6.8	-19.8	-39.9	24	P243C
0.7	2.7	6.3	11.6	18.8	-0.3	⊕	-2.2	-8.8	+0.2	+1.1	⊕	-5.5	-16.1	-32.8	24	P243D
0.7	2.8	6.5	12.0	19.6	-0.2	⊕	-3.0	-11.4	+0.5	+1.5	⊕	-6.8	-19.9	-40.4	24	P2506C
0.7	2.7	6.3	11.6	18.9	-0.2	⊕	-3.4	-12.5	+0.7	+1.7	⊕	-7.4	-21.4	-43.0	24	P270C
0.7	2.8	6.6	12.1	19.7	-0.2	⊕	-2.8	-10.7	+0.5	+1.4	⊕	-6.5	-19.0	-38.5	24	P270D
0.5	2.2	5.1	9.3	15.0	-0.3	⊕	-2.6	-9.8	+0.4	+1.3	⊕	-5.9	-17.0	-34.2	24	P7RD
0.5	2.0	4.6	8.4	13.5	-0.2	⊕	-3.0	-10.9	+0.5	+1.5	⊕	-6.4	-18.4	-36.6	24	P7RE
0.7	2.8	6.6	12.3	19.9	-0.2	⊕	-3.6	-13.2	+0.8	+1.8	⊕	-7.8	-22.4	-45.2	24	P3006D
0.7	3.0	7.1	13.4	22.0	-0.2	⊕	-3.3	-12.4	+0.6	+1.7	⊕	-7.4	-21.5	-43.7	24	P3006G
0.6	2.6	6.0	11.0	17.8	-0.1	⊕	-3.9	-13.9	+0.9	+1.9	⊕	-8.1	-23.1	-46.1	24	P3006L
0.7	3.0	7.0	13.0	21.1	-0.1	⊕	-4.0	-14.4	+0.9	+2.0	⊕	-8.4	-24.3	-49.0	24	P308C
0.5	2.2	5.0	9.2	14.9	-0.2	⊕	-3.4	-12.2	+0.7	+1.7	⊕	-7.1	-20.4	-40.5	24	P300WC

WIND DRIFT IN INCHES 10 MPH CROSSWIND					HEIGHT OF BULLET TRAJECTORY IN INCHES ABOVE OR BELOW LINE OF SIGHT IF ZEROED AT ⊕ YARDS. SIGHTS 1.5 INCHES ABOVE BORE LINE. AVERAGE RANGE				LONG RANGE						TEST BARREL LENGTH INCHES	FEDERAL LOAD NO.
100 YDS.	200 YDS.	300 YDS.	400 YDS.	500 YDS.	50 YDS.	100 YDS.	200 YDS.	300 YDS.	50 YDS.	100 YDS.	200 YDS.	300 YDS.	400 YDS.	500 YDS.		
0.8	3.3	7.9	14.7	24.1	-0.3	⊕	-2.9	-11.0	+0.5	+1.4	⊕	-6.7	-19.8	-29.0	24	P6C
0.7	3.1	7.3	13.5	22.1	-0.2	⊕	-3.2	-11.9	+0.6	+1.6	⊕	-7.1	-20.9	-42.5	24	P243E
0.8	3.3	7.7	14.3	23.5	-0.1	⊕	-3.8	-14.0	+0.8	+1.9	⊕	-8.2	-24.0	-48.9	24	P257B
0.9	3.9	9.2	17.3	28.5	-0.2	⊕	-3.7	-13.8	+0.8	+1.9	⊕	-8.3	-24.4	-50.5	24	P270E
1.3	3.2	8.2	15.4	23.4	-0.1	⊕	-4.3	-15.4	+1.0	+2.1	⊕	-9.0	-26.1	-52.9	24	P7C
0.9	3.8	9.0	16.8	27.8	-0.2	⊕	-3.6	-13.4	+0.7	+1.8	⊕	-8.0	-23.8	-49.2	24	P280A
0.8	3.3	7.7	14.1	23.4	-0.2	⊕	-3.2	-11.9	+0.6	+1.6	⊕	-7.1	-20.7	-42.0	24	P7RF
0.6	2.7	6.2	11.5	18.7	-0.3	⊕	-2.6	-9.9	+0.4	+1.3	⊕	-6.1	-17.7	-36.0	24	P7RG
0.9	8.0	19.4	36.7	59.8	-0.3	⊕	-8.3	-29.8	+2.4	+4.1	⊕	-17.4	-52.4	-109.4	24	P3030D
0.9	3.7	8.8	16.5	27.1	-0.1	⊕	-4.2	-15.3	+1.0	+2.1	⊕	-9.0	-26.4	-54.0	24	P3006F
0.8	3.3	7.7	14.3	23.3	-0.1	⊕	-4.4	-15.8	+1.0	+2.2	⊕	-9.2	-26.5	-53.6	24	P308E

These trajectory tables were calculated by computer using the best available data for each load. Trajectories are representative of the nominal behavior of each load at standard conditions (59°F temperature; barometric pressure of 29.53 inches; altitude at sea level). Shooters are cautioned that actual trajectories may differ due to variations in altitude, atmospheric conditions, guns, sights, and ammunition.

*"Nosler" and "Partition" are registered trademarks of Nosler Bullets, Inc.

FEDERAL/NORMA BALLISTICS

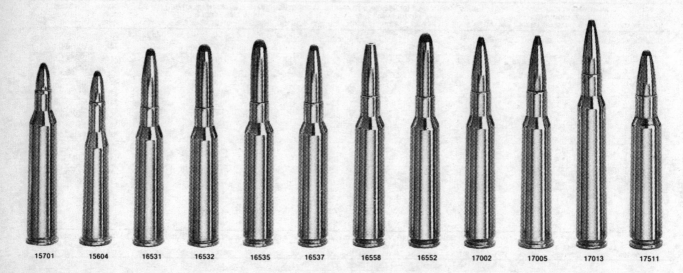

| 15701 | 15604 | 16531 | 16532 | 16535 | 16537 | 16558 | 16552 | 17002 | 17005 | 17013 | 17511 |

Norma Centerfire Rifle Ballistics (Approximate)   Usage Key: 1 = Varmints, predators, small game   2 = Medium game   3 = Large heavy game

Usage	Federal Load No.	Caliber	Bullet Wgt. in Grains	Bullet Wgt. in Grams	Bullet Style	Factory Primer	Velocity in Feet Per Second (to Nearest 10 Feet) Muzzle	100 yds.	200 yds.	300 yds.	400 yds.	500 yds.	Energy in Foot/Pounds (to Nearest 5 Foot/Pounds) Muzzle	100 yds.	200 yds.	300 yds.	400 yds.	500 yds.
1	15701	220 Swift	50	3.24	Soft Point	Large Rifle	4110	3570	3080	2640	2240	1870	1875	1415	1055	775	555	390
1	15604	22 Savage HiPwr (5.6x52Rmm)	71	4.60	Soft Point	Large Rifle	2790	2340	1930	1570	1280	1090	1225	860	585	390	260	190
2	16531	6.5x50mm Japanese	139	9.00	Boat-tail Soft Point	Large Rifle	2360	2160	1970	1790	1620	1470	1720	1440	1195	985	810	665
2	16532	6.5x50mm Japanese	156	10.10	Soft Point Alaska	Large Rifle	2070	1830	1610	1420	1260	1140	1475	1155	900	695	550	445
2	16535	6.5x52mm Carcano	156	10.10	Soft Point Alaska	Large Rifle	2430	2170	1930	1700	1500	1320	2045	1630	1285	1005	780	605
2	16537	6.5x52mm Carcano	139	9.00	Soft Point	Large Rifle	2580	2360	2160	1970	1790	1620	2045	1725	1440	1195	985	810
2	16558	6.5x55mm Swedish	139	9.00	Prot'd Power Cavity	Large Rifle	2850	2560	2290	2030	1790	1570	2515	2025	1615	1270	985	760
2	16552	6.5x55mm Swedish	156	10.10	Soft Point Alaska	Large Rifle	2650	2370	2110	1870	1650	1450	2425	1950	1550	1215	945	730
2	17002	7x57mm Mauser	154	9.97	Soft Point	Large Rifle	2690	2490	2300	2120	1940	1780	2475	2120	1810	1530	1285	1080
2	17005	7x57Rmm	154	9.97	Soft Point	Large Rifle	2630	2430	2250	2070	1900	1740	2355	2020	1725	1460	1230	1035
2	17012	7x61mm Sharpe & Hart Super	154	9.97	Soft Point	Large Rifle	3060	2720	2400	2100	1820	1580	3200	2520	1965	1505	1135	850
2	17013	7x64mm Brenneke	154	9.97	Soft Point	Large Rifle	2820	2610	2420	2230	2050	1870	2720	2335	1995	1695	1430	1200
2	17511	7.5x55mm Swiss	180	11.66	Boat-tail Soft Point	Large Rifle	2650	2450	2250	2060	1880	1720	2805	2390	2020	1700	1415	1180
3	17638	308 Norma Magnum	180	11.66	Dual Core	Large Magnum Rifle	3020	2820	2630	2440	2270	2090	3645	3175	2755	2385	2050	1750
2	17634	7.62x54Rmm Russian	180	11.66	Boat-tail Soft Point	Large Rifle	2580	2370	2180	2000	1820	1660	2650	2250	1900	1590	1325	1100
2	17637	7.62x54Rmm Russian	150	9.72	Soft Point	Large Rifle	2950	2700	2450	2220	2000	1800	2905	2420	2005	1645	1335	1075
2	17701	7.65x53mm Argentine	150	9.72	Soft Point	Large Rifle	2660	2380	2120	1880	1660	1460	2355	1895	1500	1175	915	705
2	17702	7.65x53mm Argentine	180	11.66	Soft Point	Large Rifle	2590	2390	2200	2010	1830	1670	2685	2280	1925	1615	1345	1115
2	17712	303 British	150	9.72	Soft Point	Large Rifle	2720	2440	2180	1930	1700	1500	2465	1985	1580	1240	965	745
2	17721	7.7x58mm Japanese	130	8.42	Soft Point	Large Rifle	2950	2530	2150	1800	1500	1260	2510	1850	1335	935	650	455
2	17722	7.7x58mm Japanese	180	11.66	Boat-tail Soft Point	Large Rifle	2500	2300	2100	1920	1750	1590	2490	2105	1770	1475	1225	1015
2	*18017	8x57mm JS Mauser	165	10.69	Prot'd Power Cavity	Large Rifle	2850	2520	2210	1930	1670	1440	2985	2330	1795	1360	1015	755
3	*18003	8x57mm JS Mauser	196	12.70	Soft Point Alaska	Large Rifle	2530	2200	1890	1620	1380	1200	2775	2100	1555	1140	830	625
3	19303	9.3x57mm Mauser	286	18.53	Soft Point Alaska	Large Rifle	2070	1810	1590	1390	1230	1110	2710	2090	1600	1220	955	780
3	19315	9.3x62mm Mauser	286	18.53	Soft Point Alaska	Large Rifle	2360	2090	1840	1610	1410	1240	3535	2770	2145	1645	1255	980
3	19001	358 Norma Magnum	250	16.2	Soft Point	Large Magnum Rifle	2800	2510	2230	1970	1730	1510	4350	3480	2750	2145	1655	1265

*Only for use in barrels intended for .323 inch diameter bullets. Do not use in 8x57mm J Commission Rifles (M1888) or in sporting or other military arms of .318 inch bore diameter.

Norma Pistol and Revolver Ballistics (Approximate)   Usage Key: 3 = Self defense   4 = Target shooting, training, practice

Usage	Federal Load No.	Caliber	Bullet Wgt. in Grains	Bullet Wgt. in Grams	Bullet Style	Factory Primer	Velocity in Feet Per Second Muzzle	25 yds.	50 yds.	75 yds.	100 yds.	Energy in Foot/Pounds Muzzle	25 yds.	50 yds.	75 yds.	100 yds.	Mid-Range Trajectory 25 yds.	50 yds.	75 yds.	100 yds.	Test Barrel Length Inches
3, 4	11001	10mm Auto	200	12.96	FMJ	Large Pistol	1120	1080	1040	1010	980	555	515	480	450	425	0.2	0.9	2.2	4.0	5
3	11002	10mm Auto	170	11.01	JHP	Large Pistol	1300	1210	1140	1090	1040	640	555	490	445	410	0.2	0.7	1.8	3.3	5

FEDERAL/NORMA BALLISTICS

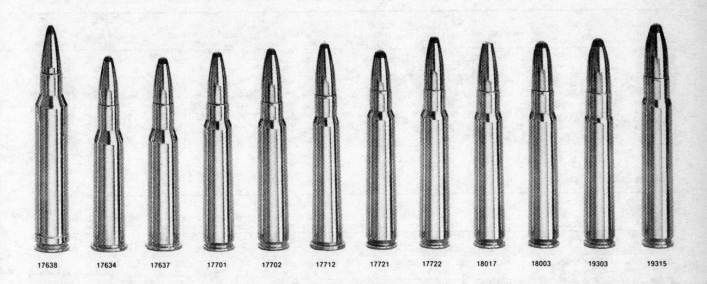

| 17638 | 17634 | 17637 | 17701 | 17702 | 17712 | 17721 | 17722 | 18017 | 18003 | 19303 | 19315 |

Wind Drift in Inches 10 mph Crosswind					Height of Bullet Trajectory in Inches Above or Below Line of Sight if Zeroed at + Yards. Sights 1.5 Inches Above Bore Line. Average Range				Long Range						Test Barrel Length Inches	Federal Load No.
100 yds.	200 yds.	300 yds.	400 yds.	500 yds.	50 yds.	100 yds.	200 yds.	300 yds.	50 yds.	100 yds.	200 yds.	300 yds.	400 yds.	500 yds.		
0.9	4.0	9.7	18.6	31.6	−0.5	⊕	−1.2	− 3.2	−0.1	+0.6	⊕	− 4.3	−13.6	− 29.9	24	15701
1.8	7.7	19.2	37.6	63.6	−0.1	⊕	−4.9	−19.3	+1.2	+2.5	⊕	−11.9	−37.7	− 83.0	24	15604
1.0	4.3	10.1	18.8	30.7	+0.1	⊕	−6.0	−21.0	+1.6	+3.0	⊕	−12.0	−34.8	− 70.7	24	16531
1.6	6.8	16.2	30.3	49.0	+0.4	⊕	−8.9	−31.2	+2.6	+4.5	⊕	−17.8	−52.7	−108.4	24	16532
1.3	5.4	12.8	24.2	40.0	+0.1	⊕	−5.9	−21.3	+1.6	+3.0	⊕	−12.4	−36.8	− 76.4	24	16535
0.9	3.7	8.8	16.5	27.0	0	⊕	−4.8	−17.1	+1.2	+2.4	⊕	− 9.9	−29.0	− 59.3	24	16537
1.0	4.3	10.4	19.6	32.6	−0.2	⊕	−3.8	−14.3	+0.8	+1.9	⊕	− 8.6	−25.7	53.6	24	16558
1.1	4.7	11.3	21.4	35.5	−0.1	⊕	−4.7	−17.3	+1.1	+2.4	⊕	−10.3	−30.6	− 63.9	24	16552
0.8	3.2	7.5	13.9	22.8	−0.1	⊕	−4.1	−14.9	+0.9	+2.1	⊕	− 8.7	−25.1	− 50.9	24	17002
0.8	3.3	7.6	14.2	23.1	−0.1	⊕	−4.4	−15.8	+1.0	−2.2	⊕	− 9.2	−26.6	− 53.9	24	17005
1.1	4.5	10.8	20.5	34.5	−0.2	⊕	−3.2	−12.6	+0.6	+1.6	⊕	− 7.7	−23.4	− 49.5	24	17012
0.7	3.0	7.1	13.1	21.3	−0.2	⊕	−3.6	−13.2	+0.7	+1.8	⊕	− 7.8	−22.7	− 46.1	24	17013
0.8	3.4	8.0	14.9	24.3	−0.1	⊕	−4.3	−15.5	+1.0	+2.2	⊕	− 9.0	−26.1	− 52.9	24	17511
0.6	2.5	5.9	10.9	17.6	−0.2	⊕	−2.9	−10.8	+0.5	+1.4	⊕	− 6.5	−18.8	− 37.8	24	17638
0.9	3.6	8.4	15.6	25.4	0	⊕	−4.7	−16.8	+1.1	+2.4	⊕	− 9.8	−28.5	− 57.9	24	17634
0.8	3.5	8.2	15.4	25.3	−0.2	⊕	−3.3	−12.3	+0.6	+1.6	⊕	− 7.4	−21.7	− 44.6	24	17637
1.1	4.7	11.3	21.4	35.6	−0.1	⊕	−4.7	−17.2	+1.1	+2.3	⊕	−10.2	−30.3	− 63.2	24	17701
0.8	3.5	8.3	15.4	25.2	0	⊕	−4.6	−16.4	+1.1	+2.3	⊕	− 9.5	−27.6	− 56.0	24	17702
1.1	4.6	10.9	20.7	34.4	−0.1	⊕	−4.4	−16.1	+1.0	+2.2	⊕	− 9.6	−28.5	− 59.5	24	17712
1.4	6.2	15.1	29.4	50.1	−0.2	⊕	−4.0	−15.6	+0.8	+2.0	⊕	− 9.6	−30.1	− 65.8	24	17721
0.9	3.8	8.9	16.5	27.0	0	⊕	−5.1	−18.0	+1.3	+2.5	⊕	−10.4	−30.2	− 61.2	24	17722
1.2	5.0	12.1	23.1	38.8	−0.1	⊕	−4.0	−15.2	+0.9	+2.0	⊕	− 9.2	−27.8	− 58.8	24	18017
1.5	6.5	15.8	30.3	50.6	0	⊕	−5.7	−21.2	+1.5	−2.9	⊕	−12.6	−38.4	− 81.8	24	18003
1.7	7.3	17.4	32.4	52.3	+0.4	⊕	−9.2	−32.3	+2.7	+3.8	⊕	−18.6	−55.2	−113.8	24	19303
1.4	6.0	14.3	27.1	44.7	+0.1	⊕	−6.5	−23.3	+1.8	+3.3	⊕	−13.6	−40.5	− 84.5	24	19315
1.1	4.6	11.0	20.8	34.7	−0.1	⊕	−4.1	−15.2	+0.9	+2.0	⊕	− 9.1	−27.2	− 57.0	24	19001

These trajectory tables were calculated by computer using the best available data for each load. Trajectories are representative of the nominal behavior of each load at standard conditions (59°F temperature; barometric pressure of 29.53 inches; altitude at sea level). Shooters are cautioned that actual trajectories may differ due to variations in altitude, atmospheric conditions, guns, sights, and ammunition.

FEDERAL BALLISTICS

Automatic Pistol Ballistics (Approximate)

Usage Key: 1=Varmints, predators, small game   2=Medium game   3=Self Defense   4=Target shooting, training, practice

USAGE	FEDERAL LOAD NO.	CALIBER	BULLET WGT. IN GRAINS	GRAMS	BULLET STYLE	FACTORY PRIMER NO.	VELOCITY IN FEET PER SECOND MUZZLE	25YDS.	50YDS.	75YDS.	100YDS.	ENERGY IN FOOT/POUNDS MUZZLE	25YDS.	50YDS.	75YDS.	100YDS.	MID-RANGE TRAJECTORY 25YDS.	50YDS.	75YDS.	100YDS.	TEST BARREL LENGTH INCHES
3, 4	25AP	25 Auto (6.35mm Browning)	50	3.24	Full Metal Jacket	100	760	750	730	720	700	65	60	59	55	55	0.5	1.9	4.5	8.1	2
3, 4	32AP	32 Auto (7.65mm Browning)	71	4.60	Full Metal Jacket	100	905	880	855	830	810	129	120	115	110	105	0.3	1.4	3.2	5.9	4
3, 4	380AP	380 Auto (9x17mm Short)	95	6.15	Full Metal Jacket	100	955	910	865	830	790	190	175	160	145	130	0.3	1.3	3.1	5.8	3³/4
3	380BP	380 Auto (9x17mm Short)	90	5.83	Hi-Shok JHP	100	1000	940	890	840	800	200	175	160	140	130	0.3	1.2	2.9	5.5	3³/4
3, 4	9AP	9mm Luger (9x19mm Parabellum)	124	8.03	Full Metal Jacket	100	1120	1070	1030	990	960	345	315	290	270	255	0.2	0.9	2.2	4.1	4
3	9BP	9mm Luger (9x19mm Parabellum)	115	7.45	Hi-Shok JHP	100	1160	1100	1060	1020	990	345	310	285	270	250	0.2	0.9	2.1	3.8	4
3, 4	45A	45 Auto	230	14.90	Full Metal Jacket	150	850	830	810	790	770	370	350	335	320	305	0.4	1.6	3.6	6.6	5
3	45C	45 Auto	185	11.99	Hi-Shok JHP	150	950	920	900	880	860	370	350	335	315	300	0.3	1.3	2.9	5.3	5

Revolver Ballistics (Approximate)

USAGE	FEDERAL LOAD NO.	CALIBER	BULLET WGT. IN GRAINS	GRAMS	BULLET STYLE	FACTORY PRIMER NO.	VELOCITY IN FEET PER SECOND MUZZLE	25YDS.	50YDS.	75YDS.	100YDS.	ENERGY IN FOOT/POUNDS MUZZLE	25YDS.	50YDS.	75YDS.	100YDS.	MID-RANGE TRAJECTORY 25YDS.	50YDS.	75YDS.	100YDS.	TEST BARREL LENGTH INCHES
4	32LA	32 S&W Long	98	6.35	Lead Wadcutter	100	780	700	630	560	500	130	105	85	70	55	0.5	2.2	5.6	11.1	4
4	32LB	32 S&W Long	98	6.35	Lead Round Nose	100	705	690	670	650	640	115	105	98	95	90	0.6	2.3	5.3	9.6	4
3	32HRA	32 H&R Magnum	95	6.15	Lead Semi-Wadcutter	100	1030	1000	940	930	900	225	210	190	185	170	0.3	1.1	2.5	4.7	4¹/2
3	32HRB	32 H&R Magnum	85	5.50	Hi-Shok JHP	100	1100	1050	1020	970	930	230	210	195	175	165	0.2	1.0	2.3	4.3	4¹/2
3	9FA	9mm Federal	115	7.45	Hi-Shok JHP	100	1280	1200	1130	1080	1040	420	370	330	300	280	0.2	0.7	1.8	3.3	4-V
4	38B	38 Special	158	10.23	Lead Round Nose	100	755	740	723	710	690	200	190	183	175	170	0.5	2.0	4.6	8.3	4-V
3, 4	38C	38 Special	158	10.23	Lead Semi-Wadcutter	100	755	740	723	710	690	200	190	183	175	170	0.5	2.0	4.6	8.3	4-V
1, 3	38E	38 Special (High Velocity +P)	125	8.10	Hi-Shok JHP	100	945	920	898	880	860	248	235	224	215	205	0.3	1.3	2.9	5.4	4-V
1, 3	38F	38 Special (High Velocity +P)	110	7.13	Hi-Shok JHP	100	995	960	926	900	870	242	225	210	195	185	0.3	1.2	2.7	5.0	4-V
1, 3	38G	38 Special (High Velocity +P)	158	10.23	Semi-Wadcutter HP	100	890	870	855	840	820	278	265	257	245	235	0.3	1.4	3.3	5.9	4-V
3, 4	38H	38 Special (High Velocity +P)	158	10.23	Lead Semi-Wadcutter	100	890	870	855	840	820	270	265	257	245	235	0.3	1.4	3.3	5.9	4-V
1, 3	38J	38 Special (High Velocity +P)	125	8.10	Hi-Shok JSP	100	945	920	898	880	860	248	235	224	215	205	0.3	1.3	2.9	5.4	4-V
2, 3	357A	357 Magnum	158	10.23	Hi-Shok JSP	100	1235	1160	1104	1060	1020	535	475	428	395	365	0.2	0.8	1.9	3.5	4-V
1, 3	357B	357 Magnum	125	8.10	Hi-Shok JHP	100	1450	1350	1240	1160	1100	583	495	427	370	335	0.1	0.6	1.5	2.8	4-V
4	357C	357 Magnum	158	10.23	Lead Semi-Wadcutter	100	1235	1160	1104	1060	1020	535	475	428	395	365	0.2	0.8	1.9	3.5	4-V
1, 3	357D	357 Magnum	110	7.13	Hi-Shok JHP	100	1295	1180	1094	1040	990	410	340	292	260	235	0.2	0.8	1.9	3.5	4-V
2, 3	357E	357 Magnum	158	10.23	Hi-Shok JHP	100	1235	1160	1104	1060	1020	535	475	428	395	365	0.2	0.8	1.9	3.5	4-V
2	357G	357 Magnum	180	11.66	Hi-Shok JHP	100	1090	1030	980	930	890	475	425	385	350	320	0.2	1.0	2.4	4.5	4-V
1, 3	41A	41 Rem. Magnum	210	13.60	Hi-Shok JHP	150	1300	1210	1130	1070	1030	790	680	595	540	495	0.2	0.7	1.8	3.3	4-V
1, 3	44SA	44 S&W Special	200	12.96	Semi-Wadcutter HP	150	900	860	830	800	770	360	330	305	285	260	0.3	1.4	3.4	6.3	6¹/2-V
2, 3	44A	44 Rem. Magnum	240	15.55	Hi-Shok JHP	150	1180	1130	1081	1050	1010	741	675	623	580	550	0.2	0.9	2.0	3.7	6¹/2-V
1, 2	44B*	44 Rem. Magnum	180	11.66	Hi-Shok JHP	150	1610	1480	1365	1270	1180	1035	875	750	640	555	0.1	0.5	1.2	2.3	6¹/2-V
1, 3	45LCA	45 Colt	225	14.58	Semi-Wadcutter HP	150	900	880	860	840	820	405	385	369	355	340	0.3	1.4	3.2	5.8	5¹/2

+P ammunition is loaded to a higher pressure. Use only in firearms so recommended by the gun manufacturer. "V" indicates vented barrel to simulate service conditions.
* Also available in 20-round box (A44B20).

Match Pistol and Revolver Ballistics (Approximate)

USAGE	FEDERAL LOAD NO.	CALIBER	BULLET WGT. IN GRAINS	GRAMS	BULLET STYLE	FACTORY PRIMER NO.	VELOCITY IN FEET PER SECOND MUZZLE	25YDS.	50YDS.	75YDS.	100YDS.	ENERGY IN FOOT/POUNDS MUZZLE	25YDS.	50YDS.	75YDS.	100YDS.	MID-RANGE TRAJECTORY 25YDS.	50YDS.	75YDS.	100YDS.	TEST BARREL LENGTH INCHES
4	9MP	9mm Luger (9x19mm Parabellum)	124	8.03	FMJ-SWC Match	100	1120	1070	1030	990	960	345	315	290	270	255	0.2	0.9	2.2	4.1	4
4	38A	38 Special	148	9.59	Lead Wadcutter Match	100	710	670	634	600	560	166	150	132	115	105	0.6	2.4	5.7	10.8	4-V
4	44D	44 Rem. Magnum	250	16.20	MC Profile Match	150	1180	1140	1100	1070	1040	775	715	670	630	600	0.2	0.8	1.9	3.6	6¹/2-V
4	45A	45 Auto	230	14.90	FMJ-Match	150	850	830	810	790	770	370	350	335	320	305	0.4	1.6	3.6	6.6	5
4	45B	45 Auto	185	11.99	FMJ-SWC Match	150	775	730	695	660	620	247	220	200	175	160	0.5	2.0	4.8	9.0	5

MC Profile Match = Metal Case Profile Match

FEDERAL BALLISTICS

Hydra-Shok™ Pistol and Revolver Ballistics (Approximate)

Usage Key: 3 =Varmints, predators, small game 2 =Medium game 3 =Self Defense 4 =Target shooting, training, practice

USAGE	FEDERAL LOAD NO.	CALIBER	BULLET WGT. IN GRAINS	GRAMS	BULLET STYLE	FACTORY PRIMER NO.	VELOCITY IN FEET PER SECOND MUZZLE	25 YDS.	50 YDS.	75YDS.	100YDS.	ENERGY IN FOOT/POUNDS MUZZLE	25 YDS.	50 YDS.	75 YDS.	100 YDS.	MID-RANGE TRAJECTORY 25 YDS.	50 YDS.	75 YDS.	100 YDS.	TEST BARREL LENGTH INCHES
3 NEW	P380HS1	380 Auto (9x17mm Short)	90	5.83	Hydra-Shok HP	100	1000	940	890	840	800	200	175	160	140	130	0.3	1.2	2.9	5.5	3³/₄
3	P9HS1	9mm Luger (9x19mm Parabellum)	124	8.03	Hydra-Shok HP	100	1120	1070	1030	990	960	345	315	290	270	255	0.2	0.9	2.2	4.1	4
3	P9HS2	9mm Luger (9x19mm Parabellum)	147	9.52	Hydra-Shok HP	100	1050	1010	980	950	920	360	335	310	295	275	0.3	1.1	2.5	4.5	4
3 NEW	P10HS1	10mm Auto	180	11.06	Hydra-Shok HP	150	950	847	767	698	638	361	287	235	195	163	0.1	1.3	3.6	7.3	5
3	P45HS1	45 Auto	230	14.90	Hydra-Shok HP	150	850	830	810	790	770	370	350	335	320	305	0.4	1.6	3.6	6.6	5
3	P38HS1	38 Special (High Velocity +P)	129	8.36	Hydra-Shok HP	100	945	930	910	890	870	255	245	235	225	215	0.3	1.3	2.9	5.3	4-V
3	P357HS1	357 Magnum	158	10.23	Hydra-Shok HP	100	1235	1160	1104	1060	1020	535	475	428	395	365	0.2	0.8	1.9	3.5	4-V
3 NEW	P44HS1	44 Rem. Magnum	240	15.55	Hydra-Shok HP	150	1180	1130	1081	1050	1010	741	675	623	580	550	0.2	0.9	2.0	3.7	6¹/₂-V

Nyclad Pistol and Revolver Ballistics (Approximate)

USAGE	FEDERAL LOAD NO.	CALIBER	BULLET WGT. IN GRAINS	GRAMS	BULLET STYLE	FACTORY PRIMER NO.	VELOCITY IN FEET PER SECOND MUZZLE	25 YDS.	50 YDS.	75YDS.	100YDS.	ENERGY IN FOOT/POUNDS MUZZLE	25 YDS.	50 YDS.	75 YDS.	100 YDS.	MID-RANGE TRAJECTORY 25 YDS.	50 YDS.	75 YDS.	100 YDS.	TEST BARREL LENGTH INCHES
3	P9BP	9mm Luger (9x19mm Parabellum)	124	8.03	Nyclad Hollow Point	100	1120	1070	1030	990	960	345	315	290	270	255	0.2	0.9	2.2	4.1	4
4	P38B	38 Special	158	10.23	Nyclad Round Nose	100	755	740	723	710	690	200	190	183	175	170	0.5	2.0	4.6	8.3	4-V
1, 3	P38G	38 Special (High Velocity +P)	158	10.23	Nyclad SWC-HP	100	890	870	855	840	820	270	265	257	245	235	0.3	1.4	3.3	5.9	4-V
3	P38M	38 Special	125	8.10	Nyclad Hollow Point	100	825	780	730	690	650	190	170	150	130	115	0.4	1.8	4.3	8.1	2-V
1, 3	P38N	38 Special (High Velocity +P)	125	8.10	Nyclad Hollow Point	100	945	920	898	880	860	248	235	224	215	205	0.3	1.3	2.9	5.4	4-V
2, 3	P357E	357 Magnum	158	10.23	Nyclad SWC-HP	100	1235	1160	1104	1060	1020	535	475	428	395	365	0.2	0.8	1.9	3.5	4-V

+P ammunition is loaded to a higher pressure. Use only in firearms so recommended by the gun manufacturer. "V" indicates vented barrel to simulate service conditions.

22 Cartridge Ballistics (Approximate)

	TYPE	FEDERAL LOAD NO.	CART-RIDGE PER BOX	CALIBER	BULLET WGT. IN GRAINS	BULLET STYLE	VELOCITY IN FEET PER SECOND MUZZLE	50 YDS.	100 YDS.	150 YDS.	ENERGY IN FOOT/POUNDS MUZZLE	50 YDS.	100 YDS.	150 YDS.	WIND DRIFT IN INCHES 10 MPH CROSSWIND 50 YDS.	100 YDS.	150 YDS.	HEIGHT OF BULLET TRAJECTORY IN INCHES ABOVE OR BELOW LINE OF SIGHT IF ZEROED AT ⊕ YARDS. SIGHTS 1.5 INCHES ABOVE BORE LINE. 50 YDS.	100 YDS.	150 YDS.	50 YDS.	100 YDS.	150 YDS.
CB	Hi-Power®	700CB	50	22 CB Long	29	Solid	730	670	610	560	35	30	25	20	1.6	6.8	16.1	⊕	-19.0	-61.5	+9.0	⊕	-32.4
Short	Hi-Power	701	50	22 Short HV	29	Solid	1095	990	905	830	77	65	53	45	1.3	5.1	11.5	⊕	-7.0	-23.0	+3.0	⊕	-14.1
Long	Hi-Power	706	50	22 Long HV	29	Solid	1240	1060	960	880	99	75	60	50	1.9	6.8	14.3	⊕	-7.0	-23.0	+3.0	⊕	-12.0
Standard Velocity	Champion™	711	50	22 Long Rifle HV	40	Solid	1150	1050	975	910	117	95	85	75	1.2	4.4	9.4	⊕	-7.3	-23.6	+3.2	⊕	-12.1
High Velocity	Hi-Power	710	50	22 Long Rifle HV	40	Solid, Copper Plated	1255	1100	1015	940	140	110	92	80	1.5	5.5	11.4	⊕	-6.5	-21.0	+2.7	⊕	-10.8
	Hi-Power	810	100	22 Long Rifle HV	40	Solid, Copper Plated	1255	1100	1015	940	140	110	92	80	1.5	5.5	11.4	⊕	-6.5	-21.0	+2.7	⊕	-10.8
	Hi-Power	712	50	22 Long Rifle HV	38	HP. Copper Plated	1255	1120	1020	950	138	105	88	75	1.6	5.8	12.1	⊕	-6.3	-20.6	+2.7	⊕	-10.6
	Hi-Power	812	100	22 Long Rifle HV	38	HP. Copper Plated	1255	1120	1020	950	138	105	88	75	1.6	5.8	12.1	⊕	-6.3	-20.6	+2.7	⊕	-10.6
Shot	Hi-Power	716	50	22 Long Rifle Shot	25	No. 12 Lead Shot	–	–	–	–	–	–	–	–	–	–	–	–	–	–	–	–	–

These ballistic specifications were derived from test barrels 24 inches in length.

LIGHTNING™ RIMFIRE 22

FEDERAL LOAD NO.	CART-RIDGES PER BOX	CALIBER	BULLET WGT. IN GRAINS	BULLET STYLE	VELOCITY IN FEET PER SECOND MUZZLE	50 YDS.	100YDS.	150YDS.	ENERGY IN FOOT/POUNDS MUZZLE	50 YDS.	100YDS.	150YDS.	WIND DRIFT IN INCHES 10 MPH CROSSWIND 50YDS.	100YDS.	150YDS.	HEIGHT OF BULLET TRAJECTORY IN INCHES ABOVE OR BELOW LINE OF SIGHT IF ZEROED AT ⊕ YARDS. SIGHTS 1.5 INCHES ABOVE BORE LINE. 50YDS.	100YDS.	150YDS.	50YDS.	100YDS.	150YDS.	TEST BARREL LENGTH INCHES
510	50	22 Long Rifle HV	40	Solid	1255	1100	1015	940	140	110	92	80	1.5	5.5	11.4	⊕	-6.5	-21.0	+2.7	⊕	-10.8	24

22 Win. Magnum Ballistics (Approximate)

	TYPE	FEDERAL LOAD NO.	CART-RIDGE PER BOX	CALIBER	BULLET WGT. IN GRAINS	BULLET STYLE	VELOCITY IN FEET PER SECOND MUZZLE	50 YDS.	100 YDS.	150 YDS.	ENERGY IN FOOT/POUNDS MUZZLE	50 YDS.	100 YDS.	150 YDS.	WIND DRIFT IN INCHES 10 MPH CROSSWIND 50 YDS.	100 YDS.	150 YDS.	HEIGHT OF BULLET TRAJECTORY IN INCHES ABOVE OR BELOW LINE OF SIGHT IF ZEROED AT ⊕ YARDS. SIGHTS 1.5 INCHES ABOVE BORE LINE. 50 YDS.	100 YDS.	150 YDS.	50 YDS.	100 YDS.	150 YDS.
	Magnum	757	50	22 Win. Magnum	50	JHP	1650	1450	1280	1150	300	235	180	145	1.1	4.5	10.3	⊕	-3.6	-12.5	+1.3	⊕	-6.5

REMINGTON BALLISTICS
CENTERFIRE RIFLE

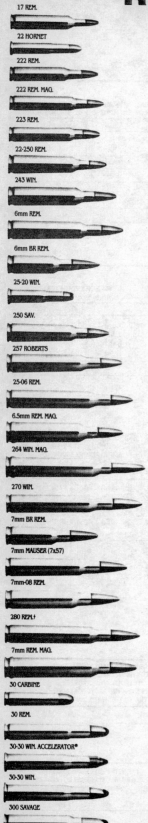

17 REM.

22 HORNET

222 REM.

222 REM. MAG.

223 REM.

22-250 REM.

243 WIN.

6mm REM.

6mm BR REM.

25-20 WIN.

250 SAV.

257 ROBERTS

25-06 REM.

6.5mm REM. MAG.

264 WIN. MAG.

270 WIN.

7mm BR REM.

7mm MAUSER (7x57)

7mm-08 REM.

280 REM.†

7mm REM. MAG.

30 CARBINE

30 REM.

30-30 WIN. ACCELERATOR®

30-30 WIN.

300 SAVAGE

Remington Ballistics

CALIBERS	REMINGTON Order No.	BULLET Wt.-Grs.	BULLET Style	Primer No.
17 REM.	R17REM	25*	Hollow Point Power-Lokt®	7½
22 HORNET	R22HN1	45*	Pointed Soft Point	6½
	R22HN2	45	Hollow Point	6½
222 REM.	R222R1	50	Pointed Soft Point	7½
	R222R3	50*	Hollow Point Power-Lokt	7½
222 REM. MAG.	R222M1	55*	Pointed Soft Point	7½
223 REM.	R223R1	55	Pointed Soft Point	7½
	R223R2	55*	Hollow Point Power-Lokt	7½
	R223R3	55	Metal Case	7½
	R223R4	60	Hollow Point Match	7½
22-250 REM.	R22501	55*	Pointed Soft Point	9½
	R22502	55	Hollow Point Power-Lokt	9½
243 WIN.	R243W1	80	Pointed Soft Point	9½
	R243W2	80*	Hollow Point Power-Lokt	9½
	R243W3	100	Pointed Soft Point Core-Lokt®	9½
6mm REM.	R6MM1	80†	Pointed Soft Point	9½
	R6MM2§	80†	Hollow Point Power-Lokt	9½
	R6MM4	100*	Pointed Soft Point Core-Lokt	9½
6mm BR REM.	R6MMBR	100	Pointed Soft Point	7½
25-20 WIN.	R25202	86*	Soft Point	6½
250 SAV.	R250SV	100*	Pointed Soft Point	9½
257 ROBERTS	R257	117	Soft Point Core-Lokt	9½
	R257AS	100*	Pointed Soft Point Core-Lokt	9½
25-06 REM.	R25061§	87	Hollow Point Power-Lokt	9½
	R25062	100*	Pointed Soft Point Core-Lokt	9½
	R25063	120	Pointed Soft Point Core-Lokt	9½
264 WIN. MAG.	R264W2	140*	Pointed Soft Point Core-Lokt	9½M
270 WIN.	R270W1	100	Pointed Soft Point	9½
	R270W2	130*	Pointed Soft Point Core-Lokt	9½
	R270W3	130	Bronze Point	9½
	R270W4	150	Soft Point Core-Lokt	9½
7mm BR REM.	R7MMBR	140*	Pointed Soft Point	7½
7mm MAUSER (7x57)	R7MSR1	140*	Pointed Soft Point	9½
7mm-08 REM.	R7M081	140	Pointed Soft Point	9½
	R7M083	120*	Hollow Point	9½
280 REM.†	R280R3	140	Pointed Soft Point	9½
	R280R1	150	Pointed Soft Point Core-Lokt	9½
	R280R2	165	Soft Point Core-Lokt	9½
	R280R4	120*	Hollow Point	9½
7mm REM. MAG.	R7MM2	150	Pointed Soft Point Core-Lokt	9½M
	R7MM3	175	Pointed Soft Point Core-Lokt	9½M
	R7MM4	140*	Pointed Soft Point	9½M
30 CARBINE	R30CAR	110*	Soft Point	6½
30 REM.	R30REM	170*	Soft Point Core-Lokt	9½
30-30 WIN. ACCELERATOR®	R3030A	55*	Soft Point	9½
30-30 WIN.	R30301	150*	Soft Point Core-Lokt	9½
	R30302	170	Soft Point Core-Lokt	9½
	R30303	170	Hollow Point Core-Lokt	9½
300 SAVAGE	R30SV3	180*	Soft Point Core-Lokt	9½
	R30SV2	150	Pointed Soft Point Core-Lokt	9½

REMINGTON BALLISTICS
CENTERFIRE RIFLE

SHORT RANGE — Bullet does not rise more than one inch above line of sight from muzzle to sighting-in range.
LONG RANGE — Bullet does not rise more than three inches above line of sight from muzzle to sighting-in range.

VELOCITY FEET PER SECOND						ENERGY FOOT-POUNDS						TRAJECTORY SHORT RANGE						LONG RANGE							BARREL LENGTH
Muzzle	100 Yds.	200 Yds.	300 Yds.	400 Yds.	500 Yds.	Muzzle	100 Yds.	200 Yds.	300 Yds.	400 Yds.	500 Yds.	50 Yds.	100 Yds.	150 Yds.	200 Yds.	250 Yds.	300 Yds.	100 Yds.	150 Yds.	200 Yds.	250 Yds.	300 Yds.	400 Yds.	500 Yds.	
4040	3284	2644	2086	1606	1235	906	599	388	242	143	85	0.1	0.5	0.0	-1.5	-4.2	-8.5	2.1	2.5	1.9	0.0	-3.4	-17.0	-44.3	24"
2690	2042	1502	1128	948	840	723	417	225	127	90	70	0.3	0.0	-2.4	-7.7	-16.9	-31.3	1.6	0.0	-4.5	-12.8	-26.4	-75.6	-163.4	24"
2690	2042	1502	1128	948	840	723	417	225	127	90	70	0.3	0.0	-2.4	-7.7	-16.9	-31.3	1.6	0.0	-4.5	-12.8	-26.4	-75.6	-163.4	
3140	2602	2123	1700	1350	1107	1094	752	500	321	202	136	0.5	0.9	0.0	-2.5	-6.9	-13.7	2.2	1.9	0.0	-3.8	-10.0	-32.3	-73.8	24"
3140	2635	2182	1777	1432	1172	1094	771	529	351	228	152	0.5	0.9	0.0	-2.4	-6.6	-13.1	2.1	1.8	0.0	-3.6	-9.5	-30.2	-68.1	
3240	2748	2305	1906	1556	1272	1282	922	649	444	296	198	0.4	0.8	0.0	-2.2	-6.0	-11.8	1.9	1.6	0.0	-3.3	-8.5	-26.7	-59.5	24"
3240	2747	2304	1905	1554	1270	1282	921	648	443	295	197	0.4	0.8	0.0	-2.2	-6.0	-11.8	1.9	1.6	0.0	-3.3	-8.5	-26.7	-59.6	24"
3240	2773	2352	1969	1627	1341	1282	939	675	473	323	220	0.4	0.8	0.0	-2.1	-5.8	-11.4	1.8	1.6	0.0	-3.2	-8.2	-25.5	-56.0	
3240	2759	2326	1933	1587	1301	1282	929	660	456	307	207	0.4	0.8	0.0	-2.1	-5.9	-11.6	1.9	1.6	0.0	-3.2	-8.4	-26.2	-57.9	
3100	2712	2355	2026	1726	1463	1280	979	739	547	397	285	0.5	0.8	0.0	-2.2	-6.0	-11.5	1.9	1.6	0.0	-3.2	-8.3	-25.1	-53.6	
3680	3137	2656	2222	1832	1493	1654	1201	861	603	410	272		0.5	0.0	-1.6	-4.4	-8.7	2.3	2.6	1.9	0.0	-3.4	-15.9	-38.9	24"
3680	3209	2785	2400	2046	1725	1654	1257	947	703	511	363		0.5	0.0	-1.5	-4.1	-8.0	2.1	2.5	1.8	0.0	-3.1	-14.1	-33.4	
3350	2955	2593	2259	1951	1670	1993	1551	1194	906	676	495	0.3	0.7	0.0	-1.8	-4.9	-9.4	2.6	2.9	2.1	0.0	-3.6	-16.2	-37.9	24"
3350	2955	2593	2259	1951	1670	1993	1551	1194	906	676	495	0.3	0.7	0.0	-1.8	-4.9	-9.4	2.6	2.9	2.1	0.0	-3.6	-16.2	-37.9	
2960	2697	2449	2215	1993	1786	1945	1615	1332	1089	882	708	0.5	0.9	0.0	-2.2	-5.8	-11.0	1.9	1.6	0.0	-3.1	-7.8	-22.6	-46.3	
3470	3064	2694	2352	2036	1747	2139	1667	1289	982	736	542	0.3	0.6	0.0	-1.6	-4.5	-8.7	2.4	2.7	1.9	0.0	-3.3	-14.9	-35.0	24"
3470	3064	2694	2352	2036	1747	2139	1667	1289	982	736	542	0.3	0.6	0.0	-1.6	-4.5	-8.7	2.4	2.7	1.9	0.0	-3.3	-14.9	-35.0	
3100	2829	2573	2332	2104	1889	2133	1777	1470	1207	983	792	0.4	0.8	0.0	-1.9	-5.2	-9.9	1.7	1.5	0.0	-2.8	-7.0	-20.4	-41.7	
2550	2310	2083	1870	1671	1491	1444	1185	963	776	620	494	0.3	0.0	-1.9	-5.6	-11.4	-19.3	2.8	2.3	0.0	-4.3	-10.9	-31.7	-65.1	15"
1460	1194	1030	931	858	797	407	272	203	165	141	121	0.0	-4.1	-14.4	-31.8	-57.3	-92.0	0.0	-8.2	-23.5	-47.0	-79.6	-175.9	-319.4	24"
2820	2504	2210	1936	1684	1461	1765	1392	1084	832	630	474	0.2	0.0	-1.6	-4.7	-9.6	-16.5	2.3	2.0	0.0	-3.7	-9.5	-28.3	-59.5	24"
2650	2291	1961	1663	1404	1199	1824	1363	999	718	512	373	0.3	0.0	-1.9	-5.8	-11.9	-20.7	2.9	2.4	0.0	-4.7	-12.0	-36.7	-79.2	24"
2980	2661	2363	2085	1827	1592	1972	1572	1240	965	741	563	0.1	0.0	-1.3	-4.0	-8.3	-14.3	2.0	1.7	0.0	-3.3	-8.3	-24.6	-51.4	
3440	2995	2591	2222	1884	1583	2286	1733	1297	954	686	484	0.3	0.6	0.0	-1.7	-4.8	-9.3	2.5	2.9	2.1	0.0	-3.6	-16.4	-39.1	24"
3230	2893	2580	2287	2014	1762	2382	1858	1478	1161	901	689	0.4	0.7	0.0	-1.9	-5.0	-9.7	1.6	1.4	0.0	-2.7	-6.9	-20.5	-42.7	
2990	2730	2484	2252	2032	1825	2382	1985	1644	1351	1100	887	0.5	0.8	0.0	-2.1	-5.6	-10.7	1.9	1.6	0.0	-3.0	-7.5	-22.0	-44.8	
3030	2782	2548	2326	2114	1914	2854	2406	2018	1682	1389	1139	0.5	0.8	0.0	-2.0	-5.4	-10.2	1.8	1.5	0.0	-2.9	-7.2	-20.8	-42.2	24"
3430	3021	2649	2305	1988	1699	2612	2027	1557	1179	877	641	0.3	0.6	0.0	-1.7	-4.6	-9.0	2.5	2.8	2.0	0.0	-3.4	-15.5	-36.4	24"
3060	2776	2510	2259	2022	1801	2702	2225	1818	1472	1180	936	0.5	0.8	0.0	-2.0	-5.5	-10.4	1.8	1.5	0.0	-2.9	-7.4	-21.6	-44.3	
3060	2802	2559	2329	2110	1904	2702	2267	1890	1565	1285	1046	0.4	0.8	0.0	-2.0	-5.3	-10.1	1.8	1.5	0.0	-2.8	-7.1	-20.6	-42.0	
2850	2504	2183	1886	1618	1385	2705	2087	1587	1185	872	639	0.7	1.0	0.0	-2.6	-7.1	-13.6	2.3	2.0	0.0	-3.8	-9.7	-29.2	-62.2	
2215	2012	1821	1643	1481	1336	1525	1259	1031	839	681	555		0.0	-2.7	-7.7	-15.4	-25.9	1.8	0.0	-4.1	-10.9	-20.6	-50.0	-95.2	15"
2660	2435	2221	2018	1827	1648	2199	1843	1533	1266	1037	844	0.2	0.0	-1.7	-5.0	-10.0	-17.0	2.5	2.0	0.0	-3.8	-9.6	-27.7	-56.3	24"
2860	2625	2402	2189	1988	1798	2542	2142	1793	1490	1228	1005	0.6	0.9	0.0	-2.3	-6.1	-11.6	2.1	1.7	0.0	-3.2	-8.1	-23.5	-47.7	24"
3000	2725	2467	2223	1992	1778	2598	1979	1621	1316	1058	842	0.5	0.8	0.0	-2.1	-5.7	-10.8	1.9	1.6	0.0	-3.0	-7.6	-22.3	-45.8	
3000	2758	2528	2309	2102	1905	2797	2363	1986	1657	1373	1128	0.5	0.8	0.0	-2.1	-5.5	-10.4	1.8	1.5	0.0	-2.9	-7.3	-21.1	-42.9	24"
2890	2624	2375	2135	1912	1702	2781	2293	1875	1518	1217	968	0.6	0.9	0.0	-2.3	-6.2	-11.8	2.1	1.7	0.0	-3.3	-8.3	-24.2	-49.7	
2820	2510	2220	1950	1701	1479	2913	2308	1805	1393	1060	801	0.2	0.0	-1.5	-4.6	-9.5	-16.4	2.3	1.9	0.0	-3.7	-9.4	-28.1	-58.8	
3150	2866	2599	2348	2110	1887	2643	2188	1800	1468	1186	949	0.5	0.7	0.0	-1.9	-5.1	-9.7	2.8	3.0	2.2	0.0	-3.6	-15.7	-35.6	
3110	2830	2568	2320	2085	1866	3221	2667	2196	1792	1448	1160	0.4	0.8	0.0	-1.9	-5.2	-9.9	1.7	1.5	0.0	-2.8	-7.0	-20.5	-42.1	24"
2860	2645	2440	2244	2057	1879	3178	2718	2313	1956	1644	1372	0.6	0.9	0.0	-2.3	-6.0	-11.3	2.0	1.7	0.0	-3.2	-7.9	-22.7	-45.8	
3175	2923	2684	2458	2243	2039	3133	2655	2240	1878	1564	1292	0.4	0.7	0.0	-1.8	-4.8	-9.1	2.6	2.9	2.0	0.0	-3.4	-14.5	-32.6	
1990	1567	1236	1035	923	842	967	600	373	262	208	173	0.9	0.0	-4.5	-13.5	-28.3	-49.9	0.0	-4.5	-13.5	-28.3	-49.9	-118.6	-228.2	20"
2120	1822	1555	1328	1153	1036	1696	1253	913	666	502	405	0.7	0.0	-3.3	-9.7	-19.6	-33.8	2.2	0.0	-5.3	-14.1	-27.2	-69.0	-136.9	24"
3400	2693	2085	1570	1187	986	1412	886	521	301	172	119	0.4	0.8	0.0	-2.4	-6.7	-13.8	2.0	1.8	0.0	-3.8	-10.2	-35.0	-84.4	24"
2390	1973	1605	1303	1095	974	1902	1296	858	565	399	316	0.5	0.0	-2.7	-8.2	-17.0	-30.0	1.8	0.0	-4.6	-12.5	-24.6	-65.3	-134.9	24"
2200	1895	1619	1381	1191	1061	1827	1355	989	720	535	425	0.6	0.0	-3.0	-8.9	-18.0	-31.1	2.0	0.0	-4.8	-13.0	-25.1	-63.6	-126.7	
2200	1895	1619	1381	1191	1061	1827	1355	989	720	535	425	0.6	0.0	-3.0	-8.9	-18.0	-31.1	2.0	0.0	-4.8	-13.0	-25.1	-63.6	-126.7	
2350	2025	1728	1467	1252	1098	2207	1639	1193	860	626	482	0.5	0.0	-2.6	-7.7	-15.6	-27.1	1.7	0.0	-4.2	-11.3	-21.9	-55.8	-112.0	24"
2650	2354	2095	1853	1631	1432	2303	1845	1462	1145	806	685	0.3	0.0	-1.8	-5.4	-11.0	-18.8	2.7	2.2	0.0	-4.2	-10.7	-31.5	-65.6	

Specifications are nominal. Ballistics figures established in test barrels. Individual rifles may vary from test-barrel specifications.   *Illustrated (not shown actual size).
**Inches above or below line of sight. Hold low for positive numbers, high for negative numbers.   †280 Rem. and 7mm Express™ Rem. are interchangeable.
†Interchangeable in 244 Rem.   §Subject to stock on hand.

REMINGTON BALLISTICS
CENTERFIRE RIFLE

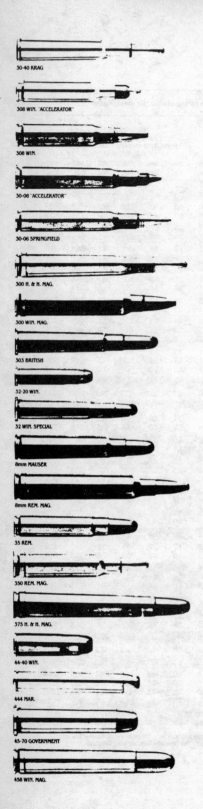

30-40 KRAG

308 WIN. "ACCELERATOR"

308 WIN.

30-06 "ACCELERATOR"

30-06 SPRINGFIELD

300 H. & H. MAG.

300 WIN. MAG.

303 BRITISH

32-20 WIN.

32 WIN. SPECIAL

8mm MAUSER

8mm REM. MAG.

35 REM.

350 REM. MAG.

375 H. & H. MAG.

44-40 WIN.

444 MAR.

45-70 GOVERNMENT

458 WIN. MAG.

Remington Ballistics

CALIBERS	REMINGTON Order No.	BULLET Wt.-Grs.	BULLET Style	Primer No.
30-40 KRAG	R30402	180°	Pointed Soft Point Core-Lokt	9½
308 WIN. ACCELERATOR®	R308W5	55°	Pointed Soft Point	9½
308 WIN.	R308W1	150	Pointed Soft Point Core-Lokt	9½
	R308W6	165	Pointed Soft Point Core-Lokt	9½
	R308W2	180	Soft Point Core-Lokt	9½
	R308W3	180	Pointed Soft Point Core-Lokt	9½
	R308W7	168°	Boattail H.P. Match	9½
30-06 ACCELERATOR	R30069	55°	Pointed Soft Point	9½
30-06 SPRINGFIELD	R30061	125	Pointed Soft Point	9½
	R30062	150	Pointed Soft Point Core-Lokt	9½
	R30063	150	Bronze Point	9½
	R3006B	165°	Pointed Soft Point Core-Lokt	9½
	R30064	180	Soft Point Core-Lokt	9½
	R30065	180	Pointed Soft Point Core-Lokt	9½
	R30066	180	Bronze Point	9½
	R30067	220	Soft Point Core-Lokt	9½
	R3006C★	168	Boattail H.P. Match	9½
300 H&H MAG.	R300HH	180°	Pointed Soft Point Core-Lokt	9½M
300 WIN. MAG.	R300W1	150	Pointed Soft Point Core-Lokt	9½M
	R300W2	180°	Pointed Soft Point Core-Lokt	9½M
300 WBY. MAG.	R300WB1★	180	Pointed Soft Point Core-Lokt	9½M
	R300WB2★	220	Soft Point Core-Lokt	9½M
303 BRITISH	R303B1	180°	Soft Point Core-Lokt	9½
7.62x39mm	R762391★	125	Pointed Soft Point	7½
32-20 WIN.	R32201	100	Lead	6½
	R32202	100°	Soft Point	6½
32 WIN. SPECIAL	R32WS2	170°	Soft Point Core-Lokt	9½
8mm MAUSER	R8MSR	170°	Soft Point Core-Lokt	9½
8mm REM. MAG.	R8MM1	185°	Pointed Soft Point Core-Lokt	9½M
	R8MM2	220	Pointed Soft Point Core-Lokt	9½M
338 WIN. MAG.	R338W1	225°	Pointed Soft Point	9½M
	R338W2	250	Pointed Soft Point	9½M
35 REM.	R35R1	150	Pointed Soft Point Core-Lokt	9½
	R35R2	200°	Soft Point Core-Lokt	9½
350 REM. MAG.	R350M1	200°	Pointed Soft Point Core-Lokt	9½M
35 WHELEN	R35WH1	200	Pointed Soft Point	9½M
	R35WH2	250°	Soft Point	9½M
	R35WH3★	250	Pointed Soft Point	9½M
375 H&H MAG.	R375M1	270°	Soft Point	9½M
	R375M2	300	Metal Case	9½M
416 REM. MAG.	R416R1★	400	Solid	9½M
	R416R2★	400	Pointed Soft Point	9½M
44-40 WIN.	R4440W	200°	Soft Point	2½
44 REM. MAG.	R44MG2	240	Soft Point	2½
	R44MG3	240	Semi-Jacketed Hollow Point	2½
	R44MG6	210	Semi-Jacketed Hollow Point	2½
444 MAR.	R444M	240	Soft Point	9½
	R444M2	265°	Soft Point	9½
45-70 GOVERNMENT	R4570O	405°	Soft Point	9½
	R4570L	300	Jacketed Hollow Point	9½
458 WIN. MAG.	R458W1	500	Metal Case	9½M
	R458W2	500°	Soft Point	9½M

*Illustrated (not shown actual size).

★ New for 1989.

REMINGTON BALLISTICS
CENTERFIRE RIFLE

TRAJECTORY** 0.0 indicates yardage at which rifle was sighted in.

SHORT RANGE: Bullet does not rise more than one inch above line of sight from muzzle to sighting-in range.

LONG RANGE: Bullet does not rise more than three inches above line of sight from muzzle to sighting-in range.

VELOCITY FEET PER SECOND						ENERGY FOOT-POUNDS						SHORT RANGE						LONG RANGE							BARREL LENGTH
Muzzle	100 Yds.	200 Yds.	300 Yds.	400 Yds.	500 Yds.	Muzzle	100 Yds.	200 Yds.	300 Yds.	400 Yds.	500 Yds.	50 Yds.	100 Yds.	150 Yds.	200 Yds.	250 Yds.	300 Yds.	100 Yds.	150 Yds.	200 Yds.	250 Yds.	300 Yds.	400 Yds.	500 Yds.	
2430	2213	2007	1813	1632	1468	2360	1957	1610	1314	1064	861	0.4	0.0	-2.1	-6.2	-12.5	-21.1	1.4	0.0	-3.4	-8.9	-16.8	-40.9	-78.1	24"
3770	3215	2726	2286	1888	1541	1735	1262	907	638	435	290	0.2	0.5	0.0	-1.5	-4.2	-8.2	2.2	2.5	1.8	0.0	-3.2	-15.0	-36.7	24"
2820	2533	2263	2009	1774	1560	2648	2137	1705	1344	1048	810	0.2	0.0	-1.5	-4.5	-9.3	-15.9	2.3	1.9	0.0	-3.6	-9.1	-26.9	-55.7	
2700	2440	2194	1963	1748	1551	2670	2180	1763	1411	1119	881	0.2	0.0	-1.7	-5.0	-10.1	-17.2	2.5	2.1	0.0	-3.9	-9.7	-28.5	-58.8	24"
2620	2274	1955	1666	1414	1212	2743	2066	1527	1109	799	587	0.3	0.0	-2.0	-5.9	-12.1	-20.9	2.9	2.4	0.0	-4.7	-12.1	-36.9	-79.1	
2620	2393	2178	1974	1782	1604	2743	2288	1896	1557	1269	1028	0.2	0.0	-1.8	-5.2	-10.4	-17.7	2.6	2.1	0.0	-4.0	-9.9	-28.9	-58.8	
2680	2493	2314	2143	1979	1823	2678	2318	1998	1713	1460	1239	0.2	0.0	-1.6	-4.7	-9.4	-15.9	2.4	1.9	0.0	-3.5	-8.9	-25.3	-50.6	
4080	3485	2965	2502	2083	1709	2033	1483	1074	764	530	356	0.4	1.0	0.9	0.0	-1.9	-5.0	1.8	2.1	1.5	0.0	-2.7	-12.5	-30.5	24"
3140	2780	2447	2138	1853	1595	2736	2145	1662	1269	953	706	0.4	0.8	0.0	-2.1	-5.6	-10.7	1.8	1.5	0.0	-3.0	-7.7	-23.0	-48.5	
2910	2617	2342	2083	1843	1622	2820	2281	1827	1445	1131	876	0.6	0.9	0.0	-2.3	-6.3	-12.0	2.1	1.8	0.0	-3.3	-8.5	-25.0	-51.8	
2910	2656	2416	2189	1974	1773	2820	2349	1944	1596	1298	1047	0.6	0.9	0.0	-2.2	-6.0	-11.4	2.0	1.7	0.0	-3.2	-8.0	-23.3	-47.5	
2800	2534	2283	2047	1825	1621	2872	2352	1909	1534	1220	963	0.7	1.0	0.0	-2.5	-6.7	-12.7	2.3	1.9	0.0	-3.6	-9.0	-26.3	-54.1	24"
2700	2348	2023	1727	1466	1251	2913	2203	1635	1192	859	625	0.2	0.0	-1.8	-5.5	-11.2	-19.5	2.7	2.3	0.0	-4.4	-11.3	-34.4	-73.7	
2700	2469	2250	2042	1846	1663	2913	2436	2023	1666	1362	1105	0.2	0.0	-1.6	-4.8	-9.7	-16.5	2.4	2.0	0.0	-3.7	-9.3	-27.0	-54.9	
2700	2485	2280	2084	1899	1725	2913	2468	2077	1736	1441	1189	0.2	0.0	-1.6	-4.7	-9.6	-16.2	2.4	2.0	0.0	-3.6	-9.1	-26.2	-53.0	
2410	2130	1870	1632	1422	1246	2837	2216	1708	1301	988	758	0.4	0.0	-2.3	-6.8	-13.8	-23.6	1.5	0.0	-3.7	-9.9	-19.0	-47.4	-93.1	
2710	2522	2346	2169	2003	1845	2739	2372	2045	1754	1497	1270	0.7	1.0	0.0	-2.5	-6.6	-12.4	2.1	1.9	0.0	-3.5	-8.6	-24.7	-49.4	
2880	2640	2412	2196	1990	1798	3315	2785	2325	1927	1583	1292	0.6	0.9	0.0	-2.3	-6.0	-11.5	2.1	1.7	0.0	-3.2	-8.0	-23.3	-47.4	24"
3290	2951	2636	2342	2068	1813	3605	2900	2314	1827	1424	1095	0.3	0.7	0.0	-1.8	-4.8	-9.3	2.6	2.9	2.1	0.0	-3.5	-15.4	-35.5	24"
2960	2745	2540	2344	2157	1979	3501	3011	2578	2196	1859	1565	0.5	0.8	0.0	-2.1	-5.5	-10.4	1.9	1.6	0.0	-2.9	-7.3	-20.9	-41.9	
3200	2942	2698	2467	2248	2040	4092	3458	2909	2433	2019	1663	0.4	0.7	0.0	-1.8	-4.7	-9.0	2.6	2.8	2.0	0.0	-3.3	-14.4	-32.4	24"
2850	2541	2283	1984	1736	1512	3967	3155	2480	1922	1471	1117	0.6	1.0	0.0	-2.5	-6.7	-12.9	2.3	1.9	0.0	-3.6	-9.1	-27.2	-56.8	
2460	2124	1817	1542	1311	1137	2418	1803	1319	950	687	517	0.4	0.0	-2.3	-6.9	-14.1	-24.4	1.7	0.0	-3.8	-10.2	-19.8	-50.5	-101.5	24"
2365	2062	1783	1533	1320	1154	1552	1180	882	652	483	370	0.4	0.0	-2.5	-7.3	-14.3	-25.7	1.7	0.0	-4.8	-10.8	-20.7	-52.3	-104.0	24"
1210	1021	913	834	769	712	325	231	185	154	131	113	0.0	-6.3	-20.9	-44.9	-79.3	-125.1	0.0	-11.5	-32.3	-63.8	-106.3	-230.3	-413.3	24"
1210	1021	913	834	769	712	325	231	185	154	131	113	0.0	-6.3	-20.9	-44.9	-79.3	-125.1	0.0	-11.5	-32.3	-63.6	-106.3	-230.3	-413.3	
2250	1921	1626	1372	1175	1044	1911	1393	998	710	521	411	0.6	0.0	-2.9	-8.6	-17.6	-30.5	1.9	0.0	-4.7	-12.7	-24.7	-63.2	-126.9	24"
2360	1969	1622	1333	1123	997	2102	1463	993	671	476	375	0.5	0.0	-2.7	-8.2	-17.0	-29.8	1.8	0.0	-4.5	-12.4	-24.3	-63.8	-130.7	24"
3080	2761	2464	2186	1927	1688	3896	3131	2494	1963	1525	1170	0.5	0.8	0.0	-2.1	-5.6	-10.7	1.8	1.6	0.0	-3.0	-7.6	-22.5	-46.8	24"
2830	2581	2346	2123	1913	1716	3912	3254	2688	2201	1787	1438	0.6	1.0	0.0	-2.4	-6.4	-12.1	2.2	1.8	0.0	-3.4	-8.5	-24.7	-50.5	
2780	2572	2374	2184	2003	1832	3860	3305	2815	2383	2004	1676	0.6	1.0	0.0	-2.4	-6.3	-12.0	2.2	1.8	0.0	-3.3	-8.4	-24.0	-48.4	24"
2660	2456	2261	2075	1898	1731	3927	3348	2837	2389	1999	1663	0.2	0.0	-1.7	-4.9	-9.8	-16.6	2.4	2.0	0.0	-3.7	-9.3	-26.6	-53.6	
2300	1874	1506	1218	1039	934	1762	1169	755	494	359	291	0.6	0.0	-3.0	-9.2	-19.1	-33.9	2.0	0.0	-5.1	-14.1	-27.8	-74.0	-152.3	24"
2080	1698	1376	1140	1001	911	1921	1280	841	577	445	369	0.8	0.0	-3.8	-11.3	-23.5	-41.2	2.5	0.0	-6.3	-17.1	-33.6	-87.7	-176.4	
2710	2410	2130	1870	1631	1421	3261	2579	2014	1553	1181	897	0.2	0.0	-1.7	-5.1	-10.4	-17.9	2.6	2.1	0.0	-4.0	-10.3	-30.5	-64.0	20"
2675	2378	2100	1842	1606	1399	3177	2510	1958	1506	1145	869	0.2	0.0	-1.8	-5.3	-10.8	-18.5	2.6	2.2	0.0	-4.2	-10.6	-31.5	-65.9	
2400	2066	1761	1492	1269	1107	3197	2369	1722	1235	893	680	0.4	0.0	-2.5	-7.3	-15.0	-26.0	1.6	0.0	-4.0	-10.9	-21.0	-53.8	-108.2	24"
2400	2197	2005	1823	1652	1496	3197	2680	2230	1844	1515	1242	0.4	0.0	-2.2	-6.3	-12.6	-21.3	1.4	0.0	-3.4	-9.0	-17.0	-41.0	-77.8	
2690	2420	2166	1928	1707	1507	4337	3510	2812	2228	1747	1361	0.2	0.0	-1.7	-5.1	-10.3	-17.6	2.5	2.1	0.0	-3.9	-10.0	-29.4	-60.7	24"
2530	2171	1843	1551	1307	1126	4263	3139	2262	1602	1138	844	0.3	0.0	-2.2	-6.5	-13.5	-23.4	1.5	0.0	-3.6	-9.8	-19.1	-49.1	-99.5	
2400	2042	1718	1436	1212	1062	5115	3702	2620	1832	1305	1001	0.4	0.0	-2.5	-7.5	-15.5	-27.0	1.7	0.0	-4.2	-11.3	-21.9	-56.7	-115.1	24"
2400	2175	1962	1761	1579	1414	5115	4201	3419	2760	2214	1775	0.4	0.0	-2.5	-6.5	-13.0	-22.0	1.5	0.0	-3.5	-9.3	-17.6	-42.9	-82.2	
1190	1006	900	822	756	699	629	449	360	300	254	217	0.0	-6.5	-21.6	-46.3	-81.8	-129.1	0.0	-11.8	-33.5	-65.5	-109.5	-237.4	-426.2	24"
1760	1380	1114	970	878	806	1650	1015	661	501	411	346	0.0	-2.7	-10.0	-23.0	-43.0	-71.2	0.0	-5.9	-17.6	-36.3	-63.1	-145.5	-273.0	
1760	1380	1114	970	878	806	1650	1015	661	501	411	346	0.0	-2.7	-10.0	-23.0	-43.0	-71.2	0.0	-5.9	-17.6	-36.3	-63.1	-145.5	-273.0	20"
1920	1477	1155	982	880	802	1719	1017	622	450	361	300	0.0	-2.2	-8.3	-19.7	-37.6	-63.2	0.0	-5.1	-15.4	-32.1	-56.7	-134.0	-256.2	
2350	1815	1377	1087	941	846	2942	1755	1010	630	472	381	0.6	0.0	-3.2	-9.9	-21.3	-38.5	2.1	0.0	-5.6	-15.9	-32.1	-87.8	-182.7	24"
2120	1733	1405	1160	1012	920	2644	1768	1162	791	603	498	0.7	0.0	-3.6	-10.8	-22.5	-39.5	2.4	0.0	-6.0	-16.4	-32.2	-84.3	-170.2	
1330	1168	1055	977	918	869	1590	1227	1001	858	758	679	0.0	-4.7	-15.8	-34.0	-60.0	-94.5	0.0	-8.7	-24.6	-48.2	-80.3	-172.4	-305.9	24"
1810	1497	1244	1073	969	895	2182	1492	1031	767	625	533	0.0	-2.3	-8.5	-19.4	-35.9	-59.0	0.0	-5.0	-14.8	-30.1	-52.1	-119.5	—	
2040	1823	1623	1442	1237	1161	4620	3689	2924	2308	1839	1469	0.7	0.0	-3.3	-9.6	-19.2	-32.5	2.2	0.0	-5.2	-13.6	-25.8	-63.2	-121.7	24"
2040	1770	1527	1319	1157	1046	4712	3547	2640	1970	1516	1239	0.8	0.0	-3.5	-10.3	-20.8	-35.6	2.4	0.0	-5.6	-14.9	-28.5	-71.5	-140.4	

*Inches above or below line of sight. Hold low for positive numbers, high for negative numbers. Specifications are nominal. Ballistics figures established in test barrels. Individual rifles may vary from test-barrel specifications.

REMINGTON BALLISTICS
PISTOL & REVOLVER

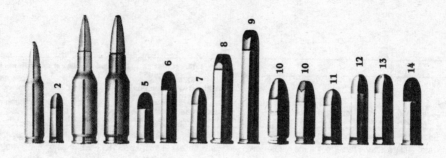

CALIBER	Order No.	Primer No.	Wt. Grs.	BULLET Style	VELOCITY (FPS) Muzzle	50 Yds.	100 Yds.	ENERGY (FT-LB) Muzzle	50 Yds.	100 Yds.	MID-RANGE TRAJECTORY 50 Yds.	100 Yds.	BARREL LENGTH
(1) 221 REM. FIREBALL®	R221F	7½	50°	Pointed Soft Point	2650	2380	2130	780	630	505	0.2″	0.8″	10
(2) 25 (6.35mm) AUTO. PISTOL	R25AP	1½	50°	Metal Case	760	707	659	64	56	48	2.0″	8.7″	2
(3) 6mm BR Rem.	R6MMBR	7½	100°	Pointed Soft Point	Refer to page 24 for ballistics.								
(4) 7mm BR Rem.	R7MMBR	7½	140°	Pointed Soft Point	Refer to page 24 for ballistics.								
(5) 32 S. & W.	R32SW	5½	88°	Lead	680	645	610	90	81	73	2.5″	10.5″	3
(6) 32 S. & W. LONG	R32SWL	1½	98°	Lead	705	670	635	115	98	88	2.3″	10.5″	4
(7) 32 (7.65mm) AUTO. PISTOL	R32AP	1½	71°	Metal Case	905	855	810	129	115	97	1.4″	5.8″	4
(8) 357 MAG.	R357M7	5½	110	Semi-Jacketed H.P.	1295	1094	975	410	292	232	0.8″	3.5″	4
Vented Barrel Ballistics	R357M1	5½	125	Semi-Jacketed H.P.	1450	1240	1090	583	427	330	0.6″	2.8″	4
(Refer to page 26 for	R357M88	5½	125	Semi-Jacketed S.P.	1450	1240	1090	583	427	330	0.6″	2.8″	4
test details)	R357M2	5½	158	Semi-Jacketed H.P.	1235	1104	1015	535	428	361	0.8″	3.5″	4
	R357M3	5½	158	Soft Point	1235	1104	1015	535	428	361	0.8″	3.5″	4
	R357M5	5½	158	Lead	1235	1104	1015	535	428	361	0.8″	3.5″	4
	R357M68	5½	158	Lead (Brass Case)	1235	1104	1015	535	428	361	0.8″	3.5″	4
	R357M9	5½	140	Semi-Jacketed H.P.	1360	1195	1076	575	444	360	0.7″	3.0″	4
	R357M10	5½	180	Semi-Jacketed H.P.	1145	1053	985	524	443	388	0.9″	3.9″	8
	R357M11	5½	125°	Semi-Jacketed H.P. (Med. Vel.)	1220	1077	984	413	322	269	0.8″	3.7″	4
	R357MB	5½	140	"Multi-Ball"	1155	829	663	418	214	136	1.2″	6.4″	4
(9) 357 REM. MAXIMUM**	357MX1	7½	158°	Semi-Jacketed H.P.	1825	1588	1381	1168	885	669	0.4″	1.7″	10
(10) 9mm LUGER	R9MM1	1½	115	Jacketed H.P.	1155	1047	971	341	280	241	0.9″	3.9″	4
AUTO. PISTOL	R9MM2	1½	124	Metal Case	1110	1030	971	339	292	259	1.0″	4.1″	4
	R9MM3	1½	115°	Metal Case	1135	1041	973	329	277	242	0.9″	4.0″	4
	R9MM5	1½	88	Jacketed H.P.	1500	1191	1012	440	277	200	0.6″	3.1″	4
	R9MM6	1½	115	Jacketed H.P. (+P)‡	1250	1113	1019	399	316	265	0.8″	3.5″	4
	R9MM7	1½	140	Semi-Jacketed H.P. (Practice)	935	889	849	272	246	224	1.3″	5.5″	4
	R9MM8★	1½	147°	Jacketed H.P. (Subsonic)	990	941	900	320	289	264	1.1″	4.9″	4
(11) 380 AUTO. PISTOL	R380AP	1½	95°	Metal Case	955	865	785	190	160	130	1.4″	5.9″	4
	R380A1	1½	88	Jacketed H.P.	990	920	868	191	165	146	1.2″	5.1″	4
(12) 38 AUTO. COLT PISTOL (A)	R38ACP8	1½	130°	Metal Case	1040	980	925	310	275	245	1.0″	4.7″	4
(13) 38 SUPER AUTO.	R38SU1	1½	115	Jacketed H.P. (+P)‡	1300	1147	1041	431	336	277	0.7″	3.3″	5
COLT PISTOL (B)	R38SUP8	1½	130°	Metal Case (+P)‡	1215	1099	1017	426	348	298	0.8″	3.6″	5
(14) 38 S. & W.	R38SW	1½	146°	Lead	685	650	620	150	135	125	2.4″	10.0″	4

REMINGTON BALLISTICS
PISTOL & REVOLVER

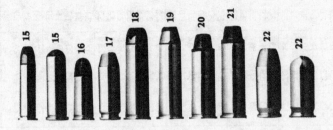

CALIBER	Order No.	Primer No.	Wt. Grs.	BULLET Style	VELOCITY (FPS) Muzzle	50 Yds.	100 Yds.	ENERGY (FT-LB) Muzzle	50 Yds.	100 Yds.	MID-RANGE TRAJECTORY 50 Yds.	100 Yds.	BARREL LENGTH
(15) 38 SPECIAL	R38S1	1½	95	Semi-Jacketed H.P. (+P)‡	1175	1044	959	291	230	194	0.9"	3.9"	4
Vented Barrel Ballistics	R38S10	1½	110	Semi-Jacketed H.P. (+P)‡	995	926	871	242	210	185	1.2"	5.1"	4
	R38S2	1½	125‡	Semi-Jacketed H.P. (+P)‡	945	898	858	248	224	204	1.3"	5.4"	4
	R38S13§	1½	125	Semi-Jacketed S.P. (+P)‡	945	908	875	248	229	212	1.3"	5.3"	4
	R38S3	1½	148	Targetmaster® Lead W.C. Match	710	634	566	166	132	105	2.4"	10.8"	4
	R38S4§	1½	158	Targetmaster Lead	755	723	692	200	183	168	2.0"	8.3"	4
	R38S5	1½	158	Lead (Round Nose)	755	723	692	200	183	168	2.0"	8.3"	4
	R38S14	1½	158	Semi-Wadcutter (+P)‡	890	855	823	278	257	238	1.4"	6.0"	4
	R38S6	1½	158	Semi-Wadcutter	755	723	692	200	183	168	2.0"	8.3"	4
	R38S7§	1½	158	Metal Point	755	723	692	200	183	168	2.0"	8.3"	4
	R38S12	1½	158	Lead H.P. (+P)‡	890	855	823	278	257	238	1.4"	6.0"	4
	R38SMB	1½	140*	"Multi-Ball"	830	731	506	216	130	80	2.0"	10.6"	4
(16) 38 SHORT COLT	R38SC	1½	125*	Lead	730	685	645	150	130	115	2.2"	9.4"	6
(17) 10mm AUTO.	R10MM1	2½	170	Jacketed H.P.	1340	1165	1047	678	512	413	0.7"	3.2"	5
	R10MM2	2½	200	Metal Case	1160	1072	1007	597	510	450	0.9"	3.8"	5
(18) 41 REM. MAG.	R41MG1	2½	210	Soft Point	1300	1162	1062	788	630	526	0.7"	3.2"	4
Vented Barrel Ballistics	R41MG2	2½	210	Lead	965	898	842	434	376	331	1.3"	5.4"	4
	R41MG3	2½	170*	Semi-Jacketed H.P.	1420	1166	1014	761	513	388	0.7"	3.2"	4
(19) 44 REM. MAG.	R44MG5	2½	180	Semi-Jacketed H.P.	1610	1365	1175	1036	745	551	0.5"	2.3"	4
Vented Barrel Ballistics	R44MG1	2½	240	Lead Gas Check	1350	1186	1069	971	749	608	0.7"	3.1"	4
	R44MG2	2½	240	Soft Point	1180	1081	1010	741	623	543	0.9"	3.7"	4
	R44MG3	2½	240	Semi-Jacketed H.P.	1180	1081	1010	741	623	543	0.9"	3.7"	4
	R44MG4	2½	240	Lead (Med. Vel.)	1000	947	902	533	477	433	1.1"	4.8"	6
	R44MG6	2½	210	Semi-Jacketed H.P.	1495	1312	1167	1042	803	634	0.6"	2.5"	6
(20) 44 S. & W. SPECIAL	R44SW	2½	246	Lead	755	725	695	310	285	265	2.0"	8.3"	6
	R44SW1	2½	200*	Semi-Wadcutter	1035	938	866	476	391	333	1.1"	4.9"	6
(21) 45 COLT	R45C	2½	250	Lead	860	820	780	410	375	340	1.6"	6.6"	5
	R45C1	2½	225*	Semi-Wadcutter (Keith)	960	890	832	460	395	346	1.3"	5.5"	5
(22) 45 AUTO.	R45AP1	2½	185	Metal Case Wadcutter Match	770	707	650	244	205	174	2.0"	8.7"	5
	R45AP2	2½	185*	Jacketed H.P.	1000	939	889	411	362	324	1.1"	4.9"	5
	R45AP4	2½	230	Metal Case	835	800	767	356	326	300	1.6"	6.8"	5
	R45AP5	2½	Shot*	Shot				Number 12 shot.					
	R45AP6	2½	185	Jacketed H.P. (+P)‡	1140	1040	971	534	445	387	0.9"	4.0"	5
BLANK CARTRIDGES													
38 S. & W.	R38SWBL§	1½	–	Blank	–	–	–	–	–	–	–	–	
32 S. & W.	R32BLNK	5½	–	Blank	–	–	–	–	–	–	–	–	
38 SPECIAL	R38BLNK	1½	–	Blank	–	–	–	–	–	–	–	–	

*Illustrated (not shown in actual size).   **Will not chamber in 357 Mag. or 38 Special handguns.   ‡Ammunition with (+P) on the case headstamp is loaded to higher pressure. Use only in firearms designated for this cartridge and so recommended by the gun manufacturer.   §Subject to stock on hand.   ★New for 1990.   (A) Adapted only for 38 Colt sporting, military and pocket model automatic pistols. These pistols were discontinued after 1928.   (B) Adapted only for 38 Colt Super and Colt Commander automatic pistols. Not for use in sporting, military and pocket models.

WEATHERBY BALLISTICS

Cartridge	BULLETS		VELOCITY in Feet per Second						ENERGY in Foot Pounds						BULLET DROP in Inches From Bore Line			PATH OF BULLET (Above or below Line-of-sight) For riflescopes mounted 1.5" above bore		
	Weight In Grains	Type	Muzzle	100 Yds.	200 Yds.	300 Yds.	400 Yds.	500 Yds.	Muzzle	100 Yds.	200 Yds.	300 Yds.	400 Yds.	500 Yds.	100 Yds.	200 Yds.	300 Yds.	100 Yds.	200 Yds.	300 Yds.
.224 WBY MAG	55	Pt-Ex	3650	3192	2780	2403	2057	1742	1627	1244	943	705	516	370	-1.4	-6.3	-15.6	2.8	3.6	0
.240 WBY MAG	87	Pt-Ex	3500	3202	2924	2663	2416	2183	2366	1980	1651	1370	1127	920	-1.5	-6.4	-15.4	2.6	3.4	0
	100	Pt-Ex	3395	3106	2835	2581	2339	2112	2559	2142	1785	1478	1215	990	-1.6	-6.8	-16.4	2.9	3.6	0
	100	Partition	3395	3069	2766	2483	2216	1966	2559	2091	1698	1368	1091	859	-1.6	-6.9	-16.8	3.0	3.8	0
.257 WBY MAG	87	Pt-Ex	3825	3456	3118	2805	2513	2239	2826	2308	1878	1520	1220	969	-1.3	-5.5	-13.2	2.1	2.9	0
	100	Pt-Ex	3555	3237	2941	2665	2404	2159	2806	2326	1920	1576	1283	1035	-1.5	-6.2	-15.1	2.6	3.3	0
	100	Partition	3555	3292	3044	2810	2589	2377	2806	2406	2058	1754	1488	1254	-1.4	-6.1	-14.5	2.4	3.1	0
	117	Semi Pt-Ex	3300	2882	2502	2152	1830	1547	2829	2158	1626	1203	870	621	-1.7	-7.7	-19.3	3.7	4.6	0
	117	Partition	3300	2998	2717	2452	2202	1967	2829	2335	1917	1561	1260	1005	-1.7	-7.3	-17.6	3.2	3.9	0
	120	Partition	3290	3074	2869	2673	2486	2306	2884	2518	2193	1904	1646	1416	-1.7	-7.0	-16.7	2.9	3.6	0
.270 WBY MAG	100	Pt-Ex	3760	3380	3033	2712	2412	2133	3139	2537	2042	1633	1292	1010	-1.3	-5.7	-13.9	2.3	3.0	0
	130	Pt-Ex	3375	3100	2842	2598	2366	2148	3287	2773	2330	1948	1616	1331	-1.6	-6.9	-16.4	2.9	3.6	0
	130	Partition	3375	3119	2878	2649	2432	2225	3287	2808	2390	2026	1707	1429	-1.6	-6.8	-16.2	2.8	3.5	0
	150	Pt-Ex	3245	3019	2803	2598	2402	2215	3507	3034	2617	2248	1922	1634	-1.7	-7.3	-17.3	3.0	3.8	0
	150	Partition	3245	3036	2837	2647	2465	2290	3507	3070	2681	2334	2023	1746	-1.7	-7.2	-17.1	3.0	3.7	0
7mm WBY MAG	139	Pt-Ex	3400	3138	2892	2659	2437	2226	3567	3039	2580	2181	1832	1529	-1.6	-6.7	-16.0	2.7	3.5	0
	140	Partition	3400	3163	2939	2726	2522	2328	3593	3110	2684	2309	1978	1684	-1.6	-6.6	-15.7	2.7	3.4	0
	150	Pt-Ex	3260	3023	2799	2586	2382	2188	3539	3044	2609	2227	1890	1595	-1.7	-7.2	-17.2	3.0	3.8	0
	154	Pt-Ex	3260	3023	2800	2586	2383	2189	3633	3125	2681	2287	1941	1638	-1.7	-7.3	-17.2	3.0	3.7	0
	160	Partition	3200	3004	2816	2637	2464	2297	3637	3205	2817	2469	2156	1875	-1.8	-7.4	-17.4	3.0	3.7	0
	175	Pt-Ex	3070	2879	2696	2520	2351	2189	3662	3220	2824	2467	2147	1861	-1.9	-8.0	-19.0	3.4	4.1	0
.300 WBY MAG	110	Pt-Ex	3900	3441	3028	2652	2305	1985	3714	2891	2239	1717	1297	962	-1.2	-5.4	-13.5	2.2	3.0	0
	150	Pt-Ex	3600	3297	3015	2751	2502	2266	4316	3621	3028	2520	2084	1709	-1.4	-6.0	-14.5	2.4	3.1	0
	150	Partition	3600	3307	3033	2776	2533	2303	4316	3642	3064	2566	2137	1766	-1.4	-6.0	-14.4	2.4	3.1	0
	165	Boat Tail	3450	3220	3003	2797	2599	2409	4360	3799	3303	2865	2475	2126	-1.5	-6.4	-15.2	2.5	3.2	0
	180	Pt-Ex	3300	3064	2841	2629	2426	2233	4352	3753	3226	2762	2352	1992	-1.7	-7.1	-16.8	2.9	3.6	0
	180	Partition	3300	3077	2865	2663	2470	2285	4352	3784	3280	2834	2438	2086	-1.7	-7.0	-16.6	2.9	3.6	0
	220	Semi Pt-Ex	2905	2498	2126	1787	1490	1250	4122	3047	2207	1560	1085	763	-2.3	-10.2	-25.8	5.3	6.5	0
.340 WBY MAG	200	Pt-Ex	3260	3011	2775	2552	2339	2137	4719	4025	3420	2892	2429	2027	-1.7	-7.3	-17.4	3.1	3.8	0
	210	Partition	3250	2991	2746	2515	2295	2086	4924	4170	3516	2948	2455	2029	-1.7	-7.4	-17.6	3.1	3.9	0
	250	Semi Pt-Ex	3000	2670	2363	2078	1812	1574	4995	3958	3100	2396	1823	1375	-2.1	-9.1	-22.4	1.7	0	-8.0
	250	Partition	3000	2806	2621	2443	2272	2108	4995	4371	3812	3311	2864	2465	-2.0	-8.5	-19.9	1.5	0	-6.5
.378 WBY MAG	270	Pt-Ex	3180	2976	2781	2594	2415	2243	6062	5308	4635	4034	3495	3015	-1.8	-7.5	-17.8	1.2	0	-5.8
	300	RN	2925	2576	2252	1952	1680	1439	5698	4419	3379	2538	1881	1379	-2.2	-9.7	-24.0	1.9	0	-8.7
.416 WBY MAG	400	Swift A-Frame	2600	2365	2141	1930	1733	1552	6003	4965	4071	3309	2668	2140	-2.7	-11.7	-28.3	5.7	6.7	0
	400	RNSP	2700	2391	2101	1834	1592	1379	6476	5077	3921	2986	2249	1688	-2.6	-11.3	-27.9	5.7	6.8	0
	400	Mono Solid®	2700	2398	2115	1852	1613	1402	6476	5108	3971	3047	2310	1746	-2.6	-11.2	-27.7	5.7	6.7	0
.460 WBY MAG	500	RN	2700	2404	2128	1869	1635	1425	8092	6416	5026	3878	2969	2254	-2.6	-11.2	-27.4	2.3	0	-9.8
	500	FMJ	2700	2425	2166	1923	1700	1497	8092	6526	5210	4105	3209	2488	-2.4	-11.1	-26.9	2.2	0	-9.5

LEGEND: Pt-Ex=Pointed-expanding. Semi Pt-Ex=Semi pointed-expanding. RN=Round nose. FMJ=Full metal jacket.
NOTE: These tables were calculated by computer using a standard modern scientific technique to predict trajectories from the best available data for each cartridge. The figures shown are expected to be reasonably accurate of ammunition behavior under standard conditions. However, the shooter is cautioned that performance will vary because of variations in rifle, ammunition and atmospheric conditions. BALLISTIC COEFFICIENTS used for these tables are as published by Hornady and Nosler ballistic data compiled using 26" barrels.

WINCHESTER BALLISTICS
CENTERFIRE PISTOL AND REVOLVER
Super-X®

Cartridge	Symbol	Bullet Wt. Grs.	Type	Velocity (fps) Muzzle	50 Yds.	100 Yds.	Energy (ft.-lbs.) Muzzle	50 Yds.	100 Yds.	Mid Range Traj. (in.) 50 Yds.	100 Yds.	Barrel Length Inches
25 Automatic (6.35mm) Expanding Point	X25AXP	45	XP**	815	729	655	66	53	42	1.8	7.7	2
25 Automatic (6.35mm) Full Metal Jacket	X25AP	50	FMJ	760	707	659	64	56	48	2.0	8.7	2
30 Luger (7.65mm) Full Metal Jacket	X30LP	93	FMJ	1220	1110	1040	305	255	225	0.9	3.5	4½
# 30 Carbine Hollow Soft Point	X30M1	110	HSP	1790	1601	1430	783	626	500	0.4	1.7	10
# 30 Carbine Full Metal Jacket	X30M2.	110	FMJ	1740	1552	1384	740	588	468	0.4	1.8	10
32 Smith & Wesson Lead Round Nose	X32SWP	85	Lead-RN	680	645	610	90	81	73	2.5	10.5	3
32 Smith & Wesson Long (Colt New Police) Lead Round Nose	X32SWLP	98	Lead-RN	705	670	635	115	98	88	2.3	10.5	4
32 Short Colt Lead Round Nose	X32SCP	80	Lead-RN	745	665	590	100	79	62	2.2	9.9	4
32 Long Colt Lead Round Nose	X32LCP	82	Lead-RN	755	715	675	105	93	83	2.0	8.7	4
32 Automatic Silvertip Hollow Point	X32ASHP	60	STHP	970	895	835	125	107	93	1.3	5.4	4
32 Automatic Full Metal Jacket	X32AP	71	FMJ	905	855	810	129	115	97	1.4	5.8	4
38 Smith & Wesson Lead Round Nose	X38SWP	145	Lead-RN	685	650	620	150	135	125	2.4	10.0	4
380 Automatic Silvertip Hollow Point	X380ASHP	85	STHP	1000	921	860	189	160	140	1.2	5.1	3¾
380 Automatic Full Metal Jacket	X380AP	95	FMJ	955	865	785	190	160	130	1.4	5.9	3¾
38 Special Silvertip Hollow Point	X38S9HP	110	STHP	945	894	850	218	195	176	1.3	5.4	4V
38 Special Lead Round Nose	X38S1P	158	Lead-RN	755	723	693	200	183	168	2.0	8.3	4V
38 Special Lead Semi-Wad Cutter	X38WCPSV	158	Lead-SWC	755	721	689	200	182	167	2.0	8.4	4V
38 Special Metal Point	X38S2P	158	Met. Pt.	755	723	693	200	183	168	2.0	8.3	4V
38 Special Silvertip Hollow Point + P	X38SSHP	95	STHP	1100	1002	932	255	212	183	1.0	4.3	4V
# 38 Special Jacketed Hollow Point + P	X38S6PH	110	JHP	995	926	871	242	210	185	1.2	5.1	4V
# 38 Special Jacketed Hollow Point + P	X38S7PH	125	JHP	945	898	858	248	224	204	1.3	5.4	4V
# 38 Special Silvertip Hollow Point + P	X38S8HP	125	STHP	945	898	858	248	224	204	1.3	5.4	4V
38 Special Lead Hollow Point + P	X38SPD	158	Lead-HP	890	855	823	278	257	238	1.4	6.0	4V
38 Special Lead Semi-Wad Cutter + P	X38WCP	158	Lead-SWC	890	855	823	278	257	238	1.4	6.0	4V
38 Special Match Lead Mid-Range (Clean Cutting) Match	X38SMRP	148	Lead-WC	710	634	566	166	132	105	2.4	10.8	4V
9mm Luger (Parabellum) Full Metal Jacket	X9LP	115	FMJ	1155	1047	971	341	280	241	0.9	3.9	4
9mm Luger (Parabellum) Silvertip Hollow Point	X9MMSHP	115	STHP	1225	1095	1007	383	306	259	0.8	3.6	4
9mm Luger (Parabellum) Silvertip Hollow Point	X9MMSTHP	147	STHP	1010	962	921	333	302	277	1.1	4.7	4
* 38 Super Automatic Silvertip Hollow Point + P	X38ASHP	125	STHP	1240	1130	1050	427	354	306	0.8	3.4	5
* 38 Super Automatic Full Metal Jacket + P	X38A1P	130	FMJ	1215	1099	1017	426	348	298	0.8	3.6	5
38 Automatic (For all 38 Automatic Pistols) Full Metal Jacket	X38A2P	130	FMJ	1040	980	925	310	275	245	1.0	4.7	4½
# 357 Magnum Jacketed Hollow Point	X3573P	110	JHP	1295	1095	975	410	292	232	0.8	3.5	4V
# 357 Magnum Jacketed Hollow Point	X3576P	125	JHP	1450	1240	1090	583	427	330	0.6	2.8	4V
# 357 Magnum Silvertip Hollow Point	X357SHP	145	STHP	1290	1155	1060	535	428	361	0.8	3.5	4V
357 Magnum Lead Semi-Wad Cutter	X3571P	158	Lead-SWC**	1235	1104	1015	535	428	361	0.8	3.5	4V
# 357 Magnum Jacketed Hollow Point	X3574P	158	JHP	1235	1104	1015	535	428	361	0.8	3.5	4V
# 357 Magnum Jacketed Soft Point	X3575P	158	JSP	1235	1104	1015	535	428	361	0.8	3.5	4V
New 40 Smith & Wesson Jacketed Hollow Point	X40SW	180	JHP	◄990	936	891	392	350	317	1.2	4.9	4
10mm Automatic Silvertip Hollow Point	X10MMSTHP	175	STHP	1290	1141	1037	649	506	418	0.7	3.3	5½
# 41 Remington Magnum Silvertip Hollow Point	X41MSTHP	175	STHP	1250	1120	1029	607	488	412	0.8	3.4	4V
41 Remington Magnum Lead Semi-Wad Cutter	X41MP	210	Lead-SWC	965	898	842	434	376	331	1.3	5.4	4V
# 41 Remington Magnum Jacketed Soft Point	X41MJSP	210	JSP	1300	1162	1062	788	630	526	0.7	3.2	4V
# 41 Remington Magnum Jacketed Hollow Point	X41MHP2	210	JHP	1300	1162	1062	788	630	526	0.7	3.2	4V
# 44 Smith & Wesson Special Silvertip Hollow Point	X44STHPS2	200	STHP	900	860	822	360	328	300	1.4	5.9	6½
44 Smith & Wesson Special Lead Round Nose	X44SP	246	Lead-RN	755	725	695	310	285	265	2.0	8.3	6½
# 44 Remington Magnum Silvertip Hollow Point	X44MSTHP2	210	STHP	1250	1106	1010	729	570	475	0.8	3.5	4V
# 44 Remington Magnum Hollow Soft Point	X44MHSP2	240	HSP	1180	1081	1010	741	623	543	0.9	3.7	4V
44 Remington Magnum Lead Semi-Wad Cutter (Med.)	X44MWCP	240	Lead-SWC	1000	937	885	533	468	417	1.2	4.9	6½V
44 Remington Magnum Lead Semi-Wad Cutter (Gas Check)	X44MP	240	Lead-SWC	1350	1186	1069	971	749	608	0.7	3.1	4V
45 Automatic Silvertip Hollow Point	X45ASHP2	185	STHP	1000	938	888	411	362	324	1.2	4.9	5
45 Automatic Full Metal Jacket	X45A1P2	230	FMJ	835	800	767	356	326	300	1.6	6.8	5
45 Automatic Super-Match Full Metal Jacket Semi-Wad Cutter	X45AWCP	185	FMJ-SWC	770	707	650	244	205	174	2.0	8.7	5
# 45 Colt Silvertip Hollow Point	X45CSHP2	225	STHP	920	877	839	423	384	352	1.4	5.6	5½
45 Colt Lead Round Nose	X45CP2	255	Lead-RN	860	820	780	420	380	345	1.5	6.1	5½
# 45 Winchester Magnum Full Metal Jacket	X45WM	230	FMJ	1400	1232	1107	1001	775	636	0.6	2.8	5

(Not for Arms Chambered for Standard 45 Automatic)

CENTERFIRE BLANK CARTRIDGES

Cartridge	Symbol	Bullet Wt. Grs.	Type	Muzzle	50 Yds.	100 Yds.	Muzzle	50 Yds.	100 Yds.	50 Yds.	100 Yds.	Barrel Length Inches
32 Smith & Wesson Black Powder	32BL2P		Black Powder	—	—	—	—	—	—	—	—	—
38 Smith & Wesson Smokeless Powder	38BLP		Smokeless Powder	—	—	—	—	—	—	—	—	—
38 Special Smokeless Powder	38SBLP		Smokeless Powder	—	—	—	—	—	—	—	—	—

FMJ-Full Metal Jacket ● JHP-Jacketed Hollow Point ●
JSP-Jacketed Soft Point ● ● RN-Round Nose ●
Met. Pt.-Metal Point ● XP-Expanding Point ● WC-Wad Cutter ●
SWC-Semi Wad Cutter ● HSP-Hollow Soft Point ●
STHP-Silvertip Hollow Point ● HP-Hollow Point ●
**Lubaloy
*For use only in 38 Super Automatic Pistols.
◄ Tentative Data

+ P Ammunition with (+ P) on the case head stamp is loaded to higher pressure. Use only in firearms designated for this cartridge and so recommended by the gun manufacturer.
V-Data is based on velocity obtained from 4" vented test barrels for revolver cartridges (38 Special, 357 Magnum, 41 Rem. Mag. and 44 Rem. Mag.)

Specifications are nominal. Test barrels are used to determine ballistics figures. Individual firearms may differ from test barrel statistics.
Specifications subject to change without notice.
Acceptable for use in rifles also.

WINCHESTER BALLISTICS
CENTERFIRE RIFLE
Super-X®

CXP Class	Examples		
1	Prairie dog, coyote, woodchuck	3D	All game in category 3 plus large dangerous game (i.e. Kodiak bear)
2	Antelope, deer, black bear	4	Cape Buffalo, elephant
3	Elk, moose		

Cartridge	Symbol	Game Selector Guide	CXP Guide Number	Wt. Grs.	Bullet Type	Barrel Length (In.)	Muzzle	100	200	300	400	500
218 Bee	X218B	V	1	46	HP	24	2760	2102	1550	1155	961	850
22 Hornet	X22H1	V	1	45	SP	24	2690	2042	1502	1128	948	840
22-250 Remington	X222501	V	1	55	PSP	24	3680	3137	2656	2222	1832	1493
222 Remington	X222R	V	1	50	PSP	24	3140	2602	2123	1700	1350	1107
222 Remington	X222R1	V	–	55	FMJ	24	3020	2675	2355	2057	1783	1537
223 Remington	X223RH	V	1	53	HP	24	3330	2882	2477	2106	1770	1475
223 Remington	X223R	V	1	55	PSP	24	3240	2747	2304	1905	1554	1270
223 Remington	X223R1	V	–	55	FMJ	24	3240	2877	2543	2232	1943	1679
223 Remington	X223R2	D	2	64	PP	24	3020	2621	2256	1920	1619	1362
225 Winchester	X2251	V	1	55	PSP	24	3570	3066	2616	2208	1838	1514
243 Winchester	X2431	V	1	80	PSP	24	3350	2955	2593	2259	1951	1670
243 Winchester	X2432	D,O/P	2	100	PP	24	2960	2697	2449	2215	1993	1786
6mm Remington	X6MMR1	V	1	80	PSP	24	3470	3064	2694	2352	2036	1747
6mm Remington	X6MMR2	D,O/P	2	100	PP	24	3100	2829	2573	2332	2104	1889
25-06 Remington	X25061	V	1	90	PEP	24	3440	3043	2680	2344	2034	1749
25-06 Remington	X25062	D,O/P	2	120	PEP	24	2990	2730	2484	2252	2032	1825
# 25-20 Winchester	X25202	V	1	86	SP	24	1460	1194	1030	931	858	798
25-35 Winchester	X2535	D	2	117	SP	24	2230	1866	1545	1282	1097	984
250 Savage	X2503	D,O/P	2	100	ST	24	2820	2467	2140	1839	1569	1339
257 Roberts + P	X257P2	D,O/P	2	100	ST	24	3000	2633	2295	1982	1697	1447
257 Roberts + P	X257P3	D,O/P	2	117	PP	24	2780	2411	2071	1761	1488	1263
264 Winchester Mag.	X2642	D,O/P	2	140	PP	24	3030	2782	2548	2326	2114	1914
270 Winchester	X2701	V	1	100	PSP	24	3430	3021	2649	2305	1988	1699
270 Winchester	X2705	D,O/P	2	130	PP	24	3060	2802	2559	2329	2110	1904
270 Winchester	X2703	D,O/P	2	130	ST	24	3060	2776	2510	2259	2022	1801
270 Winchester	X2704	D,M	3	150	PP	24	2850	2585	2336	2100	1879	1673
284 Winchester	X2842	D,O/P,M	2	150	PP	24	2860	2595	2344	2108	1886	1680
7mm Mauser (7 × 57)	X7MM1	D	2	145	PP	24	2660	2413	2180	1959	1754	1564
7mm Remington Mag.	X7MMR1	D,O/P,M	2	150	PP	24	3110	2830	2568	2320	2085	1866
7mm Remington Mag.	X7MMR2	D,O/P,M	3	175	PP	24	2860	2645	2440	2244	2057	1879
# 30 Carbine	X30M1	V	1	110	HSP	20	1990	1567	1236	1035	923	842
30-30 Winchester	X30301	D	2	150	HP	24	2390	2018	1684	1398	1177	1036
30-30 Winchester	X30306	D	2	150	PP	24	2390	2018	1684	1398	1177	1036
30-30 Winchester	X30302	D	2	150	ST	24	2390	2018	1684	1398	1177	1036
30-30 Winchester	X30303	D	2	170	PP	24	2200	1895	1619	1381	1191	1061
30-30 Winchester	X30304	D	2	170	ST	24	2200	1895	1619	1381	1191	1061
30-06 Springfield	X30062	V	1	125	PSP	24	3140	2780	2447	2138	1853	1595
30-06 Springfield	X30061	D,O/P	2	150	PP	24	2920	2580	2265	1972	1704	1466
30-06 Springfield	X30063	D,O/P	2	150	ST	24	2910	2617	2342	2083	1843	1622
30-06 Springfield	X30065	D,O/P,M	2	165	SP	24	2800	2573	2357	2151	1956	1772
30-06 Springfield	X30064	D,O/P,M	2	180	PP	24	2700	2348	2023	1727	1466	1251
30-06 Springfield	X30066	D,O/P,M,L	3	180	ST	24	2700	2469	2250	2042	1846	1663
30-06 Springfield	X30069	M,L	3	220	ST	24	2410	2192	1985	1791	1611	1448

V-Varmint; D-Deer; O/P-Open or Plains; M-Medium Game; L-Large Game; XL-Extra Large Game

SUPREME CENTERFIRE RIFLE

Cartridge	Symbol	Game Selector Guide	CXP Guide Number	Wt. (grs.)	Bullet Type	Barrel Length (In.)	Muzzle	100	200	300	400	500
22-250 Remington	S22250R52	V	1	52	HPBT	24	3750	3268	2835	2442	2082	1755
243 Winchester	S243W100	D,O/P	2	100	SPBT	24	2960	2712	2477	2254	2042	1843
270 Winchester	S270W140	D,O/P	2	140	STBT	24	2960	2753	2554	2365	2183	2009
New 7 MM Remington Mag.	S7MMRM160	D,O/P,M,L	3	160	STBT	24	2950	2745	2550	2363	2184	2012
30-30 Winchester	S3030W150	D	2	150	ST	24	2390	2018	1684	1398	1177	1036
30-06 Springfield	S3006S165	D,O/P,M	2	165	STBT	24	2800	2597	2402	2216	2038	1869
30-06 Springfield	S3006S180	D,O/P,M,L	3	180	STBT	24	2700	2503	2314	2133	1960	1797
New 308 Winchester	S308W150	D,O/P	2	150	STBT	24	2820	2559	2312	2080	1861	1659
308 Winchester	S308W180	D,O/P,M	3	180	STBT	24	2610	2424	2245	2074	1911	1756
300 Winchester Mag.	S300WM190	O/P,M,L	3D	190	STBT	24	2885	2698	2519	2347	2181	2023

	CXP Class	Examples
V-Varmint	1	Prairie dog, coyote, woodchuck
D-Deer	2	Antelope, deer, black bear
O/P-Open or Plains	3	Elk, moose
M-Medium Game	3D	All game in category 3 plus large dangerous game (i.e. Kodiak bear)
L-Large Game	4	Cape Buffalo, elephant
XL-Extra Large Game		

WINCHESTER BALLISTICS
CENTERFIRE RIFLE

Energy in Foot Pounds (ft.-lbs.)						Trajectory, Short Range Yards						Trajectory, Long Range Yards						
Muzzle	100	200	300	400	500	50	100	150	200	250	300	100	150	200	250	300	400	500
778	451	245	136	94	74	0.3	0	-2.3	-7.2	-15.8	-29.4	1.5	0	-4.2	-12.0	-24.8	-71.4	-155.6
723	417	225	127	90	70	0.3	0	-2.4	-7.7	-16.9	-31.3	1.6	0	-4.5	-12.8	-26.4	-75.6	-163.4
1654	1201	861	603	410	272	0.2	0.5	0	-1.6	-4.4	-8.7	2.3	2.6	1.9	0	-3.4	-15.9	-38.9
1094	752	500	321	202	136	0.5	0.9	0	-2.5	-6.9	-13.7	2.2	1.9	0	-3.8	-10.0	-32.3	-73.8
1114	874	677	517	388	288	0.5	0.9	0	-2.2	-6.1	-11.7	2.0	1.7	0	-3.3	-8.3	-24.9	-52.5
1305	978	722	522	369	256	0.3	0.7	0	-1.9	-5.3	-10.3	1.7	1.4	0	-2.9	-7.4	-22.7	-49.1
1282	921	648	443	295	197	0.4	0.8	0	-2.2	-6.0	-11.8	1.9	1.6	0	-3.3	-8.5	-26.7	-59.6
1282	1011	790	608	461	344	0.4	0.7	0	-1.9	-5.1	-9.9	1.7	1.4	0	-2.8	-7.1	-21.2	-44.6
1296	977	723	524	373	264	0.6	0.9	0	-2.4	-6.5	-12.5	2.1	1.8	0	-3.5	-9.0	-27.4	-59.6
1556	1148	836	595	412	280	0.2	0.6	0	-1.7	-4.6	-9.0	2.4	2.8	2.0	0	-3.5	-16.3	-39.5
1993	1551	1194	906	676	495	0.3	0.7	0	-1.8	-4.9	-9.4	2.6	2.9	2.1	0	-3.6	-16.2	-37.9
1945	1615	1332	1089	882	708	0.5	0.9	0	-2.2	-5.8	-11.0	1.9	1.6	0	-3.1	-7.8	-22.6	-46.3
2139	1667	1289	982	736	542	0.3	0.6	0	-1.6	-4.5	-8.7	2.4	2.7	1.9	0	-3.3	-14.9	-35.0
2133	1777	1470	1207	983	792	0.4	0.8	0	-1.9	-5.2	-9.9	1.7	1.5	0	-2.8	-7.0	-20.4	-41.7
2364	1850	1435	1098	827	611	0.3	0.6	0	-1.7	-4.5	-8.8	2.4	2.7	2.0	0	-3.4	-15.0	-35.2
2382	1985	1644	1351	1100	887	0.5	0.8	0	-2.1	-5.6	-10.7	1.9	1.6	0	-3.0	-7.5	-22.0	-44.8
407	272	203	165	141	122	0	-4.1	-14.4	-31.8	-57.3	-92.0	0	-8.2	-23.5	-47.0	-79.6	-175.9	-319.4
1292	904	620	427	313	252	0.6	0	-3.1	-9.2	-19.0	-33.1	2.1	0	-5.1	-13.8	-27.0	-70.1	-142.0
1765	1351	1017	751	547	398	0.2	0	-1.6	-4.9	-10.0	-17.4	2.4	2.0	0	-3.9	-10.1	-30.5	-65.2
1998	1539	1169	872	639	465	0.5	0.9	0	-2.4	-4.9	-12.3	2.9	3.0	1.6	0	-6.4	-23.2	-51.2
2009	1511	1115	806	576	415	0.8	1.1	0	-2.9	-7.8	-15.1	2.6	2.2	0	-4.2	-10.8	-33.0	-70.0
2854	2406	2018	1682	1389	1139	0.5	0.8	0	-2.0	-5.4	-10.2	1.8	1.5	0	-2.9	-7.2	-20.8	-42.2
2612	2027	1557	1179	877	641	0.3	0.6	0	-1.7	-4.6	-9.0	2.5	2.8	2.0	0	-3.4	-15.5	-36.4
2702	2267	1890	1565	1285	1046	0.4	0.8	0	-2.0	-5.3	-10.1	1.8	1.5	0	-2.8	-7.1	-20.6	-42.0
2702	2225	1818	1472	1180	936	0.5	0.8	0	-2.0	-5.5	-10.4	1.8	1.5	0	-2.9	-7.4	-21.6	-44.3
2705	2226	1817	1468	1175	932	0.6	1.0	0	-2.4	-6.4	-12.2	2.2	1.8	0	-3.4	-8.6	-25.0	-51.4
2724	2243	1830	1480	1185	940	0.6	1.0	0	-2.4	-6.3	-12.1	2.1	1.8	0	-3.4	-8.5	-24.8	-51.0
2279	1875	1530	1236	990	788	0.2	0	-1.7	-5.1	-10.3	-17.5	1.1	0	-2.8	-7.4	-14.1	-34.4	-66.1
3221	2667	2196	1792	1448	1160	0.4	0.8	0	-1.9	-5.2	-9.9	1.7	1.5	0	-2.8	-7.0	-20.5	-42.1
3178	2718	2313	1956	1644	1372	0.6	0.9	0	-2.3	-6.0	-11.3	2.0	1.7	0	-3.2	-7.9	-22.7	-45.8
967	600	373	262	208	173	0.9	0	-4.5	-13.5	-28.3	-49.9	0	-4.5	-13.5	-28.3	-49.9	-118.6	-228.2
1902	1356	944	651	461	357	0.5	0	-2.6	-7.7	-16.0	-27.9	1.7	0	-4.3	-11.6	-22.7	-59.1	-120.5
1902	1356	944	651	461	357	0.5	0	-2.6	-7.7	-16.0	-27.9	1.7	0	-4.3	-11.6	-22.7	-59.1	-120.5
1902	1356	944	651	461	357	0.5	0	-2.6	-7.7	-16.0	-27.9	1.7	0	-4.3	-11.6	-22.7	-59.1	-120.5
1827	1355	989	720	535	425	0.6	0	-3.0	-8.9	-18.0	-31.1	2.0	0	-4.8	-13.0	-25.1	-63.6	-126.7
1827	1355	989	720	535	425	0.6	0	-3.0	-8.9	-18.0	-31.1	2.0	0	-4.8	-13.0	-25.1	-63.6	-126.7
2736	2145	1662	1269	953	706	0.4	0.8	0	-2.1	-5.6	-10.7	1.8	1.5	0	-3.0	-7.7	-23.0	-48.5
2839	2217	1708	1295	967	716	0.6	1.0	0	-2.4	-6.6	-12.7	2.2	1.8	0	-3.5	-9.0	-27.0	-57.1
2820	2281	1827	1445	1131	876	0.6	0.9	0	-2.3	-6.3	-12.0	2.1	1.8	0	-3.3	-8.5	-25.0	-51.8
2873	2426	2036	1696	1402	1151	0.7	1.0	0	-2.5	-6.5	-12.2	2.2	1.9	0	-3.6	-8.4	-24.4	-49.6
2913	2203	1635	1192	859	625	0.2	0	-1.8	-5.5	-11.2	-19.5	2.7	2.3	0	-4.4	-11.3	-34.4	-73.7
2913	2436	2023	1666	1362	1105	0.2	0	-1.6	-4.8	-9.7	-16.5	2.4	2.0	0	-3.7	-9.3	-27.0	-54.9
2837	2347	1924	1567	1268	1024	0.4	0	-2.2	-6.4	-12.7	-21.6	1.5	0	-3.5	-9.1	-17.2	-41.8	-79.9

SUPREME CENTERFIRE RIFLE

Energy In Foot-Pounds (ft-lbs)						Trajectory, Short Range Yards						Trajectory, Long Range Yards						
Muzzle	100	200	300	400	500	50	100	150	200	250	300	100	150	200	250	300	400	500
1624	1233	928	689	501	356	-.1	0	-.7	-2.4	-5.1	-9.1	1.2	1.1	0	-2.1	-5.5	-16.9	-36.3
1946	1633	1363	1128	926	754	.1	0	-1.3	-3.8	-7.8	-13.3	1.9	1.6	0	-3.0	-7.6	-22.0	-44.8
2724	2356	2029	1739	1482	1256	.1	0	-1.2	-3.7	-7.5	-12.7	1.8	1.5	0	-2.9	-7.2	-20.6	-41.3
3093	2679	2311	1984	1694	1439	.1	0	-1.2	-3.7	-7.5	-12.8	1.9	1.5	0	-2.9	-7.2	-20.6	-41.4
1902	1356	944	651	461	357	.5	0	-2.6	-7.7	-16.0	-27.9	3.9	3.2	0	-6.2	-16.1	-49.4	-105.2
2873	2421	2114	1799	1522	1280	.1	0	-1.4	-4.3	-8.6	-14.6	2.1	1.8	0	-3.3	-8.2	-23.4	-47.0
2914	2504	2140	1819	1536	1290	.2	0	-1.6	-4.7	-9.4	-15.8	2.3	1.9	0	-3.5	-8.8	-25.3	-50.8
2649	2182	1782	1441	1154	917	.2	0	-1.5	-4.4	-9.0	-15.4	2.2	1.8	0	-3.5	-8.7	-25.5	-52.3
2723	2348	2015	1719	1459	1232	.2	0	-1.7	-5.0	-10.1	-17.0	2.5	2.1	0	-3.8	-9.4	-26.9	-54.0
3512	3073	2679	2325	2009	1728	.1	0	-1.3	-3.9	-7.8	-13.2	1.9	1.6	0	-3.0	-7.4	-21.1	-42.2

WINCHESTER BALLISTICS
CENTERFIRE RIFLE
Super-X®

Cartridge	Symbol	Game Selector Guide	CXP Guide Number	Wt. Grs.	Bullet Type	Barrel Length (In.)	Muzzle	100	200	300	400	500
30-40 Krag	X30401	D	2	180	PP	24	2430	2099	1795	1525	1298	1128
300 Winchester Mag.	X30WM1	D,O/P	2	150	PP	24	3290	2951	2636	2342	2068	1813
300 Winchester Mag.	X30WM2	O/P,M,L	3	180	PP	24	2960	2745	2540	2344	2157	1979
300 Winchester Mag.	X30WM3	M,L,XL	3D	220	ST	24	2680	2448	2228	2020	1823	1640
300 H. & H. Magnum	X300H2	O/P,M,L	3	180	ST	24	2880	2640	2412	2196	1991	1798
300 Savage	X3001	D,O/P	2	150	PP	24	2630	2311	2015	1743	1500	1295
300 Savage	X3003	D,O/P	2	150	ST	24	2630	2354	2095	1853	1631	1434
300 Savage	X3004	D	2	180	PP	24	2350	2025	1728	1467	1252	1098
303 Savage	X3032	D	2	190	ST	24	1890	1612	1372	1183	1055	970
303 British	X303B1	D	2	180	PP	24	2460	2233	2018	1816	1629	1459
307 Winchester	X3075	D	2	150	PP	24	2760	2321	1924	1575	1289	1091
308 Winchester	X3085	D,O/P	2	150	PP	24	2820	2488	2179	1893	1633	1405
308 Winchester	X3082	D,O/P	2	150	ST	24	2820	2533	2263	2009	1774	1560
308 Winchester	X3086	D,O/P,M	2	180	PP	24	2620	2274	1955	1666	1414	1212
308 Winchester	X3083	M,L	3	180	ST	24	2620	2393	2178	1974	1782	1604
7.62 x 39	X76239	D,V	2	123	SP	20	2365	2033	1731	1465	1248	1093
32 Win. Special	X32WS2	D	2	170	PP	24	2250	1870	1537	1267	1082	971
32 Win. Special	X32WS3	D	2	170	ST	24	2250	1870	1537	1267	1082	971
# 32-20 Winchester	X32201	V	1	100	Lead	24	1210	1021	913	834	769	712
8mm Mauser (8 × 57)	X8MM	D	2	170	PP	24	2360	1969	1622	1333	1123	997
338 Winchester Mag.	X3381	D,O/P,M	3	200	PP	24	2960	2658	2375	2110	1862	1635
338 Winchester Mag.	X3383	M,L,XL	3D	225	SP	24	2780	2572	2374	2184	2003	1832
348 Winchester	Q3167	D,M	3	200	ST	24	2520	2215	1931	1672	1443	1253
35 Remington	X35R1	D	2	200	PP	24	2020	1646	1335	1114	985	901
356 Winchester	X3561	D,M	2	200	PP	24	2460	2114	1797	1517	1284	1113
356 Winchester	X3563	M,L	3	250	PP	24	2160	1911	1682	1476	1299	1158
# 357 Magnum	X3575P	V,D	2	158	JSP	20	1830	1427	1138	980	883	809
358 Winchester	X3581	D,M	3	200	ST	24	2490	2171	1876	1610	1379	1194
375 Winchester	X375W	D,M	2	200	PP	24	2200	1841	1526	1268	1089	980
375 Winchester	X375W1	D,M	2	250	PP	24	1900	1647	1424	1239	1103	1011
375 H. & H. Magnum	X375H1	M,L,XL	3D	270	PP	24	2690	2420	2166	1928	1707	1507
375 H. & H. Magnum	X375H2	M,L,XL	3D	300	ST	24	2530	2268	2022	1793	1583	1397
375 H. & H. Magnum	X375H3	XL	4	300	FMJ	24	2530	2171	1843	1551	1307	1126
# 38-40 Winchester	X3840	D	2	180	SP	24	1160	999	901	827	764	710
38-55 Winchester	X3855	D	2	255	SP	24	1320	1190	1091	1018	963	917
# 44 Remington Magnum	X44MHSP2	D	2	240	HSP	20	1760	1362	1094	953	861	789
# 44-40 Winchester	X4440	D	2	200	SP	24	1190	1006	900	822	756	699
45-70 Government	X4570H	D,M	2	300	JHP	24	1880	1650	1425	1235	1105	1010
458 Winchester Mag.	X4580	XL	4	500	FMJ	24	2040	1823	1623	1442	1287	1161
458 Winchester Mag.	X4581	L,XL	3D	510	SP	24	2040	1770	1527	1319	1157	1046

Velocity In Feet Per Second (fps)

† Obsolete in 1989.

	CXP Class	Examples
V-Varmint		
D-Deer	1	Prairie dog, coyote, woodchuck
O/P-Open or Plains	2	Antelope, deer, black bear
M-Medium Game	3	Elk, moose
L-Large Game	3D	All game in category 3 plus large dangerous game (i.e. Kodiak bear)
XL-Extra Large Game	4	Cape Buffalo, elephant

#Acceptable for use in pistols and revolvers also.
HSP-Hollow Soft Point, PEP-Positive Expanding Point, PSP-Pointed Soft Point®, FMC-Full Metal Case, SP-Soft Point, HP-Hollow Point, ST-Silvertip*, JHP-Jacket Hollow Point, PP-Power Point

Specifications are nominal. Test barrels are used to determine ballistics figures. Individual firearms may differ from these test barrels statistics. Specifications subject to change without notice.

WINCHESTER BALLISTICS
CENTERFIRE RIFLE

#Acceptable for use in pistols and revolvers also.
HSP-Hollow Soft Point, PEP-Positive Expanding Point, PSP-Pointed Soft Point, FMJ-Full Metal Jacket, SP-Soft Point, HP-Hollow Point, ST-Silvertip®, JHP-Jacket Hollow Point, STHP-Silvertip Hollow Point, PP-Power Point®

Energy In Foot Pounds (ft.-lbs.)						Trajectory, Short Range Yards						Trajectory, Long Range Yards						
Muzzle	100	200	300	400	500	50	100	150	200	250	300	100	150	200	250	300	400	500
2360	1761	1288	929	673	508	0.4	0	-2.4	-7.1	-14.5	-25.0	1.6	0	-3.9	-10.5	-20.3	-51.7	-103.9
3605	2900	2314	1827	1424	1095	0.3	0.7	0	-1.8	-4.8	-9.3	2.6	2.9	2.1	0	-3.5	-15.4	-35.5
3501	3011	2578	2196	1859	1565	0.5	0.8	0	-2.1	-5.5	-10.4	1.9	1.6	0	-2.9	-7.3	-20.9	-41.9
3508	2927	2424	1993	1623	1314	0.2	0	-1.7	-4.9	-9.9	-16.9	2.5	2.0	0	-3.8	-9.5	-27.5	-56.1
3315	2785	2325	1927	1584	1292	0.6	0.9	0	-2.3	-6.0	-11.5	2.1	1.7	0	-3.2	-8.0	-23.3	-47.4
2303	1779	1352	1012	749	558	0.3	0	-1.9	-5.7	-11.6	-19.9	2.8	2.3	0	-4.5	-11.5	-34.4	-73.0
2303	1845	1462	1143	886	685	0.3	0	-1.8	-5.4	-11.0	-18.8	2.7	2.2	0	-4.2	-10.7	-31.5	-65.5
2207	1639	1193	860	626	482	0.5	0	-2.6	-7.7	-15.6	-27.1	1.7	0	-4.2	-11.3	-21.9	-55.8	-112.0
1507	1096	794	591	469	397	1.0	0	-4.3	-12.6	-25.5	-43.7	2.9	0	-6.8	-18.3	-35.1	-88.2	-172.5
2418	1993	1627	1318	1060	851	0.3	0	-2.1	-6.1	-12.2	-20.8	1.4	0	-3.3	-8.8	-16.6	-40.4	-77.4
2538	1795	1233	826	554	397	0.2	0	-1.9	-5.6	-11.8	-20.8	1.2	0	-3.2	-8.7	-17.1	-44.9	-92.2
2648	2061	1581	1193	888	657	0.2	0	-1.6	-4.8	-9.8	-16.9	2.4	2.0	0	-3.8	-9.8	-29.3	-62.0
2648	2137	1705	1344	1048	810	0.2	0	-1.5	-4.5	-9.3	-15.9	2.3	1.9	0	-3.6	-9.1	-26.9	-55.7
2743	2066	1527	1109	799	587	0.3	0	-2.0	-5.9	-12.1	-20.9	2.9	2.4	0	-4.7	-12.1	-36.9	-79.1
2743	2288	1896	1557	1269	1028	0.2	0	-1.8	-5.2	-10.4	-17.7	2.6	2.1	0	-4.0	-9.9	-28.9	-58.8
1527	1129	818	586	425	327	.5	0	-2.6	-7.6	-15.4	-26.7	3.8	3.1	0	-6.0	-15.4	-46.3	-98.4
1911	1320	892	606	442	356	0.6	0	-3.1	-9.2	-19.0	-33.2	2.0	0	-5.1	-13.8	-27.1	-70.9	-144.3
1911	1320	892	606	442	356	0.6	0	-3.1	-9.2	-19.0	-33.2	2.0	0	-5.1	-13.8	-27.1	-70.9	-144.3
325	231	185	154	131	113	0	-6.3	-20.9	-44.9	-79.3	-125.1	0	-11.5	-32.3	-63.6	-106.3	-230.3	-413.3
2102	1463	993	671	476	375	0.5	0	-2.7	-8.2	-17.0	-29.8	1.8	0	-4.5	-12.4	-24.3	-63.8	-130.7
3890	3137	2505	1977	1539	1187	0.5	0.9	0	-2.3	-6.1	-11.6	2.0	1.7	0	-3.2	-8.2	-24.3	-50.4
3862	3306	2816	2384	2005	1677	1.2	1.3	0	-2.7	-7.1	-12.9	2.7	2.1	0	-3.6	-9.4	-25.0	-49.9
2820	2178	1656	1241	925	697	0.3	0	-2.1	-6.2	-12.7	-21.9	1.4	0	-3.4	-9.2	-17.7	-44.4	-87.9
1812	1203	791	551	431	360	0.9	0	-4.1	-12.1	-25.1	-43.9	2.7	0	-6.7	-18.3	-35.8	-92.8	-185.5
2688	1985	1434	1022	732	550	0.4	0	-2.3	-7.0	-14.3	-24.7	1.6	0	-3.8	-10.4	-20.1	-51.2	-102.3
2591	2028	1571	1210	937	745	0.6	0	-3.0	-8.7	-17.4	-30.0	2.0	0	-4.7	-12.4	-23.7	-58.4	-112.9
1175	715	454	337	274	229	0	-2.4	-9.1	-21.0	-39.2	-64.3	0	-5.5	-16.2	-33.1	-57.0	-128.3	-235.8
2753	2093	1563	1151	844	633	0.4	0	-2.2	-6.5	-13.3	-23.0	1.5	0	-3.6	-9.7	-18.6	-47.2	-94.1
2150	1506	1034	714	527	427	0.6	0	-3.2	-9.5	-19.5	-33.8	2.1	0	-5.2	-14.1	-27.4	-70.1	-138.1
2005	1506	1126	852	676	568	0.9	0	-4.1	-12.0	-24.0	-40.9	2.7	0	-6.5	-17.2	-32.7	-80.6	-154.1
4337	3510	2812	2228	1747	1361	0.2	0	-1.7	-5.1	-10.3	-17.6	2.5	2.1	0	-3.9	-10.0	-29.4	-60.7
4263	3426	2723	2141	1669	1300	0.3	0	-2.0	-5.9	-11.9	-20.3	2.9	2.4	0	-4.5	-11.5	-33.8	-70.1
4263	3139	2262	1602	1138	844	0.3	0	-2.2	-6.5	-13.5	-23.4	1.5	0	-3.6	-9.8	-19.1	-49.1	-99.5
538	399	324	273	233	201	0	-6.7	-22.2	-47.3	-83.2	-130.8	0	-12.1	-33.9	-66.4	-110.6	-238.3	-425.6
987	802	674	587	525	476	0	-4.7	-15.4	-32.7	-57.2	-89.3	0	-8.4	-23.4	-45.6	-75.2	-158.8	-277.4
1650	988	638	484	395	332	0	-2.7	-10.2	-23.6	-44.2	-73.3	0	-6.1	-18.1	-37.4	-65.1	-150.3	-282.5
629	449	360	300	254	217	0	-6.5	-21.6	-46.3	-81.8	-129.1	0	-11.8	-33.3	-65.5	-109.5	-237.4	-426.2
2355	1815	1355	1015	810	680	0	-2.4	-8.2	-17.6	-31.4	-51.5	0	-4.6	-12.8	-25.4	-44.3	-95.5	
4620	3689	2924	2308	1839	1496	0.7	0	-3.3	-9.6	-19.2	-32.5	2.2	0	-5.2	-13.6	-25.8	-63.2	-121.7
4712	3547	2640	1970	1516	1239	0.8	0	-3.5	-10.3	-20.8	-35.6	2.4	0	-5.6	-14.9	-28.5	-71.5	-140.4

Trajectory Illustration

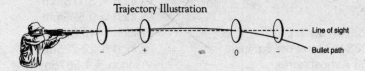

Line of sight
Bullet path

TRAJECTORY inches above (+) or below (−) line of sight. 0 = yardage at which rifle is sighted in.

CONVERSION FACTORS

Common inch calibers converted to metric

.25 inch = 6.35mm
.256 inch = 6.5mm
.270 inch = 6.858mm
.280 inch = 7.11mm
.297 inch = 7.54mm
.300 inch = 7.62mm
.301 inch = 7.62mm
.303 inch = 7.696mm
.308 inch = 7.82mm
.311 inch = 7.899mm
.312 inch = 7.925mm
.380 inch = 9.65mm
.400 inch = 10.16mm
.402 inch = 10.21mm
.450 inch = 11.43mm
.455 inch = 11.557mm
.500 inch = 12.7mm
.550 inch = 13.97mm
.577 inch = 14.65mm
.600 inch = 15.24mm
.661 inch = 16.79mm

Pressure

1 kg per sq. cm = 14.223 lb. per sq. inch
1 kg per sq. cm = 0.0063493 tons per sq. inch
1 kg per sq. cm = 0.968 Atmospheres
1 Atmosphere = 14.7 lb. per sq. inch
1 Atmosphere = 0.00655 tons per sq. inch
1 ton per sq. inch = 152.0 Atmospheres
1 lb. per sq. inch = 0.0680 Atmospheres
1 Atmosphere = 1.03 kg per sq. cm
1 lb. per sq. inch = 0.070309 kg per sq. cm
1 ton per sq. inch = 157.49 kg per sq. cm

Energy

1 m.kg = 7.2331 foot lb.
1 foot lb. = 0.13825 m.kg

Velocity

1 meter per second = 3.2809 feet per second
1 foot per second = 0.30479 meters per second

Weight

1 gram = 15.432 grains
1 grain = 0.0648 grams
1 oz. = 28.349 grams

Linear

1 meter = 1.0936 yards
1 meter = 3.2808 feet
1 yard = 0.91438 meters
1 foot = 0.30479 meters
1 inch = 25.4mm
$1/4$ inch = 6.35mm
$1/2$ inch = 12.7mm
$3/4$ inch = 19.05mm
$1/8$ inch = 3.175mm
$3/8$ inch = 9.525mm
$5/8$ inch = 15.875mm
$7/8$ inch = 22.225mm
$1/16$ inch = 1.5875mm
$3/16$ inch = 4.7625mm
$5/16$ inch = 7.9375mm
$7/16$ inch = 11.1125mm
$9/16$ inch = 14.2875mm
$11/16$ inch = 17.4625mm
$13/16$ inch = 20.6375mm
$15/16$ inch = 23.8125mm

Reloading

FOR ADDRESSES AND PHONE NUMBERS OF MANUFACTURERS AND DISTRIBUTORS INCLUDED IN THIS SECTION, SEE *DIRECTORY OF MANUFACTURERS AND SUPPLIERS*

BUFFALO BULLET

.45 Caliber 285 Grain Hollow Point Hollow Base	.45 Caliber 325 Grain Hollow Point Flat Base	.50 Caliber 385 Grain Hollow Point Hollow Base	.50 Caliber 410 Grain Hollow Point Hollow Base	.54 Caliber 425 Grain Hollow Point Hollow Base	.54 Caliber 435 Grain Round Nose Hollow Base	.54 Caliber 460 Grain Round Nose Flat Base

BUFFALO MAXI BULLETS

Buffalo's black powder bullets are cold formed in precision dies from pure lead, eliminating the air voids, sprue marks or parting lines that spoil consistent accuracy. Other features include increased barrel-to-bullet bearing surface, uniform lubrication, smaller base diameter for easy "thumb starting,"

hollow point for better expansion, double gas seals, plus a choice of hollow or flat base. Available in 45, 50 or 54 calibers (see below). Prices range from $6.75 (285 grain) for a 20-bullet box to $9.00 (460 grain).

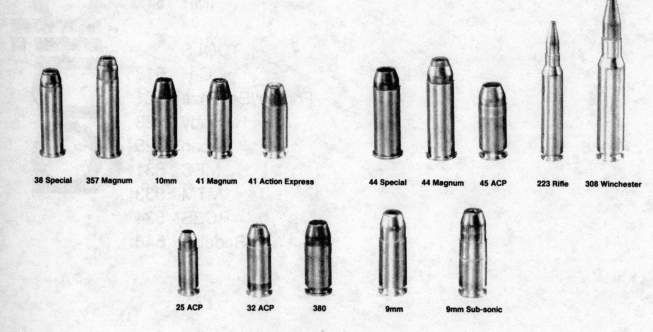

38 Special   357 Magnum   10mm   41 Magnum   41 Action Express   44 Special   44 Magnum   45 ACP   223 Rifle   308 Winchester

25 ACP   32 ACP   380   9mm   9mm Sub-sonic

BUFFALO BULLET CORE-SHOT

Core-Shot ammunition is custom-loaded with a pre-fragmented projectile containing a small lead core swaged over #12 shot. While maintaining the advantages of fragmented ammunition, Core-Shot also yields moderate penetration. Upon eruption of the thin copper jacket and core, hundreds of sub-particles are released into the target medium, creating a substantial wound

channel. Sure-Shot is designed to expend all of the bullet's energy into the target medium without over-penetration. It also reduces hazardous ricochet action, an important safety factor. Core-Shot is available in the calibers pictured below. Prices range from $14.25 per 6-round pack to $19.25.

REMINGTON BULLETS

REMINGTON RIFLE BULLETS

Remington component rifle bullets bring the renown performance of "Core-Lokt", "Power-Lokt" and "Bronze Point" to reloaders.

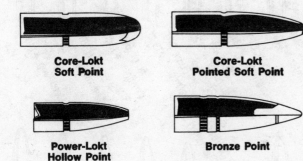

Core-Lokt Soft Point

Core-Lokt Pointed Soft Point

Power-Lokt Hollow Point

Bronze Point

"Core-Lokt" Pointed Soft Point and Soft Point bullets for controlled expansion and high weight retention—ideal for medium and big game.

"Power-Lokt" hollow points for pin point accuracy on targets, small game and varmints.

"Bronze Point" for flat trajectory and excellent accuracy at extended ranges.

Order No.	Caliber	Bullet weight	Bullet style	Boxes per case*
B1705	17 Cal	25 gr.	Hollow Point "Power-Lokt"	40
B2240	22 Cal	50 gr.	Hollow Point "Power-Lokt"	40
B2265	22 Cal	55 gr.	Hollow Point "Power-Lokt"	40
B2430	6mm	80 gr.	Hollow Point "Power-Lokt"	24
B2460	6mm	100 gr.	Pointed Soft Point "Core-Lokt"	24
B2510	25 Cal	87 gr.	Hollow Point "Power-Lokt"	24
B2540	25 Cal	120 gr.	Pointed Soft Point "Core-Lokt"	24
B2720	270	130 gr.	Pointed Soft Point "Core-Lokt"	24
B2730	270	130 gr.	"Bronze Point"	20
B2830	7mm	150 gr.	Pointed Soft Point "Core-Lokt"	20
B2850	7mm	175 gr.	Pointed Soft Point "Core-Lokt"	20
B3020	30 Cal	150 gr.	"Bronze Point"	20
B3030	30 Cal	150 gr.	Pointed Soft Point "Core-Lokt"	20
B3060	30 Cal	180 gr.	"Bronze Point"	20
B3080	30 Cal	180 gr.	Pointed Soft Point "Core-Lokt"	20

*Packed 100 per box.

REMINGTON HANDGUN BULLETS

The Choice of Champions

Semi-Jacketed Hollow Point
Scalloped jacket delivers maximum expansion and stopping power, with controlled expansion even at high velocities.

Soft Point
Delivers deeper penetration than the semi-jacketed hollow point.

Metal Case
Helps ensure positive functioning in autoloaders.

Jacketed Hollow Point
Controlled expansion with no exposed lead to impair functioning in autoloaders.

Wadcutter
Solid lead for precision target shooting. Leave an easy-to-see hole in the target.

Lead Round Nose
A general purpose bullet and standard for law enforcement.

Order No.	Caliber	Bullet weight	Bullet style	Boxes per case*
B2525	25	50 gr.	Metal Case	40
B3550	9mm	115 gr.	Jacketed Hollow Point	24
B3552	9mm	124 gr.	Metal Case	24
B3572	357	125 gr.	Semi-Jacketed Hollow Point	24
B3576	357	158 gr.	Semi-Jacketed Hollow Point	20
B3578	357	158 gr.	Lead	20
B3810	38	95 gr.	Semi-Jacketed Hollow Point	24
B3830D	38	148 gr.	Wadcutter	20*
B4110	41 Mag	210 gr.	Soft Point	20
B4120	41 Mag	210 gr.	Lead	20
B4410	44 Mag	240 gr.	Soft Point	20
B4420	44 Mag	240 gr.	Semi-Jacketed Hollow Point	20
B4405	44 Mag	180 gr.	Semi-Jacketed Hollow Point	20
B4520	45	185 gr.	Jacketed Hollow Point	20
B4530	45	230 gr.	Metal Case	20

*Packed 100 per box except B3830D, 500 per box.

SIERRA BULLETS

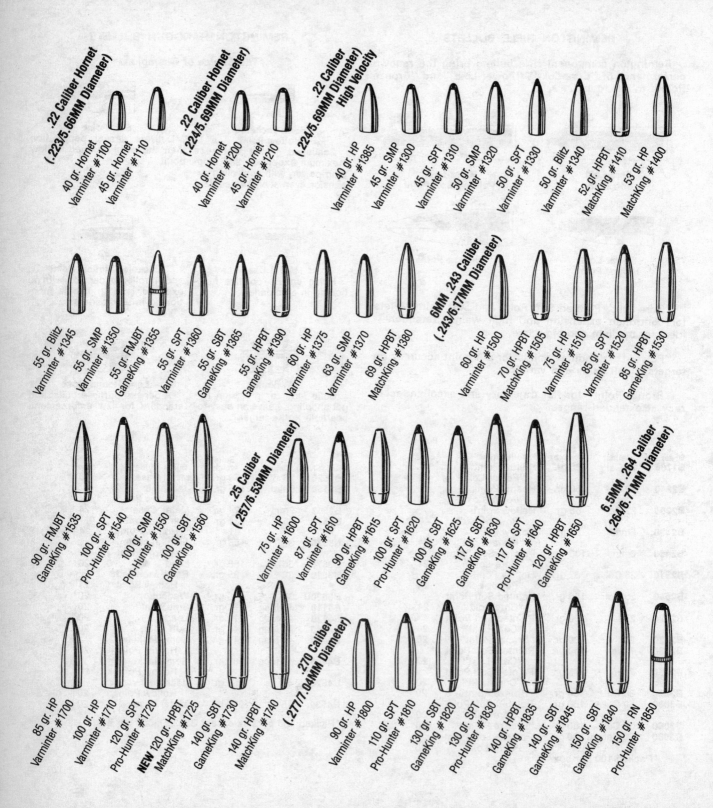

.22 Caliber Hornet (.223/5.66MM Diameter)
- 40 gr. Hornet Varminter #1100
- 45 gr. Hornet Varminter #1110

.22 Caliber Hornet (.224/5.69MM Diameter)
- 40 gr. Hornet Varminter #1200
- 45 gr. Hornet Varminter #1210

.22 Caliber (.224/5.69MM Diameter) High Velocity
- 40 gr. HP Varminter #1385
- 45 gr. SMP Varminter #1300
- 45 gr. SPT Varminter #1310
- 50 gr. SMP Varminter #1320
- 50 gr. SPT Varminter #1330
- 50 gr. Blitz Varminter #1340
- 52 gr. HPBT MatchKing #1410
- 53 gr. HP MatchKing #1400
- 55 gr. Blitz Varminter #1345
- 55 gr. SMP Varminter #1350
- 55 gr. FMJBT GameKing #1355
- 55 gr. SPT Varminter #1360
- 55 gr. SBT GameKing #1365
- 55 gr. HPBT GameKing #1390
- 60 gr. HP Varminter #1375
- 63 gr. SMP Varminter #1370
- 69 gr. HPBT MatchKing #1380

6MM .243 Caliber (.243/6.17MM Diameter)
- 60 gr. HP Varminter #1500
- 70 gr. HPBT MatchKing #1505
- 75 gr. HP Varminter #1510
- 85 gr. SPT Varminter #1520
- 85 gr. HPBT GameKing #1530
- 90 gr. FMJBT GameKing #1535
- 100 gr. SPT Pro-Hunter #1540
- 100 gr. SMP Pro-Hunter #1550
- 100 gr. SBT GameKing #1560

.25 Caliber (.257/6.53MM Diameter)
- 75 gr. HP Varminter #1600
- 87 gr. SPT Varminter #1610
- 90 gr. HPBT GameKing #1615
- 100 gr. SPT Pro-Hunter #1620
- 100 gr. SBT GameKing #1625
- 117 gr. SBT GameKing #1630
- 117 gr. SPT Pro-Hunter #1640
- 120 gr. HPBT GameKing #1650

6.5MM .264 Caliber (.264/6.71MM Diameter)
- 85 gr. HP Varminter #1700
- 100 gr. HP Varminter #1710
- 120 gr. SPT Pro-Hunter #1720
- **NEW** 120 gr. HPBT MatchKing #1725
- 140 gr. SBT GameKing #1730
- 140 gr. HPBT MatchKing #1740

.270 Caliber (.277/7.04MM Diameter)
- 90 gr. HP Varminter #1800
- 110 gr. SPT Pro-Hunter #1810
- 130 gr. SBT GameKing #1820
- 130 gr. SPT Pro-Hunter #1830
- 140 gr. HPBT GameKing #1835
- 140 gr. SBT GameKing #1845
- 150 gr. SBT GameKing #1840
- 150 gr. RN Pro-Hunter #1850

SIERRA BULLETS

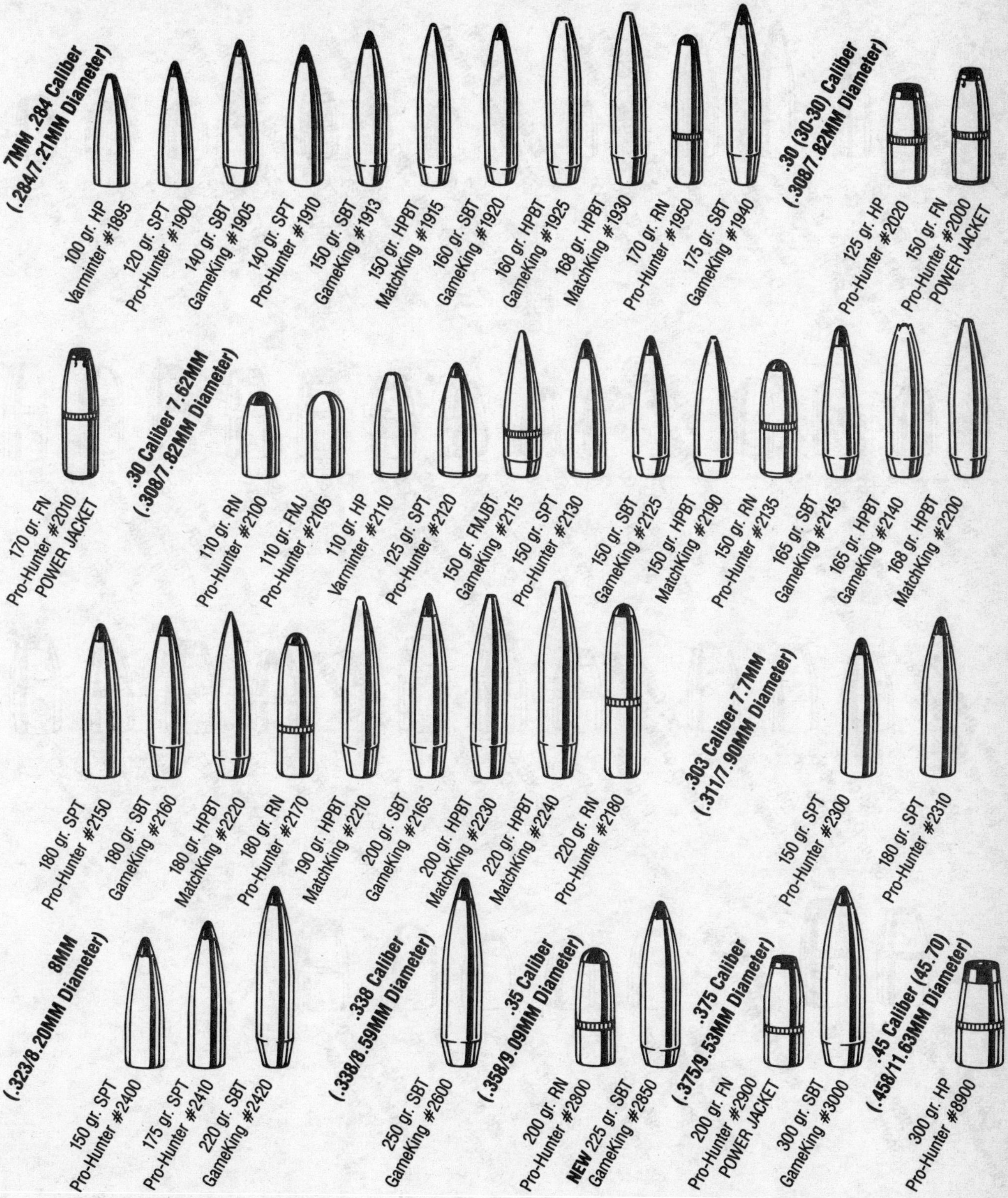

7MM .284 Caliber (.284/7.21MM Diameter)

- 100 gr. HP Varminter #1895
- 120 gr. SPT Pro-Hunter #1900
- 140 gr. SBT GameKing #1905
- 140 gr. SPT Pro-Hunter #1910
- 150 gr. SBT GameKing #1913
- 150 gr. HPBT MatchKing #1915
- 160 gr. SBT GameKing #1920
- 160 gr. HPBT GameKing #1925
- 168 gr. HPBT MatchKing #1930
- 170 gr. RN Pro-Hunter #1950
- 175 gr. SBT GameKing #1940

.30 (30-30) Caliber (.308/7.82MM Diameter)

- 125 gr. HP Pro-Hunter #2020
- 150 gr. FN Pro-Hunter #2000 POWER JACKET
- 170 gr. FN Pro-Hunter #2010 POWER JACKET

.30 Caliber 7.62MM (.308/7.82MM Diameter)

- 110 gr. RN Pro-Hunter #2100
- 110 gr. FMJ Pro-Hunter #2105
- 110 gr. HP Varminter #2110
- 125 gr. SPT Pro-Hunter #2120
- 150 gr. FMJBT GameKing #2115
- 150 gr. SPT Pro-Hunter #2130
- 150 gr. SBT GameKing #2125
- 150 gr. HPBT MatchKing #2190
- 150 gr. RN Pro-Hunter #2135
- 165 gr. SBT GameKing #2145
- 165 gr. HPBT GameKing #2140
- 168 gr. HPBT MatchKing #2200
- 180 gr. SPT Pro-Hunter #2150
- 180 gr. SBT GameKing #2160
- 180 gr. HPBT MatchKing #2220
- 180 gr. RN Pro-Hunter #2170
- 190 gr. HPBT MatchKing #2210
- 200 gr. SBT GameKing #2165
- 200 gr. HPBT MatchKing #2230
- 220 gr. HPBT MatchKing #2240
- 220 gr. RN Pro-Hunter #2180

.303 Caliber 7.7MM (.311/7.90MM Diameter)

- 150 gr. SPT Pro-Hunter #2300
- 180 gr. SPT Pro-Hunter #2310

8MM (.323/8.20MM Diameter)

- 150 gr. SPT Pro-Hunter #2400
- 175 gr. SPT Pro-Hunter #2410
- 220 gr. SBT GameKing #2420

.338 Caliber (.338/8.59MM Diameter)

- 250 gr. SBT GameKing #2600

.35 Caliber (.358/9.09MM Diameter)

- 200 gr. RN Pro-Hunter #2800
- NEW 225 gr. SBT GameKing #2850

.375 Caliber (.375/9.53MM Diameter)

- 200 gr. FN Pro-Hunter #2900 POWER JACKET
- 300 gr. SBT GameKing #3000

.45 Caliber (45-70) (.458/11.63MM Diameter)

- 300 gr. HP Pro-Hunter #8900

SIERRA BULLETS

Single Shot Pistol Bullets

6MM .243 Dia. 80 gr. SPT Pro-Hunter #7150

7MM .284 Dia. 130 gr. SPT Pro-Hunter #7250

.30 cal .308 Dia. 135 gr. SPT Pro-Hunter #7350

25 Caliber (.251/6.38MM Diameter)

50 gr. FMJ Tournament Master #8000

32 Caliber 7.65MM (.312/7.92MM Diameter)

71 gr. FMJ Tournament Master #8010

32 Mag. .312/7.92MM Diameter

90 gr. JHC Sports Master #8030 POWER JACKET

9MM .355 Caliber (.355/9.02MM Diameter)

90 gr. JHP Sports Master #8100 POWER JACKET

95 gr. FMJ Tournament Master #8105

115 gr. JHP Sports Master #8110 POWER JACKET

.38 Caliber (.357/9.07MM Diameter)

115 gr. FMJ Tournament Master #8115

125 gr. FMJ Tournament Master #8120

130 gr. FMJ Tournament Master #8345

110 gr. JHC Blitz Sports Master #8300 POWER JACKET

125 gr. JSP Sports Master #8310

125 gr. JHC Sports Master #8320 POWER JACKET

140 gr. JHC Sports Master #8325 POWER JACKET

158 gr. JHC Sports Master #8360 POWER JACKET

158 gr. JSP Sports Master #8340

170 gr. JHC Sports Master #8365 POWER JACKET

170 gr. FMJ Match Tournament Master #8350

180 gr. FPJ Match Tournament Master #8370

10MM .400 Caliber (.400/10.16MM Diameter)

150 gr. JHP Sports Master #8430 POWER JACKET

180 gr. JHP Sports Master #8460 POWER JACKET

NEW 190 gr. FPJ Sports Master #8480

.41 Caliber (.410/10.41MM Diameter)

170 gr. JHC Sports Master #8500 POWER JACKET

210 gr. JHC Sports Master #8520 POWER JACKET

220 gr. FPJ Match Tournament Master #8530

.44 Magnum (.4295/10.91MM Diameter)

180 gr. JHC Sports Master #8600 POWER JACKET

210 gr. JHC Sports Master #8620 POWER JACKET

220 gr. FPJ Match Tournament Master #8605

240 gr. JHC Sports Master #8610 POWER JACKET

.45 Caliber (.4515/11.47MM Diameter)

250 gr. FPJ Match Tournament Master #8615

NEW 300 gr. JSP Sports Master #8630

185 gr. JHP Sports Master #8800 POWER JACKET

185 gr. FPJ Match Tournament Master #8810

200 gr. FPJ Match Tournament Master #8825

230 gr. FMJ Match Tournament Master #8815

240 gr. JHC Sports Master #8820 POWER JACKET

SPEER BULLETS

HANDGUN BULLETS—JACKETED

CALIBER & TYPE	25 TMJ	9mm JHP	32 JHP	9mm TMJ	9mm JHP	9mm TMJ	9mm JHP	9mm TMJ	9mm PSP	38 JHP	38 JSP	38 JHP	38 TMJ	38 JHP
WEIGHT (GRS.)	50	88	100	95	100	115	115	124	124	110	125	125	125	140
DIAMETER	.251″	.355″	.312″	.355″	.355″	.355″	.355″	.355″	.355″	.357″	.357″	.357″	.357″	.357″
USE	P	P,V	P,V	P	P,V	P,T,V	P,V	P,T,V	P,V	P,V	P,V	P,V	P,T	P,V
PART NUMBER	3982	4000	3981	4001	3983	3995*	3996	4004	3997	4007	4011	4013	4015	4203

NEW

CALIBER & TYPE	38 JHP-SWC	38 TMJ	38 JHP	38 JSP	38 JSP-WC	38 TMJ-Sil.	38 TMJ-Sil.	10mm TMJ	41 JHP-SWC	41 JSP-SWC	41 TMJ-Sil.	44 Mag.-JHP	44 JHP-SWC	44 JSP-SWC
WEIGHT	146	150	158	158	160	180	200	190	200	220	210	200	225	240
DIAMETER	.357″	.357″	.357″	.357″	.357″	.357″	.357″	.400″	.410″	.410″	.410″	.429″	.429″	.429″
USE	P,V	P,T,V	P,V,S	P,V,S	P,V,S	P,S	P,S	P,S,M	P,V,SG,S	P,V,S,D	S,T	P,V,SG,S	P,V,SG,S,D	P,V,SG,S,D
PART NUMBER	4205	4207	4211	4217	4223	4229*	4231*	4403	4405	4417	4420	4425	4435	4447

CALIBER & TYPE	44 Mag.-JHP	44 Mag.-JSP	44 TMJ-Sil.	45 TMJ-Match	45 TMJ-Match	45 JHP	45 Mag.-JHP	45 TMJ	45 JHP
WEIGHT	240	240	240	185	200	200	225	230	260
DIAMETER	.429″	.429″	.429″	.451″	.451″	.451″	.451″	.451″	.451″
USE	P,V,SG,S,D	P,V,SG,S,D	P,V,S	P,T,M	P,T,M	P,V,SG	P,V,SG,S	P,T,S	P,V,S,D
PART NUMBER	4453	4457	4459*	4473	4475	4477	4479	4480*	4481

HANDGUN BULLETS—LEAD

CALIBER & TYPE	32 HB-WC	9mm RN	38 BB-WC
WEIGHT (GRS.)	98	125	148
DIAMETER	.314″	.356″	.358″
USE	P,T,M	P,T	P,T
PART NUMBER	4600**	4601*	4605*

CALIBER & TYPE	38 HB-WC	38 SWC	38 HP-SWC	38 RN	44 SWC	45 SWC	45 RN	45 SWC
WEIGHT	148	158	158	158	240	200	230	250
DIAMETER	.358″	.358″	.358″	.358″	.430″	.452″	.452″	.452″
USE	P,T,M	P,T,V,SG	P,T,V,SG	P,T	P,T,V,SG,D	P,T,M	P,T	P,T,V,SG,D
PART #	4617*	4623*	4627*	4647*	4660*	4677*	4690*	4683*

PLASTIC INDOOR AMMO

NOTE: Shown are 44 bullet and 44 case. 45 bullet is used with regular brass case.

PART #		BULLETS	CASES
NO PER BOX		50	50
	38 CAL.	8510	8515
	44 CAL.	8520	8525
	45 CAL.	8530	See Note

Abbreviation Guide:
JHP–Jacketed Hollow Point
TMJ™–Totally Metal Jacketed™
PSP–Plated Soft Point
JSP–Jacketed Soft Point
Sil.–Silhouette
WC–Wadcutter
SWC–Semi-Wadcutter
HB–Hollow Base
BB–Bevel Base
RN–Round Nose
P–Plinking; T–Target
V–Varmint; M–Match
SG–Small Game
S–Silhouette; D–Deer.
* Also available in 500-bullet Bulk-Pak.
** Available in bulk quantities only.

LEAD BALLS

WT. (GRS.)	64	80	120	128	133	138	141	144	177	182	224	230	278
DIAMETER	.350″	.375″	.433″	.440″	.445″	.451″	.454″	.457″	.490″	.495″	.530″	.535″	.570″
PART #	5110	5113	5127	5129	5131	5133	5135	5137	5139	5140	5142	5150	5180
GUN TYPE	Some 36 Pistols & Rifles	36 Sheriffs Revolver / 36 Leech & Rigdon Revolver / 36 Navy Revolver	45 Hawken / 45 Kentucky / 45 Percussion Pistols	45 Thompson Center Rifle / Senecca / Hawken	45 Kentucky (F&P) / 45 Mountain / 45 Springfield / 45 Huntsman / 45 Yorkshire / 45 Michigan Carbine	44 Revolvers / 44 Percussion Revolving Carb. / 44 Ballister Revolver	44 Percussion Revolving Carb.	Ruger New Old Army	50 Thompson Center Hawken	50 Douglas / 50 Sharon / 50 Morse Navy	54 Thompson Center Renegade	54 Douglas / 54 Sharon / 54 Mountain	58 Harpers Ferry Pistol / 58 Morse Navy

SPEER BULLETS

RIFLE BULLETS

BULLET CALIBER AND TYPE	22 Spire Soft Point	22 Spitzer Soft Point	22 Spire Soft Point	22 Spitzer Soft Point	22 Spitzer Soft Point	22 Hollow Point	22 Full Metal Jacket	22 Spitzer Soft Point	22 Spitzer S.P. w/ Cannelure	22 Semi-Spitzer Soft Point	6mm Hollow Point	6mm Spitzer Soft Point	6mm Spitzer Soft Point B.T.	6mm Full Metal Jacket
DIAMETER	.223″	.223″	.224″	.224″	.224″	.224″	.224″	.224″	.224″	.224″	.243″	.243″	.243″	.243″
WEIGHT (GRS.)	40	45	40	45	50	52	55	55	55	70	75	80	85	90
USE	V	V	V	V	V	V	V	V	V	HV	V	V	HV,LG	HV
PART NUMBER	1005	1011	1017	1023	1029	1035	1045	1047	1049	1053	1205	1211	1213	1215

CAL. & TYPE	270 Spitzer Soft Point B.T.	270 Spitzer Soft Point	7mm Hollow Point	7mm Spitzer Soft Point	7mm Spitzer Soft Point B.T.	7mm Spitzer Soft Point B.T.	7mm Spitzer Soft Point	7mm Match B.T.	7mm Spitzer Soft Point B.T.	7mm Spitzer Soft Point	7mm Mag-Tip Soft Point	7mm Mag-Tip Soft Point	30 Round Soft Point Plinker®	30 Hollow Point	30 Round Soft Point
DIA.	.277″	.277″	.284″	.284″	.284″	.284″	.284″	.284″	.284″	.284″	.284″	.284″	.308″	.308″	.308″
WT.	150	150	115	130	130	145	145	145	160	160	160	175	100	110	110
USE	BG	BG	V	HV,LG	HV,LG	BG	BG	M	BG	BG	BG	BG	V	V	V
PART #	1604	1605	1617	1623	1624	1628	1629	1631	1634	1635	1637	1641	1805	1835	1845

CAL. & TYPE	30 Mag-Tip Soft Point	30 Match B.T.	30 Spitzer Soft Point	303 Spitzer Soft Point	303 Round Soft Point	32 Flat Soft Point	8mm Spitzer Soft Point	8mm Semi-Spitzer Soft Point	8mm Spitzer Soft Point	338 Spitzer Soft Point	338 Semi-Spitzer Soft Point	35 Flat Soft Point	35 Flat Soft Point	35 Spitzer Soft Point	9.3mm Semi-Spitzer Soft Point
DIA.	.308″	.308″	.308″	.311″	.311″	.321″	.323″	.323″	.323″	.338″	.338″	.358″	.358″	.358″	.366″
WT.	180	190	200	150	180	170	150	170	200	200	275	180	220	250	270
USE	BG	M	BG	BG	BG	BG	BG	BG	BG	BG	BG	BG	BG	BG	BG
PART #	2059	2080	2211	2217	2223	2259	2277	2283	2285	2405	2411	2435	2439	2453	2459

V–Varmint; HV–Heavy Varmint (coyote); LG–Light Game (whitetail, antelope); BG–Big Game; M–Match. 🔴 Hot-Cor.

SPEER BULLETS

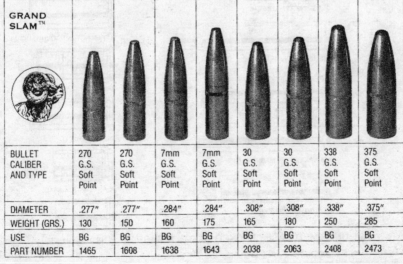

6mm Spitzer Soft Point	6mm Spitzer Soft Point	6mm Round Soft Point	6mm Spitzer Soft Point	25 Spitzer Soft Point	25 Spitzer Soft Point	25 Hollow Point	25 Spitzer Soft Point B.T.	25 Spitzer Soft Point B.T.	25 Spitzer Soft Point	6.5mm Spitzer Soft Point	6.5mm Spitzer Soft Point	270 Hollow Point	270 Spitzer Soft Point	270 Spitzer Soft Point B.T.	270 Spitzer Soft Point
.243"	.243"	.243"	.243"	.257"	.257"	.257"	.257"	.257"	.257"	.263"	.263"	.277"	.277"	.277"	.277"
90	100	105	105	87	100	100	100	120	120	120	140	100	100	130	130
HV,LG	LG	LG	LG	HV	HV,LG	HV	HV,LG	BG	BG	HV,LG	BG	V	V	BG	BG
1217	1220	1223	1229	1241	1405	1407	1408	1410	1411	1435	1441	1447	1453	1458	1459

30 Spire Soft Point	30 Hollow Point	30 Flat Soft Point	30 Flat Soft Point	30 Round Soft Point	30 Spitzer Soft Point B.T.	30 Spitzer Soft Point	30 Mag-Tip Soft Point	30 Round Soft Point	30 Spitzer Soft Point	30 Spitzer Soft Point B.T.	30 Match B.T.	30 Flat Soft Point	30 Round Soft Point	30 Spitzer Soft Point B.T.	30 Spitzer Soft Point
.308"	.308"	.308"	.308"	.308"	.308"	.308"	.308"	.308"	.308"	.308"	.308"	.308"	.308"	.308"	.308"
110	130	130	150	150	150	150	150	165	165	165	168	170	180	180	180
V	V	HV,LG	BG	BG	BG	BG	BG	BG	BG	BG	M	BG	BG	BG	BG
1855	2005	2007	2011	2017	2022	2023	2025	2029	2034	2035	2040	2041	2047	2052	2053

375 Semi-Spitzer Soft Point	45 Flat Soft Point
.375"	.458"
235	400
BG	BG
2471	2479

GRAND SLAM™

BULLET CALIBER AND TYPE	270 G.S. Soft Point	270 G.S. Soft Point	7mm G.S. Soft Point	7mm G.S. Soft Point	30 G.S. Soft Point	30 G.S. Soft Point	338 G.S. Soft Point	375 G.S. Soft Point
DIAMETER	.277"	.277"	.284"	.284"	.308"	.308"	.338"	.375"
WEIGHT (GRS.)	130	150	160	175	165	180	250	285
USE	BG	BG	BG	BG	BG	BG	BG	BG
PART NUMBER	1465	1608	1638	1643	2038	2063	2408	2473

New

REMINGTON CASES & PRIMERS

Remington brass cases with 5% more brass for extra strength in head section — annealed neck section for longer reloading life — primer pocket dimension controlled to .0005 inch to assure precise primer fit — heavier bridge and sidewalls — formed and machined to exacting tolerances for consistent powder capacity.

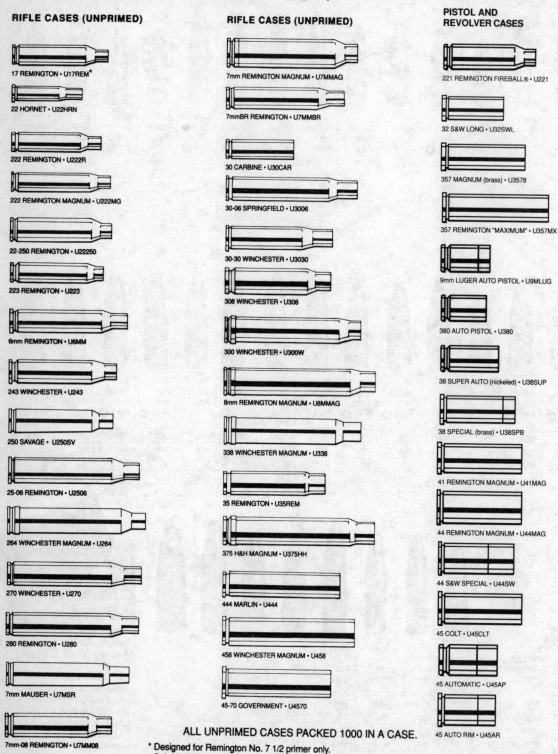

RIFLE CASES (UNPRIMED)

17 REMINGTON • U17REM*

22 HORNET • U22HRN

222 REMINGTON • U222R

222 REMINGTON MAGNUM • U222MG

22-250 REMINGTON • U22250

223 REMINGTON • U223

6mm REMINGTON • U6MM

243 WINCHESTER • U243

250 SAVAGE • U250SV

25-06 REMINGTON • U2506

264 WINCHESTER MAGNUM • U264

270 WINCHESTER • U270

280 REMINGTON • U280

7mm MAUSER • U7MSR

7mm-08 REMINGTON • U7MM08

RIFLE CASES (UNPRIMED)

7mm REMINGTON MAGNUM • U7MMAG

7mmBR REMINGTON • U7MMBR

30 CARBINE • U30CAR

30-06 SPRINGFIELD • U3006

30-30 WINCHESTER • U3030

308 WINCHESTER • U308

300 WINCHESTER • U300W

8mm REMINGTON MAGNUM • U8MMAG

338 WINCHESTER MAGNUM • U338

35 REMINGTON • U35REM

375 H&H MAGNUM • U375HH

444 MARLIN • U444

458 WINCHESTER MAGNUM • U458

45-70 GOVERNMENT • U4570

ALL UNPRIMED CASES PACKED 1000 IN A CASE.

* Designed for Remington No. 7 1/2 primer only.
Substitutions not recommended. U number is unprimed.

PISTOL AND REVOLVER CASES

221 REMINGTON FIREBALL® • U221

32 S&W LONG • U32SWL

357 MAGNUM (brass) • U3578

357 REMINGTON "MAXIMUM" • U357MX

9mm LUGER AUTO PISTOL • U9MLUG

380 AUTO PISTOL • U380

38 SUPER AUTO (nickeled) • U38SUP

38 SPECIAL (brass) • U38SPB

41 REMINGTON MAGNUM • U41MAG

44 REMINGTON MAGNUM • U44MAG

44 S&W SPECIAL • U44SW

45 COLT • U45CLT

45 AUTOMATIC • U45AP

45 AUTO RIM • U45AR

WINCHESTER PRIMERS & UNPRIMED CASES

Centerfire primers are recommended for use as follows:

SYMBOL	PRIMER	TYPE
W209	#209	Shotgun Shells
WLR	#8½-120	Large Rifle
WLRM	#8½M-120	Large Rifle Magnum
WSR	#6½-116	Small Rifle
WSP	#1½-108	Small (Regular) Pistol
WSPM	#1½M-108	Small (Magnum) Pistol
WLP	#7-111	Large (Regular Pistol)

Large Rifle
220 Swift
22-250 Rem.
225 Winchester
243 Winchester
6mm Remington
250 Savage
25-06 Rem.
257 Roberts
264 Win. Mag.
270 Winchester
284 Winchester
7mm Mauser
280 Remington
7mm Express Rem.
7mm Rem. Mag.
30-30 Winchester
30 Rem.
30-06 Springfield
30-40 Krag

300 Win. Mag.
300 H&H Mag.
300 Savage
303 British
308 Winchester
32 Win. Special
32-20 Winchester
32 Remington
32-40 Win.
8mm Mauser
8mm Rem. Mag.
338 Win. Mag.
348 Winchester
35 Remington
356 Winchester
358 Winchester
350 Rem. Mag.
375 Winchester
375 H&H Mag.
38-55 Winchester
444 Marlin

45-70 Gov.
458 Win. Mag.

Small Rifle
218 Bee
22 Hornet
222 Remington
22 Rem. Mag.
223 Remington
25-20 Winchester
256 Win. Mag.
30 Carbine
357 Rem. Max.

Small (Reg.) Pistol
25 Automatic
30 Luger
32 Automatic
32 S&W
32 S&W Long
32 Short Colt
32 Long Colt
32 Colt New Police

9mm Luger
9mm Win. Mag.
38 S&W
38 Special
38 Short Colt
38 Long Colt
38 Colt New Police
38 Super-Auto
38 Automatic
380 Automatic

Small (Mag.) Pistol
357 Magnum

Large (Reg.) Pistol
38-40 Winchester
41 Mag.
44 Mag.
44 S&W Special
45 Colt
45 Automatic
45 Win. Mag.

UNPRIMED BRASS CASES

UNPRIMED RIFLE

SYMBOL	CALIBER
U218	*218 Bee
U22H	*22 Hornet
U22250	22-250 Rem.
U220S	220 Swift
U222R	222 Rem.
U223R	223 Rem.
U225	225 Win.
U243	243 Win.
U6mmR	6mm Rem.
U2520	*25-20 Win.
U256	*256 Win. Mag.
U250	250 Savage
U2506	25-06 Rem.
U257 + P	257 Roberts + P
U264	264 Win. Mag.
U270	270 Win.
U284	284 Win.
U7mm	7mm Mauser
U7MAG.	7mm Rem. Mag.
U30C	*30 Carbine
U3030	30-30 Win.
U3006	30-06 Springfield
U3040	30-40 Krag
U300WM	300 Win. Mag.

SYMBOL	CALIBER
U300H	300 H&H Mag.
U300	300 Savage
U307	307 Win.
U308	308 Win.
U303	303 British
U32W	32 Win. Special
U3220	*32-20 Win.
U32-40	32-40 Win.
U8mm	8mm Mauser
U338	338 Win. Mag.
U348	348 Win.
U35R	35 Rem.
U356	356 Win.
U358	358 Win.
U357H	375 H&H Mag.
U357W	375 Win.
U3840	*38-40 Win.
U3855	38-55 Win.
U4440	*44-40 Win.
U44M	*44 Rem. Mag.
U4570	45-70 Govt.
U458	458 Win. Mag.

UNPRIMED PISTOL/REVOLVER

SYMBOL	CALIBER
U25A	*25 Auto.
U32A	*32 Auto. (7.65mm Browning)
U32SW	32 S&W
U32SWL	*32 S&W Long (32 Colt New Police)
U357	*357 Mag.
U357RM	*357 Rem. Max.
U9MM	*9mm Luger (9mm Parabellum)
U9MMWM	*9mm Win. Mag.
U38SW	*38 S&W (38 Colt New Police)
U38SP	*38 Special
U38A	*38 Auto (and 38 Super)
U380A	*380 Auto (9mm Short-9mm Corto)
U41	*41 Rem. Mag.
U44S	*44 S&W Special
U44M	*44 Rem. Mag.
U45C	*45 Colt
U45A	*45 Auto
U45WM	*45 Win. Mag.

*50 cases per box—all others are 20 cases per box.

ACCURATE SMOKELESS POWDERS

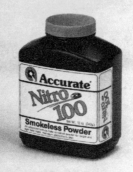  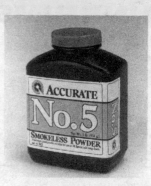 

 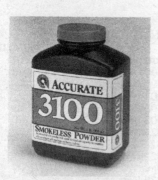 

NITRO 100 SHOTSHELL POWDER: For Target and Light Loads

PISTOL PROPELLANTS

NO. 2: For .38 Special (with 148 grain wadcutter)
NO. 5: For .45 ACP and .38 Special
NO. 7: For 9mm NATO, .38 Super, .357 Magnum, 10mm Auto
NO. 9: For .44 Magnum

RIFLE PROPELLANTS

NO. 1680: For 7.62×39 Cartridge
NO. 2230: For .223 Remington, plus 7 T/CU, 22-250, .243 Winchester, 30-30
NO. 2460: For .308 Winchester, .223 Winchester, 30-30, 30-06, .308 Winchester (under 168 grains)
NO. 2520: For 22-250 to 30-06
NO. 3100: For .243 Winchester to 7mm Remington Magnum
NO. 8700: For .264 Winchester Magnum, 7mm Remington Magnum, .300 Weatherby Magnum

HERCULES SMOKELESS SPORTING POWDERS

Twelve types of Hercules smokeless sporting powders are available to the handloader. These have been selected from the wide range of powders produced for factory loading to provide at least one type that can be used efficiently and economically for each type of ammunition. These include:

BULLSEYE® A high-energy, quick-burning powder especially designed for pistol and revolver. The most popular powder for .38 special target loads. Can also be used for 12 gauge-1 oz. shotshell target loads.

RED DOT® The preferred powder for light-to-medium shotshells; specifically designed for 12-gauge target loads. Can also be used for handgun loads.

GREEN DOT® Designed for 12-gauge medium shotshell loads. Outstanding in 20-gauge skeet loads.

UNIQUE® Has an unusually broad application from light to heavy shotshell loads. As a handgun powder, it is our most versatile, giving excellent performance in many light to medium-heavy loads.

HERCO® A long-established powder for high velocity shotshell loads. Designed for heavy and magnum 10-, 12-, 16- and 20-gauge loads. Can also be used in high-performance handgun loads.

BLUE DOT® Designed for use in magnum shotshell loads, 10-, 12-, 16-, 20- and 28-gauge. Also provides top performance with clean burning in many magnum handgun loads.

HERCULES 2400® For use in small-capacity rifle cartridges and .410-Bore shotshell loads. Can also be used for large-caliber magnum handgun cartridges.

RELODER® SERIES Designed for use in center-fire rifle cartridges. Reloder 7, 12, 15, 19 and 22 provide the right powder for the right use. From small capacity to magnum loads. All of them deliver high velocity, clean burn, round-to-round consistency, and economy.

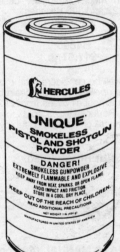
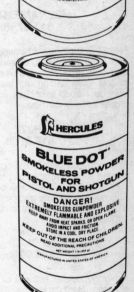

PACKAGING

POWDER	1-LB CANISTERS	4-LB CANISTERS	5-LB CANISTERS	8-LB KEG
Bullseye	●	●		●
Red Dot	●	●		●
Green Dot	●	●		●
Unique	●	●		●
Herco	●	●		●
Blue Dot	●		●	
Hercules 2400	●	●		●
Reloder Series	●		●	

HODGDON SMOKELESS POWDER

RIFLE POWDER

H4227 AND H4198
$17.67/lb.

H4227 is the fastest burning of the IMR series. Well adapted to Hornet, light bullets in 222 and all bullets in 357 and 44 Magnum pistols. Cuts leading with lead bullets. H4198 was developed especially for small and medium capacity cartridges.

H322
$17.67/lb.

Any extruded bench rest powder which has proved to be capable of producing fine accuracy in the 22 and 308 bench rest guns. This powder fills the gap between H4198 and BL-C(2). Performs best in small to medium capacity cases.

SPHERICAL BL-C®, Lot No. 2
$14.98/lb.

A highly popular favorite of the bench rest shooters. Best performance is in the 222, and in other cases smaller than 30/06.

SPHERICAL H335®
$14.98/lb.

Similar to BL-C(2), H335 is popular for its performance in medium capacity cases, especially in 222 and 308 Winchester.

H4895®
$17.67/lb.

4895 may well be considered the most versatile of all propellants. It gives desirable performance in almost all cases from 222 Rem. to 458 Win. Reduced loads, to as low as 3/5 of maximum, still give target accuracy.

SPHERICAL H380®
$17.67/lb.

This number fills a gap between 4320 and 4350. It is excellent in 22/250, 220 Swift, the 6mm's, 257 and 30/06.

#25 DATA MANUAL (544 pp.)
$15.50/lb.

SPHERICAL H414®
$14.82/lb.

In many popular medium to medium-large calibers, pressure velocity relationship is better.

SPHERICAL H870®
$8.36/lb.

Very slow burning rate adaptable to overbore capacity Magnum cases such as 257, 264, 270 and 300 Mags with heavy bullets.

H4350
$17.67/lb.

This powder gives superb accuracy at optimum velocity for many large capacity metallic rifle cartridges.

H4831®
$17.67/lb.

The most popular of all powders. Outstanding performance with medium and heavy bullets in the 6mm's, 25/06, 270 and Magnum calibers.

H1000 EXTRUDED POWDER
$17.67

Fills the gap between H4831 and H870. Works especially well in overbore capacity cartridges (1,000-yard shooters take note).

SHOTGUN AND PISTOL POWDER

HP38
$14.91/lb.

A fast pistol powder for most pistol loading. Especially recommended for mid-range 38 specials.

TRAP 100
$13.96/lb.

Trap 100 is a spherical trap and light field load powder, also excellent for target loads in centerfire pistols. Mild recoil.

HS-6 and HS-7
$14.56/lb.

HS-6 and HS-7 for Magnum field loads are unsurpassed, since they do not pack in the measure. They deliver uniform charges and are dense to allow sufficient wad column for best patterns.

H110
$15.77

A spherical powder made especially for the 30 M1 carbine. H110 also does very well in 357, 44 Spec., 44 Mag. or .410 ga. shotshell. Magnum primers are recommended for consistent ignition.

IMR SMOKELESS POWDERS

SHOTSHELL POWDER

Hi-Skor 700-X Double-Base Shotshell Powder. Specifically designed for today's 12-gauge components. Developed to give optimum ballistics at minimum charge weight (means more reloads per pound of powder). 700-X is dense, easy to load, clean to handle, and loads uniformly.

PB Shotshell Powder. Produces exceptional 20- and 28-gauge skeet reloads; preferred by many in 12-gauge target loads, it gives 3-dram equivalent velocity at relatively low chamber pressures.

Hi-Skor 800-X Shotshell Powder. An excellent powder for 12-gauge field loads and 20- and 28-gauge loads.

SR-4756 Powder. Great all-around powder for target and field loads.

SR-7625 Powder. A fast growing "favorite" for reloading target as well as light and heavy field loads in 4 gauges. Excellent velocity-chamber pressure.

IMR-4227 Powder. Can be used effectively for reloading .410-gauge shotshell ammunition.

RIFLE POWDER

IMR-3031 Rifle Powder. Specifically recommended for medium-capacity cartridges.

IMR-4064 Rifle Powder. Has exceptionally uniform burning qualities when used in medium- and large-capacity cartridges.

IMR-4198. Made the Remington 222 cartridge famous. Developed for small- and medium-capacity cartridges.

IMR-4227 Rifle Powder. Fastest burning of the IMR Series. Specifically designed for the 22 Hornet class of cartridges.

SR-4759. Brought back by shooter demand. Available for cast bullet loads.

IMR-4320. Recommended for high-velocity cartridges.

IMR-4350 Rifle Powder. Gives unusually uniform results when loaded in Magnum cartridges. Slowest burning powder of the IMR series.

IMR-4831. Produced as a canister-grade handloading powder. Packaged in 1 lb. canister, 8 lb. caddy and 20 lb. kegs.

IMR-4895 Rifle Powder. The time-tested standard for caliber 30 military ammunition; slightly faster than IMR-4320. Loads uniformly in all powder measures. One of the country's favorite powders.

IMR-7828 Rifle Powder. The slowest-burning DuPont IMR cannister powder, intended for large capacity and magnum-type cases with heavy bullets.

PISTOL POWDER

PB Powder. Another powder for reloading a wide variety of centerfire handgun ammunition.

IMR-4227 Powder. Can be used effectively for reloading "Magnum" handgun ammunition.

"Hi-Skor" 700-X Powder. The same qualities that make it a superior powder contribute to its exellent performance in all the popular handguns.

SR-7625 Powder. For reloading a wide variety of centerfire handgun ammunition.

SR-4756, IMR-3031 and IMR-4198. Three more powders in a good selection—all clean burning and with uniform performance.

C-H RELOADING ACCESSORIES

ZINC BASE SWAGE DIE

- Maximum Energy
- 100% expansion, every time
- Zinc Base coats the bore with every shot
- Actually cleans the bore as you shoot
- No leading, even using maximum loads
- Perfect gas seal
- Use with any standard loading press
- Simple to use—one stroke of the handle and tap the finished bullet out.
- The perfect lubricating qualities of zinc combined with the perfect expansion

of pure lead produce outstanding, accurate bullets and will appreciably increase bore life.

No. 105-Z Zinc Base Swage Dies, 38/357 SWC
Shipping weight, 1 lb. $29.95
No. 105 Z1 Nose Punch, SWC, caliber 38/357 . . . . 4.00
38/357 caliber Zinc Base Washer, per 1000 (shipping weight per M, 1 lb.) 23.20

308 WINCHESTER AND 223 REMINGTON TAPER CRIMP DIE

- No longer necessary to have perfect trimmed cases
- Use as a separate die to form a perfect taper crimp each time
- Eliminates time-consuming trimming
- Produces Match Grade ammo
- Perfect feeding in semiauto rifles
- Load your ammo just like the factory does

Taper Crimp Die
Shipping weight 1 lb. $17.00

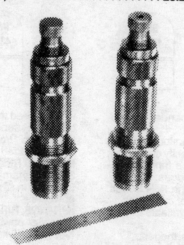

50 CALIBER BMG LOADING DIES

With **50 BMG Priming Accessories** the priming post and the shell holder can be used as is with any Hollywood tool. With the addition of the shell holder die, the priming can be accomplished with any existing loading tool with 7/8-inch top threads. The shell holder die screws into the top of the tool and the threaded shell holder is screwed into this. By adding the priming post you have a complete separate priming system.

Priming Post complete $11.95
Shell Holder Die 9.95
Shell Holder with lock ring 17.95

50 BMG DIE SET

C-H offers a die set for loading 50 caliber BMG. To give you an idea of the massive size of these dies they are shown with a 6-inch steel rule alongside a standard 308 Win. die and cartridge. They are threaded 1 1/2 × 12.

50 BMG Die set (full-length sizer and crimp seater) $275.00

DEBURRING/CHAMFERING TOOL

Standard size: Bevels both the inside and outside of the case mouth for easy bullet insertion. Hardened for long life. Extra sharp cutters. Fits 17 to 45 calibers.
Magnum size: For those who load 45 caliber and over, a Magnum Deburring Tool is available from C-H. Fits all cases from 45 to 60 caliber.

Standard Deburring Tool . . . . $ 8.95
Magnum Deburring Tool 14.95

C-H RELOADING TOOLS

Available for 38 Special/357, 45 ACP, 44 Mag. and 9mm Luger. Features reloading capability of 500 rounds per hour. Fully progressive loading. Powder measure cam allows you to "jog" the machine without dispensing powder. Simple powder measure emptying device included with each unit. Tungsten-carbide sizing die at no extra cost. Unit comes with your choice of powder bushing and seating stem (round nose, wadcutter or semi-wadcutter). Seating die cavity tapered for automatic alignment of the bullet. One 100-capacity primer tube, two 15-capacity case tubes and tube coupling also included at no extra cost **$699.00**

MODEL 444 "H" PRESS

Offers 4-station versatility—two, three or four-piece die sets may be used. New casting design offers increased strength, and there is sufficient room for the longest magnum cases.

Model 444 4-Station "H" Press (includes 4 rams, 4 shell-holders, primer arm, and primer catcher **$158.00**
Same model but with one standard caliber die set **176.00**

AUTO CHAMPION MARK V-a PROGRESSIVE RELOADING PRESS

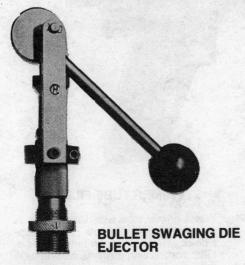

BULLET SWAGING DIE EJECTOR

A helpful accessory for use with the new C-H jacketed bullet swaging dies. The ejector attaches easily to the swaging die body with one screw. Can be used with either the core seating die or the swage die. Ejects the seated core or finished bullet with ease. No more tapping the top of the die.

Price **$24.65**

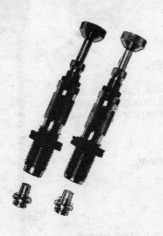

¾ JACKETED PISTOL BULLET SWAGING DIES

- Any bullet weight from 110 gr. to 250 gr. with same set of dies
- Can be used in any good ⅞" × 14 loading tool
- Absolutely no leading
- Complete no extras to buy
- Increased velocity
- Solid nose or hollow point
- Available in 38/357, 41 S & W, 44 Mag. and 45 Colt calibers

Price: **$44.45**

CANNELURE TOOL

- Solid steel
- Will work on all sizes of bullets, from 17 to 45
- Completely adjustable for depth and height
- One set will process thousands of bullets
- Necessary for rolling in grooves on bullets prior to crimping
- Hardened cutting wheel, precision-machined throughout

Price: **$34.95**

C-H RELOADING ACCESSORIES

NO. 725 POWDER and BULLET SCALE

Chrome-plated, brass beam. Graduated in 10 gr., 1 gr. and 1/10th gr. increments. Convenient pouring spout on pan. Leveling screw on base. All metal construction. 360 gr. capacity.

Price **$37.95**

C-HAMPION PRESS

Compound leverage press for all phases of reloading. Heavyweight (26#) C-Hampion comes complete with primer arms, $7/8 \times 14$ bushing for use with all reloading dies. Spent primers fall through back of press into waste basket. 'O' frame design will not spring under any conditions. Ideal press for swaging bullets. Top of frame bored $1^{1}/_{4} \times 18$ for use with special dies and shotshell dies.

C-Hampion Press **$199.50**

NO. 301 CASE TRIMMER

This design features a unique clamp to lock case holder in position. Ensures perfect uniformity from 22 through 45 caliber whether rifle or pistol cases. Complete including hardened case holder.

No. 301 Case Trimmer **$24.95**
Extra case holders (hardened & hand-lapped) **4.00**

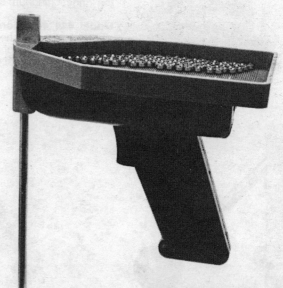

PRIMER TUBE FILLER

Fills a primer tube with 100 primers in seconds. Adjustable gate prevents upside-down primers from entering tube. Filler comes with three tubes and tube rack.

Model L (Large Primers)....... **$39.95**
Model S (Small Primers) **39.95**

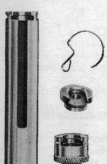

UNIVERSAL SHELL HOLDERS

Up to now, shell holders came in one piece—you needed as many shell holders as the calibers you wished to reload. With the C-H Universal Shell Holder all the reloader needs is the Shell Holder ram.

**No. 408 Universal "C" or "H" Shell
  Holder Head** **$4.00**
**No. 407 Universal "H" Shell Holder
  Ram** **5.25**
**No. 412 Universal "C" Shell Holder
  Ram** **10.50**

FORSTER/BONANZA RELOADING TOOLS

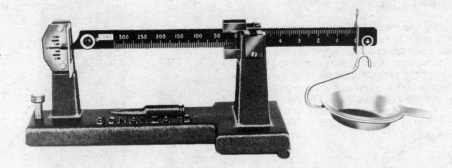

POWDER AND BULLET SCALE
MODEL "D"™ $45.00

330-grain capacity, tempered stainless steel right-hand poise, diamond-polished agate "V" bearings, non-glare white markings. Die cast aluminum base, strengthened beam at pivot points, powder pan for right or left pouring. Easy to read pointer and reference point. Guaranteed accurate to $1/10$ grain; sensitivity guaranteed to $1/20$ grain.

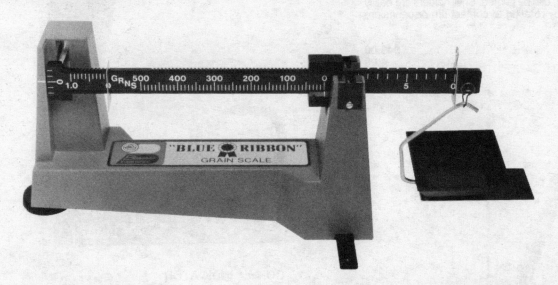

BLUE RIBBON GRAIN SCALE

511-grain capacity for ease of weighing powder. "Blue Ribbon" scales have three poises for better accuracy and convenience. White markings on non-glare enhance reading with less eye strain. Comparator scale and resting point locator lie in the same plane, which eliminates errors in reading due to parallax. Base has three point suspension, eliminating rocking. Guaranteed accurate to $1/10$ grain. Sensitivity to $1/20$ grain.

"Blue Ribbon"™ Magnetic Dampened Grain Scale $64.00

FORSTER/BONANZA RELOADING TOOLS

CO-AX® BENCH REST® RIFLE DIES

Bench Rest Rifle Dies are glass hard for long wear and minimum friction. Interiors are polished mirror smooth. Special attention is given to headspace, tapers and diameters so that brass will not be overworked when resized. Our sizing die has an elevated expander button which is drawn through the neck of the case at the moment of the greatest mechanical advantage of the press. Since most of the case neck is still in the die when expanding begins, better alignment of case and neck is obtained. **Bench Rest® Seating Die** is of the chamber type. The bullet is held in alignment in a close-fitting channel. The case is held in a tight-fitting chamber. Both bullet and case are held in alignment while the bullet is being seated. Cross-bolt lock ring included at no charge.

Bench Rest® Die Set	$52.00
Full Length Sizer	23.00
Bench Rest Seating Die	30.00

PRIMER SEATER
with "E-Z-Just" Shellholder

The Bonanza Primer Seater is designed so that primers are seated Co-Axially (primer in line with primer pocket). Mechanical leverage allows primers to be seated fully without crushing. With the addition of one extra set of Disc Shell Holders and one extra Primer Unit, all modern cases, rim or rimless, from 222 up to 458 Magnum, can be primed. Shell holders are easily adjusted to any case by rotating to contact rim or cannelure of the case.

Primer Seater	$49.00
Primer Tube	4.00

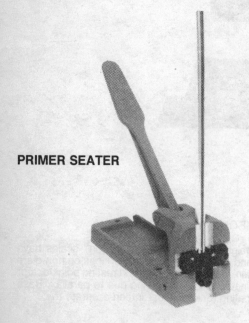

PRIMER SEATER

CO-AX® INDICATOR

Bullets will not leave a rifle barrel at a uniform angle unless they are started uniformly. The Co-Ax Indicator provides a reading of how closely the axis of the bullet corresponds to the axis of the cartridge case. The Indicator features a spring-loaded plunger to hold cartridges against a recessed, adjustable rod while the cartridge is supported in a "V" block. To operate, simply rotate the cartridge with the fingers; the degree of misalignment is transferred to an indicator which measures in one-thousandths.

Price without dial	$40.00
with Indicator Dial	50.00

HORNADY

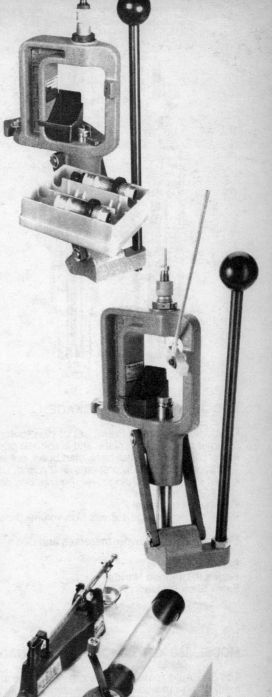

THE 00-7 PRESS PACKAGE
A reloading press complete with dies and shell holder

Expanded and improved to include Automatic Primer Feed. It sets you up to load any caliber in the list below and includes: Choice of a basic 00-7 complete with • Set of Durachrome Dies • Primer catcher • Removable head shell holder • Positive Priming System • Automatic Primer Feed.

00-7 Package (13 lbs.) $156.00
00-7 Package Series II Titanium Nitride (13 lbs.) 168.50

00-7 PRESS

- "Power-Pac" linkage multiplies lever-to-arm power.
- Frame of press angled 30° to one side, making the "O" area of press totally accessible.
- More mounting area for rock-solid attachment to bench.
- Special strontium-alloy frame provides greater stress, resistance. Won't spring under high pressures needed for full-length resizing.

00-7 Press (does not include dies or shell holder) $106.00
00-7 Automatic Primer Feed (complete with large and small primer
   tubes) 15.00

THE HANDLOADER'S ACCESSORY PACK I

Here's everything you need in one money-saving pack. It includes: • Deluxe powder measure • Powder scale • Two non-static powder funnels • Universal loading block • Primer turning plate • Case lube • Chamfering and deburring tool • 3 case neck brushes • Large and small primer pocket cleaners • Accessory handle. Plus one copy of the Hornady Handbook of Cartridge Reloading.

Handloader's Accessory Pack I No. 030300 . . . . $165.00

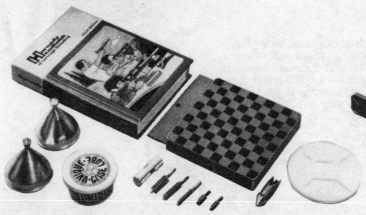

HORNADY

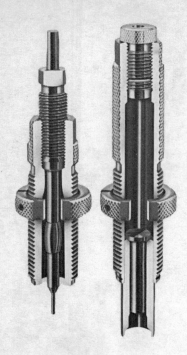

NEW DIMENSION RELOADING DIES

Features an Elliptical Expander that minimizes friction and reduces case neck stretch, plus the need for a tapered expander for "necking up" to the next larger caliber. Other recent design changes include a hardened steel decap pin that will not break, bend or crack even when depriming stubborn military cases. A bullet seater alignment sleeve guides the bullet and case neck into the die for in-line benchrest alignment. All New Dimension Reloading Dies include collar and collar lock to center expander precisely; one-piece expander spindle with tapered bottom for easy cartridge insertion; wrench flats on die body, Sure-Loc™ lock rings and collar lock for easy tightening; and built-in crimper.

New Dimension Reloading Dies:

Series I Two-die Rifle Set	$23.50
Series I Three-die Rifle Set	25.50
Series II Three-die Pistol Set (w/Titanium Nitride)	36.00
Series III Two-die Rifle Set	30.00
Series IV Custom Die Set	53.00

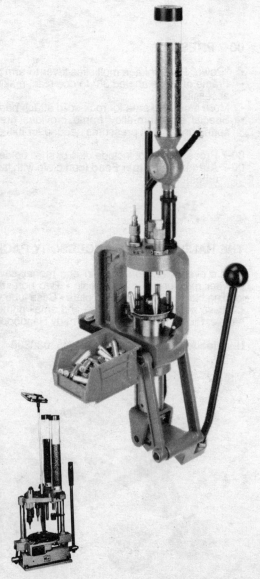

PRO-JECTOR PRESS PACKAGE

- Includes Pro-Jector Press, set of dies, automatic primer feed, brass kicker, primer catcher, shell plate, and automatic primer shut-off
- Just place case in shell plate, start bullet, pull lever and drop powder. Automatic rotation of shell plate prepares next round.
- Fast inexpensive changeover requires only shell plate and set of standard ⅞ × 14 threaded dies.
- Primes automatically.
- Power-Pac Linkage assures high-volume production even when full-length sizing.
- Uses standard powder measures and dies.

Series I	$360.00
Series II Titanium Nitride	372.50
Extra Shell Plates	21.50

MODEL 366 AUTO SHOTSHELL RELOADER

The 366 Auto features full-length resizing with each stroke, automatic primer feed, swing-out wad guide, three-stage crimping featuring Taper-Loc for factory tapered crimp, automatic advance to the next station and automatic ejection. The turntable holds 8 shells for 8 operations with each stroke. The primer tube filler is fast. The automatic charge bar loads shot and powder. Right- or left-hand operation; interchangeable charge bushings, die sets and Magnum dies and crimp starters for 6 point, 8 point and paper crimps.

Model 366 Auto Shotshell Reloader:

12, 20 or 28 Gauge	$450.00
.410 Bore	470.00
Model 366 Auto Die Set	90.00
Auto Advance	43.85
Swing-out Wad Guide & Shell Drop Combo	108.50

LYMAN BULLET SIZING EQUIPMENT

MAG 20 ELECTRIC FURNACE

The MAG 20 is a new furnace offering several advantages to cast bullet enthusiasts. It features a steel crucible of 20-pound capacity and incorporates a proven bottom-pour valve system and a fully adjustable mould guide. The improved design of the MAG 20 makes it equally convenient to use the bottom-pour valve, or a ladle. A new heating coil design reduces the likelihood of pour spout "freeze." Heat is controlled from "Off" to nominally 825° F by a calibrated thermostat which automatically increases temperature output when alloy is added to the crucible. A pre-heat shelf for moulds is attached to the back of the crucible. Availalbe for 100 V and 200 V systems.

Price: 110 V $229.95
220 V 240.95

UNIVERSAL CARBIDE FOUR-DIE SET

Universal Decapping Die
Covers all calibers .22 through .45 (except .378 and .460 Weatherby). Can be used before cases are cleaned or lubricated. Requires no adjustment when changing calibers; fits all popular makes of $7/8\times14$ presses, single station or progressive, and is packaged with 10 replacement pins.

Universal Decapping Die $8.95

Also available: **Universal Carbide Four-Die Set** in calibers 38 Spec./357 Mag., 9mm, 10mm and 45 ACP $43.95

Gas Checks
Gas checks are gilding metal caps which fit to the base of cast bullets. These caps protect the bullet base from the burning effect of hot powder gases and permit higher velocities. Easily seated during the bullet sizing operation. Only Lyman gas checks should be used with Lyman cast bullets.

22 through 35 caliber (per 1000) $20.95
375 through 45 caliber (per 1000) 23.95
Gas check seater 7.95

Lead Pot
The cast-iron pot allows the bullet caster to use any source of heat. Pot capacity is about 8 pounds of alloy and the flat bottom prevents tipping $11.95

Deburring Tool
Lyman's deburring tool can be used for chamfering or deburring of cases up to 45 caliber. For precise bullet seating, use the pointed end of the tool to bevel the inside of new or trimmed cases. To remove burrs left by trimming, place the other end of the deburring tool over the mouth of the case and twist. The tool's centering pin will keep the case aligned . . **$11.95**

Mould Handles
These large hardwood handles are available in three sizes single-, double- and four-cavity.
Single-cavity handles (for small block, black powder and specialty moulds; 12 oz.) **$20.95**
Double-cavity handles (for two-cavity and large-block single-cavity moulds; 12 oz.) 20.95
Four-cavity handles (1 lb.) 23.95

Rifle Moulds
All Lyman rifle moulds are available in double cavity only, except those moulds where the size of the bullet necessitates a single cavity (12 oz.) **$46.95**

Hollow-Point Bullet Moulds
Hollow-point moulds are cut in single-cavity blocks only and require single-cavity handles (9 oz.) **$46.95**

Shotgun Slug Moulds
Available in 12 or 20 gauge; do not require rifling. Moulds are single cavity only, cut on the larger double-cavity block and require double-cavity handles (14 oz.) **$46.95**

Pistols Moulds
Cover all popular calibers and bullet designs in double-cavity blocks and, on a limited basis, four-cavity blocks.
Double-cavity mould block **$46.95**
Four-cavity mould block 76.95

Lead Casting Dipper
Dipper with cast-iron head. The spout is shaped for easy, accurate pouring that prevents air pockets in the finished bullet **$11.95**

LYMAN RELOADING TOOLS
FOR RIFLE OR PISTOL CARTRIDGES

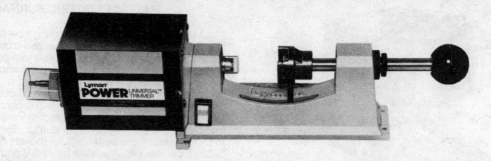

POWERED CASE TRIMMER

The new Lyman Power Trimmer is powered by a fan-cooled electric motor designed to withstand the severe demands of case trimming. The unit, which features the Universal™ Chuckhead, allows cases to be positioned for trimming or removed with fingertip ease. The Power Trimmer package includes Nine Pilot Multi-Pack. In addition to two cutter heads, a pair of wire end brushes for cleaning primer pockets are included. Other features include safety guards, on-off rocker switch, heavy cast base with receptacles for nine pilots, and bolt holes for mounting on a work bench. Available for 110 V or 220 V systems.

Prices: 110 V Model **$189.95**
        220 V Model **199.95**

ACCULINE OUTSIDE NECK TURNER
(not shown)

To obtain perfectly concentric case necks, Lyman's Outside Neck Turner assures reloaders of uniform neck wall thickness and outside neck diameter. The unit fits Lyman's Universal Trimmer and AccuTrimmer. In use, each case is run over a mandrel, which centers the case for the turning operation. The cutter is carefully adjusted to remove a minimum amount of brass. Rate of feed is adjustable and a mechanical stop controls length of cut. Mandrels are available for calibers from .17 to .375; cutter blade can be adjusted for any diameter from .195″ to .405″.

Outside Neck Turner w/extra blade, 6 mandrels . . . **$27.95**
Outside Neck Turner only **19.95**
Individual Mandrels **4.00**

BEGINNING RELOADERS' KIT
$179.95

Includes "Orange Crusher" Press, loading block, case lube kit, primer tray, Model 500 scale, powder funnel and Lyman Reloading Handbook.

LYMAN "ORANGE CRUSHER" RELOADING PRESS

The only press for rifle or pistol cartridges that offers the advantage of powerful compound leverage combined with a true magnum press opening. A unique handle design transfers power easily where you want it to the center of the ram. A 4½-inch press opening accommodates even the largest cartridges.

"Orange Crusher" Press:
With Priming Arm and Catcher **$94.95**

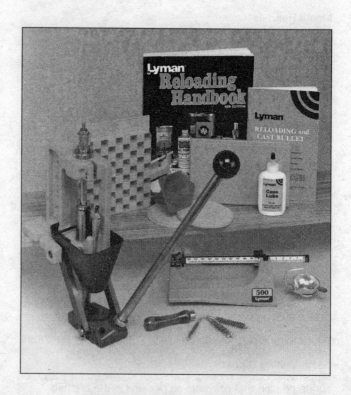

BEGINNING RELOADERS' KIT

LYMAN RELOADING TOOLS

T-MAG TURRET RELOADING PRESS

With the T-Mag you can mount up to six different reloading dies on our turret. This means you can have all your dies set up, precisely mounted, locked in and ready to reload at all times. The T-Mag works with all $7/8 \times 14$ dies. The T-Mag turret with its quick-disconnect release system is held in rock-solid alignment by a $3/4$-inch steel stud.

Also featured is Lyman's Orange Crusher compound leverage system. It has a longer handle with a ball-type knob that mounts easily for right- or left-handed operation.

T-Mag Press w/Priming Arm & Catcher **$134.95**
    Extra Turret Head **19.95**

Now available: **EXPERT KIT** that includes T-MAG Press, Universal Case Trimmer and pilot Multi-Pak, Model 500 powder scale and Model 50 powder measure, plus accessories. Available in calibers 9mm Luger, 38/357, 44 Mag., 45 ACP and 30-06 . . . . **$359.95**.

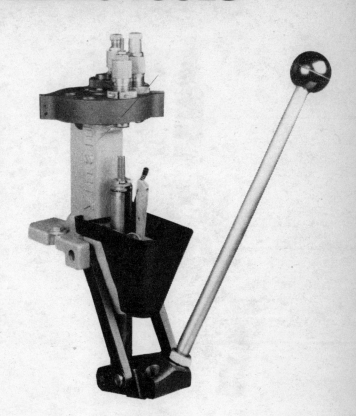

PISTOL ACCUMEASURE

Lyman's Pistol AccuMeasure uses changeable brass rotors pre-drilled to drop precise charges of ball and flake pistol propellants (the tool is not intended for use with long grain IMR-type powders). Most of the rotors are drilled with two cavities for maximum accuracy and consistency. The brass operating handle, which can be shifted for left or right hand operation, can be removed. The Pistol AccuMeasure can be mounted on all turret and single station presses; it can also be hand held with no loss of accuracy.

Pistol AccuMeasure **$21.00**
    With 3-rotor starter kit **31.95**

Now available: **AMMO HANDLER KIT** that includes every tool (except reloading press) needed to produce high-quality ammunition **$159.95**

Also, a **ROTOR SELECTION SET** including 8 dual-cavity rotors and 4 single-cavity units. Enables reloaders to throw a variety of charges for all pistol calibers through 45 . . . . **$49.95**
Extra Double Charge Rotor **7.00**

LYMAN RELOADING TOOLS

DRILL PRESS CASE TRIMMER

Intended for competitive shooters, varmint hunters, and other sportsmen who use large amounts of reloaded ammunition, this new drill press case trimmer consists of the Universal™ Chuckhead, a cutter shaft adapted for use in a drill press, and two quick-change cutter heads. Its two major advantages are speed and accuracy. An experienced operator can trim several hundred cases in a hour, and each will be trimmed to a precise length.

Price:...$42.95

DRILL PRESS CASE TRIMMER

UNIVERSAL TRIMMER WITH NINE PILOT MULTI-PACK

This trimmer with patented chuckhead accepts all metallic rifle or pistol cases, regardless of rim thickness. To change calibers, simply change the case head pilot. Other features include coarse and fine cutter adjustments, an oil-impregnated bronze bearing, and a rugged cast base to assure precision alignment and years of service. Optional carbide cutter available. Trimmer Stop Ring includes 20 indicators as reference marks.

Trimmer less pilots $62.95
Extra pilot (state caliber)......................2.95
Replacement carbide cutter 39.95
Trimmer Multi-Pack (incl. 9 pilots: 22, 24, 27, 28/7mm,
    30, 9mm, 35, 44 and 45A 67.95
Nine Pilot Multi-Pack 9.95

ACCU TRIMMER

Lyman's new Accu Trimmer can be used for all rifle and pistol cases from 22 to 458 Winchester Magnum. Standard shell-holders are used to position the case, and the trimmer incorporates standard Lyman cutter heads and pilots. Mounting options include bolting to a bench, C-clamp or vise.

Accu Trimmer...............................$34.95
    With 9-pilot multi-pak 39.95

MINI-MAG FURNACE
$39.95 ($44.95 with Ladle)

Holds 10 lbs. Sits on stable sheet metal base. Metal shroud protects user from heat (400-watt, 115-volt heating element reaches casting temperature of 750° in 30 minutes).

LYMAN RELOADING ACCESSORIES

PRIMER POCKET REAMER

Cleans and removes rough metal edges from a primer pocket. This tool is a must for military-type primers. Available in large or small see priming punch size in cartridge table.

Price $8.50

POWDER FUNNEL

This plastic powder funnel is designed to fill cases from 22 Hornet through 45-70 without inserts or adjustments.

Price $2.95

POWDER DRIBBLER

Assures full measure of accuracy; an ideal companion for any powder scale.

Price $10.50

NO. 55 POWDER MEASURE

This Powder Measure and dispensing device charges any number of cases with black or smokeless powder loads that are consistant within a fraction of a grain. The 2400-grain capacity plastic reservoir gives a clear view of the powder level. The reservoir is fabricated from blue-tinted polyvinyl-chloride plastic that resists chemical action of double base powders, and filters out light rays that would damage powders. An optional 7000-grain reservoir is available. The measure clamps securely to the loading bench, or mounts directly to any turret press by means of threaded drop tubes (supplied with measure). A knocker mounted on the side of the measure insures complete discharge of powder directly into the cartridge case. No funnel is required.

The unique three-slide micrometer adjustable cavity is the key to the unfailing accuracy of the 55 Powder Measure. Micrometer adjustments for both width and depth provide a dependable, consistent measure that minimizes cutting of coarse powder.

No. 55 Powder Measure $74.95
Optional 7000-grain capacity reservoir 9.95

STAINLESS STEEL DIAL CALIPER
$59.95

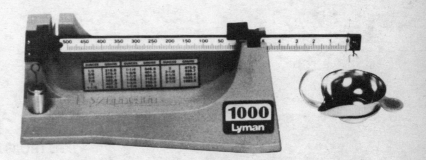

LYMAN M-1000 SCALE

Dial markings are white on jet black for easy reading. The pointer and dial are placed on the same plane to eliminate parallax error. Its high capacity of up to 1005 grains permits the heaviest charges and even bullets to be weighed. Features magnetic damping, one-tenth of a grain of sensitivity.

M-500 Scale $63.95
M-1000 Scale 88.95
Accuscale 37.95

LYMAN RELOADING ACCESSORIES

TURBO TUMBLERS

Lyman's Turbo Tumblers process cases twice as fast as old style tumblers. Their unique design allows the media to swirl around totally immersed cases in a high-speed, agitated motion that cleans and polishes interior and exterior surfaces simultaneously; it also allows inspection of cases without stopping the polishing operation. The Turbo 3200 cleans and polishes up to 1,000 .38 Special cartridge cases. The Turbo 1200 can handle the equivalent of over 300 .38 Specials or 100 .30-06 cartridges. The Turbo 600 cleans half the Model 1200 capacity.

Prices:
Turbo 600 (7 lbs.) 110V	$121.95
Turbo 1200 (10 lbs.) 110V	151.95
Turbo 2200 (12 lbs.) 110V	174.95
Turbo 3200 (13 lbs.) 110V	224.95

Turbo™ Tumbler Capacities

Model	Lyman Media	Number of .38 Special Cases	Nominal Capacity*
600	1 lb.	175	3 Pints
1200	2 lbs.	350	4 Quarts
2200	4 lbs.	750	1.5 Gallons
3200	5 lbs.	1000	2.2 Gallons

*Refer to product instructions for suggested operating procedures and weight guidelines for best results.

"POP TOP" MODEL 600 TURBO TUMBLER
$119.95

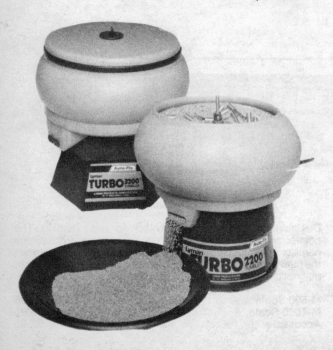

RETRO-FIT AUTO-FLO MEDIA DRAINING SYSTEMS

Lyman introduces a major option for its Model 2200 and high-capacity Model 3200 Turbo Tumblers. Auto-Flo allows automatic, hands-off separation of media from cases following the cleaning-polishing process. Using the Turbo Tumbler's agitating motion, the media is expelled through a post (in the unit's bowl) into a drain pan. Draining of the media takes 2-3 minutes. The vibration of the cases in the near-empty bowl tends to loosen media from flash holes.

Prices:
Retro-Fit (to Model 600/1200 Turbo Tumbler)	$44.95
Retro-Fit (to Model 2200 Turbo Tumbler)	59.95
Retro-Fit (to Model 3200 Turbo Tumbler)	69.95

MEC SHOTSHELL RELOADERS

MODEL 600 JR. MARK 5
$145.97

MODEL 8567 GRABBER
$411.91

This single-stage reloader features a cam-action crimp die to ensure that each shell returns to its original condition. MEC's 600 Jr. Mark 5 can load 8 to 10 boxes per hour and can be updated with the 285 CA primer feed. Press is adjustable for 3″ shells. Die sets are available in all gauges at **$54.90**.

This reloader features 12 different operations at all 6 stations, producing finished shells with each stroke of the handle. It includes a fully automatic primer feed and Auto-Cycle charging, plus MEC's exclusive 3-stage crimp. The "Power Ring" resizer ensures consistent, accurately sized shells without interrupting the reloading sequence. Simply put in the wads and shell casings, then remove the loaded shells with each pull of the handle. Optional kits to load 3″ shells and steel shot make this reloader tops in its field. Resizes high and low base shells. Available in 12, 16, 20, 28 gauge and .410 bore. No die sets are available.

MODEL 8120 SIZEMASTER
$219.95

Sizemaster's "Power Ring" collet resizer returns each base to factory specifications. This new generation resizing station handles brass or steel heads, both high and low base. An 8-fingered collet squeezes the base back to original dimensions, then opens up to release the shell easily. The E-Z Prime auto primer feed is standard equipment. Press is adjustable for 3″ shells and is available in 10, 12, 16, 20, 28 gauge and .410 bore. Die sets are available at: **$81.98**. (**$96.21** in .410).

MODEL 650
$287.06

This reloader works on 6 shells at once. A reloaded shell is completed with every stroke. The MEC 650 does not resize except as a separate operation. Automatic Primer feed is standard. Simply fill it with a full box of primers and it will do the rest. Reloader has 3 crimping stations: the first one starts the crimp, the second closes the crimp, and the third places a taper on the shell. Available in 12, 16, 20 and 28 gauge and .410 bore. No die sets are available.

HUSTLER (not shown)
$1073.56

The fastest and most precise reloader available, the Hustler features a powerful hydraulic system that operates on conventional 110-volt household current. Control is maintained by a foot pedal, leaving hands free to add wads and remove loaded shells. When the pedal is released, the press returns automatically to the top of the stroke. Available in 12, 16, 20, 28 gauge and .410 bore. No die sets are available.

MEC RELOADING

ACCESSORY EQUIPMENT

SPINDEX CRIMP STARTER
(not shown)

Rotates automatically and realigns perfectly on the original crimp of the shell. This precision-built one-piece crimp starter is made of rugged Celcon and can be changed from 6 point to 8 point in a matter of seconds.

ACCESSORIES

301L 13X BH & Cap Assy.	$3.84
453P Wad Finger Ptlc.	1.19
634P Paper Crimp St.	1.30
8042 Magnum Container	5.46
15CA E-Z Pak Accy.	6.72

E-Z PRIME "V"
For 600 Jr. and
700 Versamec

E-Z PRIME "S"
For 650 and
Super 600

E-Z PRIME "S" AND "V"
AUTOMATIC PRIMER FEEDS

From carton to shell with security, these primer feeds provide safe, convenient primer positioning and increase rate of production. Reduce bench clutter, allowing more free area for wads and shells.
- Primers transfer directly from carton to reloader, tubes and tube fillers
- Positive mechanical feed (not dependent upon agitation of press)
- Visible supply
- Automatic. Eliminate hand motion
- Less susceptible to damage
- Adapt to all domestic and most foreign primers with adjustment of the cover
- May be purchased separately to replace tube-type primer feed or to update your present reloader

E-Z Prime "S" (for Super 600 and 650) or **E-Z Primer "V"** (for 600 Jr. and Versa MEC 700) **$35.64**

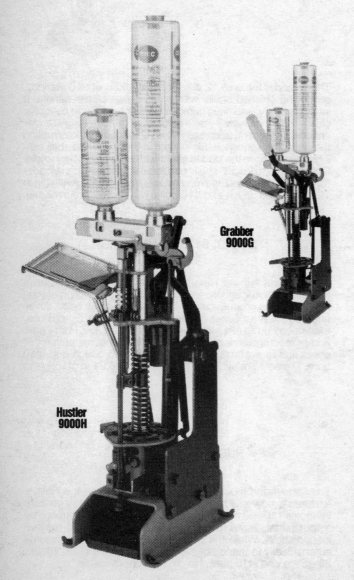

Grabber
9000G

Hustler
9000H

MEC 9000 SERIES SHOTSHELL RELOADER

MEC's new 9000 Series features automatic indexing and finished shell ejection for quicker and easier reloading. The factory set speed provides uniform movement through every reloading stage. Dropping the primer into the reprime station no longer requires operator "feel." The reloader requires only a minimal adjustment from low to high brass domestic shells, any one of which can be removed for inspection from any station.
MEC 9000H (Hustler) or 9000G (Grabber) **$500.00**

MTM

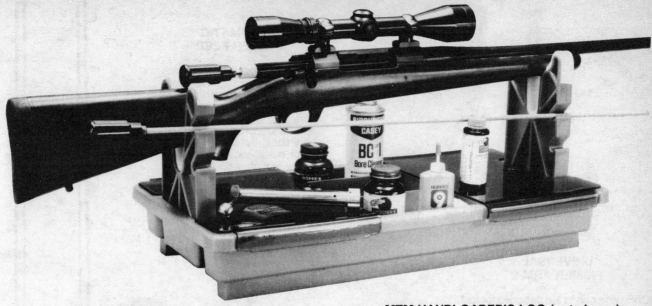

PORTABLE RIFLE MAINTENANCE CENTER

Holds rifles and shotguns for easy cleaning and maintenance (can also be used as a shooting rest). Features gun forks with built-in cleaning rod holders; sliding see-through dust covers; tough polypropylene material; fits conveniently on top of Case-Gard A-760.

Price: **$26.95**

50 ROUND HANDGUN AMMO BOXES

Designed with the shooter in mind, these 50-round ammo boxes feature a new "Step Design" on the partitions inside (for "E-Z" ammo extraction). The specially grooved lid is designed to match up with the feet on the bottom so that they nest into each other. Each box is supplied with its own label for recording custom loads.

Price: **$1.15**

MTM HANDLOADER'S LOG (not shown)

Space is provided for 1,000 entries covering date, range, group size or score, components, and conditions. Book is heavy-duty vinyl, reinforced 3-ring binder.

HL-74 . . . . **$9.41**
HL-50 (incl. 50 extra log sheets) **4.09**

CASE-GARD 100 AMMO CARRIER
FOR SKEET AND TRAP (not shown)

The MTM™ Case-Gard® 100-round shotshell case carries 100 rounds in 2 trays; or 50 rounds plus 2 boxes of factory ammo; or 50 rounds plus sandwiches and insulated liquid container; or 50 round with room left for fired hulls. Features include:
- Recessed top handle for easy storage.
- High-impact material supports 300 pounds, and will not warp, split, expand or contract.
- Dustproof and rainproof.
- Living hinge guaranteed 3 years.
- Available in deep forest green.

S-100-12 (12 gauge) **$16.00**
S-100-20 (20 gauge) **16.00**

FUNNELS

MTM Benchrest Funnel Set is designed specifically for the bench-rest shooter. One fits 222 and 243 cases only; the other 7mm and 308 cases. Both can be used with pharmaceutical vials popular with bench-rest competitors for storage of pre-weighed charges. Funnel design prevents their rolling off the bench.

MTM Universal Funnel fits all calibers from 222 to 45.
UF-1 . . . . **$2.76**
Patented MTM Adapt 5-in-1 Funnel Kit includes funnel, adapters for 17 Rem., 222 Rem. and 30 through 45. Long drop tube facilitates loading of maximum charges: 222 to 45.
AF-5 . . . . **$3.99**

RCBS RELOADING TOOLS

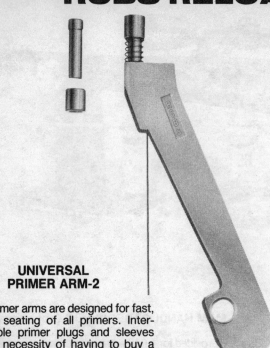

AUTOMATIC PRIMER FEED

Stop misfires greasy hands never need to touch primers. Automatically drops primers one at a time into the primer plug and sleeve of the primer arm. Adjustable primer stop pin eliminates jamming found in other automatic primer feeds. Easily mounted on RCBS and most "C" type presses. The primer tubes for large and small primers are completely interchangeable with the body.

**Automatic Primer
Feed** **$19.00**

UNIVERSAL PRIMER ARM-2

RCBS primer arms are designed for fast, accurate seating of all primers. Interchangeable primer plugs and sleeves eliminate necessity of having to buy a completely new primer arm for each primer size. Primer plugs and sleeves furnished for large and small primers. Body cast of rust-resistant zinc alloy. The Universal Primer Arm-2 is designed for use with RCBS Rock Chucker and J.R. as well as most "C" type presses.

Universal Primer Arm-2 . . . . . . **$9.50**
Plug and Sleeve (sm. or lg.) . . . **2.60**

PRIMER TRAY-2

For fast, easy handling of primers and loading automatic primer feed tubes, place primers in this tray, shake tray horizontally, and primers will automatically position themselves anvil side up. Sturdy plastic case.

Primer Tray-2 . . . . **$3.40**

AUTOMATIC PRIMING TOOL

Precision-engineered to provide fast, accurate and uniform seating of primers in one simple step. Single-stage leverage system is so sensitive it enables you actually to "feel" the primer being seated to the bottom of the primer pocket. This priming tool permits you to check visually each primer pocket before seating the primer, thus eliminating wasted motion or slowing down the reloading process.

Primers are released one at a time through the RCBS automatic primer feed, eliminating contamination caused by handling primers with oily fingers. Both primer rod assemblies furnished with this tool will handle all large and small American-made Boxer-type rifle and pistol primers.

Economy Features: If you already have RCBS automatic primer feed tubes and RCBS shell holders, they will fit this RCBS Priming Tool, thus eliminating the need to buy extras.

Berdan Primer Rod Assemblies: Optional Berdan Primer Rod Assemblies are available in three sizes and are interchangeable with the American Boxer-type Primer Rod Assemblies, furnished with the Priming Tool.

Priming Tool (less shell holder) **$60.00**

PRIMER TRAY-2

PRIMING TOOL

RCBS RELOADING TOOLS

ROCK CHUCKER "COMBO"

The Rock Chucker Press, with patented RCBS compound leverage system, delivers up to 200% more leverage than most presses for heavy-duty reloading of even the largest rifle and pistol cases. Rugged, Block "O" Frame prevents press from springing out of alignment even under the most strenuous operations. It case-forms as easily as most presses full-length size; it full-length sizes and makes bullets with equal ease. Shell holders snap into sturdy, all-purpose shell holder ram. Non-slip handle with convenient grip. Operates on downstroke for increased leverage. Standard 7/8-inch×14 thread.

Rock Chucker Press
 (Less dies) $129.00
Rock Chucker Combo,
 Rifle 162.50
Rock Chucker Combo,
 Pistol 164.60

Combos include interchangeable primer plugs and sleeves for seating large and small rifle and pistol primers, shell holder, and primer catcher.

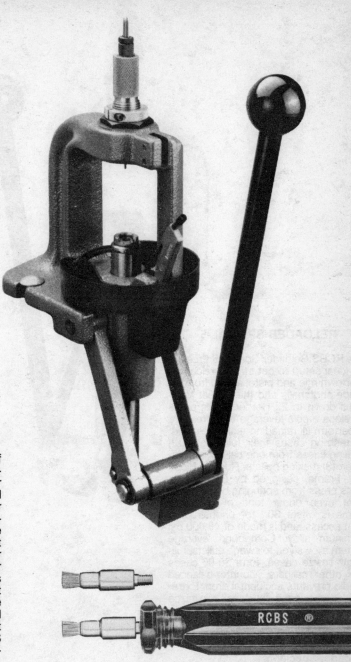

PRIMER POCKET SWAGER COMBO

For fast, precision removal of primer pocket crimp from military cases. Leaves primer pocket perfectly rounded and with correct dimensions for seating of American Boxer-type primers. Will not leave oval-shaped primer pocket that reaming produces. Swager Head Assemblies furnished for large and small primer pockets no need to buy a complete unit for each primer size. For use with all presses with standard 7/8-inch×14 top thread, except RCBS "A-3" Press. The RCBS "A-2" Press requires the optional Case Stripper Washer.

Pocket
Swager Combo $22.00

PRIMER POCKET BRUSH COMBO

A slight twist of this tool thoroughly cleans residue out of primer pockets. Interchangeable stainless steel brushes for large and small primer pockets attach easily to accessory handle.

Primer Pocket Brush Combo: $11.50

RCBS RELOADING TOOLS

RELOADING SCALE MODEL 5-0-5

This 511-grain capacity scale has a three-poise system with widely spaced, deep beam notches to keep them in place. Two smaller poises on right side adjust from 0.1 to 10 grains, larger one on left side adjusts in full 10-grain steps. The first scale to use magnetic dampening to eliminate beam oscillation, the 5-0-5 also has a sturdy die-cast base with large leveling legs for stability. Self-aligning agate bearings support the hardened steel beam pivots for a guaranteed sensitivity to 0.1 grains.

Model 5-0-5 (09071 1½ lbs.): **$72.50**

RELOADER SPECIAL-5

This RCBS Reloader Special-5 Press is the ideal setup to get started reloading your own rifle and pistol ammo from 12 gauge shotshells and the largest Magnums down to 22 Hornets. This press develops ample leverage and pressure to perform all reloading tasks including: (1) resizing cases their full length; (2) forming cases from one caliber into another; (3) making bullets. Rugged Block ''O'' Frame, designed by RCBS, prevents press from springing out of alignment even under tons of pressure. Frame is offset 30° for unobstructed front access, and is made of 48,000 psi aluminum alloy. Compound leverage system allows you to swage bullets, full-length resize cases, form 30-06 cases into other calibers. Counter-balanced handle prevents accidental drop. Extra-long ram-bearing surface minimizes wobble and side play. Standard 7/8-inch-14 thread accepts all popular dies and reloading accessories.

RELOADING SCALE MODEL 10-10

Up to 1010 Grain Capacity
Normal capacity is 510 grains, which can be increased, without loss in sensitivity, by attaching the included extra weight.

Features include micrometer poise for quick, precise weighing, special approach-to-weight indicator, easy-to-read graduations, magnetic dampener, agate bearings, anti-tip pan, and dustproof lid snaps on to cover scale for storage. Sensitivity is guaranteed to 0.1 grains.

Model 10-10 Scale (09073 3 lbs.): **$115.50**

Reloader Special-5
(Less dies) . . . . **$ 97.60**
Reloader Special-5 Combo,
Rifle **126.50**
Reloader Special-5 Combo,
Pistol **128.60**

RCBS RELOADING TOOLS

SIDEWINDER CASE TUMBLER

This RCBS case tumbler cleans cases inside and out and was designed exclusively for handloaders. Instead of just vibrating, the tilted easy-access drum rotates for fast, thorough cleaning. Its built-in timer adjusts for automatic shut-offs from five minutes to 12 hours. A perforated cap doubles as a screen to separate either liquid or dry RCBS cleaning medium from cleaned cases. Capacity is up to 300 38 Special cases or 150 30-06 cases. Available in 120 or 240 volt models. An 8-ounce bottle of Liquid Case Cleaner is included.

Sidewinder Case Tumbler

120 V	**$204.00**
240 V	**206.00**

ROTARY CASE TRIMMER-2

Much like a miniature lathe, this Precisioneer® tool is the ideal way to trim stretched cases, shorten a quantity of them to the same exact length, or correct slightly uneven case mouths. This improved model has been redesigned for absolute case length control. Adjustments have been simplified and refined for near-perfect precision in trimming fired cases.

Case is locked into trimmer collet, the cutting blade is adjusted to desired case length, the handle is turned a few times, and it's done. You then bevel and deburr the trimmed case, and it's ready to reload.

The interchangeable collets are available for all popular calibers (17 to 45) and are designed to lock cases securely for accurate trimming. Special trimmer pilots come in 20 sizes to fit 17 to 45 caliber cases. Each is Precisioneered®, and locks into the cutter with set screw. This type of lock ensures perfect case alignment, both vertically and horizontally.

The cutting assembly features a lock ring so that any quantity of cases can be trimmed to the exact same length with a single adjustment. Cutter blades are made of hardened steel for prolonged service life. Case trimmer also has sockets for holding extra collets and pilots and holes for screwing base to bench.

Rotary Case Trimmer-2	**$51.90**
Kit	**78.00**

CASE TRIMMER PILOT
$2.80

PART NO.	PILOT CAL.	PART NO.	PILOT CAL.
09377	17	09387	33
09378	22	09388	34
09379	24	09389	35
09380	25	09390	36
09381	26	09391	37
09382	27	09392	40
09383	28	09393	41
09384	30	09394	44
09385	31	09395	45
09386	32	09396	.45-R

This tool is used to: (1) trim to standard length those cases which have stretched after repeated firings; (2) trim a quantity of cases to the same length for uniform bullet seating; (3) correct uneven case mouths.

CASE TRIMMER COLLET
$6.80

PART NO.	COLLET NO.	PART NO.	COLLET NO.
09371	1	09373	3
09372	2	09374	4

RCBS RELOADING TOOLS

STAINLESS STEEL DIAL CALIPER

Features include easy-to-read dial, 6″ capacity, and measures four ways: outside, inside, depth and step. Dial graduations are in .001″; vernier measures are in millimeters. An ideal companion to RCBS Rotary Case Trimmer.

Stainless Steel Dial Caliper/Case Length Gauge . . **$61.00**

VIBRATORY CASE CLEANER

Large 3½-quart bowl cleans up to 550 .38 Special cases or 190 .30-06 cases at one time. Thermally protected 1/30 hp (2900 rpm) ball-bearing motor is available in 120 or 240 VAC. Steel case and thick ¼″ bowl ensure durability. Other features include removable lid (for fast inspection while motor is running) and 2 lb. package of Walnut shell Dry Media Case.

Vibratory Case Cleaner
120 VAC	**$157.00**
240 VAC	**176.00**

PIGGYBACK CONVERSION UNIT

A simple, inexpensive way to convert a single-stage press to a five-station, fully automatic progressive reloading tool (and back again). Mounts easily to RCBS Rock Chucker or RS-3 in less than 10 minutes. For pistol ammo and up to .223 caliber cartridges.

Piggyback Conversion Unit **$130.00**
Five Station Shell Plates **26.50**

RCBS RELOADING TOOLS

ELECTRONIC SCALE

This new RCBS Electronic Scale brings solid state electronic accuracy and convenience to handloaders. The LCD digital readings are ideal for weighing bullets and cases. The balance gives readings in grains, from zero to 500. The tare feature allows direct reading of the sample's weight with or without using the scale pan. The scale can be used on the range, operating on 8 AA batteries (approx. 50 hours).

Price: **$375.00**

POWDER CHECKER

Operates on a free-moving rod for simple, mechanical operation with nothing to break. Standard $7/8 \times 14$ die body can be used in any progressive loader that takes standard dies. Black oxide finish provides corrosion resistance with good color contrast for visibility.

Price: **$21.60**

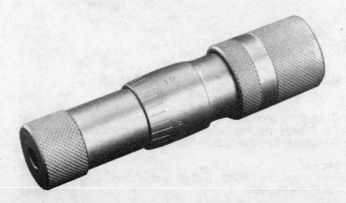

PRECISION MIC

This "Precisioneered Cartridge Micrometer" provides micrometer readings of case heads to shoulder lengths, improving accuracy by allowing the best possible fit of cartridge to chamber. By allowing comparison of the chamber to SAAMI specifications, it alerts the handloader to a long chamber or excess headspace situation. It also ensures accurate adjustment of seater die to provide optimum seating depth. Available in 12 popular calibers.

Price: **$35.00**

REDDING RELOADING TOOLS

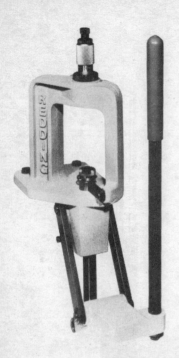

MODEL 721
"THE BOSS" PRESS

This "O" type reloading press features a rigid cast iron frame whose 36° offset provides the best visibility and access of comparable presses. Its "Smart" primer arm moves in and out of position automatically with ram travel. The priming arm is positioned at the bottom of ram travel for lowest leverage and best feel. Model 721 accepts all standard 7/8-14 threaded dies and universal shell holders.

Model 721 "The Boss" . . . . $ 98.00
   With Shellholder and 10A Dies 126.00

Now available: **Boss Pro-Pak Deluxe Reloading Kit.** Includes Boss Reloading Press, #2 Powder and Bullet Scale, Powder Trickler, Reloading Dies, and more $252.50

ULTRAMAG MODEL 700

Unlike other reloading presses that connect the linkage to the lower half of the press, the Ultramag's compound leverage system is connected at the top of the press frame. This allows the reloader to develop tons of pressure without the usual concern about press frame deflection. Huge frame opening will handle 50 × 3¼-inch Sharps with ease.

No. 700 Press, complete $210.00
No. 700K Kit, includes shell holder and one set of dies 238.00

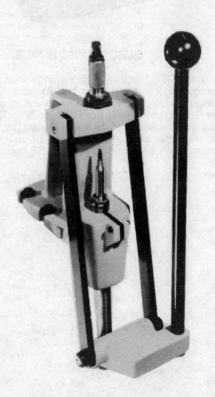

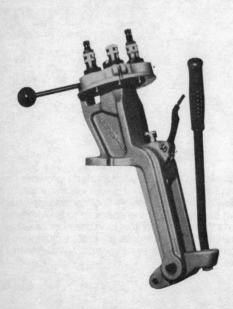

METALLIC TURRET RELOADING PRESS
MODEL 25

Extremely rugged, ideal for production reloading. No need to move shell, just rotate turret head to positive alignment. Ram accepts any standard snap-in shell holder. Includes primer arm for seating both small and large primers.

No. 25 Press, complete $234.00
No. 25K Kit, includes press, shell holder, and one set of dies 262.00
No. 19T Automatic Primer Feeder 18.00

REDDING RELOADING TOOLS

MATCH GRADE POWDER MEASURE MODEL 3BR

Designed for the most demanding reloaders—bench rest, silhouette and varmint shooters. The Model 3BR is unmatched for its precision and repeatability. Its special features include a powder baffle and zero backlash micrometer.

No. 3BR with Universal or Pistol Metering Chamber **$104.00**
No. 3 BRK includes both metering chambers **132.50**
No. 3-30 Benchrest metering chambers (fit only 3BR) . . . **30.00**

MASTER POWDER MEASURE MODEL 3

Universal- or pistol-metering chambers interchange in seconds. Measures charges from 1/2 to 100 grains. Unit is fitted with lock ring for fast dump with large "clear" plastic reservoir. "See-thru" drop tube accepts all calibers from 22 to 600. Precision-fitted rotating drum is critically honed to prevent powder escape. Knife-edged powder chamber shears coarse-grained powders with ease, ensuring accurate charges.

No. 3 Master Powder Measure (specify Universal- or Pistol-Metering chamber) . . . . . . **$ 85.00**
No. 3K Kit Form, includes both Universal and Pistol chambers **104.00**
No. 3-12 Universal or Pistol chamber **21.00**

POWDER TRICKLER MODEL 5

Brings underweight charges up to accurate reading, adding powder to scale pan a granule or two at a time by rotating knob. Speeds weighing of each charge. Solid steel, low center of gravity. "Companion" height to all reloading scales; weighs a full pound.

No. 5 Powder Trickler **$15.50**

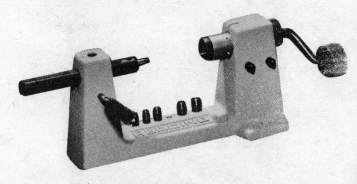

MASTER CASE TRIMMER MODEL 1400

This unit features a universal collet that accepts all rifle and pistol cases. The frame is solid cast iron with storage holes in the base for extra pilots. Both coarse and fine adjustments are provided for case length.

The case-neck cleaning brush and primer pocket cleaners attached to the frame of this tool make it a very handy addition to the reloading bench. Trimmer comes complete with:
• New speed cutter shaft
• Six pilots (22, 6mm, 25, 270, 7mm and 30 cal.)
• Universal collet
• Two neck cleaning brushes (22 thru 30 cal.)
• Two primer pocket cleaners (large and small)

No. 1400 Master Case Trimmer complete **$74.50**
No. 1500 Pilots **3.00**

STANDARD POWDER AND BULLET SCALE MODEL RS-1

For the beginner or veteran reloader. Only two counterpoises need to be moved to obtain the full capacity range of 1/10 grain to 380 grains. Clearly graduated with white numerals and lines on a black background. Total capacity of this scale is 380 grains. An over-and-under plate graduate in 10th grains allows checking of variations in powder charges or bullets without further adjustments.

Model No. RS-1 . . . . **$51.00**

Also available: **Master Powder & Bullet Scale.** Same as standard model, but includes a magnetic dampened beam swing for extra fast readings. 505-grain capacity **$62.50**

Reference

THE SHOOTER'S BOOKSHELF

An up-to-date listing of book titles, old and new, of interest to shooters and gun enthusiasts. Most of these books can be found at your local library, bookstore, or gun shop. If not available, contact the publisher. Names and addresses of leading publishers in the field are listed at the end of this section.

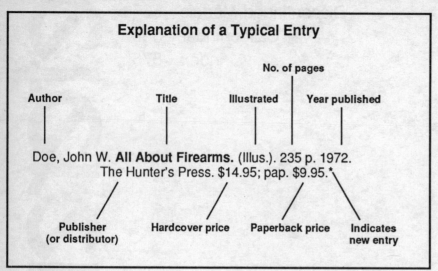

Explanation of a Typical Entry

No. of pages

Author   Title   Illustrated   Year published

Doe, John W. **All About Firearms.** (Illus.). 235 p. 1972.
The Hunter's Press. $14.95; pap. $9.95.*

Publisher (or distributor)   Hardcover price   Paperback price   Indicates new entry

AIR GUNS
Churchill, Bob & Davies, Granville. **Modern Airweapon Shooting,** (Illus.), 1981. David & Charles. $25.95.
Galan, J. I. **Air Guns Digest,** 2d ed. (Illus.). 256 p. 1988. DBI. pap. $12.95.

AMMUNITION
Brown, Ronald. **Homemade Guns & Homemade Ammo.** 191 p. 1986. Loompanics. pap. text ed. $12.95.
Buttweiler, Robert T. **Buttweiler's Guide to Ammunition Prices: The Complete Handbook of Values for the Collector.** 224 p. 1988. R. T. Buttweiler. pap. $14.95.*
Donnelly, John J. **Handloader's Manual of Cartridge Conversions.** (Illus.) 1056 p. 1987. Stoeger Pub. Co. pap. $29.95; spiral bound $44.95; hardcover $49.95.
Evaluation of Police Handgun Ammunition. (Law Enforcement Series) 1986. Gordon Press. $79.95 (lib. bdg.).
Geary, Don. **The Reloader's Bible: The Complete Guide to Making Ammunition at Home.** (Illus.) 256 p. 1986. Prentice-Hall. $17.95.
Goad, K.J. & Halsey, D. H. **Ammunition, Grenades & Mines.** 1982. Pergamon Press. $39.00; pap. $21.00.
Long, Duncan. **Combat Ammunition: Everything You Need to Know.** (Illus.). 136 p. 1986. Palladin Pr. text. ed. $19.95.
Parkerson, Codman. **A Brief History of Bullet Moulds.** Pioneer Press. $1.75.
Sears & Roebuck 1910 **Ammunition Catalog** (Illus.). pap. Sand Pond $2.00.
Stegen, Arthur E. **Biathlon.** (Illus.). 144 p. National Rifle Assn. $30.00.
Steindler, R. A. **Reloader's Guide.** 3rd ed. (Illus.). 1975. softbound. Stoeger. $9.95.
Trzoniec, Stanley W. **Handloader's Guide.** (Illus.). 256 p. pap. 1985. Stoeger. $12.95.

ARCHERY (see also Bow and Arrow)
Athletic Institute, ed. **Archery: A Sport for Everyone.** (Illus.). 96 p. 1984. Athletic Inst. pap. $7.95.
Barrett, Jean. **Archery.** 3rd ed. 1980. Scott, Foresman & Co.
Bear, Fred. **Archer's Bible.** (Illus.). 1980. pap. Doubleday, $7.95.

Combs, Roger. **Archers Digest,** 4th ed. (Illus.) 256 p. 1986. DBI. pap. $13.95.
Cub Scouts Sports Archery. (Illus.). 32 p. 1985. BSA. pap. $1.35.
Glogan, Joseph. **Sportsman's Book of U.S. Records.** (Illus.). 96 p. 1980. pap. text ed. NY Outdoor Guide. $4.95.
Haywood, Kathleen & Lewis, Catherine. **Archery: Steps to Success.** (Illus.). 1988. Leisure Press. pap. text ed. $12.00.
Henderson, Al. **Understanding Winning Archery.** Helgeland, G., ed. (Illus.). 114 p. 1983. Target Comm. pap. $8.95.
Johnson, Dewayne J. & Oliver, Robert A. **Archery.** 1980. pap. American Press. $5.95.
Kember-Smith, Jackson S. **Archery Today: Techniques & Philosophies in Action.** (Illus.). 160 p. 1988. David & Charles. $22.95.*
Klann, Margaret L. **Target Archery.** 1970. pap. Addison-W.
Laubin, Reginald & Laubin, Gladys. **American Indian Archery.** (Illus.). 1980. University of Oklahoma Press. $24.95.
McKinney, Wayne C. & McKinney, Mike W. **Archery.** 5th ed. (Illus.). 176 p. 1985. Wm. C. Brown. Price on request.
Mosely, Walter M. **An Essay on Archery.** 1976. Charles River Books. $17.50.
Neade, William. **The Double Armed Man.** facs. ed. (Illus.). 1971. George Shumway Publisher. $10.00.
Odums, R.I. & Allen, D.G. **Career Guide to Officiating Archery & Riflery.** Tessman, Rita, ed. (Illus.) 150 p. 1986. Guideposts Pub. Dists. $12.95.
Thompson, J. Maurice. **The Witchery of Archery.** 1986. Fundingsland. pap. $8.95.
Wood, William. **The Bowman's Glory, or, Archery Revived.** 1976. Charles River Books. $7.50

ARMS AND ARMOR (see also Firearms)
Albion, Robert G. **Introduction to Military History.** (Illus.). 1971. Repr. of 1929 ed. AMS Press. $29.00.
American Machines & Foundry Co. **Silencers: Patterns & Principles, Vol. 2.** (Illus.). 1969. pap. Paladin Press. $12.95.
Beckett, Brian. **Weapons of Tomorrow.** 160 p. 1983. Plenum Pub. $17.95.
Berman, Vladimir. **Masterpieces of the Gunsmiths.** (Illus.). 144 p. 1981. State Mutual Books. $81.00.

Bivens, John. **Art of the Fire-Lock, Twentieth Century: Being a Discourse Upon the Present and Past Practices of Stocking and Mounting the Sporting Fire-Lock Rifle Gun.** 1982. Shumway. $49.50.
Blair, Claude. **Arms, Armour & Base Metalwork.** (Illus.). 532 p. 1985. Sotheby Pubns. text ed. $85.00.
Constant, James N. **Fundamentals of Strategic Weapons.** 940 p. 1981. Sijthoff & Nordoff. $140.00.
Daniel, Larry J. & Gunter, Riley W. **Confederate Cannon Foundries.** Pioneer Press. ed. Pioneer Press. $17.95.
Diagram Group. **Weapons** (Illus.). 1980. St. Martin's Press. $27.50.
Dunnigan, James F. **How to Make War: A Comprehensive Guide to Modern Warfare.** (Illus.). 416 p. 1981. Morrow. pap. $8.95.
Dupuy, Trevor N. **The Evolution of Weapons & Warfare.** (Illus.). 360 p. 1984. Repr. of 1980 ed. Hero Bks. text ed. $19.95.
Ezell, Edward C. **Small Arms Today: Latest Reports on the World's Weapons & Ammunition.** 256 p. (Orig.). 1984. pap. Stackpole. $16.95.
Foss, Christopher F., ed. **Jane's Armour & Artillery, 1989–90.** (Illus.). 1000 p. 1989. Janes Info Group. $145.00.*
Frost, H. Gordon. **Blades and Barrels: Six Centuries of Combination Weapons.** Walloon Press. $16.95. deluxe ed. $25.00; presentation ed. $50.00.
Funcken, Lilane & Funcken, Fred. **Arms & Uniforms: The Second World War,** vols. I, III & IV. 128 p. 1984. P-H. $17.95 (ea.).
Gruzanski, C. V. **Spike and Chain.** Wehman Brothers, Inc. $7.50.
Guthman, William, ed. **Guns and Other Arms.** (Illus.). 1980. pap. Mayflower Books. $7.95.
Hamilton, T. M. **Firearms on the Frontier: Guns at Fort Michilimackinac 1715–1781.** Armour, David A., ed. (Illus.). 1976. pap. Mackinac Island State Park Commission. $3.00.
—**Colonial Frontier Guns.** 1987. Pioneer Press. $13.95.
Hogg, Ian. **The Weapons That Changed the World.** (Illus.). 1986. Morrow. $22.95.
Hogg, Ian, ed. **Jane's Infantry Weapons 1989–90.** (Illus.). 600 p. 1989. Janes Info Group. $170.00.
Holmes, Bill. **Home Workshop Guns for Defense & Resistance: The Handgun, Vol. II.** (Illus.). 144 p. 1979. Paladin Press. pap. $10.00.
Illustrations of United States Military Arms 1976–1903: And Their Inspector's Marks. 1987. Pioneer Press. $4.95.
Jane's Infantry Weapons 1987–88. Hogg, Ian, ed. (Illus.). 1000 p. 1987. Janes Info Group. $150.00.
Jane's Infantry Weapons 1988–1990. Hogg, Ian, ed. (Illus.). 600 p. 1989. Janes Info Group. $170.00.*
Johnson, Thomas M. **Collecting the Edged Weapons of the Third Reich.** 4 vols. Bradach, Wilfrid, tr. (Illus.). Johnson Reference Books. $25.00 (per volume).
Johnson, Thomas M. & Wasmus, A. **Collecting the Edged Weapons of the Third Reich: Five Volume Cross-Index.** Johnson Reference Books Staff, ed. 100 p. 1988. Johnson Reference Books. $12.00.*
Journal of the Arms and Armour Society. Vol. 1. (Illus.). 240 p. 1970. George Shumway Publisher. $12.00.
Klare, Michael T. **American Arms Supermarket.** (Illus.). 336 p. 1985. pap. U. of Texas Pr. $12.95.
Kozan, S. **Manufacture of Armour and Helmets in Sixteenth Century Japan.** Albert Saifer, Publisher. $35.00.
Laking, Guy F. **A Record of European Armour and Arms Through Seven Centuries.** 5 vols. (Illus.). Repr. AMS Press. set $295.00.
McAulay, John D. **Carbines of the Civil War, 1861–1865.** 1981. Pioneer Press. $8.95.

Macksey, Kenneth. **Technology in War:** The Impact on Science of Weapon Development & Modern Battles. (Illus.) 224 p. 1986. Arco. $19.95.

Marchant-Smith, D. J. & Haslem, P. R. **Small Arms & Cannons.** (Brassey's Battlefield Weapons System & Technology: Vol. 5) 160 p. 1982. Pergamon. $18.95.

Matunas, Edward. **Handbook of Metallic Cartridge Reloading.** (Illus.) 272 p. 1981. New Century. $19.95.

Mowbray, E. Andrew, ed. **Arms-Armor: From the Atelier of Ernst Schmidt, Munich.** (Illus.). 1967. Mowbray Inc. $15.00.

Officers of the U.S. Army Ordnance Dept. Staff. **Small Arms Eighteen Fifty-Six: Reports of Experiments with Small Arms for the Military Service.** (Illus.). 168 p. 1984. Repr. of 1856 ed. Thomas Pubns. $15.00.

Owen, J. I. ed. **Infantry Weapons of the Armies of Africa, the Orient and Latin America.** 1980. pap. Pergamon Press. $35.95.

—**Infantry Weapons of the NATO Armies.** 2nd ed. 1980. pap. Pergamon Press. $35.95.

—**Infantry Weapons of the Warsaw Pact Armies.** 2nd ed. 1979. Pergamon Press. $35.95.

Peterson, Harold L. **The American Sword. 1775–1945.** (Illus.). 1983. Ray Riling. $35.00.

Pierre, Andrew, J. **The Global Politics of Arms Sales.** 1981. Princeton University Press. pap. $14.00.

Rossner-Owen, Davis. **Vietnam Weapons Handbook.** (Illus.) 128 p. 1986. Sterling. pap. $7.99.

Royal United Service Institute for Defense Studies, ed. **International Weapon Developments: A Survey of Current Developments in Weapons Systems,** 4th ed. (Illus.). 1980. Pergamon Press. pap. $19.00.

Schuyler-Hartley-Graham Military Furnishers. **Illustrated Catalog Arms and Military Goods.** facs. ed. (Illus.). 1864. Flayderman, N. & Co. $9.50.

Sedov, Alexander & Portnov, Mikhail. **Russian Arms & Armour: The Armoury of the Moscow Kremlin & The Historical Museum,** Moscow. 208 p. 1982. State Mutual Bks. $154.00.

Smith, Mark. **Hidden Threat: A Guide to Covert Weapons.** (Illus.). 168 p. 1989. Paladin Press. pap. $14.00.*

Smith, W. H. **Small Arms of the World: A Basic Manual of Small Arms,** 12th ed. 896 p. 1983. Stackpole, $49.95.

Suenega, M. **Pictorial History of Ancient Japanese Weapons, Armour & Artifacts.** (Illus.). 100 p. 1983. pap. Saifer. $17.50.

Temesvary, Ferenc. **Arms & Armour.** (Illus.). 126 p. 1982. Int'l Spec. Books. $19.95.

Thomas, Dean S. **Ready . . . Aim . . . Fire! Small Arms Ammunition in the Battle of Gettysburg.** (Illus.). 76 p. 1981. Thomas Pubns. pap. $7.50.

Truby, J. David. **Silencers, Snipers & Assassins.** (Illus.). 214 p. 1972. Paladin Press. $21.95.

Warry, John. **Warfare in the Classical World: An Illustrated Encyclopedia of Weapons, Warriors and Warfare in the Ancient Civilizations of Greece and Rome.** 1981. St. Martin. $24.95.

Whisker, James B. **Arms Makers of Pennsylvania.** (Illus.). 1988. Susquehanna U. Press. $60.00.

Wintringham, Thomas H. **Story of Weapons and Tactics.** facs. ed. 1943. Arno Press. $18.00.

Wright, James & Rossi, Peter. **Under the Gun: Weapons, Crime & Violence in America.** 360 p. 1983. Aldine de Gruyter Pub. $39.95.

Zaloga, Stephen J. & Grandsen, James. **The Eastern Front.** 96 p. 1983. Squad Sig. Pubns. $7.95.

ARTILLERY

Bidwell, Shefford, ed. **Brassey's Artillery of the World.** 2nd rev. ed. 1981. Pergamon Press. $67.50.

Downey, Fairfax. **The Guns of Gettysburg.** 290 p. 1958. Olde Soldier Books. Repr. $25.00.

Foss, Christopher. **Artillery of the World.** 2nd ed. (Illus.). 1976. Scribner's. $8.95.

Foss, Christopher F., ed. **Jane's Armour & Artillery 1987–88** (Illus.). 1000 p. 1987 Janes Info Group. $152.50.

—**Jane's Armour & Artillery, 1988–89.** (Illus.). 800 p. 1988. Janes Info Group. $127.50

Gander, Terry. **Artillery** (Modern Military Techniques Service). (Illus.). 48 p. (gr. 5 up). 1987. Lerner Publications. $9.95

Karwan, Chuck. **Gun Digest Book of Combat Handgunnery,** 2d ed. (Illus.). 256 p. 1989. DBI. pap. $14.95.*

Macchiavelli, Nicolo. **The Arte of Warre (Certain Wales of the Orderying of Souldiours).** Whitehorne, P., tr. 1969. Repr. of 1562 ed. W. J. Johnson. $85.00.

Manucy, Albert. **Artillery through the Ages:** A Short Illus. History of Cannon Emphasizing Types Used in America. (Illus.) 96 p. 1985. Govt. Ptg. Off. pap. $2.75.

Rogers. H. B. **A History of Artillery.** (Illus.). 230 p. 1974. Carol Pub. Group. $7.95.

Rogers, H. C. **A History of Artillery.** (Illus.). 1977. Citadel Press. pap. $4.95.

Simienowicz, Casimir. **The Great Art of Artillery.** 1976. Charles River Books. $20.00.

BALLISTICS

Farrar, C. L. & Leeming, D. W. **Military Ballistics: A Basic Manual.** 225 p. 1983. Pergamon Press. pap. $18.95.

FBI Wound Ballistic Evaluation. (Illus.). 48 p. 1988. Paladin Press. pap. $8.00.

Krier, Herman & Summerfield, Martin, eds. **Interior Ballistics of Guns.** 385 p. 1979. AIAA. $79.95.

Laible, Roy C. **Ballistic Materials & Penetration Mechanics.** 1980. Elsevier. $100.00

Mann, Franklin W. **The Bullet's Flight to Target From Powder: The Ballistics of Small Arms.** 391 p. 1980. Wolfe Pub. Co. Repr. text ed $22.50.

Mannes, Philip. **Tables of Bullet Performance.** Wolfe, Dave, ed. 407 p. (Orig.). 1980. pap. text ed. Wolfe Pub. Co. $17.50.

Pejsa, Arthur J. **Modern Practical Ballistics.** (Illus.). 200 p. 1989. Kenwood Pub. $19.95.*

Wilber, Charles G. **Ballistic Science for the Law Enforcement Officer.** (Illus.). 1977. C. C. Thomas. $40.75.

—**Forensic Biology for the Law Enforcement Officer.** (Illus.). 1974. C. C. Thomas. $49.50.

Williams, M. **Practical Handgun Ballistics.** 1980. C. C. Thomas. $28.00.

Wolfe, Dave, ed. **The Art of Bullet Casting.** (Illus.). 258 p. pap. 1981. Wolfe Pub. Co. pap. $12.95.

—**Propellant Profiles.** (Illus.) 158 p. 1982. Wolfe Pub. Co. pap. text ed. $12.95.

BIRD DOGS

Falk, John R. **The Complete Guide to Bird Dog Training.** rev. ed. 1986. Winchester Press. $15.95.

Rafe, Stephen C. **Training Your Dog For Birdwork.** (Illus.). 96 p. 1987. Denlingers. pap. $16.95.

Stuart, Jack. **Bird Dogs and Upland Game Birds.** (Illus.) 1983. Denlingers. $24.95.

Waterman, Charles F. **Gun Dogs & Bird Guns: A Charley Waterman Reader.** (Illus.). 244 p. 1987. GSJ Press (South Hamilton, Mass.). text ed. $25.00.

BLACK POWDER GUNS (see also Firearms)

Bridges, Toby. **Advanced Muzzleloader's Guide.** (Illus.). 256 p. 1985. pap. Stoeger. $11.95.

Elliot, Brook. **Complete Smoothbore Hunter.** (Illus.) 240 p. 1986. New Century. $16.95.

Fadala, Sam. **The Complete Black Powder Handbook.** (Illus.). 288 p. 1979. DBI. pap. $12.95.

—**Gun Digest Black Powder Loading Manual.** (Illus.). 224 p. 1982. DBI. pap. $13.95.

Nonte, George C. Jr., **Black Powder Guide.** 2d ed. (Illus.). 256 p. pap. Stoeger Pub. Co. $11.95.

BOW AND ARROW (see also Archery, Crossbows)

Adams, Chuck. **Bowhunter's Digest.** 2nd ed. pap. 1981. DBI Books. $13.95.

Bear, Fred. **The Archer's Bible.** rev. ed. (Illus.). 1980. Doubleday. pap. $7.95.

Bowring, Dave. **Bowhunting for Whitetails: Your Best Methods for Taking North America's Favorite Deer.** (Illus.). 304 p. 1985. Stackpole. $24.95.

Helgeland, G. **Archery World's Complete Guide to Bow Hunting.** 1975. P-H. pap. $6.95.

—**Complete Bowhunting.** (Illus.). 261 p. 1987. American Hunt Club. $19.95.

Kinton, Tony. **The Beginning Bowhunter.** (Illus.). 128 p. 1985. ICS Books. pap. $9.95.

Maynard, Roger. **Advanced Bowhunting Guide.** (Illus.). 224 p. 1984. Stoeger Pub. Co. pap. $14.95.

Schuh, Dwight. **Hunting Open Country Mule Deer.** 1986. Stoneydale Press Pub. pap. $12.95.

—**Bowhunter's Encyclopedia: Practical, Easy-to-Find Answers to Your Bowhunting Questions.** (Illus.). 576 p. 1987. Stackpole. $39.95.

Smyth, John & Barwick, Humphrey. **Bow vs. Gun.** 1976. Reprint. Charles River Books. $15.00

Thayer, Dixon. **Bow Hunting Basics: Fundamentals for Successful Hunting.** (Illus.). 32 p. 1985. Blue Sky. pap. $2.95.

Wise, Larry. **Tuning Your Compound Bow.** Helgeland, Glenn, ed. (Illus.). 132 p. 1985. Target Comm. pap. $6.95.

Wise, Larry, et al. **Tuning Your Broadheads.** (Illus.). 100 p. 1988. Target Comm. pap. $8.95.

Wood, William. **The Bowman's Glory, or, Archery Revived.** 1976. Charles River Books. $7.50.

BOWHUNTING (see Bow and Arrow)

CARTRIDGES

Barnes, Frank C. **Cartridges of the World,** 6th ed. (Illus.). 416 p. 1989. DBI. pap. $18.95.*

Bartlett, W. A. & Gallatin, D. B. **B and G Cartridge Manual,** Pioneer Press. $2.00.

Datig, Fred A. **Cartridges for Collectors,** 3 vols. Borden, $10.95 ea.

Donnelly, John J. **Handloader's Manual of Cartridge Conversions.** (Illus.) 1056 p. 1987. Stoeger Pub. Co. pap. $29.95; spiral bound $44.95; hardcover $49.95.

Keith, Elmer. **Sixgun Cartridges & Loads.** 1985. Repr. of 1936 ed. Gun Room. $19.95.

Manual of Pistol & Revolver Cartridges. 2 vols. 1987. Gordon Press. lib. bdg. $79.75.

Matthews, Charles. **Shoot Better With Centerfire Rifle Cartridges-Ballistics Tables.** (Illus.). 560 p. 1984. Matthews Inc. pap. $16.45.

Nonte, George. **The Home Guide to Cartridge Conversions.** rev. ed. Gun Room Press. $19.95.

Suydam, Charles R. **American Cartridge.** Borden. $12.95.

Thomas, Gough. **Shotguns and Cartridges for Game and Clays.** 3rd ed. (Illus.). 1976. Transatlantic Arts, Inc. $25.00.

COLLECTING (see Firearms—Collectors and Collecting)

COLT REVOLVERS

Bady, Donald B. **Colt Automatic Pistols,** rev. ed. 1973. Borden. $19.95.

Cochran, Keith. **Colt Peacemaker Ready-Reference Handbook.** (Illus.) 76 p. 1985. Cochran Pub. pap. $12.95.

—**Colt Peacemaker Encyclopedia.** (Illus.). 434 p. 1986. Cochran Pub. $59.95.

—**Colt Peacemaker Yearly Variations.** (Illus.). 96 p. 1987. Cochran Pub. $17.95. pap. $12.95.

—**Colt Peacemaker British Model.** (Illus.). 160 p. 1989. Cochran Pub. $35.00.*

The Colt .45 Exotic Weapons System. (Illus.). 88 p. 1984. Paladin Pr. pap. $15.00.

Graham, Ron, et al. **A Study of the Colt Single Action Army Revolver.** (Illus.) 523 p. 1985. Repr. of 1976 ed. Kopec Pubns. $69.95.

Shumaker, P. L. **Colt's Variations of the Old Model Pocket Pistol.** 1957. Borden. $10.95.

Whittington, Robert D. III. **The Colt Whitneyville-Walker Pistol.** (Illus.). 96 p. 1984. Brownlee Books. $20.00.

CROSSBOWS (see also Bow & Arrow)

Benson, Ragnar. **Bull's-Eye Crossbows by Ragnar Benson.** (Illus.). 96 p. 1985. Paladin Press. pap. $10.00.

Combs, Roger, ed. **Crossbows.** (Illus.). 192 p. 1987. DBI. $12.95.

Payne-Gallwey, Ralph. **Cross-Bow, Medieval and Modern.** Saifer, Albert, Pub. pap. $35.00.
Wilbur, C. Martin. **History of the Crossbow.** (Illus.). Repr. of 1936 ed. pap. Shorey. $2.95.

DECOYS (see also Duck Shooting)
Art, Brad & Kimball, Scott. **The Fish Decoy,** vol. II. 192 p. 1987. Aardvark WL. $60.00.
Barber, Joel. **Wild Fowl Decoys.** (Illus.). pap. Dover. $8.95.
Berkey, Barry R., et al. **Pioneer Decoy Carvers: A Biography of Lemuel and Stephen Ward.** (Illus.). 1977. Tidewater. $17.50.
Bridenhagen, Keith. **Decoy Pattern Book.** (Illus.). 224 p. (Orig.). 1984. Sterling. pap. $10.95.
—**Realistic Decoys.** 224 p. 1985. Stoeger Pub. Co. pap. $14.95.
Bridenhagen, Keith & Spielman, Patrick. **Realistic Decoys: Carving, Texturing, Painting & Finishing.** (Illus.). 224 p. (Orig.). 1985. Sterling. pap. $15.95.
Carpenter, Pearl E. **The Duck Book One & Two: Basics for Painting Wood-Carved Ducks & Birds.** (Illus.) 1984. Shades Mother Nature wkbk. $12.75.
Chapell, Carl & Sullivan, Clark. **Wildlife Woodcarvers: A Complete How-to-do-it Book for Carving & Painting Wildfowl.** (Illus.) 216 p. 1986. Stackpole. $39.95.
Chitwood, Henry C., et al. **Connecticut Decoys.** (Illus.). 256 p. 1987. Schiffer. $45.00.
Connett, Eugene. **Duck Decoys.** 1980. Durrell. $12.50.
Coykendall, Ralf, Sr. **Duck Decoys & How To Rig Them.** Coykendall, Ralf, Jr., ed. (Illus.). 135 p. 1987. New Century. pap. $14.95.
Delph, John and Delph, Shirley. **Factory Decoys of Mason, Stevens, Dodge & Peterson.** 168 p. (Illus.). Schiffer. $35.00.
Earnest, Adele. **The Art of the Decoy: American Bird Carvings.** (Illus.). 1982. pap. Schiffer. $14.95.
Frank, Chas. W., Jr. **Wetland Heritage: The Louisiana Duck Decoy.** 192 p. 1985. Pelican. $49.95.
Hillman, Anthony. **Carving Famous Antique Bird Decoys: Patterns & Instructions for Reproducing 16 Masterpieces from Shelburne Museum.** 72 p. 1988. Dover. pap. $5.95.
—**Carving Classic Swan & Goose Decoys.** 72 p. 1987. Dover. pap. $5.95.
—**Miniature Duck Decoys for Woodcarvers.** 40 p. 1985. Dover. $4.95.
—**Painting Duck Decoys: 24 Full-Color Plates.** 56 p. 1985. Dover. pap. $4.95.
—**Painting Shorebird Decoys.** (Illus.). 40 p. 1987. Dover. pap. $4.95.
Johnsgard, Paul A. ed. **The Bird Decoy: An American Art Form.** (Illus.). 1976. University of Nebraska Press. $17.95.
Luckey, Carl F. **Collecting Antique American Bird Decoys: An Identification and Value Guide.** (Illus.). 208 p. 1983. pap. Books Americana. $14.95.
Parmalee, Paul W. & Loomis, Forrest D. **Decoys and Decoy Carvers of Illinois.** 1969. pap. Northern Illinois University Press. $25.00.
Reiger, George. **Floaters & Stick-Ups.** 208 p. 1986. Godine. $45.00.
Schroeder, Roger. **How To Carve Wildfowl: Nine North American Masters Reveal the Carving and Painting Techniques That Win Them International Blue Ribbons.** 256 p. 1984. Stackpole. $39.95.
Shourds, Harry V. & Hillman, Anthony. **Carving Duck Decoys.** 1981. pap. Dover. $5.95.
—**Carving & Painting Duck Decoys** (2 vols.). 126 p. 1985. Dover. pap. $10.90 (set).
Spielman, Patrick. **Making Wood Decoys.** 1982. Sterling. pap. $9.95.
Veasey, William. **Head Patterns.** (Illus.). 58 p. 1983. pap. Schiffer. $14.95.
—**Making Hunting Decoys.** (Illus.). 256 p. 1986. Schiffer. $45.00.
—**Miniature Decoy Patterns.** (Illus.). 58 p. 1983. pap. $14.95.
Veasey, William & Hull, Cary S. **Waterfowl Carving: Blue Ribbon Techniques.** (Illus.). 1982. Schiffer. $35.00.

Walsh, Clune, Jr. & Jackson, Lowell G., eds. **Waterfowl Decoys of Michigan and the Lake St. Clair Region.** (Illus.). 175 p. 1983. Gale. $65.00.

DEER HUNTING (see also Hunting)
Adams, Chuck. **Complete Guide to Bowhunting Deer.** 256 p. 1984. pap. DBI. $13.95.
Bowring, Dave. **Bowhunting for Whitetails: Your Best Methods for Taking North America's Favorite Deer.** (Illus.). 304 p. 1985. Stackpole. $24.95.
Cameron, Donald. **Among The Red Deer: The Stalking Portfolio of Henry Hope Creslock.** 1985. State Mutual Bks. $300.00.
Chalmers, Patrick R. **Deer-Stalking.** 256 p. 1985. State Mutual Bks. $60.00.
Conway, Bryant W. **Successful Hints on Hunting White Tail Deer.** 2nd ed. 1967. pap. Claitors. $3.98.
Cunningham, Marci. **The Deerhunter's Guide to Success: From the Woods to the Skillet.** 1985. Backwoods Bks. $3.50.
Dalrymple, Bryon W. **The Complete Book of Deer Hunting.** 256 p. pap. Stoeger. $9.95.
—**Deer Hunting with Dalrymple: A Lifetime of Lore on The Whitetail and Mule Deer.** 256 p. 1983. pap. Arco. $7.95.
Deer Hunter's Guide. (Illus.). 160 p. Nat'l Rifle Assn. $4.95.
Elman, Robert, ed. **All About Deer Hunting in America.** 1976. New Century. $16.95.
Guide to Deer Hunting in the Catskill Mountains. pap. Outdoor Pubns. $2.00.
Hayes, Tom. **How to Hunt the White Tail Deer.** A. S. Barnes, rev. ed. pap. $6.95.
Horner, Kent. **Art & Science of Whitetail Hunting: How to Interpret the Facts & Find the Deer.** (Illus.) 192 p. 1986. Stackpole. pap. $11.95.
Lapinski, Mike. **Whitetail Deer Hunting.** (Illus.). 64 p. 1988. Stoneydale Press. pap. $3.50.
Laycock, George. **Deer Hunter's Bible.** rev. ed. (Illus.). 1986. pap. Doubleday. $7.95.
Moody, Warren G. **Hunting Deer: Long Range, Short Range—One Point of Aim to 350 Yards.** (Illus.). 88 p. 1989. Pioneer A. C. pap. $6.95.*
Nelson, Norm. **Mule Deer: How To Bring Home North America's Big Deer of the West.** (Illus.). 208 p. 1987. Stackpole. $16.95.
Ozoga, John J. **Whitetail Country.** Petrie, Chuck, ed. (Illus.). 157 p. 1988. Willow Creek Press. $39.00.
Patridge, Ray. **The Deer Hunter Log Book.** 36 p. 1984. Bootstrap Pubns. softcover $6.95.
Peterson, B. R. **Buck Peterson's Guide to Deer Hunting.** (Illus.). 132 p. 1989. Ten Speed Press. pap. $6.95.*
Sell, Francis E. **Art of Successful Deer Hunting.** 1980. pap. Willow Creek. $5.95.
Sisley, Nick. **Deer Hunting Across North America.** (Illus.). 1975. Freshet Press. $12.95.
Smith, Richard P. **Deer Hunting.** rev. ed. (Illus.). 1981. pap. Stackpole Books. $10.95.
VanDyke, Theodore S. **The Still-Hunter.** (Illus.). 390 p. 1989. Repr. of 1882 ed. Gunnerman Press. $21.95.*
Wegner, Robert. **Deer & Deer Hunting: The Serious Hunter's Guide.** 324 p. 1984. Stackpole. $24.95.
—**Deer & Deer Hunting.** Book 2. (Illus.). 400 p. 1987. Stackpole. $29.95.
Wolff, Ed. **Taking Big Bucks: Solving the Whitetail Riddle.** (Illus.). 176 p. 1987. Stoneydale Pr. Pub. pap. $12.95.
Wooters, John. **Hunting Trophy Deer.** rev. ed. (Illus.). 265 p. 1983. pap. New Century. $13.95.
Zumbo, Jim & Elman, Robert. **All-American Deer Hunter's Guide.** (Illus.) 320 p. 1983. New Century. $29.95.

DUCK & GEESE SHOOTING (see also Decoys)
Cadieux, Charles L. **Successful Goose Hunting.** (Illus.) 240 p. 1986. Stone Wall Press. $24.95.
Hinman, Bob. **The Duck Hunter's Handbook.** (Illus.). 1976. softbound. Stoeger. $9.95.
McGrath, Brian J. **Duck Calls & Other Game Calls.** (Illus.). 1988. Thos. B. Reel. $40.00.
MacQuarrie, Gordon. **The Last Stories of the Old Duck Hunters.** (Illus.). 204 p. 1985. Willow Creek. $17.50.

—**Stories of the Old Duck Hunters & Other Drivel.** repr. of 1967 ed. Willow Creek. $17.50.
Milner, Robert, **Retriever Training for the Duck Hunter.** (Illus.) 150 p. 1985. Repr. of 1983 ed. Junction Press. $18.95.
Smith, Steve. **Hunting Ducks & Geese: Hard Facts, Good Bets and Serious Advice From a Duck Hunter You Can Trust.** 160 p. 1984. Stackpole. $14.95.

FALCONRY (see also Fowling)
Beebe, Frank L. **A Falconry Manual.** (Illus.). 128 p. 1983. pap. Hancock House. $12.95.
Bert, Edmund. **An Approved Treatise of Hawkes and Hawking Divided into Three Bookes.** 1968. Repr. of 1619 ed. W. J. Johnson. $45.00.
Fisher, Charles H. **Falconry Reminiscences.** 1972. Falcon Head Press. $15.00; deluxe ed. $45.00.
Fox, David G. **Garden of Eagles: The Life & Times of a Falconer.** (Illus.). 216 p. 1984. Merrimack Pub. Cir. $16.95.
Frederick II of Hohenstaufen. **The Art of Falconry.** Wood, Casey A. & Fyfe, F. Marjorie, eds. (Illus.). 1943. Stanford University Press. $60.00.
Freeman, Gage E. & Salvin, Francis H. **Falconry: Its Claims, History and Practice.** 1972. Falcon Head Press. $25.00.
Gryndall, William. **Hawking, Hunting, Fouling and Fishing;** Newly Corrected by W. Gryndall Faulkener. 1972. Repr. of 1596 ed. Walter J. Johnson, Inc. $25.00.
Harting, James E. **Bibliotheca Accipitraria, a Catalogue of Books Ancient and Modern Relating to Falconry.** 1977. Repr. of 1963 ed. Oak Knoll Books. $45.00.
Jameson, E. W. Jr. & Peeters, Hans J. **Introduction to Hawking.** 2nd ed. (Illus.). 1977. pap. E. W. Jameson, Jr. $8.95.
Latham, Simon. **Lathams Falconry, 2 pts.** 1977. Repr. of 1615 ed. Walter J. Johnson, Inc. $32.50.
Madden, D. H. **Chapter of Medieval History.** 1969. Repr. of 1924 ed. Kennikat. lib. bdg. $55.00.
Mellor, J. E. **Falconry Notes by Mellor.** 1972. Falcon Head Press. $15.00.
Mitchell, E. B. **Art & Practice of Falconry.** (Illus.). 303 p. Saifer. $25.00.
O'Brien, Dan. **Rites of Autumn: A Falconer's Journey Across the American West.** 1988. Atlantic Monthly. $17.95.
Phillott, D. C. & Harcourt, E. S., trs. from Persian Urdu. **Falconry—Two Treatises.** 1968. text ed. Falcon Head Press. $45.00.
Rowley, Sam R. **Discovering Falconry: A Comprehensive Guide to Contemporary Falconry.** (Illus.). 160 p. 1985. New Dawn. pap. $11.95.
Samson, Jack. **Modern Falconry: Your Illustrated Guide To The Art & Sport of Hunting With North American Hawks.** 160 p. 1984. Stackpole. pap. $13.95.
Schlegel, H. & Verster De Wulverhorst, J. A. **The World of Falconry.** 1980. Vendome Press. $60.00.
Schlegel, H. & Wulverhorst, A. H. **Traite De Fauconnerie: Treatise of Falconry.** Hanlon, Thomas, tr. (Illus.). 1973. Chasse Pubns. $32.50.

FIREARMS (see also Arms and Armor, Pistols, Revolvers, Rifles, Shotguns)
Askins, Charles. **Askins on Pistols and Revolvers.** Bryant, Ted & Askins, Bill. eds., 1980. National Rifle Association, $25.00; pap. $8.95.
Bartone, John C. **Firearms & Gunshot Wounds: Index of Modern Information.** 150 p. 1988. ABBE Pubs. Assn. pap. $26.50.
Barwick, Humphrey. **Concerning the Force and Effect of Manual Weapons of Fire.** 1974. Repr. of 1594 ed. W. J. Johnson. $20.00.
Berger, Robert J. **Know Your Broomhandle Mausers.** (Illus.). 96 p. 1985. Blacksmith Corp. pap. $6.95.
Bodio, Stephen. **Good Guns.** 128 p. 1986. N. Lyons Bks. $14.95.
Bridges, Toby. **Advanced Muzzleloader's Guide.** 256 p. 1985. Stoeger Pub. Co. pap. $11.95.
Brown, Ronald. **Homemade Guns & Homemade Ammo.** 191 p. 1986. Loompanics. pap. text ed. $12.95.

Browne, Bellmore H. **Guns and Gunning.** (Illus.). Repr. of 1908 ed. pap. Shorey. $4.95.

Cameron, Frank. **Micro Guns.** (Illus.). 48 p. 1982. Mosaic Press, OH. $24.00.

Clapp, Wiley M. **Handguns, 1989.** (Illus.). 224 p. 1988. DBI. pap. $12.95.

Clede, Bill. **Police Handgun Manual: How To Get Street-Smart Survival Habits.** (Illus.). 128 p. Stackpole. $13.95.

Cromwell, Giles. **The Virginia Manufactory of Arms.** 1975. University Press of Virginia. $20.00.

Davis, John E. **Introduction to Tool Marks, Firearms and the Striagraph.** (Illus.). 1958. C. C. Thomas. $31.25.

Donnelly, John. **Handloader's Manual of Cartridge Conversions.** (Illus.). 1056 p. 1987. Stoeger Pub. $49.95. sp. bd. $44.95. pap. $29.95.

Edsall, James. **Volcanic Firearms and Their Successors.** Pioneer Press. $2.50.

Erickson, Wayne R. & Pate, Charles E. **The Broomhandle Pistol: 1896-1936.** 300 p. E&P Enter. $49.95.

Ezell, Edward C. **Handguns of the World.** (Illus.). 1981. Stackpole Books, $39.95.

—**Small Arms Today: Latest Reports on the World's Weapons & Ammunition.** 256 p. (Orig.). 1984. pap. Stackpole. $16.95.

Farnum, John. **The Street Smart Gun Book.** Police Bookshelf. pap. $11.95.

Fjestad, Steven P. **Blue Book of Gun Values.** 9th ed. 704 p. 1988. Investment Rarities. pap. $17.50.

Flayderman, Norm. **Flayderman's Guide to Antique American Firearms & Their Values,** 4th ed. (Illus.). 624 p. 1987. DBI. pap. $23.95.

Flores, Eliezer, ed. **How To Make Disposable Silencers,** Vol. II. (Illus.). 120 p. 1985. J.O. Flores. pap. $12.00.

Flynn, George & Gottlieb, Alan. **Guns for Women: The Complete Handgun Buying Guide for Women.** 108 p. 1988. Merril Pr. pap. $9.95.

Galan, J. I. **Air Guns Digest,** 2d ed. (Illus.). 256 p. 1988. DBI. pap. $12.95.

Gates, Elgin. **Gun Digest Book of Metallic Silhouette Shooting.** 2d ed. (Illus.). 256 p. 1988. DBI. pap. $12.95.

George, John N. **English Pistols and Revolvers.** Albert Saifer, Pub. $20.00.

Grennell, Dean A. **ABC's of Reloading.** 4th ed. (Illus.). 1988. pap. DBI Books. $14.95.

—**Gun Digest Book of 9MM Handguns.** 256 p. 1986. DBI. pap. $13.95.

—**Handgun Digest.** (Illus.). 256 p. 1987. DBI. pap. $13.95.

Grennell, Dean & Clapp, Wiley M. **Gun Digest Book of Handgun Reloading.** (Illus.). 256 p. 1987. DBI. pap. $13.95.

Gresham, Grits. **Grits on Guns.** (Illus.). 352 p. 1988. Cane River AK. $25.00.

Hacker, Larry. **The Colt Single Action Army.** 1989. Pioneer Press, $4.00.*

Gun Digest 1990. 44th ed. (Illus.). DBI. pap. $17.95.

Hamilton, T. M. **Early Indian Trade Guns: 1625–1775.** (Contributions of the Museum of the Great Plains Ser.: No. 3). (Illus.). 1968. pap. Museum of the Great Plains Pubns. Dept. pap. $6.95.

Hatcher. **The Book of the Garand.** Gun Room Press. $17.95.

Hatcher, Julian S. **Hatcher's Notebook.** rev. ed. (Illus.). 1962. Stackpole Books. $24.95.

Hoffschmidt, Edward J. **Know Your Gun,** Incl. **Know Your .45 Auto Pistols; Know Your Walther P. .38 Pistols; Know Your Walther P. P. and P. P. K. Pistols; Know Your M1 Garand Rifles; Know Your Mauser Broomhandle Pistol.** 1976. Borden pap. $6.95. ea.

Hogg, Brig., fwrd. by. **The Compleat Gunner.** (Illus.). 1976. Repr. Charles River Books. $10.50.

Hogg, Ian V. ed. **Jane's Infantry Weapons 1988–89.** (Illus.). 800 p. 1988. Janes Info Group. $165.00.*

Home Workshop Silencers 1. 1980. pap. Paladin Enterprises. $12.00.

Huebner, Siegfried. **Silencers for Hand Firearms.** Schreier, Konrad & Lund, Peter C., eds. 1976. pap. Paladin Enterprises. $13.95.

Huntington, R. T. **Hall's Breechloaders: John H. Hall's Invention and Development of a Breechloading Rifle with Precision-Made Interchangeable Parts, and Its Introduction Into the United States Service.** (Illus.). 1972. pap. George Shumway Publisher. $22.50.

James, Edsall. **The Story of Firearm Ignition.** Pioneer Press. $3.50.

Kelly, Palo. **An American Tradition: Handguns.** (Illus.). 250 p. 1986. Tarantula Press. pap. $9.95.

Kelvin, Martin Dr. **Collecting Antique Firearms.** (Illus.). 224 p. 1988. David & Charles. $55.00.

Kennedy, Monty. **Checkering and Carving of Gunstocks.** rev. ed. (Illus.). 1952. Stackpole Books. $29.95.

King, Peter. **The Shooting Field: One Hundred Fifty Years with Holland & Holland.** (Illus.). 176 p. 1985. Blacksmith. $39.95.

Kukla, Robert J. **Gun Control.** 449 p. Nat'l Rifle Assn. pap. $4.95.

Lacy, John F. **The Remington 700: A History & User's Manual.** (Illus.). 200 p. 1989. J. F. Lacy (price not set).*

Larson, E. Dixon. **Remington Tips.** Pioneer Press. $4.95.

Lauber, George. **How to Build Your Own Flintlock Rifle or Pistol.** Seaton. Lionel tr. from Ger. (Illus.). 1976. pap. Jolex. $6.95.

—**How To Build Your Own Wheellock Rifle or Pistol.** Seaton, Lionel, tr. from Ger. (Illus.). 1976. pap. Jolex. $12.50.

—**How To Build Your Own Percussion Rifle or Pistol.** Seaton, Lionel transl. from German. Jolex. pap. $6.95.

Laycock, George. **Shotgunner's Bible.** (Illus.). 176 p. 1987. Doubleday. pap. $7.95.

Lewis, Jack. **Gun Digest Book of Modern Gun Values,** 6th ed. (Illus.). 448 p. 1987. DBI. pap. $15.95.

Lindsay, Merrill. **Twenty Great American Guns.** (Illus.). 1976. Repr. pap. Arma Press. $1.75.

Long, Duncan. **Automatics: Fast Firepower, Tactical Superiority.** (Illus.). 144 p. 1986. Paladin Pr. pap. text ed. $14.95.

—**Firearms for Survival.** (Illus.). 144 p. 1987. Paladin Press. pap. $16.95.

Matunas, Edward A. **Metallic Cartridge Reloading.** 2d ed. (Illus.). 320 p. 1988. DBI. pap. $15.95.

Miller, Martin. **Collector's Illustrated Guide to Firearms.** (Illus.). 1978. Mayflower Books. $24.95.

Murtz, Harold A. **Guns Illustrated.** 21st ed. (Illus.) 320 p. 1988. DBI. pap. $15.95.

Myatt, F. **An Illustrated Guide to Rifles and Automatic Weapons.** (Illus.). 1981. Arco. $9.95.

National Muzzle Loading Rifle Association. Muzzle Blasts: Early Years Plus Vol. I and II 1939–41. 1974. pap. George Shumway Publisher. $18.00.

Norton (R. W.) Art Gallery. **E. C. Prudhomme: Master Gun Engraver.** (Illus.). 1973. pap. Norton Art Gallery. $3.00.

NRA Gun Collectors Guide. 336 p. Nat'l Rifle Assn. $4.50.

Painter, Doug. **Hunting & Firearms Safety Primer.** 128 p. 1986. N. Lyons Bks. pap. $8.95.

Pollard, Hugh B. **The History of Firearms.** 1974. Burt Franklin, Pub. pap. $8.95.

Price, Robert M. **Firearms Self-Defense: An Introductory Guide.** (Illus.). 1986. Gordon Press. lib. bdg. $79.95.

Rees, Clair F. **Beginner's Guide to Guns & Shooting,** rev. ed. 224 p. 1988. DBI. pap. $12.95.

Reese, Michael, II. **Nineteen Hundred Luger—U.S. Test Trials.** 2nd rev. ed. Pioneer Press, ed. (Illus.). Pioneer Press. pap. $4.95.

Reilly, Robert M. **United States Military Small Arms, 1816–1865.** 1983. Gun Room. $35.00.

Riling, Ray. **Guns and Shooting: A Bibliography.** (Illus.). 1981. Ray Riling. $75.00.

Riviere, Bill & Elman, Robert. **Gunner's Bible.** 3d rev. ed. (Illus.). 192 p. 1985. Doubleday. pap. $7.95.

The Ruger Pistol Exotic Weapons System. (Illus.). 96 p. (Orig.). 1984. pap. Paladin Pr. $15.00.

Rutherford, Ken. **Collecting Shotgun Cartridges.** (Illus.). 126 p. 1988. David & Charles. $45.00.

Saxon, K. **The Poor Man's James Bond Homemade Poisons, Explosives, Improvised Firearms, Pyrotechny.** 1986. Atlantic Formularies. $17.00.

Sharpe, Phil. **Complete Guide to Handloading.** 230 p. 1988. Repr. of 1949 ed. Wolfe Pub. Co. $60.00.

Shelsby, Earl, ed. **NRA Gunsmithing Guide:** Updated rev. ed. (Illus.). 336 p. (Orig.). 1980. pap. Nat'l Rifle Assn. $11.95.

Shooter's Bible 1991, Vol. 82. (Illus.). 576 p. 1990. Stoeger Pub. Co. $17.95.*

Shooter's Bible 1990. Vol. 81. (Illus.). 576 p. 1989. Stoeger Pub. Co. $16.95.

Smythe, John & Barwick, Humphrey. **Bow vs. Gun.** 1976. Repr. Charles River Books. $15.00.

Spearing, G. W. **The Craft of the Gunsmith.** (Illus.). 128 p. 1989. Sterling. pap. $8.95.*

Steindler, R. A. **Reloader's Guide.** (Illus.). 3rd ed. 1975. softbound. Stoeger. $11.95.

Steiner, Bradley. **The Death Dealer's Manual.** (Illus.). 120 p. 1982. pap. Paladin Press. $12.00.

Stockbridge, V. D. **Digest of U.S. Patents Relating to Breech-loading & Magazine Small Arms, 1836–1873.** (Illus.). 1963. N. Flayderman & Co. $12.50.

Sybertz, Gustav. **Technical Dictionary for Weaponry.** (Ger.-Eng.). 1969. French & European Pubns. Inc. pap. $24.95.

Taylor, Chuck. **The Combat Shotgun & Submachine Gun: A Special Weapons Analysis.** 176 p. 1985. Paladin Pr. pap. $16.95.

Thomas, Donald G. **Complete Book of Thompson Patents.** 1985. Gun Room. pap. $15.95.

Thompson, Leroy & Smeets, Rene. **Great Combat Handguns.** (Illus.). 224 p. 1987. Sterling. $29.95.

Thompson Submachine Gun. 1986. Gordon Press. lib. bdg. $79.95.

Traister, John E. **How To Buy and Sell Used Guns.** (Illus.). 1982. softbound. Stoeger. $10.95.

—**Gunsmithing at Home.** (Illus.). 256 p. pap. (Orig.). 1985. Stoeger. $14.95.

—**Professional Care & Finishing of Gun Stocks.** (Illus.). 208 p. 1985. TAB Bks. pap. $15.95.

Trzoniec, Stanley. **Handloader's Guide.** 256 p. 1985. Stoeger Pub. Co. pap. $12.95.

Van Rensselaer, S. **American Firearms.** (Illus.). 1948. pap. American Life Foundation. pap. $15.00.

Waite, Malden & Ernst, Bernard. **Trapdoor Springfield.** 1985. Gun Room. $29.95.

Walsh, J. H. **The Modern Sportsman's Gun & Rifle.** Vol I & II. (Illus.). 536 p. 1986. Wolfe Pub. Co. Price on request.

Walter, John. **The Luger Book.** (Illus.). 288 p. 1987. Sterling. $45.00.

Warner, Ken, ed. **Handloader's Digest.** 11th ed. 1987. DBI Books. $16.95.

Walsh, J. H. **The Modern Sportsman's Gun & Rifle,** Vols. I & II. (Illus.). 536 p. 1986. Wolfe Pub. Co. (write for price info).

West, Bill. **Winchester Encyclopedia.** (Illus.). B. West. $15.00.

—**Winchester Lever-Action Handbook.** (Illus.). B. West. $25.00.

—**The Winchester Single Shot.** (Illus.). B. West. $19.00.

—**Winchesters, Cartridges, & History.** (Illus.). B. West. $42.00.

Williams, John J. **Survival Guns and Ammo.** (Illus.). 1979. pap. Consumertronics. pap. $15.00.

Williams, Mason. **The Law Enforcement Book of Weapons, Ammunition & Training Procedures: Handguns, Rifles and Shotguns.** (Illus.). 1977. C. C. Thomas. $67.50.

Wirnsberger, Gerhard. **Standard Directory of Proof Marks.** Steindler, R. A. tr. from Ger. (Illus.). 1976. pap. Jolex. $9.95.

Withers, John. **Precision Handloading.** 224 p. 1985. Stoeger Pub. Co. pap. $12.95.

Wood, J. B. **Gun Digest Book of Firearm Assembly-Disassembly: Law Enforcement Weapons, Pt. VI** (Illus.). 1981. pap. DBI Books. $13.95.

Zellman, Aaron & Neuens, Michael L. **Consumer's Guide to Handguns.** (Illus.). 208 p. 1986. Stackpole. pap. $16.95.

Zhuk, A. B. **Revolvers & Pistols.** 304 p. 1987. State Mutual Bks. $40.00.

FIREARMS—CATALOGS

Barnes, Frank L. **Cartridges of the World,** 5th ed. (Illus.). 416 p. 1985. DBI. pap. $18.95.

Grennell, Dean A. **Gun Digest Book of the 45.** (Illus.). 256 p. 1989. DBI. pap. $14.95.*

Hoxie Bullet Catalog. Pioneer Press. $0.75.

Murtz, Harold A. **Guns Illustrated. 1990.** 22d ed. 320 p. 1989. DBI. pap. $15.95.*

Remington Gun Catalog 1877. Pioneer Press. $1.50.

Sears & Roebuck c1910 Ammunition Catalog. (Illus.). pap. Sand Pond. $2.00.

Tarassuk, Leonid, ed. **Antique European and American Firearms at the Hermitage Museum.** (Illus., Eng. & Rus.). 1976. Arma Press. ltd. ed. $40.00.

Tinkham, Sandra S., ed. **Catalog of Tools, Hardware, Firearms, and Vehicles.** 1979. Chadwyck-Healey. pap. $40.00.

United States Cartridge Co.-Lowell, Mass. 1891 Catalog. (Illus.). Sand Pond. $3.50.

Wahl, Paul. **Gun Trader's Guide,** 13th ed. 464 p. 1989. Stoeger Pub. Co. pap. $14.95.

Walmer, Max, et al, eds. **The Illustrated Directory of Modern American Weapons.** (Illus.). 480 p. 1986. P-H. pap. $14.95.

West, Bill. **Remington Arms Catalogues, 1877–1899.** 1st ed. (Illus.). 1971. B. West. $10.00.

Winchester Shotshell Catalog 1897. (Illus.). pap. Sand Pond. $1.50.

FIREARMS—COLLECTORS AND COLLECTING

Chapel, Charles E. **The Gun Collector's Handbook of Values.** 1984. Putnam Pub. Gp. pap. $11.95.

Dicarpegna, N. **Firearms in the Princes Odescalchi Collection in Rome.** (Illus.). 1976. Repr. of 1969 ed. Arma Press. $20.00.

Dixie Gun Works Antique Arms Catalog. Pioneer Press. $2.00.

Flayderman, Norm. **Flayderman's Guide to Antique American Firearms and Their Values.** 4th ed. (Illus.). 1987. pap. DBI Books. $23.95.

Gopstein, Herbert. **Gunbook Priceguide—Bibliography.** 160 p. 1989. Bert Pubn. $25.00.*

Gusler, Wallace B. & Lavin, James D. **Decorated Firearms 1540–1870, from the Collection of Clay P. Bedford.** 242 p. 1977. University Press of Virginia. $29.50.

Koenig, Klaus-Peter & Hugo, Martin. **Service Handguns: A Collector's Guide.** (Illus.). 264 p. 1989. David & Charles. $45.00 *

Lewis, Jack, ed. **Gun Digest Book of Modern Gun Values.** 7th ed. (Illus.). 496 p. 1989. DBI. pap. $17.95.*

Madaus, H. Michael. **The Warner Collector's Guide to American Long Arms.** 1981. pap. Warner Books. $9.95.

Quertermous, Russel & Quertermous, Steve. **Modern Guns, Identification and Values.** 7th ed. 1988. pap. Collector Books., $12.95.

Schroeder, Joseph J., ed. **Gun Collector's Digest.** 5th ed. (Illus.). 224 p. 1989. DBI. pap. $14.95.

Serven, James. **Rare and Valuable Antique Arms.** 1976. Pioneer Press. $4.95.

Shumaker, P. L. **Colt's Variations of the Old Model Pocket Pistol.** 1957. Borden. $10.95.

Stevenson, Jan. **Modern Sporting Guns.** 1988. Doubleday. $19.95.

Traister, John E. **How To Buy and Sell Used Guns.** (Illus.). 1982. softbound. Stoeger. $10.95.

—**Antique Guns: The Collector's Guide.** (Illus.). 288 p. 1989. Stoeger Pub. Co. pap. $16.95.*

Wahl, Paul. **Gun Trader's Guide.** 13th ed. (Illus.). Stoeger. $14.95.

Wilson, R. L. **Colt—Christie's Rare and Historic Firearms Auction Catalogue.** (Illus.). 1981. Arma Press. $25.00.

FIREARMS—HISTORY

Ayalon, David. **Gunpowder and Firearms in the Mamluk Kingdom: A Challenge to Medieval Society.** 2nd ed. 1978. Biblio Distribution Centre. $25.00.

Barnes, Duncan. **History of Winchester Firearms 1866–1980.** 5th ed. rev. (Illus.). 256 p. New Century. $18.95.

Batchelor, John & Walter, John. **Handgun: From Matchlock to Laser-Sited Weapon.** (Illus.). 160 p. 1988. Sterling. $19.95.

Blanch, H. J. A. **A Century of Guns: A Sketch of the Leading Types of Sporting and Military Small Arms.** (Illus.). 1977. Repr. of 1909 ed. Charles River Books. $25.00.

Brown, M. L. **Firearms in Colonial America: The Impact of History and Technology 1492–1792.** 1980. Smithsonian Institution Press. $55.00.

Buchele, W. & Shumway, G. **Recreating the American Long Rifle.** 4th ed. 175 p. 1988. George Shumway Publisher. pap. $20.00.

Fuller, Claude E. **Breech-Loader in the Service 1816–1917.** (Illus.). 1965. Flayderman, N. & Co. $14.50.

Garavaglia, Louis A. & Worman, Charles G. **Firearms of the American West, 1803–1865.** (Illus.). 1984. U of NM Press. $35.00.

—**Firearms of the American West,** 1866–1895. (Illus.). 423 p. 1985. U. of NM Press. $40.00.

Gusler, Wallace B. & Lavin, James D. **Decorated Firearms, 1540–1870 from the Collection of Clay P. Bedford.** 1977. (Colonial Williamburg Foundation). University Press of Virginia. $29.50.

Hackley, F. W. et al. **History of Modern U.S. Military Small Arms Ammunition: Vol. 2, 1940–1945.** Gun Room Press. $35.00.

Hamilton, T. M. ed. **Indian Trade Guns.** 1983. Pioneer Press. $10.95.

Helmer, William J. **The Gun That Made the Twenties Roar.** Gun Room Press. $17.95.

Hetrick, Calvin. **The Bedford County Rifle and Its Makers.** (Illus.). 1975. pap. George Shumway Publisher. (OP). pap. $7.50.

Holme, N. & Kirby, E. L. **Medal Rolls: Twenty-Third Foot Royal Welch Fusiliers, Napoleonic Period.** 1979. S. J. Durst. $45.00.

Hutslar, Donald A. **Gunsmiths of Ohio: 18th and 19th Centuries.** Vol. I. (Illus.). Shumway Publisher. $40.00.

Kennett, Lee & Anderson, James L. **The Gun in America: The Origins of a National Dilemma.** (Illus., Orig). 1975. Greenwood Press. lib. bdg. $38.95.

Lindsay, Merrill. **The New England Gun: The First 200 Years.** (Illus.). 1976. Arma Press. pap. $12.50.

Meadows, Edward S. **U.S. Military Holsters & Pistol Cartridge Boxes.** (Illus.). 432 p. 1987. Ordnance Pubns $45.00.

Nonte, George C., Jr. **Black Powder Guide.** 2nd ed. (Illus.). pap. Stoeger, $11.95.

North & North. **Simeon North: First Official Pistol Maker of the United States.** Repr. Gun Room Press. $12.95.

Peterson, Harold. **Historical Treasury of American Guns.** Benjamin Co. pap. $2.95.

Pollard, Hugh B. **History of Firearms.** (Illus.). 1974. B. Franklin. $29.50; pap. $8.95.

Reese, Michael II. **Nineteen-hundred Luger-U.S. Test Trials.** 2nd rev. ed. (Illus.). pap. Pioneer Press. $4.95.

Remington Arms & History, Vols. 1 and 2. B. West. $42.00 ea.

Rosebush, Waldo E. **American Firearms and the Changing Frontier.** 1962. pap. Eastern Washington State Historical Society. $4.50.

Sawyer, C. W. **Firearms in American History 1600–1800.** Repr. of 1886 ed. Saifer. $25.00.

Schreier, Konrad F., Jr. **Remington Rolling Block Firearms.** (Illus.). Pioneer Press. pap. $6.95.

Sellers, Frank M. **Sharps Firearms.** (Illus.). 1982. Sellers Pubns. $39.95.

Shelton, Lawrence P. **California Gunsmiths.** (Illus.). 302 p. 1977. George Shumway Publisher. casebound. $29.95.

Tonso, William R. **Gun & Society: The Social and Existential Roots of the American Attachment to Firearms.** 1982. U Press of America. pap. $16.75 lib bdg. $36.75.

Truby, J. David. **The Lewis Gun.** 2d ed. (Illus.). 216 p. 1988. Paladin Press. text ed. $25.00.

West, Bill. **Marlin and Ballard, Arms and History, 1861–1978.** (Illus.). 1978. B. West. $42.00.

—**Savage & Stevens, Arms and History, 1849–to date.** (Illus.). 1971. B. West. $60.00.

FIREARMS—IDENTIFICATION

Baer, Larry L. **The Parker Gun.** Gun Room. $29.95.

Brophy, Williams S. **The Krag Rifle.** Gun Room. $29.95.

—**L.C. Smith Shotguns.** Gun Room. $29.95.

Garton, George. **Colt's SAA Post-War Models.** Gun Room. $21.95.

Madaus, H. Michael. **The Warner Collector's Guide to American Long Arms.** 1981. Warner Books. pap. $9.95.

Nelson, Thomas B. & Lockhaven, Hans B. **The World's Submachine Guns: Developments from 1915 to 1963.** Vol. I rev. ed. 1985. TBN Ent. $29.95.

Ruth, Larry. **M-1 Carbine.** pap. Gun Room. $17.95.

Small Arms Training: Sten Machine Carbine, Vol. I. 1983. pap. Ide House $0.95.

Wilber, Charles G. **Ballistic Science for the Law Enforcement Officer.** (Illus.). 1977. C. C. Thomas. $40.75.

FIREARMS—INDUSTRY AND TRADE

Grancsay, Stephen V. & Lindsay, Merrill. **Illustrated British Firearms Patents 1718–1853.** limited ed. (Illus.). Arma Press. $75.00.

Hartzler, Daniel D. **Arms Makers of Maryland.** 1975. George Shumway Publisher. $40.00.

Kirkland, Turner. **Southern Derringers of the Mississippi Valley.** Pioneer Press. $2.00.

Noel-Baker, Phillip. **The Private Manufacture of Armaments.** 1971. pap. Dover. $7.95.

Russell, Carl P. **Guns on the Early Frontiers: A History of Firearms from Colonial Times through the Years of the Western Fur Trade.** 1980. University of Nebraska Press. $27.95.

Stiefel, Ludwig, ed. **Gun Propulsion Technology.** 500 p. 1988. AJAA. $79.00.

Stockholm International Peace Research Institute (SIPRI). **The Arms Trade Registers.** 1975. MIT Press. $29.50.

West, Bill. **Browning Arms and History, 1842–1973.** (Illus.). 1972. B. West. $42.00.

FIREARMS—LAWS AND REGULATIONS

Casey, Verna. **Gun Control: A Selected Bibliography.** 11 p. 1988. Vance Biblios. pap. $3.75.

Cook, Phillip J. & Lambert, Richard D., eds. **Gun Control.** 250 p. 1981. American Academy of Political and Social Science. pap. $8.95.

Garrison, William L. **Women's Views on Guns & Self-Defense.** 114 p. (Orig.). 1983. pap. Second Amend. $5.50.

Gottlieb, Alan. **The Rights of Gun Owners.** 216 p. 1986. Gordon Press. lib. bdg. $79.95.

—**Gun Rights Fact Book.** 168 p. 1988. Merril Pr. $3.95.

Halbrook, Stephen P. **A Right to Bear Arms: State & Federal Bills of Rights & Constitutional Guarantees.** 1989. Greenwood. Write for price info.*

Hardy, David T. **Origins & Development of the 2nd Amendment.** 96 p. 1986. Blacksmith Corp. $11.95.

Hill, J. B. **Weapons Law.** 96 p. 1989. Pergamon. pap. $17.95.*

Kates, Don B., ed. **Firearms & Violence: Issues of Public Policy.** 475 p. 1983. Pacific Inst. Pub. pap. $15.95.

Kennett, Lee & Anderson, James L. **The Gun in America.** (Illus.). 1975. text ed. pap. Greenwood Press. lib. bdg. $38.95.

Krema, Vaclav. **Identification and Registration of Firearms.** (Illus.). 1971. C. C. Thomas. $28.00.

Kruschke, Earl R. **The Right To Keep and Bear Arms.** 230 p. 1985. C.C. Thomas. $29.75.

Kukla, Robert J. **Gun Control: A Written Record of Efforts to Eliminate the Private Possession of Firearms in America.** Orig. Title: Other Side of Gun Control. 1973. Stackpole Books. pap. $9.95.

Leddy, Edward B. **Magnum Force Lobby: The NRA Fights Gun Control.** 1987. U. Pr. of Amer. $30.00.

Lester, David. **Gun Control: Issues & Answers.** 146 p. 1984. C. Thomas. pap. $18.00.

The Right To Keep & Bear Arms: A Presentation of Both Sides. 1986. Gordon Pr. $79.95 (lib. bdg.).

Siegel, Mark A., et al. **Gun Control: Restricting Rights or Protecting People?** 112 p. 1989. pap. $16.95.*

Stewart, Alva W. **Gun Control: Its Pros & Cons. A Checklist.** 12 p. 1986. Vance Biblios. $3.75.

Whisker, James B. **The Citizen Soldier and U.S. Military Policy.** 1979. North River Press. $10.00.

Zimring, Franklin E. & Hawkins, Gordon. **The Citizen's Guide to Gun Control.** 224 p. 1987. Macmillan. $17.95.

FOWLING (see also Decoys, Duck & Geese Shooting, Falconry)

Bauer, Erwin A. **Duck Hunter's Bible.** pap. Doubleday. $4.95.

Bell, Bob. **Hunting the Long Tailed Bird.** (Illus.). 1975. Freshet Press. $14.95.

Churchill, James. **Field Dressing Small Game & Fowl: The Illustrated Guide to Dressing 20 Birds & Mammals.** (Illus.). 112 p. 1987. Stackpole. pap. $10.95.

Dalrymple, Byron W. **Bird Hunting with Dalrymple: The Rewards of Shotgunning Across North America.** (Illus.) 288 p. 1987. Stackpole. $24.95.

Elliot, Charles. **Turkey Hunting With Charlie Elliot.** 288 p. Arco. pap. $8.95.

Gryndall, William. **Hawking, Hunting, Fowling and Fishing; Newly Corrected by W. Gryndall Faulkner.** 1972. Repr. of 1596 ed. W. J. Johnson. $25.00.

Norman, Geoffrey. **The Orvis Book of Upland Game Shooting.** (Illus.). 160 p. 1988. Lyons & Burford. $15.95.

Smith, Steve. **Hunting Ducks & Geese: Hard Facts, Good Bets and Serious Advice From a Duck Hunter You Can Trust.** 160 p. 1984. Stackpole. $14.95.

Woolmer, Frank. **Grouse & Grouse Hunting.** (Illus.). 192 p. Repr. of 1970 ed. N Lyons Bks. $18.95.

Zutz, Don. **Modern Waterfowl Guns & Gunning.** 288 p. 1985. Stoeger Pub. Co. pap. $11.95.

GAME AND GAME BIRDS (see also Duck & Geese Hunting, Fowling, Hunting)

Beasom, Sam L. & Roberson, Sheila F., eds. **Game Harvest Management.** (Illus.) 300 p. 1985. CK Wildlife Res. $20.00; pap. $15.00.

Billmeyer, Patricia. **The Encyclopedia of Wild Game and Fish Cleaning and Cooking.** Yeshaby Pubs. $3.95.

Blair, Gerry. **Predator Caller's Companion.** 1981. Winchester Press. $18.95.

Candy, Robert. **Getting The Most From Your Game & Fish.** (Illus.). 278 p. (Orig.). 1984. pap. A. C. Hood Pub. $16.95.

Churchill, James. **Field Dressing Big Game.** Atwater, Sally, ed. (Illus.). 96 p. 1989. Stackpole. pap. $10.95.*

Churchill, James. **Field Dressing Small Game & Fowl: The Illustrated Guide to Dressing 20 Birds & Mammals.** (Illus.). 112 p. 1987. Stackpole. pap. $10.95.

Duffy, David N. **Bird Hunting Tactics,** rev. ed. 167 p. 1989. Willow Creek Press. $17.50.*

Grooms, Steve. **Modern Pheasant Hunting.** (Illus.). 224 p. 1984. pap. Stackpole. $10.95.

Hagerbaumer, David. **Selected American Game Birds.** 1972. Caxton. $30.00.

Harbour, Dave. **Advanced Wild Turkey Hunting & World Records.** (Illus.) 264 p. 1983. New Century. $19.95.

McDaniel, John M. **Spring Turkey Hunting: The Serious Hunter's Guide.** (Illus.) 224 p. 1986. Stackpole. $21.95.

Nesbitt, W. H., ed. **Boone & Crockett 18th Big Game Awards.** (Illus.). 306 p. 1984. Boone & Crockett. $25.00.

Nesbitt, W. H. & Wright, Phillip L., eds. **Records at North American Big Game.** 8th ed. 412 p. 1981. Boone & Crockett. $195.00.

Robbins, Charles T., ed. **Wildlife Feeding and Nutrition.** 1983. Academic Press. $55.00.

Sherwood, Morgan. **Big Game in Alaska.** 1981. Yale University Press. $37.50.

Smith, Steve. **Hunting Upland Game Birds: What the Wingshooter Needs to Know about the Birds, the Guns & the New Clay Games.** (Illus.). 160 p. 1987. Stackpole. $16.95.

Stuart, Jack. **Bird Dogs & Upland Game Birds.** (Illus.). 1983. Denlinger. $24.95.

GAME AND GAME BIRDS—NORTH AMERICA

Bent, Arthur C. **Life Histories of North American Wild Fowl.** 685 p. 1987. Dover. pap. $12.95.

Boddington, Craig. **Campfires & Game Trails: Hunting North American Big Game.** (Illus.). 256 p. 1985. New Century. $19.95.

Brown, David E. **Arizona Game Birds.** (Illus.). 335 p. 1989. U. of Ariz. Press. $19.95.*

Foster. **New England Grouse Shooting.** 1983. Willow Creek. $45.00.

Johnsgaard, Paul. **North American Game Birds of Upland & Shoreline.** (Illus.). 231 p. 1975. U. of Nebraska Pr. pap. $8.95.

Nesbitt, W. H. & Wright, Phillip L., eds. **Records of North American Big Game.** 8th ed. 1981. Boone & Crockett Club. $30.00.

Phillips, John C. **American Game Mammals and Birds: A Catalog of Books, Sports, Natural History and Conservation. 1582–1925.** 1978. Repr. of 1930 ed. Ayer Co. Pubns. lib. bdg. $49.50

Sanderson, Glen C., ed. **Management of Migratory Shore & Upland Game Birds in North America.** 1980. pap. University of Nebraska Press. $10.95.

Tinsley, Russell, ed. **All About Small-Game Hunting in America.** 1976. Winchester Press. $16.95.

Walsh, Roy. **Gunning the Chesapeake: Duck & Goose Shooting on the Eastern Shore.** 130 p. 1960. Cornell Maritime. $14.95

Yarnall, Rea W. **Turkey Hunting (& Other Hunting) At Its Best.** (Illus.). 170 p. 1989. Lil Jewel Enterprises. $14.95.*

GAME & FISH COOKERY (see also Outdoor Cookery)

Barbour, Judy. **Elegant Elk: Delicious Deer.** 3rd ed. (Illus.). 196 p. 1983 reprint of 1978 ed. Peters Studio. $13.95.

Bashline, Sylvia G. **Sylvia Bashline's Savory Game Cookbook.** (Illus.). 176 p. 1989. Iron Blue. Write for price info.*

Billmeyer, Patricia. **The Complete Encyclopedia of Wild Game and Fish Cleaning and Cooking.** 3 vols. Yesnaby Pubs. pap. $3.95 ea.

Cameron, Angus & Jones, Judith. **The L. L. Bean Game & Fish Cookbook.** 1983. Random. $21.95.

Camp, Raymond. **Game Cookery.** (Illus.). 176 p. 1988. Price Stern. pap. $9.95.

Canino, Thomas L. **Mountain Man Cookbook: Venison & Other Recipes.** 85 p. 1985. TLC Enterprises. pap. $7.95.

Chicken and Game Hen Menus. 1983. Silver. $18.60.

Cone, Joan. **Fish and Game Cooking.** 1981. pap. EPM Publications. $5.95.

De Gouy, Louis V. **The Derrydale Game Cookbook,** 2 Vols. Game Book 308 p. Fish Book 330 p. 1987. Willow Creek Pr. $25.00 ea.

Del Guidice, Paula J. **Microwave Game & Fish Cookbook.** (Illus.) 160 p. 1985. Stackpole. pap. $12.95.

Dempsey, Jim (compiled by). **Wild Game Cookbook.** (Illus.). 156 p. 1987. UCS Press. pap. $8.95.

D'Ermo. Dominique. **Dominique's Famous Fish, Game & Meat Recipes.** 1981. Acropolis. pap. $8.95.

Fadala, Sam. **Complete Guide to Game Care & Cookery.** 288 p. 1989 DBI. pap. $14.95.*

French, Jack. **Pioneer Heritage Wild Game Cookbook.** (Illus.). 416 p. 1987. Realco Pub. pap. $14.95.

Gaida, Urban & Marchello, Martin. **Going Wild: A Guide to Field Dressing, Butchering, Sausage-Making & Cooking Wild Game & Fish.** (Illus.). 240 p. 1987. Watab Mktg. pap. $16.95.

Goolsby, Sam. **Great Southern Wild Game Cookbook.** 193 p. 1984. Pelican. $14.95.

Gorton, Audrey A. **Venison Book: How to Dress, Cut Up and Cook Your Deer.** 1957. pap. Greene. $4.95.

Gray, Rebecca & Reeve, Cintra. **Gray's Wild Game Cookbook: A Menu Cookbook.** 220 p. 1983. Grays Sporting. $25.00.

Hargreaves, Barbara, ed. **The Sporting Wife: A Guide to Game & Fish Cooking.** (Illus.). 336 p. 1988. David & Charles. pap. $15.95.

Holmes, Ferne. **Easy Recipes for Wild Game & Fish.** (Illus.). 160 p. 1988. Golden West Pubns. pap. $6.50.

Hull, Raymond & Sleight, Jack. **Home Book of Smoke Cooking Meat, Fish & Game.** (Illus.). 160 p. 1971. Stackpole. $10.95.

Humphreys, Angela. **Game Cookery.** (Illus.) 144 p. 1986. David & Charles. $24.95.

Hunting & Fishing Library: Dressing & Cooking Wild Game. (Illus.). 160 p. 1987. P-H. pap. $12.95.

Jaxson, Jay. **Wild Country All Game & Fish Recipes.** (Illus.). 81 p. 1982. pap. Jackson G. B. $7.95.

Johnson, L. W., ed. **Wild Game Cookbook: A Remington Sportsmen's Library Bk.** Benjamin Co. pap. $3.95.

Knight, Jacqueline E. **The Hunter's Game Cookbook.** (Illus.). 1978. Winchester Press. pap. $12.95.

Lamagna, Joseph. **Wild Game Cookbook for Beginner and Expert.** J. Lamagna. $6.95.

Little, Carolyn. **The Game Cookbook.** (Illus.). 224 p. 1989. David & Charles. $29.95.*

Mabbutt, Bill & Mabbutt, Anita: **North American Wild Game Cookbook.** 216 p. 1982. NC Book Exp. $9.95.

Mabbutt, Bill, et al. **North American Game Fish Cookbook.** 192 p. 1983. NC Bk. Exp. $9.95.

MacIlquham, Frances. **Complete Fish & Game Cookery of North America.** (Illus.). 304 p. 1983. Winchester Press. $29.95.

Manion, Timothy E. **The Game & Fish Menu Cookbook.** (Illus.). 320 p. 1987. Weidenfeld. pap. $10.95.

—**Wild Game & Country Cooking.** 200 p. 1983. Manion Outdoors Co. spiral bd. $9.95.

Morris, Dan & Morris, Inez. **The Complete Fish Cookbook.** 1989. Stoeger Pub. Co. $10.95.

Oakland, Ann. **Buffalo at Steak.** 32 p. 1983. One Percent. pap. $3.95.

Obern, Jane & Waldron, Valerie, eds. **NAHC Wild Game Cookbook.** 192 p. 1987. N. Am. Hunt Club. pap. $14.95.

Pederson, Rolf. **Our Wild Harvest: Sowing, Reaping, Cooking, Eating.** (Illus.). 174 p. 1982. Rolf's Gallery. pap. $9.95.

Perkins, Romi. **Game in Season: The Orvis Cookbook.** (Illus.). 224 p. 1988. Lyons & Burford. $19.95.

Robertson, Dale & Robertson, Phyllis. **Texas Wild Game Recipes Cookbook.** 215 p. 1989. Keepem Running. $12.95.*

Rojas-Lombardi, Felipe. **Game Cookery.** (Illus.). 1973. Harrowood Books. $3.95.

Rywell, Martin. **Wild Game Cook Book.** 1952. pap. Buck Hill. $6.75.

Sagstetter, Brad. **The Venison Handbook.** (Illus.). 80 p. 1981. Larksdale. $5.95.

Smith, Capt. James A. **Dress 'Em Out.** (Illus.). 256 p. pap. (Orig.). Stoeger. $12.95.

Smith, John A. **Wild Game Cookbook.** 64 p. 1986. Dover. pap. $4.95.

Steindler, Geraldine. **Game Cookbook.** New Revised Edition. 1985. softbound. Stoeger. $12.95.

Turkey & Duck Menus. 1985. (Pub. by Time-Life) Silver. $18.60.

Upland Game Birds, Vol. I. (Illus.). 174 p. pap. Rolf's Galley. $9.95.

Vail, Mike & Miller, Bill, eds. **NAHC Wild Game Cookbook.** (Illus.). 192 p. 1987. N. Amer. Hunt Club. pap. $14.95.

Wary, Carol. **Wild Game Cookery: The Hunter's Home Companion.** (Illus.). 1984. pap. (Orig.). Countryman. $12.95.

Willard, John. **Game Is Good Eating.** 4th rev. ed. (Illus.). 111 p. repr. of 1954 ed. J.A. Willard. $7.95.

Wongrey, Jan. **Southern Wildfowl and Wildgame Cookbook.** 2d ed. 1976. Sandlapper Store. $7.95.

GUNPOWDER (see Black Powder Guns, Ammunition)

GUNS (see Firearms, Pistols, Revolvers, Rifles, Shotguns)

GUNSMITHING

Angier, R. H. **Firearms Blueing and Browning.** 1936. Stackpole Books. $12.95.

Demeritt, Dwight B., Jr. **Maine Made Guns and Their Makers.** (Illus.). Maine State Museum Pubns. $22.00.

Dubino, Andrew D. **Gunsmithing with Simple Hand Tools: How to Repair, Improve & Add a Touch of Class to the Guns You Own.** (Illus.). 224 p. 1987. Stackpole. $19.95.

Dunlap, Roy F. **Gunsmithing.** 1963. Stackpole Books. $29.95.

Fry, Franklin. **Gunsmithing Fundamentals: A Guide for Professional Results.** (Illus.). 176 p. 1988. TAB Books. pap. $10.95.

Gunsmith Tips & Projects. 1989. Wolfe Pub. Co. $25.00.*

Hartzler, Daniel D. **Arms Makers of Maryland.** (Illus.). 1977. George Shumway Publisher. $40.00.

Hutslar, Donald A. **Gunsmiths of Ohio: 18th and 19th Centuries.** Vol. 1. (Illus.). 1973. George Shumway Publisher. $40.00.

Mitchell, Jack. **Gun Digest Book of Pistolsmithing.** 1980. pap. DBI Books. $12.95.

—**Gun Digest Book of Riflesmithing.** 256 p. 1982. pap. DBI Books. $12.95.

Norton Art Gallery. **Artistry in Arms: The Art of Gunsmithing and Gun Engraving.** (Illus.). 1971. pap. Norton Art Gallery. $2.50.

NRA Gunsmithing Guide. 336 p. Natl Rifle Assn. $9.95.

Sellers, Frank M. **American Gunsmiths: A Source Book.** 1983. Gun Room. $39.95.

Shelsby, Earl, ed. **NRA Gunsmithing Guide: Updated.** rev. ed. (Illus.). 336 p. 1980. pap. Natl. Rifle Assn. $11.95.

Shelton, Lawrence P. **California Gunsmiths.** (Illus.). 1977. George Shumway Publisher. $29.65.

Spearing, G. W. **The Craft of the Gunsmith.** (Illus.). 128 p. 1989. Borgo Press. $22.95.*

Stelle & Harrison. **The Gunsmith's Manual: A Complete Handbook for the American Gunsmith.** (Illus.). Repr. of 1883 ed. Gun Room Press. $15.00.

Stiefel, Ludwig, ed. **Gun Propulsion Technology, AAS 109.** 500 p. 1988. AIAA. $79.50.

Traister, John. **Gunsmithing at Home.** (Illus.). 256 p. pap. (Orig.). Stoeger. $12.95.

Vickery, W. F. **Advanced Gunsmithing.** 422 p. 1988. Repr. of 1940 ed. Wolfe Pub. Co. $42.00.

Walker, Ralph. **Shotgun Gunsmithing: Gun Digest Book.** 256 p. 1983. pap. DBI. $12.95.

HAWKEN RIFLES

Baird, John D. **Fifteen Years in the Hawken Lode.** (Illus.). Gun Room Press. $17.95.

—**Hawken Rifles. The Mountain Man's Choice.** Gun Room Press. $17.95.

HUNTING (see also Bird Dogs, Decoys, Deer Hunting, Duck & Geese Shooting, Fowling, Hunting Dogs)

Acerrano, Anthony J. **The Practical Hunter's Handbook.** (Illus.). 1978. pap. Winchester Press. $13.95.

Bashline, L. James. ed. **The Eastern Trail.** (Illus.). 1972. Freshet Press. $8.95.

Bland, Dwain. **Turkey Hunter's Digest.** (Illus.) 256 p. 1986. DBI. pap. $13.95.

Brister, Bob. **Shotgunning: The Art and the Science.** 1976. Winchester Press. $17.95.

Burnham, Murry & Tinsley, Russell. **Murry Burnham's Hunting Secrets.** (Illus.). 244 p. 1983. New Century. $17.95.

Cadieux, Charles L. **Goose Hunting.** 208 p. 1983. Stoeger. $9.95.

Camp, Doug. **Turkey Hunting: Spring & Fall.** (Illus.). 176 p. 1983. pap. Outdoor Skills. $12.95.

Cappossela, Jim. **How to Turn Your Fishing-Hunting Experiences Into Cash: Twenty-Five Ways to Earn Cash from Your Hobbies.** 1982. pap. Northeast Sportsmans. $5.00.

Capstick, Peter H. **Last Horizons: Hunting, Fishing & Shooting on Five Continents.** (Illus.). 288 p. 1988. St. Martin. $19.95.

Carlisle, G. L. **Grouse & Gun.** 184 p. 1988. David & Charles. $24.95.

Coles, Charles, ed. **Shooting & Stalking: A Basic Guide.** (Illus.). 204 p. 1988. David & Charles. $34.95.

Coon, Carlton. **The Hunting Peoples.** 423 p. 1987. N Lyons Bks. $15.95.

Douglas, James. **The Sporting Gun.** (Illus.). 240 p. 1983. David & Charles. $29.95.

Duffey, David M. **Bird Hunting Tactics,** rev. ed. (Illus.). 167 p. 1989. Willow Creek Press. $17.50.*

Elliott, William. **Carolina Sports by Land and Water: Incidents of Devil-Fishing. Wild-Cat, Deer and Bear Hunting.** (Illus.). 1978. Repr. of 1859 ed. Attic Press. $12.50.

Ellsberg, Bob. **Bob Ellsberg's 1988 Hunting & Fisherman's Planning Yearbook.** (Illus.). 192 p. 1987. Outdoor Enterprises. pap. $12.95.

Elman, Robert. **The Hunter's Field Guide to the Game Birds and Animals of North America.** 1982. Knopf. $15.95.

—**One Thousand One Hunting Tips.** rev. ed. 1983. pap. New Century. $14.95.

Fears, J. Wayne. **Successful Turkey Hunting.** 92 p. 1984. Target Comm. pap. $5.95.

Fergus, Charles, et al. **Rabbit Hunting.** 1985. Allegheny. pap. $7.95.

Field & Stream. **Field and Stream Reader.** facs. ed. 1946. Ayer Co. Pub. $21.50.

Geer, Galen. **Meat On The Table: Modern Small-Game Hunting.** (Illus.). 216 p. 1985. Paladin Pr. $16.95.

Gilsvik, Bob. **The Guide to Good Cheap Hunting.** (Illus.). 1979. Scarborough House. pap. $5.95.

Grinnell, George B. & Sheldon, Charles, eds. **Hunting and Conservation.** 1970. Repr. of 1925 ed. Arno. $33.00.

Gryndall, William. **Hawking, Hunting, Fouling and Fishing: Newly Corrected by W. Gryndall Faulkener.** 1972. Repr. of 1596 ed. W. J. Johnson. $25.00.

Hagel, Bob. **Game Loads and Practical Ballistics for the American Hunter.** (Illus.). 1978. Knopf. $14.95.

—**Guns, Loads & Hunting Tips.** Wolfe, Dave, ed. (Illus.) 536 p. 1986. Wolfe Pub. Co. $19.50.

Harbour, Dave. **Advanced Wild Turkey Hunting & World Records.** (Illus.). 264 p. 1983. New Century. $19.95.

Heacox, Cecil E. & Heacox, Dorothy. **The Gallant Grouse: All About the Hunting & Natural History of Old Ruff.** (Illus.). 1980. McKay. $14.95.

Henckel, Mark. **Hunter's Guide to Montana.** (Illus.). 224 p. 1985. Falcon Pr. MT. pap. $9.95.

Hill, Gene. **A Hunter's Fireside Book: Tales of Dogs, Ducks, Birds and Guns.** (Illus.). 1972. Winchester Press. $14.95.

—**Mostly Tailfeathers.** 1975. Winchester Press. $14.95.

Hill, Gene & Smith, Steve. **Outdoor Yarns & Outright Lies.** 168 p. 1983. Stackpole. $16.95.

Hunter's Guide to Professional Outfitters. (Illus.). 223 p. 1988. Safari Press. $25.00.

James, David & Stephens, Wilson, eds. **In Praise of Hunting.** (Illus.). 1961. Devin-Adair Co. $16.00.

Janes, Edward C. **Ringneck! Pheasants and Pheasant Hunting.** (Illus.). 1975. Crown. $8.95.

Johnson, et al. **Outdoor Tips.** pap. Benjamin Co. $2.95.

Keith, Elmer. **Keith's Rifles for Large Game.** (Illus.). 424 p. 1987. Repr. of 1946 ed. Wolfe Pub. Co. $54.00.

Knight, John A. **Ruffed Grouse.** (Illus.). 288 p. 1989. Repr. of 1947 ed. Wolfe Pub. Co. $21.95.*

Laubach, Don & Henckel, Mark. **The Elk Hunter: The Ultimate Source Book on Elk & Elk Hunting.** 224 p. 1989. Falcon Press MT. pap. $12.95.*

Liu, Allan J. **The American Sporting Collector's Handbook.** (Illus.). pap. Stoeger. $5.95.

McClane, A. J., ed. **McClane's Great Fishing & Hunting Lodges of North America.** 176 p. 1984. HR&W. $29.95.

McIntyre, Thomas. **The Way of the Hunter: The Art & Spirit of Modern Hunting.** 256 p. 1988. Dutton. $18.95.

Madden, D. H. **Chapter of Mediaeval History.** 1969. Repr. of 1924 ed. Kennikat Press. $26.50.

Madden, Dodgson H. **Diary of Master William Silence: A Study of Shakespeare and Elizabethan Sport.** 1970. Repr. of 1897. ed. Haskell Booksellers. $61.95.

Merrill, Wm. & Rees, Clair. **Hunter's Bible,** rev. ed. (Illus.) 192 p. 1986. Doubleday. pap. $7.95.

Meyer, Jerry. **Bear Hunting.** 224 p. 1983. Stackpole. $16.95.

Money, Albert W. **Pigeon Shooting.** Gould, A. C., ed. (Illus.). 109 p. 1987. Repr. of 1896 ed. Gunnerman Pr. $19.95.

NRA Guidebook for Hunters. 144 p. Nat'l Rifle Assn. $5.00.

O'Connor, Jack. **The Shotgun Book.** 2d rev. ed. 1978. Knopf. pap. $13.95.

Ortega y Gasset, Jose. **Meditations on Hunting.** 144 p. 1986. Scribner. pap. $7.95.

Ottman, Jim. **Hunting on Horseback.** (Illus.). 151 p. 1987. Paladin Press. $16.95.

Painter, Doug. **Hunting & Firearms Safety Primer.** 128 p. 1986. N. Lyons Bks. pap. $8.95.

Pyle, Wilf E. **Hunting Predators for Hides & Profit.** 224 p. Stoeger Pub. Co. pap. $11.95.

—**Small Game & Varmint Hunting.** (Illus.). 1989. Stoeger Pub. Co. $14.95.

Ricketts, Mitchell S. **Bobcat Trapper's Guide.** (Illus.). 116 p. 1987. Elk River Pr. pap. $10.95.

Shelsby, Earl & Gilford, James eds. **Basic Hunter's Guide.** rev. ed. (Illus.). 280 p. 1982. pap. Nat'l Rifle Assn. $14.95.

Shooter's Bible 1990, vol. 81. (Illus.). 576 p. 1989. Stoeger Pub. Co. pap. $16.95.

Shooter's Bible 1991. Vol. 82. (Illus.). 576 p. 1990. Stoeger Pub. Co. pap. $17.95.*

Shooter's Bible 1940. Repr. of 1940 ed. 512 p. 1989. Stoeger Pub. Co. pap. $16.95.*

Smith, James A. **Dress 'Em Out.** (Illus.). pap. Stoeger. $12.95.

Smith, Steve. **More & Better Pheasant Hunting.** (Illus.). 192 p. 1987. New Century. $15.95.

Stehsel, Donald. L. **Hunting the California Black Bear.** (Illus.). pap. Donald Stehsel. $7.00.

Strung, Norman. **The Art of Hunting.** (Illus.). 160 p. 1985. Prentice-Hall. $17.95.

Tapley, William G. **Those Hours Spent Outdoors: Reflections on Hunting & Fishing.** 224 p. 1988. Scribner. $17.95.

Walrod, Dennis. **More Than a Trophy.** (Illus.). 256 p. 1983. pap. Stackpole. $12.95.

—**Grouse Hunter's Guide.** 192 p. 1985. Stackpole. $16.95.

Waterman, C. F. **The Hunter's World.** (Illus.). 250 p. 1983. reprint of 1973 ed. New Century. $29.95.

Whelen, Townsend. **The Hunting Rifle.** 464 p. 1984. Repr. of 1924 ed. Wolfe Pub. Co. $39.00.

—**Wilderness Hunting & Wildcraft.** (Illus.). 368 p. 1987. Repr. of 1927 ed. Wolfe Pub. Co. $39.00.

White, S. E. **The Forest.** 296 p. 1987. Repr. of 1903 ed. Wolfe Pub. Co. $25.00.

—**The Land of Footprints.** (Illus.). 448 p. 1987. Repr. of 1912 ed. Wolfe Pub. Co. $25.00.

—**The Mountains.** (Illus.). 328 p. 1987. Repr. of 1904 ed. Wolfe Pub. Co. $25.00.

—**The Rediscovered Country.** (Illus.). 440 p. 1987. Repr. of 1914 ed. Wolfe Pub. Co. $25.00.

Whitney, Leon F. & Underwood, Acil B. **The Coon Hunter's Handbook.** Hart, Ernest, ed. (Illus.). 1952. Holt. $13.95.

Wolff, Ed. **Elk Hunting in the Northern Rockies.** 164 p. 1984. Stoneydale Pr. Pub. pap. $12.95.

Timberdoodle! A Guide to Woodcock. (Illus.). 192 p. 1987. Repr. of 1974 ed. Lyons & Burford. $18.95.

Young, Ralph. W. **Grizzlies Don't Come Easy.** (Illus.). 200 p. 1981. Winchester Press. $15.95.

—**My Lost Wilderness.** (Illus.). 196 p. 1984. New Century. $15.95.

Zern, Ed. **Hunting & Fishing From A to Zern.** (Illus.). 288 p. 1985. Lyons & Burford. $17.95.

Zumbo, Jim. **Hunting America's Mule Deer.** 1981. Winchester Press. $17.95.

HUNTING—DICTIONARIES

Frevert, W. **Woerterbuch der Jaegerei.** 4th ed. (Ger.) 1975. French & European Pubns. Inc. $24.95.

Kehrein, Franz. **Woerterbuch der Weldmannssprache.** (Ger.) 1969. French & European Pubns. Inc. $110.00.

Kirchoff, Anne. **Woerterbuch der Jagel. (Ger., Eng. & Fr. Dictionary of Hunting.)** 1976. French & European Pubns. Inc. $75.00.

Sparano, Vin T. **The Sportsman's Dictionary of Fishing & Hunting Lingo.** (Illus.). 1987. McKay. $12.45.

Wisconsin Hunting Encyclopedia. 1976. pap. Wisconsin Sportsman. $2.95.

HUNTING—HISTORY

Petersen, Eugene T. **Hunters' Heritage: A History of Hunting in Michigan.** Lowe, Kenneth S. ed. (Illus.). 1979. Michigan United Conservation Clubs. $4.65.

Rick, John W. **Prehistoric Hunters of the High Andes.** (Studies in Archaeology Ser.). 1980. Academic Press. $34.50.

Speth, John D. **Bison Kills and Bone Counts: Decision Making by Ancient Hunters.** 272 p. 1983. pap. U of Chicago. $8.00.

Spiess, Arthur E. **Reindeer and Caribou Hunters: An Archaeological Study.** (Studies in Archaeology Ser.). 1979. Academic Press. $29.50.

HUNTING—AFRICA

Bell, Walter D. **The Wanderings of an African Hunter: African Collection.** 187 p. 1990. Repr. of 1923 ed. Briar Patch. $49.95.*

Bosman, Paul & Hall-Martin, Anthony. **Elephants of Africa.** (Illus.). 176 p. 1988. Safari Press. $42.50.

Brander, Michael. **The Big Game Hunters.** (Illus.). 192 p. 1988. St. Martin. $24.95.

Buckley, William. **Big Game Hunting in Central Africa.** (Illus.). 320 p. 1988. St. Martin. $15.95.

Capstick, Peter H. **Death in the Long Grass.** (Illus.). 1978. St. Martin's Press. $15.95.

—**Death in the Dark Continent.** (Illus.). 320 p. 1983. St. Martin. $14.95.

Cloudsley-Thompson, J. L. **Animal Twilight, Man and Game in Eastern Africa.** (Illus.). 1967. Dufour Editions, Inc. $13.95.

Finaughty, William. **The Recollections of William Finaughty, Elephant Hunter.** 272 p. 1990. Repr. of 1916 ed. Briar Patch. $49.95.*

Findlay, Frederick R. N. & Croonwright-Schreiner, S. C. **Big Game Shooting and Travel in Southeast Africa: Account of Shooting Trips in the Cheringoma and Gorongoza Divisions of Portuguese South-East Africa and in Zululand.** Repr. of 1903 ed. Arno. $44.25.

Foa, Eduoard. **After Big Game in Central Africa.** (Illus.). 330 p. 1986. Safari Press. $45.00.

Foran, Robert. **Kill or Be Killed: The Rambling Reminiscences of an Amateur Hunter.** (Illus.). 400 p. 1988. St. Martin. $15.95.

Gillmore, Parker. **Days and Nights by the Desert.** Repr. of 1888 ed. Arno. $22.50.

Hemingway, Ernest. **Green Hills of Africa.** 1935. Scribner's. pap. $9.95.

Lechter, Owen. **Big Game Hunting in North-Eastern Rhodesia.** (Illus.). 272 p. 1987. St. Martin. $15.95.

Lyell, Denis D. **Memories of an African Hunter.** (Illus.). 288 p. 1987. St. Martin. $15.95.

—**African Adventures: Letters from Famous Big-Game Hunters.** (Illus.). 304 p. St. Martin. $15.95.

Mellon, James. **African Hunter.** (Illus.). 522 p. 1988. Safari Press. $100.00.

Roosevelt, Theodore. **African Game Trials.** (Illus.). 620 p. 1988. Repr. of 1910 ed. St. Martin. $19.95.

Ruark, Robert. **Horn of the Hunter.** (Illus.). 315 p. 1988. Safari Press. $35.00.

Selous, Frederick. **Hunter's Wanderings in Africa.** 526 p. 1986. repr. of 1920 ed. Wolfe Pub. Co. $47.00.

Stigand, Chauncey H. **Hunting the Elephant in Africa.** (Illus.) 400 p. 1985. St. Martin. $14.95.

White, S. E. **Lions in the Path.** (Illus.). 352 p. 1987. Repr. of 1926 ed. Wolfe Pub. Co. $25.00.

—**African Campfires.** (Illus.). 456 p. 1987. Repr. of 1910 ed. Wolfe Pub. Co. $25.00.

HUNTING—ALASKA

Batin, Christopher M. **Hunting in Alaska.** (Illus.). 416 p. 1987. Alaska Angler. pap. $24.95.*

Keim, Charles J. **Alaska Game Trails with a Master Guide.** pap. Alaska Northwest. $8.95.

Schetzle, Harold. **Alaska Wilderness Hunter.** (Illus.). 224 p. 1987. Great Northwest. $19.95.

HUNTING—GREAT BRITAIN

Jeffries, Richard. **The Gamekeeper at Home and the Amateur Poacher.** 1978. pap. Oxford University Press. $6.95.

Martin, Brian. **The Great Shoots: Britain's Premier Sporting Estates.** (Illus.). 240 p. 1988. David & Charles. $34.95.

Watson, J. N. **British and Irish Hunts and Huntsmen: Vols. I & II.** (Illus.). 1981. David & Charles. $90.00.

HUNTING—NORTH AMERICA

Dalrymple, Byron W. **Bird Hunting with Dalrymple: The Rewards of Shotgunning Across North America.** (Illus.) 288 p. 1987. Stackpole. $24.95.

Irwin, R. Stephen. **Hunters of the Buffalo.** (Illus.). 52 p. 1984. Hancock House. pap. $3.95.

Leopold, Luna. B., ed. **Round River: From the Journals of Aldo Leopold.** (Illus.). 1972. pap. Oxford University Press. $3.95.

Selous, F. C. **Hunting Trips in North America.** (Illus.). 528 p. 1988. Repr. of 1907 ed. Wolfe Pub. Co. $52.00.

Suits, Chauncey. **Big Game, Big Country.** (Illus.). 224 p. 1987. Great Northwest. $19.95.

HUNTING—U.S.

Abbott, Henry. **Birch Bark Books of Henry Abbott: Sporting Adventures and Nature Observations in the Adirondacks in the Early 1900s).** Illus., Repr. of 1914 & 1932 eds.). 1980. Harbor Hill Books. $22.50.

Baily's Hunting Directory. 1978–79. (Illus.). 1978. J. A. Allen. $25.00.

Baker, Ron. **The American Hunting Myth.** 287 p. 1985. Vantage. $10.95.

Barsness, John. **Hunting the Great Plains.** 164 p. 1979. pap. Mountain Press. $6.95.

Burk, Dale A. **Elk Hunting.** (Illus.). 64 p. 1988. Stoneydale Press. pap. $3.50.

Burk, R. L. **Mule Deer Hunting.** (Illus.). 64 p. 1988. Stoneydale Press. pap. $3.50.

Cory, Charles B. **Hunting and Fishing in Florida, Including a Key to the Water Birds.** 1970. Repr. of 1896 ed. Ayer Co. Pubs. $19.00.

Dahl, Ruby W., et al. **Lander: One-Shot Antelope Hunt.** 129 p. 1986. $19.95; leather bound lmtd. ed. $50.00.

Darner, Kirt I. **Hunting the Rockies—Home of the Giants.** (Illus.). 291 p. 1988. Darner Books. $25.00.

Donnell, Rich & Lamar, May. **Hunting: The Southern Tradition.** 208 p. 1987. Taylor Pub. $35.00.

Dorsey, Chris & Babbit, Patrick. **Hunt Wisconsin: A Comprehensive Guide to Wisconsin Public Hunting Areas.** 1989. Pine River Press. pap. $14.95.*

Elman, Robert, ed. **All About Deer Hunting in America 1976.** New Century. $16.95.

Gilchrist, Duncan. **Antelope Hunting.** (Illus.). 64 p. 1988. Stoneydale Press. pap. $3.50.

—**Moose Hunting.** (Illus.). 64 p. 1988. Stoneydale Press. pap. $3.50.

—**Mountain Goat Hunting.** (Illus.). 64 p. 1988. Stoneydale press. pap. $3.50.

Hirsch, Bob. **Outdoors in Arizona: A Guide to Fishing & Hunting.** 192 p. 1986. Arizona Highway. pap. $12.95.

Huggler, Tom. **Hunt Michigan: How to, Where to, When to.** (Illus.). 1985. Mich. United Conserv. pap. $12.95.

Johnson, John A. **Oregon Hunting Guide.** (Illus.). 176 p. 1988. Stoneydale Press. pap. $12.95.

Kozickey, Edward L. **Hunting Preserves for Sport or Profit.** 250 p. 1987. CK Wildlife Res. $24.95.

Lapinski, Mike, et al. **All About Elk.** Miller, Bill, ed. 253 p. 1987. N Amer. Hunt Club. text ed. $15.95.

Lowenstein, Bill. **Hunting in Michigan: The Early 80's.** Arnold, David A., ed. 1981. pap. Michigan Natural Resources Michigan. $6.95.

Manion, Timothy E. **American Hunting & Fishing Guide.** 292 p. Manion Outdoors Co. pap. $9.95.

Mitchell, John G. **The Hunt.** 320 p. 1980. Knopf. $12.45.

Norris, Charles C. **Eastern Upland Shooting.** (Illus.). 408 p. 1989. Repr. of 1946 ed. Countrysport Press. $29.50.*

O'Connor, Jack. **Hunting in the Rockies.** (Illus.). 297 p. 1988. Safari Press. $29.95.

Pennaz, Steve, ed. **North American Hunting Adventures.** (Illus.). 208 p. 1988. Amer. Hunt Club. $19.95.

Roosevelt, Theodore. **Outdoor Pastimes of an American Hunter.** 1970. Repr. of 1905 ed. Arno Press. $29.00.

—**Ranch Life and the Hunting-Trail.** 208 p. 1985. Repr. of 1901 ed. Hippocrene. pap. $8.95.

—**Theodore Roosevelt's America.** Wiley, Farida, ed. (Illus.). 1955. Devin-Adair Co. $14.95.

—**Wilderness Hunter.** 279 p. 1970. Repr. of 1900 ed. Irvington.

Sandoz, Mari. **The Buffalo-Hunters: The Story of the Hide Men.** 1978. pap. University of Nebraska Press. $7.95.

Tome, Philip. **Pioneer Life or Thirty Years a Hunter: Being Scenes and Adventures in the Life of Philip Tome.** (Illus.). 1989. Repr. of 1928 ed. Ayer Co. Pubns. $18.95.

Zumbo, Jim. **Hunt Elk.** 256 p. 1985. New Century. $17.95.

HUNTING DOGS (see also Bird Dogs)

Bernard, Art. **Dog Days.** 1969. Caxton. $5.95.

Duffey, David M. **Hunting Dog Know-How** (Illus.). 1983. Winchester Press. pap. $10.95.

Hartley, Oliver. **Hunting Dogs.** pap. A. R. Harding Pub. $4.00.

Hobson, J. C. **Beagling.** (Illus.). 192 p. 1988. David & Charles. $29.95.

Irving, Joe. **Training Spaniels.** (Illus.). 1980. David & Charles. $19.95.

—**Gun Dogs: Their Learning Chain.** 231 p. 1983. State Mutual Bks. $35.00.

Petrie, Chuck, ed. **Just Dogs: A Photographic & Literary Tribute to the Great Hunting Breeds.** (Illus.). 160 p. 1988. Willow Creek Press. $35.00.

Robinson, Jerome. **Training the Hunting Retriever.** (Illus.). 233 p. 1987. B. Robinson. $18.95.

Roebuck, Kenneth C. **Gun-Dog Training Spaniels and Retrievers.** 1982. Stackpole. $14.95.

—**Gun-Dog Training Pointing Dogs.** 192 p. 1983. Stackpole. $14.95.

Rutherford, Clarice & Loveland, Cherylon. **Retriever Puppy Training: The Right Start for Hunting.** (Illus.). 109 p. 1988. Alpine Pub. pap. $8.98.

Salmon, H. M. **Gazehounds and Coursing.** (Illus.). 1977. North Star Press. $18.50.

Sjrotuck, William G. **Scent & The Scenting Dog.** 3d ed. (Illus.). 102 p. 1972. Arner Pubns. pap. $7.95.

Tarrant, Bill. **Best Way to Train Your Gun Dog: The Dalmar Smith Method.** 1977. David McKay Co. $11.95.

Waterman, Charles F. **Gun Dogs & Bird Guns: A Charley Waterman Reader.** (Illus.). 244 p. 1987. GSJ Press. text ed. $25.00.

Wehle, Robert G. **Wing and Shot.** 1964. Country Press NY. $25.00.

HUNTING STORIES

Hinckley, Gerald A. **The Great Green Mountain Horn Hunt.** 112 p. 1987. Carleton. $9.50.

MacQuarrie. Gordon. **The Last Stories of the Old Duck Hunters.** 1985. pap. Willow Creek Press. $17.50.

—**More Stories of the Old Duck Hunters.** 1983. Willow Creek. $17.50.

—**Stories of the Old Duck Hunters & Other Drivel.** 228 p. 1985. repr. of 1967 ed. Willow Creek. $17.50.

Sassoon, Siegfried. **Memoirs of a Fox-Hunting Man.** 320 p. 1960. pap. Faber & Faber. $6.95.

Shields, George O. **Hunting in the Great West: Rustlings in the Rockies.** (Illus.). 175 p. J. A. Willard. pap. $9.95.

Smith, Steve. **Picking Your Shots & Other Stories of Dogs & Birds & Guns & Days Afield.** (Illus.). 160 p. 1986. Stackpole. $16.95.

Sobol, Donald. **Encyclopedia Brown's Book of the Wacky Outdoors.** (gr. 5 up). 1988. Bantam. pap. $2.50.

Sparano, Vin., ed. **Classic Hunting Tales,** Vol. II. 256 p. 1987. Beaufort Bks. NY. $18.95.

HUNTING WITH BOW AND ARROW (see Bow and Arrow)

KNIVES

Berner, Douglas C. **Survival Knife Reference Guide.** (Illus.) 207 p. 1986. Bee Tree. pap. $12.95.

Blandford, Percy W. **Making Knives & Tools.** 2d ed. (Illus.). 256 p. 1985. TAB Books. pap. $12.60.

Boye, David. **Step-By-Step Knifemaking.** 1977. Rodale Press. $14.95.

Erhardt, Roy & Ferrell, J. **Encyclopedia of Pocket Knives: Book One and Book Two Price Guide.** rev. ed. (Illus.). 1977. Heart of America Press. $7.00.

Goins, John E. **Pocketknives—Markings, Manufacturers & Dealers.** 2d ed. 280 p. 1982. pap. Knife World. $8.95.

Hardin, Albert N., Jr. & Hedden, Robert W. **Light but Efficient: A Study of the M1880 Hunting and M1890 Intrenching Knives and Scabbards.** (Illus.). 1973. Albert N. Hardin. $7.95.

Hughes, B. R. **Modern Hand-Made Knives.** Pioneer Press. $9.95.

Latham, Sid. **Knives and Knifemakers.** (Illus.). 1974. pap. Macmillan. $13.50.

Levine, Bernard R. **Levine's Guide to Knife Values.** (Illus.). 480 p. 1985. DBI. pap. $19.95.

Lewis, Jack. **Gun Digest Book of Knives.** 3d ed. (Illus.). 256 p. 1988. DBI. pap. $12.95.

Lewis, Jack & Combs, Roger. **Gun Digest Book of Knifemaking.** (Illus.). 224 p. 1989. DBI. pap. $13.95.*

McCreight, Tim. **Custom Knifemaking: 10 Projects from a Master Craftsman.** (Illus.). 234 p. 1985. Stackpole. pap. $14.95.

Parker, James, ed. **The Official Price Guide to Knives,** 9th ed. 1988. Ballantine. pap. $12.95.

Paul, Don. **Everybody's Knife Bible.** (Illus.). 128 p. 1987. Pathfinder. pap. $9.95.

Peterson, Harold L. **American Knives.** 1980. Gun Room. $17.95.

Sanchez, John. **Blade Master: Advanced Survival Skills for the Knife Fighter.** (Illus.). 96 p 1982. pap. Paladin Press. $10.00.

Stephens, Frederick J. **Fighting Knives.** (Illus.). 144 p. 1985. Arco. pap. $11.95.

Tappan, Mel. ed. **A Guide to Handmade Knives and the Official Directory of the Knifemaker's Guild.** (Illus.). 1977. Janus Press. $9.95.

Warner, Ken. **Practical Book of Knives.** (Illus.). 1976. softbound. Stoeger. $10.95.

—**Knives '89.** 9th ed. (Illus.). 256 p. 1988. DBI. pap. $13.95.

Watson, Jim. **Sharpening & Knife Making.** (Illus.). 150 p. 1987. Schiffer. $12.95.

NATURAL HISTORY—OUTDOOR BOOKS

Bedichek, Roy. **Adventures with a Texas Naturalist.** (Illus.). 1961. pap. University of Texas Press. $9.95.

Errington, Paul L. **The Red Gods Call.** (Illus.). 1973. Iowa State University Press. $9.50.

Fuller, Raymond T. **Now That We Have to Walk: Exploring the Out-of-Doors.** facsimile ed. Repr. of 1943 ed. Ayer Co. $19.00.

Godfrey, Michael A. **A Sierra Club Naturalist's Guide to the Piedmont of Eastern North America.** (Illus.). 432 p. 1980. pap. Sierra. $9.95.

Jefferies, Richard. **Old House at Coate.** 1948. Arno Press. $18.00.

Kieran, John F. **Nature Notes.** facs. ed. 1941. Arno Press. $16.50.

Olson, Sigurd F. **Listening Point.** (Illus.). 1958. Knopf. $13.45.

—**Sigurd Olson's Wilderness Days.** (Illus.). 1972. Knopf. $29.45.

Pearson, Haydn S. **Sea Flavor.** facs. ed. 1948. Ayer Co. Pubns. $12.50.

Rowlands, John J. **Cache Lake County.** (Illus.). 1959. W. W. Norton & Co. $12.95.

Sharp, Dallas L. **Face of the Fields.** facs. ed. 1911. Ayer Co. Pubns. $17.00.

—**Sanctuary! Sanctuary!** facs. ed. 1926. Ayer Co. Pubns. $12.00.

Sharp, William. **Where the Forest Murmurs.** 1906. Ayer Co. Pubns. $21.50.

Shepard, Odell. **Harvest of a Quiet Eye: A Book of Digressions.** facs. ed. Repr. of 1927 ed. Ayer Co. Pubns. $21.50.

Wiley, Farida, ed. **John Burroughs' America.** (Illus.). Devin-Adair Co. $10.50; pap. $9.95.

ORDNANCE (see also Ballistics)

Colby, C. B. **Civil War Weapons: Small Arms and Artillery of the Blue and Gray.** (Illus.). 1962. Coward, McCann & Geoghegan. $6.99.

Derby, Harry L. **The Hand Cannons of Imperial Japan.** Reidy, John and Welge, Albert, eds., 1981. Derby Publishing Co. $37.95.

Marchant-Smith, D. J. & Haslem, P. R. **Small Arms and Cannons.** 1982. Pergamon Press. pap. $18.95.

Norton, Robert. **The Gunner, Shewing the Whole Practise of Artillerie.** 1973. Repr. of 1628 ed. W. J. Johnson. $70.00.

ORIENTATION

Henley, B. M. **Orienteering.** (Illus.). 1976. Charles River Books. $6.95.

Kals, W. S. **Land Navigation Handbook: The Sierra Club Guide to Map & Compass.** (Illus.). 288 p. 1983. pap. Sierra. $8.95.

Ratliff, Donald E. **Map Compass and Campfire.** (Illus.). 1970. Binford & Mort Pubs. pap. $3.95.

Vassilevsky, B. **Where is the North?** 1977. pap. Imported Pubns. $3.95.

Watson, J. D. **Orienteering.** (Illus.). 1975. Charles River Books. pap. $2.50.

Williams, Charles W. **Direction: The Essential Dimension.** 1960. Speller. $8.95.

OUTDOOR COOKERY (see also Game Cookery)

Anderson, Beverly M. & Hamilton, Donna M. **The New High Altitude Cookbook.** (Illus.). 1980. Random House. $17.95.

Antell, Steven. **Backpacker's Recipe Book.** (Illus.). 1980. pap. Pruett. $7.95.

Banks, James E. **Alfred Packer's Wilderness Cookbook.** (Illus.). 1969. Filter Press. $8.00. pap. $2.00.

Barker, Harriett. **The One-Burner Gourmet.** rev. ed. 1981. pap. Contemporary Books. $10.95.

Beard, James & Brown, Helen E. **The Complete Book of Outdoor Cooking.** (Illus.). 256 p. 1989. Harper & Row. pap. $8.95.*

Braun, Robert L. **Wilderness Recipie.** 96 p. 1988. Todd & Honeywell. $8.95.

Brent, Carol D., ed. **Barbecue: The Fine Art of Charcoal, Gas and Hibachi Outdoor Cooking.** (Illus.). 1971. Test Recipe. $5.95.

Bunnelle, Hasse & Sarvis, Shirley. **Cooking for Camp and Trail.** 1972. pap. Sierra Club. $7.95.

Drew, Edwin P. **The Complete Light-Pack Camping and Trail-Food Cookbook.** 1977. pap. McGraw-Hill. $4.95.

Fleming, June. **The Well-Fed Backpacker.** (Illus.). 1981. pap. Random House. $4.95.

Heffron, Lauren. **Cycle Food: A Guide to Satisfying Your Inner Tube.** (Illus.). 96 p. 1983. pap. Ten Speed Press. $4.95.

Hemingway, Joan & Maricich, Connie. **The Picnic Gourmet.** (Illus.). 1978. pap. Random House. $10.95.

Holm, Don. **Old-Fashioned Dutch Oven Cookbook.** 1969. pap. Caxton Printers. $5.95.

Hughes, Stella. **Chuck Wagon Cookin'.** 1974. pap. University of Arizona Press. $9.95.

Jacobson, Cliff. **Cooking in the Outdoors: The Basic Essentials.** (Illus.). 72 p. 1989. ICS Books. pap. $4.95.*

Krenzel, Kathleen & Heckendorf, Robyn. **The Sporting Life Gourmet.** (Illus.). 74 p 1980. R. Louis Pub. $9.95.

Lund, Duane R. **Camp Cooking.** 198 p. 1990. Adventure Pubns. $7.95.*

McElfresh, Beth. **Chuck Wagon Cookbook.** pap. Swallow Press. 72 p. 1960. $4.95.

McHugh, Gretchen. **The Hungry Hiker's Book of Good Cooking.** (Illus.). 1982. Alfred A. Knopf. $17.50. pap. $11.95.

Macmillan, Diane D. **The Portable Feast.** rev. ed. (Illus.). 1984. 101 Productions. pap. $7.95.

Mendenhall, Ruth D. **Backpack Cookery.** (Illus.). 1974. pap. La Siesta. $1.95.

Nagy, Jean. **Brown Bagging It: A Guide to Fresh Food Cooking in the Wilderness.** 1976 pap. Marty-Nagy Bookworks. $2.50.

Outdoor Cooking. (Illus.). 176 p. 1983. Time Life. $14.95.

Picnic and Outdoor Menus. 1984. Silver. $18.60.

Prater, Yvonne & Mendenhall, Ruth D. **Gorp, Glop and Glue Stew: Favorite Foods from 165 Outdoor Experts.** (Illus.). 1981. pap. Mountaineers. $9.95.

Ragsdale, John. **Camper's Guide to Outdoor Cooking: Tips, Techniques & Delicious Eats.** (Illus.). 138 p. 1989. Gulf Pubns. pap. $8.95.*

Raup, Lucy G. **Camper's Cookbook.** 1967. pap. C. E. Tuttle. $3.75.

Schultz, Philip S. **Cooking with Fire and Smoke.** 273 p. 1986. S&S. $17.95.

Small, Dan & Frank, Nancy. **The Official Outdoor Wisconsin Cookbook.** 144 p. 1988. Northwood. $19.95.

Tarr, Yvonne Y. **The Complete Outdoor Cookbook.** (Illus.). 1973. Times Books. $8.95.

Thomas, Dian. **Roughing It Easy: A Unique Ideabook on Camping and Cooking.** (Illus.). 1974. pap. Brigham Young University Press. $6.95.

Wary, Carol & Wary, William. **Fish & Fowl Cookery: The Outdoorsman's Home Companion.** 224 p. 1987. Countryman. pap. $10.95.

Woodall's Campsite Cookbook. Woodall. pap. $4.95.

OUTDOOR LIFE

Acerrano, Anthony. **The Outdoorsman's Emergency Manual.** 1976. 352 p. softbound. Stoeger. $9.95.

Anderson, Steve. **The Orienteering Book.** (Illus.). 1980. pap. Anderson World. $3.95.

Angier, Bradford. **How to Stay Alive in the Woods.** Orig. Title: **Living off the Country.** 1962. pap. Macmillan. $5.95.

Bass, Rick. **Wild to the Heart.** 144 p. 1988. Stackpole. $11.95.

Brown, Vinson. **Reading the Outdoors at Night.** (Illus.). 192 p. 1982. pap. Stackpole Books. $9.95.

Camazine, Scott. **The Naturalist's Year: Twenty-Six Outdoor Explorations.** 1987. Wiley. pap. $14.95.

Carter, Jimmy. **An Outdoor Journal.** 443 p. 1989. Repr. of 1988 ed. Thorndike Press. $18.95.*

Douglas & McIntyre. **Outdoor Safety & Survival.** (Illus.). 154 p. 1986. Salem Hse Pub. $4.95.

Eastman, P. F. **Advanced First Aid for All Outdoors.** 1976. pap. Cornell Maritime Press. $6.00.

Fear, Gene. **Fundamentals of Outdoor Enjoyment.** (Illus.). 1976. pap. Survival Ed. Assoc. $5.00.

Grow, Laurence. **The Old House Book of Outdoor Living Places.** (Illus.). 1981. Warner Books. $15.00; pap. $8.95.

Hamper, Stanley R. **Wilderness Survival.** 3rd ed. 1975. Repr. of 1963 ed. Peddlers Wagon. $1.79.

Hanley, Wayne. **A Life Outdoors: A Curmudgeon Looks at the Natural World.** (Illus.). 1980. Stephen Greene Press. pap. $5.95.

Hickin, Norman. **Beachcombing for Beginners.** 1976. pap. Wilshire Book Co. $2.00.

Humphreys, John. **The Country Sportsman's Record Book & Journal.** (Illus.). 224 p. 1989. David & Charles. $45.00.*

Johnson, et al. **Outdoor Tips: A Remington Sportsman's Library Book.** pap. Benjamin Co. $2.95.

Kodet, E. Russell & Angier, Bradford. **Being Your Own Wilderness Doctor.** (Illus.). 1975. Stackpole Books. $8.95.

Lund, Duane R. **Nature's Bounty for Your Table.** 1982. Adventure Pubns. $7.95.

Maguire, Jack. **Outdoor Spaces.** 1987. H. Holt. $19.95.

Mills, Robert & Haines, Olin, eds. **National Outdoor Guides Directory.** (Illus.). 434 p. 1987. Professional Guides Pub. $12.95.

Olsen, Larry D. **Outdoor Survival Skills.** rev. ed. 1973. Brigham Young University Press. $7.95.

Olson, Sigurd F. **Olson's Wilderness Days.** (Illus.). 1972. Knopf. $29.45.

Outdoor Living Skills Instructor's Manual. 1979. pap. American Camping Association. $6.50.

Patmore, J. Allan. **Land and Leisure In England and Wales.** 1971. Fairleigh Dickinson. $27.50.

Paul, Don, ed. **Great Livin' in Grubby Times.** (Illus.) 140 p. 1986. Pathfinder HL. pap. $12.95.

—**Green Beret's Guide to Outdoor Survival.** (Illus.). 134 p. 1986. Pathfinder HL. pap. $12.95.

Rae, William E., ed. **A Treasury of Outdoor Life.** (Illus.). 520 p. 1983. Stackpole. $24.95.

Rafferty, Milton D. **The Ozarks Outdoors:** A Guide for Fishermen, Hunters & Tourists. (Illus.) 408 p. 1985. U of Okla. Press. $26.95.

Rawick, George P. **From Sundown to Sunup.** 1972. pap. Greenwood Press. pap. $9.95.

Roberts, Harry. **Keeping Warm and Dry.** (Illus.). 1982. pap. Stone Wall Press. $7.95.

Russell, Andy. **Trail of a Wilderness Wanderer.** 336 p. 1988. N. Lyons Bks. $12.95.

Rutstrum, Calvin. **Once Upon a Wilderness.** (Illus.). 1973. Macmillan. $10.95.

Shepherd, Laurie. **A Dreamer's Log Cabin: A Woman's Walden.** (Illus.). 1981. Dembner Books. $8.95.

Van Der Smissen, Betty. **Leader's Guide to Nature-Oriented Activities.** 3rd ed. (Illus.). 1977. pap. Iowa State University Press. $14.95.

Wood, Dave. **Wisconsin Life Trip.** 1982. Adventure Pubns. $5.95.

Wurman, Richard S. et al. **The Nature of Recreation: A Handbook in Honor of Frederick Law Olmstead.** 1972. pap. MIT Press. $6.95.

PISTOL SHOOTING

Antal, Laslo. **Competitive Pistol Shooting.** 190 p. 1982. State Mutual Bks. $30.00.

Duncan, Mark. **On Target with Mark Duncan:** An Illustrated Pocket Guide to Handgun Accuracy. (Illus.) 52 p. 1984. Duncan Gun. pap. $4.95.

Given, T. **Survival Shooting: Handguns & Shotguns.** 1986. Gordon Pr. $79.95 (lib. bdg.).

Leatherdale, Frank & Leatherdale, Paul. **Successful Pistol Shooting.** (Illus.). 144 p. 1989. David & Charles. $24.95.*

Mason, James D. **Combat Handgun Shooting.** (Illus.) 286 p. 1980. C. C. Thomas. $34.75.

PISTOLS

American Historical Foundation Staff, ed. **M1911A1 Automatic Pistol:Proud American Legend.** (Illus.) 1985. Am. Hist. Found. pap. $8.95.

Antaris, Leonardo. **Astra Automatic Pistols.** 260 p. 1988. Firac Pub. Co. $40.00.

Askins, Charles. **Askins on Pistols and Revolvers.** Bryant, Ted & Askins, Bill, eds. 1980. National Rifle Association. $25.00; pap. $8.95.

Buxton, Warren H. **The P-38 Pistol,** Vol. 2. 1940–1945. (Illus.). 256 p. 1985. Ucross Bks. $45.50.

Datig, Fred A. **Luger Pistol.** rev. ed. Borden, $16.95.

Dyke, S. E. **Thoughts on the American Flintlock Pistol.** (Illus.). 1974. George Shumway Publisher. $7.50.

Erickson, Wayne & Pate, Charles E. **The Broomhandle Pistol, 1896 to 1936.** 300 p. 1985. E&P Enter. $49.95.

Gould, A. C. **Modern American Pistols & Revolvers.** (Illus.). 244 p. 1987. Repr. of 1888 ed. Wolfe Pub. Co. $37.00.

Hacker, Larry. **The Colt 1911 Automatic Pistol: Its Predecessor & Variations.** 1989. Pioneer Press. $4.00.*

Hoffschmidt, E. J. **Know Your Forty-Five Caliber Auto Pistols.** (Illus.). 1973. pap. Blacksmith Corp. $5.95.

—**Know Your Walther PP and PPK Pistols.** (Illus.). 1975. pap. Blacksmith Corp. $5.95.

—**Know Your Walther P.38 Pistols.** (Illus.). pap. 1974. Blacksmith Corp. $5.95.

Hogg, Ian. **Military Pistols & Revolvers.** (Illus.). 128 p. 1988. Sterling. $24.95.

Horlacher, R., ed. **The Famous Automatic Pistols of Europe.** Seaton, L. & Steindler, R. A. trs. from Ger. (Illus.). 1976. pap. Jolex. $6.95.

Kirkland, Turner. **Southern Derringers of the Mississippi Valley.** Pioneer Press. $2.00.

Klay, Frank. **The Sammuel E. Dyke Collection of Kentucky Pistols.** 1980. Gun Room Press. $2.50.

Landskron, Jerry. **Remington Rolling Block Pistols.** (Illus.). 1981. Rolling Block Press. $34.95; deluxe ed. $39.95.

Long, Duncan. **Assault Pistols, Rifle & Submachine Guns.** 152 p. 1986. Paladin Pr. pap. $19.95.

Manual of Pistol & Revolver Cartridges, Vols 1 & 2. 1987. Gordon Pr. lib. bdg. $79.75.

Mitchell, Jack. **The Gun Digest of Pistolsmithing.** 1980. pap. DBI Books. $12.95.

Myatt, F. **An Illustrated Guide to Pistols and Revolvers.** 1981. Arco. $9.95.

Nonte, George C. Jr. **Pistol Guide.** (Illus.). 1980. Stoeger. $11.95.

—**Pistolsmithing.** (Illus.). 560 p. 1974. Stackpole. $27.95.

North & North. **Simeon North: First Official Pistol Maker of the United States.** Repr. Gun Room Press. $12.95.

Reese. Michael. **Collector's Guide to Luger Values.** 1972. pap. Pelican. $1.95.

Seaton, Lionel, tr. **Famous Auto Pistols and Revolvers, Vol. II.** (Illus.). 1971. Jolex. $6.95.

Small Arms Identification & Operations Guide: Pistols. 1986. Gordon Press. $79.95.

Van Der Mark, Kist & Van Der Sloot, Puype. **Dutch Muskets and Pistols.** (Illus.). 1974. George Shumway Publisher. $35.00.

Walther P-38 Auto Pistol Caliber 9mm Parabellum. 1986. Gordon Pr. lib. bdg. $79.95.

Whittington, Robert D. **German Pistols and Holsters, 1943–45: Military-Police-NSDAP.** (Illus.). Gun Room Press. $17.95.

Whittington, Robert D. III. **The Colt Whitneyville-Walker Pistol.** 96 p. 1984. Brownlee Books. $20.00.

—**German Pistols & Holsters, 1934–1945,** Vol. II. (Illus.). 312 p. 1989. Brownlee Books. $45.00.*

Williams, Mason. **The Sporting Use of the Handgun.** (Illus.). 1979. C. C. Thomas. $18.00.

Wood, J. B. **Gun Digest Book of Firearms Assembly-Disassembly. Pt. 1: Automatic Pistols.** (Illus.). 1979. pap. DBI Books. $13.95.

—**Beretta Automatic Pistols: The Collector's & Shooter's Comprehensive Guide.** (Illus.). 192 p. 1985. Stackpole. $19.95.

RELOADING (see also Firearms, Rifles, Shotguns)

Donnelly, John J. **Handloader's Manual of Cartridge Conversions.** (Illus.). 1056 p. 1987. Stoeger Pub. Co. pap. $29.95; spiral bound $44.95; hardcover $49.95.

Matunas, Edward. **Handbook of Metallic Cartridge Reloading.** (Illus.). 1981. Winchester Press. $15.95.

Steindler, R. A. **Reloader's Guide.** 3rd ed. (Illus.). 1975. softbound. Stoeger, $11.95.

REVOLVERS (see also Colt Revolvers)

Askins, Charles. **Askins on Pistols and Revolvers.** Bryant, Ted & Askins, Bill, eds. 1980. National Rifle Association. $25.00; pap. $8.95.

Dougan, John C. **Know Your Ruger Single Action Revolvers: 1953–1963.** Amber, John T., ed. 1981. Blacksmith Corp. $35.00.

Gould, A. C. **Modern American Pistols & Revolvers.** (Illus.). 244 p 1987. Repr. of 1888 ed. Wolfe Pub. Co. $37.00.

Hogg, Ian V. **Military Pistols & Revolvers.** (Illus.). 128 p. 1988. Sterling. $24.95.

Long, Duncan. **Combat Revolvers: The Best (and Worst) Modern Wheelguns.** (Illus.). 152 p. 1989. Paladin Press. pap. $16.95.*

Manual of Pistol & Revolver Cartridges, 2 vols. 1987. Gordon Press. $79.95.

Munnell, J. C. **A Blacksmith Guide to Ruger Rimfire Revolvers.** (Illus.). 56 p. 1982. pap. Blacksmith Corp. $7.50.

Myatt, F. **An Illustrated Guide to Pistols & Revolvers.** 160 p. 1981. Arco. (Illus.). $9.95.

Nonte, George C. Jr. **Revolver Guide.** (Illus.). 1980. Stoeger. $10.95.

Ross, H. W. **A Blacksmith Guide to Ruger Flattops & Super Blackhawks.** (Illus.). 96 p. 1982. pap. Blacksmith Corp. $9.95.

Seaton, Lionel, tr. **Famous Auto Pistols and Revolvers, Vol. II.** (Illus.). 1979. Jolex. $6.95.

Williams, Mason. **The Sporting Use of the Handgun.** (Illus.). 1979. C. C. Thomas. $18.00.

Wood, J. B. **Gun Digest Book of Firearms Assembly-Disassembly: Part II: Revolvers.** (Illus.). 320 p. 1979. pap. DBI. $13.95.

RIFLES (see also Firearms, Hawken Rifles, Sharps Rifles, Winchester Rifles)

Bridges, Toby. **Custom Muzzleloading Rifles:** An Illustrated Guide to Building or Buying a Handcrafted Muzzleloader. (Illus.) 224 p. 1986. Stackpole. pap. $16.95.

Buchele, William and Shumway, George. **Recreating the American Longrifle.** Orig. Title: Recreating the Kentucky Rifle. (Illus.). 1973. pap. George Shumway Publisher. pap. $20.00.

Clayton, Joseph D. **The Ruger Number One Rifle.** (Illus.). 212 p. 1982. Blacksmith Corp. $39.95.

Colvin & Viall. **The Manufacture of Model 1903 Springfield Service Rifle.** 392 p. 1984. repr. of 1917 ed. Wolfe Pub. Co. $19.50.

Davis, Henry. **A Forgotten Heritage: The Story of the Early American Rifle.** 1976. Repr. of 1941 ed. Gun Room Press. $9.95.

De Haas, Frank. **Bolt Action Rifle.** rev. ed. 448 p. 1984. DBI. pap. $15.95.

Ezell, Edw. C. **The Great Rifle Controversy: Search for The Ultimate Infantry Weapon From World War II Through Vietnam & Beyond.** 352 p. 1984. Stackpole. $29.95.

—**The AK47 Story: Evolution of the Kalishnokov Weapons.** (Illus.). 256 p. 1986. Stackpole. pap. $12.95.

Fadala, Sam. **Rifleman's Bible.** (Illus.). 192 p. 1987. Doubleday. pap. $7.95.

—**The Book of the Twenty-Two.** (Illus.). 1989. Stoeger Pub. Co. $16.95.

Fremantle, J. F. **The Book of the Rifle.** (Illus.). 576 p. 1985. repr. of 1901 ed. Wolfe Pub. Co. $54.00.

Grant James J. **More Single Shot Rifles.** (Illus.). Gun Room Press. $25.00.

—**Single-Shot Rifles.** Gun Room Press. $25.00.

—**Still More Single Shot Rifles.** 1979. Pioneer Press. $17.50.

Grissom, Ken. **Buckskins & Black Powder: A Mountain Man's Guide to Muzzle Loading.** (Illus.). 224 p. New Century. $15.95.

Hanson. **The Plains Rifle.** Gun Room Press. $19.95.

Hoffschmidt, E. J. **Know Your M-1 Garand Rifles.** 1976. pap. Blacksmith Corp. $5.95.

Huddleston, Joe D. **Colonial Riflemen in the American Revolution.** (Illus.). 1978. George Shumway Publisher. $20.00.

James, Edsall. **The Golden Age of Single Shot Rifles.** Pioneer Press. $2.75.

—**The Revolver Rifles.** Pioneer Press. $2.50.

Keith, Elmer. **Big Game Rifles & Cartridges.** 176 p. 1985. repr of 1936 ed. Gun Room. $19.95.

—**Big Game Rifles & Cartridges.** (Illus.). 176 p. 1984. Deluxe ed. Wolfe Pub. Co. $30.00.

—**Keith's Rifles for Large Game.** (Illus.). 424 p. 1987. Repr. of 1946 ed. Wolfe Pub. Co. $54.00.

Kindig, Joe, Jr. **Thoughts on the Kentucky Rifle in Its Golden Age.** annotated 2nd ed. (Illus.). 1982. George Shumway Publisher. $75.00.

Kindig, Joe K. III. **Artistic Ingredients of the Long Rifle.** (Illus.). 102 p. Shumway. $10.00.

Kirton, Jonathan G. **British Falling Block Breechloading Rifles From 1865.** (Illus.). 250 p. 1985. Armory Pubns. $39.95.

Long, Duncan. **Assault Pistols, Rifles & Submachine Guns.** (Illus.). 152 p. 1986. Paladin Pr. text ed. $19.95.

—**The Mini-14: The Plinker, Hunter, Assault & Everything Else Rifle.** (Illus.).120 p. 1987. Paladin Pr. pap. text ed. $10.00.

—**Modern Sniper Rifle.** (Illus.). 120 p. 1988. Paladin Press. pap $16.95.

McAulay, John D. **Carbines of the Civil War, 1861–1865.** 1981. Pioneer Press. $8.95.

Mallory, Franklin B. & Olson, Ludwig. **The Krag Rifle Story.** 1980. Springfield Research Service. $20.00.

Matthews, Charles W. **Shoot Better With Centerfire Rifle Cartridges-Ballistic Tables.** (Illus.). 560 p. 1984. Matthews Inc. pap. $16.45.

Myatt, F. **An Illustrated Guide to Rifles and Automatic Weapons.** (Illus.). 1981. Arco. $9.95.

O'Connor, Jack, **The Rifle Book.** 3rd ed. (Illus.). 1978. Knopf. pap. $13.95.

Ottenson, Stuart. **The Bolt Action.** 2 vols. rev. ed. 1984. Wolfe Pub. Co. cased set $39.00.

—**Benchrest Actions & Triggers.** Wolfe, Dave, ed. 61 p. 1983. Wolfe Pub. Co. pap. $8.50.

Page, Warren. **The Accurate Rifle.** (Illus.). 1975. softbound. Stoeger. $9.95.

Pitman, John. **Breechloading Carbines of the U.S. Civil War Period.** (Illus.). 94 p. 1987. Armory Pubns. $29.95.

Rywell, Martin. **American Antique Rifles.** Pioneer Press. $2.00.

Sharpe, Philip. **The Rifle in America.** (Illus.). 726 p. 1987. Repr. of 1938 ed. Wolfe Pub. Co. $59.00.

Shelsby, Earl, ed. **NRA Gunsmithing Guide.** Updated rev. ed. (Illus.). 336 p. (Orig.). 1980. pap. Nat'l Rifle Assn. $11.95.

Shumway, George. **Pennsylvania Longrifles of Note.** (Illus.). 1977. pap. George Shumway Publisher. $7.50.

—**Rifles of Colonial America.** 2 vols. incl. Vol. 1; Vol. 2. (Illus.). 1980. casebound. George Shumway Publisher. ea. $49.50.

Steindler, R. A. **Rifle Guide.** 304 p. 1978. softbound. Stoeger. $9.95.

Taylor, C. **African Rifles and Cartridges.** 448 p. Gun Room Press. $21.95.

Tryon, T. B. **The Complete Rehabilitation of the Flintlock Rifle.** 1987. Pioneer Press. $5.95.

U.S. Rifle Caliber .30 Model 1903. Pioneer Press. $2.00.

U.S. Rifle Model 1866 Springfield. Pioneer Press. $1.75.

U.S. Rifle Model 1870 Remington. Pioneer Press. $1.75.

Walsh, J. H. **The Modern Sportsman's Gun & Rifle.** Vol. I & II. (Illus). 536 p. 1986. Wolfe Pub. Co. price on request.

Whelen, Townsend. **The Hunting Rifle.** 464 p. 1984. Repr. of 1924 ed. Wolfe Pub. Co. $39.00.

White, S. E. **The Long Rifle.** (Illus). 544 p. 1987. Repr. of 1930 ed. Wolfe Pub. Co. $25.00.

Wood, J. B. **Gun Digest Book of Firearms Assembly/Disassembly. Pt. III: Rimfire Rifles.** (Illus). 1980. pap. DBI Books.

—**Gun Digest Book of Firearms Assembly/ Disassembly. Part IV: Centerfire Rifles.** (Illus). 1979. pap. $13.95.

Workman, William E. **Know Your Ruger 10-22 Carbine.** (Illus.) 96 p. 1986. Blacksmith Corp. pap. $9.95.

SHARPS RIFLES
Manual of Arms for the Sharps Rifle. Pioneer Press. $1.50.

Rywell, Martin. **Sharps Rifle: The Gun That Shaped American Destiny.** Pioneer Press. $5.00.

SHOOTING (see also Firearms, Trap & Skeet Shooting)
Berger, Robert J. **Know Your Broomhandle Mauser.** (Illus). 96 p. 1985. Blacksmith Corp. pap. $6.95.

Bogardus, A. H. **Field, Cover & Trap Shooting.** (Illus). 500 p. 1987. Repr. of 1878 ed. Wolfe Pub. Co. $43.00.

Bowles, Bruce. **The Orvis Wing Shooting Handbook.** 96 p. 1985. N Lyons Bks. pap. $8.95.

Brister, Bob. **Shotgunning: The Art and the Science.** (Illus). 1976. Winchester Press. $17.95.

Cooper, Jeff. **To Ride, Shoot Straight & Speak the Truth.** (Illus.). 400 p. 1988. Gunsite Press. $26.00.

Crossman, E. C. **Military & Sporting Rifle Shooting.** (Illus). 536 p. 1986. Repr. of 1920 ed. Wolfe Pub. Co. $45.00.

Crossman, Jim. **Olympic Shooting.** (Illus). 144 p. Natl Rifle Assn. $12.95.

Day, J. Wentworth. **The Modern Shooter.** 1976. Repr. of 1952 ed. Charles River Books. $15.00.

Farrow, W. M. **How I Became a Crack Shot With Hints to Beginners.** (Illus). 204 p. Wolfe Pub. Co. $16.50.

Hagel, Bob. **Guns, Loads & Hunting Tips.** Wolfe, Dave, ed. (Illus.). 536 p. 1986. Wolfe Pub. Co. $19.50.

Hill, Gene. **Shotgunners Notebook: The Advice & Reflections of a Wingshooter.** (Illus.). 1989. Countrysport Press. $24.50.*

Humphreys, John. **Learning To Shoot.** (Illus.) 192 p. 1985. David & Charles. $20.95.

Jarrett, William S., ed. **Shooter's Bible 1990.** (Illus.) 576 p. 1989. Stoeger Pub. Co. $16.95.

—**Shooter's Bible 1991.** (Illus.). 576 p. 1990. Stoeger Pub. Co. $17.95.*

King, Peter. **The Shooting Field: 150 Years With Holland & Holland.** (Illus.). 176 p. 1985. Blacksmith. $39.95.

Lind, Ernie. **Complete Book of Trick and Fancy Shooting.** (Illus). 1977. pap. Citadel Press. $3.95.

McGivern, Ed. **Fast and Fancy Revolver Shooting.** New Century. $15.95.

Merkley, Jay P. **Marksmanship with Rifles: A Basic Guide.** (Illus.). pap. American Press. $5.95.

Rees, Clair. **Be An Expert Shot: With Rifle, Handgun, or Shotgun.** (Illus.). 192 p. 1984. New Century. $19.95.

Riling, Ray. **Guns and Shooting: A Bibliography.** (Illus.). 1981. Ray Riling. $75.00.

Ruffer, J. E. **Good Shooting.** (Illus.). 1980. David & Charles. $22.50.

Set Your Sights: A Guide to Handgun Basics. (Illus.). 1982. Outdoor Empire. $1.95.

Shooter's Bible 1940. 512 p. 1989. Stoeger Pub. Co. pap. $16.95.*

Slahor, Stephen, et al. **Shooting Guide for Beginners.** (Illus.). 144 p. 1986. Allegheny. pap. $7.95.

Stanbury, Percy & Carlisle, G. L. **Shotgun Marksmanship.** (Illus). 188 p. 1988. David & Charles. $24.95.

Weston, Paul B. **Combat Shooting for Police.** 2nd ed. (Illus). 1978. C. C. Thomas. $18.00.

Willock, Colin. **Duck Shooting.** (Illus). 144 p. 1981. Andre Deutsch. $18.95.

Yochem, Barbara. **Barbara Yochem's Inner Shooting.** 1981. By By Productions. pap. $3.95.

SHOTGUNS
Anderson, Robert S., ed. **Reloading for Shotgunners.** 2d ed. (Illus). 256 p. 1985. pap. DBI. $12.95.

Askins, Charles. **The American Shotgun.** (Illus). 336 p. 1987. Repr. of 1910 ed. Wolfe Pub. Co. $39.00.

Bowlen, Bruce. **The Orvis Wing Shooting Handbook.** 96 p. 1985. N. Lyons Bks. pap. $8.95.

Brockway, William R. **Recreating the Double Barrel Muzzleloading Shotgun.** (Illus). 1985. Shumway. pap. $20.00.

Elliott, Robert W. & Cobb, Jim. **Lefevre: Guns of Lasting Fame.** 174 p. 1987. R. W. Elliott. $29.95.

Grozik, Richard S. **Game Gun.** (Illus.) 160 p. 1986. Willow Creek. $39.00.

Hastings, Macdonald. **The Shotgun: A Social History.** 1981. David & Charles. $34.95.

Hinman, Bob. **The Golden Age of Shotgunning.** 2nd ed. Wolfe, Dave, ed. (Illus.) 175 p. Wolfe Pub. Co. $17.95.

Keith, Elmer. **Shotguns by Keith.** 1988. Wolfe Pub. Co. $39.00.

Lewis, Jack & Mitchell, Jack. **Shotgun Digest.** 2nd ed. 1980. pap. DBI Books. $13.95.

McIntosh, Michael. **Best Guns.** (Illus). 1989. Countrysport Press. $39.50.*

O'Connor, Jack. **The Shotgun Book,** 2nd ed. rev. (Illus.). 1978. Knopf. pap. $13.95.

Robinson, Roger H. **The Police Shotgun Manual.** (Illus.). 1973. C. C. Thomas. $24.00.

Skillen, Charles R. **Combat Shotgun Training.** (Illus). 1982. C. C. Thomas. $32.50.

Swearengen, Thomas F. **World's Fighting Shotguns.** 1978. TBN Ent. $29.95.

Thomas, Gough. **Shotguns and Cartridges for Game and Clays.** 3rd ed. (Illus.). 1976. Transatlantic Arts, Inc. $25.00.

Zutz, Don. **The Double Shotgun,** rev. ed. 304 p. (Illus). 1985. New Century. $19.95.

SURVIVAL (see also Outdoor Life)
Angier, Bradford. **How to Stay Alive in the Woods.** Orig. Title: **Living Off the Country.** 1962. pap. Macmillan. $5.95.

Benson, Ragnar. **Live Off the Land in The City and Country.** (Illus). 1981. Paladin Enterprises. $19.95.

Canadian Government. **Never Say Die: The Canadian Air Force Survival Manual.** (Illus). 208 p. 1979. Paladin Pr. pap. $10.00.

Churchill, James. **Survival: The Basic Essentials.** (Illus.). 72 p. 1989. ICS Books. pap. $4.95.*

Dennis, Lawrence. **Operational Thinking for Survival.** 1969. R. Myles. $5.95.

Fear, Daniel E., ed. **Surviving the Unexpected: A Curriculum Guide for Wilderness Survival and Survival from Natural and Man Made Disasters.** (Illus.). rev. ed. 1974. Survival Education Association. $6.00.

Fear, Eugene H. **Surviving the Unexpected Wilderness Emergency.** 6th ed. (Illus.). 1979. pap. Survival Education Association. $7.00.

Freeman, Daniel B. **Speaking of Survival.** (Illus.). Oxford University Press. pap. $7.95.

Olsen, Larry D. **Outdoor Survival Skills.** 4th rev. ed. 1973. Brigham Young University Press. $7.95.

—**Outdoor Survival Skills.** 1984. pap. Pocket Books. $3.95.

Read, Piers Paul. **Alive: The Story of the Andes Survivors.** (Illus.). 1975. pap. Avon. pap. $4.95.

Survival Improvised Weapons. 1986. Gordon Press. $79.95 (lib. bdg.).

Wiseman, John. **Survive Safely Anywhere:** The SAS Survival Manual. (Illus.) 1986. Crown. $29.95.

TAXIDERMY
Billard, Ruth S. **Ralph C. Morrill's Museum Quality Fish Taxidermy.** (Illus.). 257 p. 1984. BillArt Pubns. $32.75.

Dahmes, Sallie. **The Sallie Dahmes Whitetail-Mule Deer Taxidermy System.** (Illus.). 160 p. 1987. Breakthrough Pub. pap. $19.95.

Farnham, Albert B. **Home Taxidermy for Pleasure and Profit.** (Illus.). pap. A. R. Harding Publishing. $4.00.

Grantz, Gerald J. **Home Book of Taxidermy and Tanning.** (Illus.). 1985. Stackpole. pap. $9.95.

Metcalf, John C. **Taxidermy: A Computer Manual.** (Illus.). 166 p. 1981. pap. Biblio Dist. $15.00.

Moyer, John W. **Practical Taxidermy.** 2nd ed. 1984. Wiley. pap. $12.95.

Phillips, John E. **How to Make Extra Profits in Taxidermy.** (Illus.). 160 p. 1984. New Century. pap. $12.95.

Pray, Leon L. **Taxidermy.** (Illus.). 1943. Macmillan. $11.95.

Tinsley, Russell. **Taxidermy Guide.** 3d ed. (Illus.). 1990. softbound. Stoeger. $14.95.*

Williamson, Bob & Sexton, Tom. **The Breakthrough Whitetail Taxidermy Manual.** rev. ed. (Illus.). 112 p. 1987. Breakthrough Pubns. pap. $19.95.

TRAP AND SKEET SHOOTING
Blatt, Art. **Gun Digest Book of Trap & Skeet Shooting.** 2d ed. 288 p. 1989. pap. DBI. $14.95.*

Campbell, Robert, ed. **Trapshooting with D. Lee Braun and the Remington Pros.** pap. Benjamin Co. $5.95.

—**Skeet Shooting with D. Lee Braun:** A Remington Sportsman's Library Book. Benjamin Co. $4.95.*

Cradock, Chris. **Manual of Clayshooting.** (Illus.) 192 p. 1986. David & Charles. $34.95.

National Skeet Shooting Association Record Annual. p. Natl. Skeet Shoot. Assn. $9.00.

Smith, A. J. & Upton, Philip. **Sporting Clays.** (Illus.). 156 p. 1989. Willow Creek Press. $19.50.*

Stanbury, Percy & Carlisle, G. L. **Clay Pigeon Marksmanship.** (Illus.). 220 p. 1989. David & Charles. $24.95.*

TRAPPING
Errington, Paul L. **Muskrats and Marsh Management.** (Illus.). 1978. University of Nebraska Press. pap. $4.50.

Geary, Steven. **Fur Trapping in North America.** (Illus.). 384 p. 1985. Stackpole. pap. $10.95.

Get Set To Trap. (Illus.). 1982. Outdoor Empire. $2.95.

Gilsvik, Bob. **The Complete Book of Trapping.** (Illus.). 172 p. Repr. of 1976 ed. AR Harding Pubns. $10.95.

Harding, A. R. **Deadfalls and Snares.** (Illus.). pap. A. R. Harding Publishing. $4.00.

—**Fox Trapping.** (Illus.). pap. A. R. Harding Publishing. $4.00.

—**Mink Trapping.** (Illus.). pap. A. R. Harding Publishing. $4.00.

—**Trappers' Handbook.** 1975. pap. A. R. Harding Publishing. $2.00.

—**Trapping as a Profession.** 1975. pap. A. R. Harding Publishing. $2.00.

—**Wolf & Coyote Trapping.** (Illus.) 252 p. A. R. Harding Pub. pap. $4.00.

Jamison, Rick. **Trapper's Handbook.** 224 p. 1983. pap. DBI. $12.95.

Krause, Tom. **NTA Trapping Handbook: A Guide for Better Trapping.** (Illus.). 205 p. 1984. National Trap Assn. pap. $8.00.

Kreps, E. **Science of Trappings.** (Illus.). pap. A. R. Harding Publishing. $4.00.

Lindsey, Neil M. **Tales of A Wilderness Trapper.** 1973. pap. A. R. Harding Publishing. $2.00.

Lund, Duane R. **A Beginner's Guide to Hunting & Trapping Secrets.** 1988. Adventure Pubns. $7.95.

Lynch, V. E. **Trails to Successful Trapping.** 170 p. 1935. A. R. Harding Publishing. pap. $4.00.

McCracken, Harold & Van Cleve, Harry. **Trapping.** (Illus.). 1974. A. S. Barnes. $8.95.

Martin, Dale. **The Trapper's Bible: Traps, Snares & Pathguards.** (Illus.). 72 p. 1987. Paladin Press. $8.00.

Mascall, Leonard. **A Booke of Fishing with Hooke and Line.** 1973. Repr. of 1590 ed. Walter J. Johnson. $25.00.

Montgomery, David. **Mountain Man Crafts & Skills.** (Illus.). 1981. Horizon Utah. $13.95.

Musgrove, Bill & Blair, Gerry. **Fur Trapping.** (Illus.). 1984. New Century. $12.95.

Russell, Andy. **Trails of a Wilderness Wanderer.** 1975. Knopf. $15.45.

Sandoz, Mari. **The Beaver Men: Spearheads of Empire.** (Illus.). 1978. pap. University of Nebraska Press. $7.50.

The Trapper's Companion. (Illus.). pap. A. R. Harding Publishing. $3.00.

Walters, Keith. **The Book of the Free Trapper.** 1981. Pioneer Press. $7.95.

WINCHESTER RIFLES

Fadala, Sam. **Winchester's 30-30, Model 94:** The Rifle America Loves. (Illus.) 224 p. 1986. Stackpole. $24.95.

Madis, George. **The Winchester Model Twelve.** (Illus.). 1982. Art & Ref. $19.95.

—**The Winchester Book.** 3rd ed. (Illus.). 1979. Art & Reference House. $45.00.

—**The Winchester Handbook.** (Illus.). 1981. Art & Reference House. $19.50.

Twesten, Gary. **Winchester 1894 Carbine: A 90-Year History of the Variations of the Winchester Carbine 1894–1984.** (Illus.). 1984. G. Twesten. $20.00; pap. $20.00.

—**Winchester Model 1892 Carbine.** 1985. G. Tuesten. Pap. $10.00.

West, Bill. **Winchester Encyclopedia.** (Illus.). B. West. $15.00.

—**Winchester Lever-Action Handbook.** (Illus.). B. West. $25.00.

—**Winchester Single Shot.** (Illus.). B. West. $19.00.

—**Winchesters, Cartridges and History.** (Illus.). B. West. $42.00.

Williamson, Snooky. **The Winchester Lever Legacy.** (Illus.). 650 p. 1988. Buffalo Press Pubns. $59.95.

Winchester—Complete Volume I: All Early Winchester Arms 1849–1919. (Illus.) 1981. B. West. $42.00

Winchester—Complete Volume II: All Winchester Arms 1920–1982. 1981. B. West. $42.00.

Names and Addresses of Leading Gun Book Publishers

ARCO PUBLISHING INC.
(see Prentice-Hall Inc.)

ARMORY PUBLICATIONS
P.O. Box 4206
Oceanside, California 92054

BLACKSMITH CORP.
P.O. Box 1752
Chino Valley, Arizona 86323

COCHRAN PUBLISHING
Suburban Route
Box 193
Rapid City, South Dakota 57701

DAVID & CHARLES INC.
P.O. Box 257
North Pomfret, Vermont 05053

DBI BOOKS, INC.
4092 Commercial Avenue
Northbrook, Illinois 60062

DENLINGER'S PUBLISHERS LTD.
P.O. Box 76
Fairfax, Virginia 22030

DOUBLEDAY & CO.
666 Fifth Ave.
New York, New York 10103

DOVER PUBLICATIONS
180 Varick Street
New York, New York 10014

E & P ENTERPRISES
P.O. Box 2613
Lawton, Oklahoma 73502

GUN ROOM PRESS
127 Raritan Avenue
Highland Park, N.J. 08904

JANE'S INFORMATION GROUP
1340 Braddock Place, Suite 300
Alexandria, Virginia 22313

ALFRED A. KNOPF, INC.
201 E. 50 Street
New York, N.Y. 10022

KOPEC PUBLICATION
P.O. Box 157
Whitmore, California 96096

LONGWOOD PUBLISHING GROUP INC.
Box 2069
Wolfeboro, New Hampshire 03894-2069

NATIONAL RIFLE ASSOCIATION
1600 Rhode Island Avenue NW
Washington, D.C. 20036

NEW CENTURY PUBLISHERS, INC.
220 Old New Brunswick Road
Piscataway, N.J. 08854
(also handles title published under
Winchester Press imprint)

PALADIN PRESS
P.O. Box 1307
Boulder, Colorado 80306

PRENTICE-HALL
Englewood Cliffs, N.J. 07632

ROLLING BLOCK PRESS
P.O. Box 853
Ramsey, New Jersey 07446

ALBERT SAIFER, PUBLISHERS
P.O. Box 7125
Watchung, N.J. 07060

SAIGA PUBLISHING CO. LTD.
(see under Longwood Pub. Group Inc.)

SAND POND PUBLISHERS
Box 405, Shady Lane
Hancock, New Hampshire 03449

GEORGE SHUMWAY PUBLISHERS
RD 7, P.O. Box 388B
York, Pennsylvania 17402

STACKPOLE BOOKS
P.O. Box 1831
Harrisburg, Pennsylvania 17105

STATE MUTUAL BOOK & PERIODICAL
SERVICE LTD.
521 Fifth Avenue, 17th Floor
New York, New York 10175

STERLING PUBLISHING CO., INC.
387 Park Avenue South
New York, N.Y. 10016-8810

STOEGER PUBLISHING COMPANY
55 Ruta Court
South Hackensack, N.J. 07606

TAB BOOKS INC.
Blue Ridge Summit
Pennsylvania 17214

TARGET COMMUNICATIONS CORP.
7626 West Donges Bay Road
P.O. Box 188
Mequon, Wisconsin 53902

B. WEST
536 E. Ada Avenue
Glendora, California 91740

WILLOW CREEK PRESS INC.
P.O. Box 300
Wautoma, Wisconsin 54982

WOLFE PUBLISHING COMPANY, INC.
6471 Airpark Drive
Prescott, Arizona 86301

Directory of Manufacturers
and Suppliers

Action Arms, Ltd. (handguns, rifles, scopes, ammunition)
P.O. Box 9573
Philadelphia, Pennsylvania 19124
(215) 744-0100

Aimpoint (sights, scopes, mounts)
203 Elden Street, Suite 302
Herndon, Virginia 22070
(703) 471-6828

American Arms (handguns, rifles, shotguns)
715 E. Armour Road
N. Kansas City, Missouri 64116
(816) 474-3161

American Derringer Corp. (handguns)
127 North Lacy Drive
Waco, Texas 76705
(817) 799-9111

American Military Arms Corp. (Iver Johnson pistols, rifles)
2202 Redmond Road
Jacksonville, Arkansas 72076
(501) 982-1633

Anschutz (handguns, rifles)
Available through Precision Sales International

Arcadia Machine & Tool Inc. (AMT and IAI handguns)
6226 Santos Diaz Street
Irwindale, California 91702
(818) 334-6629

Armes de Chasse (Chapuis, Francotte and Merkel shotguns)
P.O. Box 827
Chadds Ford, Pennsylvania 19317
(215) 388-1146

Armsport, Inc. (shotguns, black powder, scopes)
3590 NW 49th Street
Miami, Florida 33142
(305) 635-7850

Astra (handguns)
Available through Interarms

Auto-Ordnance Corp. (handgun, rifles)
Williams Lane
West Hurley, New York 12491
(914) 679-7225

Bausch & Lomb (scopes)
See Bushnell (Division of)

Beeman Precision Arms, Inc. (imported handguns, rifles, scopes, mounts)
3440-SBL Airway Drive
Santa Rosa, California 95403-2040
(707) 578-7900

Benelli (shotguns)
Available through Heckler & Koch

Beretta U.S.A. Corp. (handguns, shotguns)
17601 Beretta Drive
Accokeek, Maryland 20607
(301) 283-2191

Bernardelli (handguns, shotguns)
Available through Magnum Research

Bersa (handguns)
Available through Eagle Imports Inc.

Blaser USA, Inc. (rifles)
c/o Autumn Sales, Inc.
1320 Lake Street
Fort Worth, Texas 76102
(817) 335-1634

Bonanza (reloading tools)
See Forster Products

Brno (rifles)
Available through Saki International

Browning (handguns, rifles, shotguns)
Route One
Morgan, Utah 84050
(801) 876-2711

B-Square Company (mounts)
P.O. Box 11281
Fort Worth, Texas 76110
(817) 923-0964

Maynard P. Buehler, Inc. (mounts)
17 Orinda Way
Orinda, California 94563
(415) 254-3201

Buffalo Bullet Co., Inc. (reloading, ammunition)
7352 Whittier Avenue
Whittier, California 90602
(213) 696-5738

Burris Company, Inc. (scopes, mounts)
331 East Eighth Street, P.O. Box 1747
Greeley, Colorado 80632
(303) 356-1670

Bushnell (scopes)
Division of Bausch & Lomb
300 North Lone Hill Avenue
San Dimas, California 91773
(714) 592-8000

C-H Tool & Die Corp. (reloading)
106 N. Harding St., P.O. Box L
Owen, Wisconsin 54460
(715) 229-2146

CVA (black powder guns)
5988 Peachtree Corners East
Norcross, Georgia 30071
(404) 449-4687

Chapuis (shotguns)
Available through Armes de Chasse

Charter Arms Corp. (handguns)
430 Sniffens Lane
Stratford, Connecticut 06497
(203) 377-8080

Chinasports, Inc. (handguns)
2010 S. Balboa Ave.
Ontario, California 91761
(714) 923-1411

Churchill (rifles, shotguns)
Available through Ellett Brothers, Inc.

Classic Doubles (shotguns)
1982 Innerbelt Business Center
St. Louis, Missouri 63114
(314) 423-6191

Colt Industries Firearms Division (handguns, rifles)
Talcott Road, Box 1868
Hartford, Connecticut 06101
(203) 236-6311

Coonan Arms, Inc. (handguns)
830 Hampden Ave.
St. Paul, Minnesota 55114
(612) 646-6672

Dakota (handguns, rifles)
Available through E.M.F. Co., Inc.

Dakota Arms, Inc. (rifles)
HC 55, Box 326
Sturgis, South Dakota 57785
(605) 347-4686

Davis Industries (handguns)
15150 Sierra Bonita Lane
Chino, California 91710
(714) 597-4726

Detonics (handguns)
See under New Detonics Manufacturing Corp.

Dixie Gun Works (black powder guns)
Reelfoot Avenue, P.O. Box 130
Union City, Tennessee 38261
(901) 885-0561

Eagle Imports Inc. (Bersa handguns)
1907 Highway 35
Ocean, New Jersey 07712
(201) 531-8375

Ellett Brothers, Inc. (Churchill rifles, shotguns)
P.O. Box 128
Chapin, South Carolina 29036
(803) 345-3751

Emerging Technologies (sights)
P.O. Box 581
Little Rock, Arkansas 72203
(501) 375-2227

E.M.F. Company, Inc. (Dakota handguns, rifles,
black powder)
1900 East Warner Avenue 1-D
Santa Ana, California 92705
(714) 261-6611

Erma (handguns)
Available through Precision Sales (target guns only),
Beeman (PO8 model)

Euroarms of America Inc. (black powder guns)
1501 Lenoir Drive, P.O. Box 3277
Winchester, Virginia 22601
(703) 662-1863

Excam (Targa and Tanarmi pistols)
4480 E. 11th Avenue
Hialeah, Florida 33013
(305) 681-4661-2

Federal Cartridge Corporation (Federal/Norma
ammunition, bullets, primers, cases)
900 Ehlen Drive
Anoka, Minnesota 55303-7503
(612) 422-2840

Federal Ordnance (handguns)
1443 Potrero Avenue, P.O. Box 6050
South El Monte, California 91733
(800) 423-4552

Ferlib (shotguns)
Available through W. L. Moore & Co.

FIE Firearms Corporation (pistols, black powder
guns)
4530 Northwest 135th Street
Opa-Locka, Florida 33054
(305) 685-5966

Forster Products (Bonanza and Forster reloading)
82 East Lanark Avenue
Lanark, Illinois 61046
(815) 493-6360

Francotte (shotguns)
Available through Armes de Chasse

Freedom Arms (handguns)
One Freedom Lane, P.O. Box 1776
Freedom, Wyoming 83120
(307) 883-2468

Galaxy Imports, Ltd., Inc. (Laurona shotguns)
P.O. Box 3361
Victoria, Texas 77903
(512) 573-GUNS

Garbi (shotguns)
Available through W. L. Moore & Co.

Glock, Inc. (handguns)
6000 Highlands Parkway
Smyrna, Georgia 30082
(404) 432-1202

Gonic Arms (black powder rifles)
134 Flagg Road
Gonic, New Hampshire 03867
(603) 332-8457

Grendel, Inc. (handguns)
P.O. Box 908
Rockledge, Florida 32955
(407) 636-1211

Gun South Inc. (Steyr, Steyr Mannlicher rifles)
108 Morrow Ave., P.O. Box 129
Trussville, Alabama 35173
(205) 655-8299

Hammerli (handguns)
Available through Beeman Precision Arms

Heckler & Koch (handguns, rifles, Heym rifles,
Benelli and Gamba shotguns)
21480 Pacific Boulevard
Sterling, Virginia 22170-8903
(703) 450-1900

Hercules Inc. (powder)
Hercules Plaza
Wilmington, Delaware 19894
(302) 594-5000

Heym America, Inc. (rifles)
Available through Heckler & Koch

Hodgdon Powder Co., Inc. (gunpowder)
6231 Robinson, P.O. Box 2932
Shawnee Mission, Kansas 66201
(913) 362-9455

J.B. Holden Co. (scope mounts)
975 Arthur
Plymouth, Michigan 48170
(313) 455-4850

Hornady Manufacturing Company (reloading,
ammunition)
P.O. Box 1848
Grand Island, Nebraska 68802-1848
(308) 382-1390

Howa (rifles)
Available through Interarms

IAI (handguns)
Available through Arcadia Machine & Tool

IMR Powder Company (gunpowder)
R.D. 5, Box 247E
Plattsburgh, New York 12901
(518) 561-9530

Interarms (handguns, shotguns and rifles, including
Astra, Howa, Mark X, Rossi, Star, Walther,
Whitworth)
10 Prince Street
Alexandria, Virginia 22314
(703) 548-1400

InterAims (sights)
Available through Stoeger Industries

Ithaca Acquisition Corp. (shotguns)
891 Route 34B
King Ferry, New York 13081
(315) 364-7171

Iver Johnson/AMAC (handguns, rifles)
Available through American Military Arms Corp.

Paul Jaeger, Inc. (Schmidt & Bender scopes, mounts)
P.O. Box 449
1 Madison Ave.
Grand Junction, Tennessee 38039
(901) 764-6909

K.B.I., Inc. (Kassnar shotguns, rifles, black powder,
Omega shotguns)
P.O. Box 11933
Harrisburg, Pennsylvania 17108
(717) 540-8518

K.D.F. Inc. (rifles)
2485 Highway 46 North
Seguin, Texas 78155
(512) 379-8141

Kimber (rifles, scopes)
9039 S.E. Jannsen Road
Clackamas, Oregon 97015
(503) 656-1704

Krico (rifles)
Available through Beeman Precision Arms

Krieghoff International Inc. (rifles, shotguns)
337A Route 611
Ottsville, Pennsylvania 18942
(215) 847-5173

L.A.R. Manufacturing, Inc. (Grizzly handguns)
4133 West Farm Road
West Jordan, Utah 84084
(801) 255-7106

Laurona (shotguns)
Available through Galaxy Imports

Leupold & Stevens, Inc. (scopes, mounts)
P.O. Box 688
Beaverton, Oregon 97005
(503) 646-9171

Llama (handguns)
Available through Stoeger Industries

Lyman Products Corp. (black powder guns, sights, reloading tools)
Route 147
Middlefield, Connecticut 06455
(203) 349-3421

M.O.A. Corp. (handguns)
7996 Brookville-Salem Road
Brookville, Ohio 45309
(513) 833-5559

MTM Case Gard Co. (reloading tools)
3370 Obco Court
Dayton, Ohio 45414
(513) 890-7461

Magnum Research Inc. (Desert Eagle handguns, Bernardelli and Victory Arms handguns, Bernardelli shotguns)
7110 University Avenue
Minneapolis, Minnesota 55432
(612) 574-1868

Mark X (rifles)
Available through Interarms

Marlin Firearms Company (rifles, shotguns)
100 Kenna Drive
North Haven, Connecticut 06473
(203) 239-5621

Marocchi (Avanza shotguns)
Available through Precision Sales

Mauser/Precision Imports, Inc. (Mauser rifles)
5040 Space Center Drive
San Antonio, Texas 78218
(512) 666-3033

Maverick Arms, Inc. (shotguns)
Industrial Blvd., P.O. Box 586
Eagle Pass, Texas 78853
(512) 773-9007

McMillan & Co., Inc. (rifles)
21438 7th Avenue, Suite E
Phoenix, Arizona 85027
(602) 582-9627

MEC Inc. (reloading tools)
% Mayville Engineering Co.
715 South Street
Mayville, Wisconsin 53050
(414) 387-4500

Merit Corporation (sights, optical aids)
Box 9044
Schenectady, New York 12309
(518) 346-1420

Merkel (shotguns)
Available through Armes de Chasse

Millett Sights (sights and mounts)
16131 Gothard Street
Huntington Beach, California 92647
(714) 842-5575

Mitchell Arms (handguns, black powder, rifles)
3400-1 West MacArthur Blvd.
Santa Ana, California 92704
(714) 957-5711

Modern Muzzle Loading Inc. (black powder guns)
Highway 136 East, P.O. Box 130
Lancaster, Missouri 63548
(816) 457-2125

William L. Moore & Co. (Garbi, Ferlib and Piotti shotguns)
31360 Via Colinas, No. 109
Westlake Village, California 91361
(818) 889-4160

O.F. Mossberg & Sons, Inc. (shotguns)
7 Grasso Avenue
North Haven, Connecticut 06473
(203) 288-6491

Navy Arms Company, Inc. (shotguns, black powder guns, replicas)
689 Bergen Boulevard
Ridgefield, New Jersey 07657
(201) 945-2500

New Detonics Manufacturing Corp. (handguns)
21438 North 7th Avenue
Phoenix, Arizona 85027
(602) 582-4867

New England Firearms Co., Inc. (handguns)
Industrial Rowe
Gardner, Massachusetts 01440
(508) 632-9393

Norma (ammunition, gunpowder, reloading cases)
Available through Federal Cartridge Corp.

North American Arms (handguns)
1800 North 300 West
P.O. Box 707
Spanish Fork, Utah 84660
(801) 798-7401 or (800) 821-5783

Olin/Winchester (ammunition, primers, cases)
East Alton, Illinois 62024
(618) 258-2000

Omark Industries, Inc. (RCBS reloading tools, Speer bullets, Weaver mount rings)
Box 856
Lewiston, Idaho 83501
(208) 746-2351

Omega (shotguns)
Available through K.B.I.

Parker-Hale (rifles, shotguns)
Available through Precision Sports

Parker Reproduction (shotguns)
124 River Road
Middlesex, New Jersey 08846
(201) 469-0100

Pentax (scopes)
35 Inverness Drive East
Englewood, Colorado 80112
(303) 799-8000

Perazzi U.S.A. (shotguns)
1207 S. Shamrock Ave.
Monrovia, California 91016
(818) 303-0068

Piotti (shotguns)
Available through W.L. Moore & Co.

Precision Sales International (Anschutz pistols, rifles; Marocchi shotguns; Erma pistols)
P.O. Box 1776
Westfield, Massachusetts 01086
(413) 562-5055

Precision Sports (Parker-Hale rifles, shotguns)
3736 Kellogg Road, P.O. Box 5588
Cortland, New York 13045-5588
(607) 756-2851

Raven Arms (handguns)
1300 Bixby Drive
Industry, California 91745
(818) 961-2511

RCBS, Inc. (reloading tools)
See Omark Industries, Inc.

Redding Reloading Equipment (reloading tools)
1089 Starr Road
Cortland, New York 13045
(607) 753-3331

Redfield (scopes)
5800 East Jewell Avenue
Denver, Colorado 80224
(303) 757-6411

Remington Arms Company, Inc. (handguns, rifles, shotguns, ammunition, primers)
1007 Market Street
Wilmington, Delaware 19898
(302) 773-5291

Rossi (handguns, rifles, shotguns)
Available through Interarms

Ruger (handguns, rifles, shotguns, black powder guns)
See Sturm, Ruger & Company, Inc.

Saki International (Brno handguns, rifles)
19800 Center Ridge Road
P.O. Box 16189
Rocky River, Ohio 44116
(216) 331-3533

Sako (rifles, actions, scope mounts)
Available through Stoeger Industries

Savage Arms (rifles, shotguns)
Springdale Road
Westfield, Massachusetts 01085
(413) 562-2361

Schmidt and Bender (scopes)
Available through Paul Jaeger, Inc.

Shilo Rifle Mfg. Co., Inc. (Shiloh Sharps black powder rifles)
P.O. Box 279, Industrial Park
Big Timber, Montana 59011
(406) 932-4454

Sierra Bullets (bullets)
10532 S. Painter Avenue
Santa Fe Springs, California 90670
(213) 941-0251 or (800) 223-8799

Sigarms Inc. (handguns, Sauer rifles)
470 Spring Park Place, Unit 900
Herndon, Virginia 22070
(703) 481-6660

Sig-Sauer (handguns)
Available through Sigarms Inc.

Simmons Outdoor Corp. (scopes)
14530 SW 119th Ave.
Miami, Florida 33186
(305) 252-0477

SKB Shotguns (shotguns)
c/o Ernie Simmons Enterprises
709 E. Elizabethtown Rd.
Manheim, Pennsylvania 17545
(717) 664-4040

Smith & Wesson (handguns)
2100 Roosevelt Avenue
Springfield, Massachusetts 01102-2208
(413) 781-8300

Southern Gun Distributors (Tanarmi and Targa handguns)
13490 N.W. 45th Avenue
Opa-Locka (Miami), Florida 33054-0025
(305) 685-8451

Speer (bullets)
See Omark Industries, Inc.

Springfield Armory (handguns, rifles, scopes)
420 West Main Street
Geneseo, Illinois 61254
(309) 944-5631

Star (handguns)
Available through Interarms

Steyr (handguns)
Available through Gun South Inc.

Steyr-Mannlicher (rifles)
Available through Gun South Inc.

Stoeger Industries (Sako rifles, Llama handguns, Stoeger shotguns, Tikka rifles, shotguns; InterAims sights; mounts, actions)
55 Ruta Court
South Hackensack, New Jersey 07606
(201) 440-2700

Sturm, Ruger and Company, Inc. (Ruger handguns, rifles, shotguns)
Lacey Place
Southport, Connecticut 06490
(203) 259-7843

Swarovski American (scopes)
2 Slater Road
Cranston, Rhode Island 02920
(401) 463-3000

Tanarmi and Targa (pistols)
Available through Southern Gun Distributors

Tasco (scopes and mounts)
7600 N.W. 26th Street
Miami, Florida 33122
(305) 591-3670

Taurus International, Inc. (handguns)
4563 Southwest 71st Avenue
Miami, Florida 33155
(305) 662-2529

Thompson/Center Arms (handguns, rifles, black powder guns, scopes)
Farmington Road, P.O. Box 5002
Rochester, New Hampshire 03867
(603) 332-2394

Tikka (rifles, shotguns)
Available through Stoeger Industries

Traditions, Inc. (black powder guns)
P.O. Box 235
Deep River, Connecticut 06417
(203) 526-9555

Uberti USA, Inc. (handguns, rifles, black powder rifles and revolvers)
362 Limerock Rd., P.O. Box 469
Lakeville, Connecticut 06039
(203) 435-8068

Ultra Light Arms Company (rifles, black powder rifles)
214 Price Street, P.O. Box 1270
Granville, West Virginia 26534
(304) 599-5687

U.S. Repeating Arms Co. (Winchester rifles, shotguns)
275 Winchester Avenue
New Haven, Connecticut 06511
(203) 789-5000

Varner Sporting Arms (rifles)
1004F Cobb Parkway, N.E.
Marietta, Georgia 30062
(404) 422-5468

Victory Arms (handguns)
Available through Magnum Research

Walther (handguns, rifles)
Available through Interarms

Weatherby, Inc. (rifles, shotguns, scopes, ammunition)
2781 Firestone Boulevard
South Gate, California 90280
(213) 569-7186

Weaver (scopes, mount rings)
% Omark Industries
Route 2, Box 39
Onalaska, Wisconsin 54650
(800) 635-7656

Dan Wesson Arms, Inc. (handguns)
293 Main Street
Monson, Massachusetts 01057
(413) 267-4081

Whitworth (rifles)
Available through Interarms

Wildey Inc. (handguns)
P.O. Box 475
Brookfield, Connecticut 06804
(203) 355-9000

Wilkinson Arms (handguns, rifles)
Route 2, Box 2166
Parma, Idaho 83660
(208) 722-6771-2

Williams Gun Sight Co. (sights, scopes, mounts)
7389 Lapeer Road, P.O. Box 329
Davison, Michigan 48423
(313) 653-2131

Winchester (ammunition, primers, cases)
See Olin/Winchester

Winchester (domestic rifles, shotguns)
See U.S. Repeating Arms Co.

Winslow Arms Co. (rifles)
P.O. Box 783
Camden, South Carolina 29020
(803) 432-2938

Zeiss Optical, Inc. (scopes)
1015 Commerce Street
Petersburg, Virginia 23803
(804) 861-0033

Antonio Zoli U.S.A., Inc. (shotguns)
P.O. Box 6190
Fort Wayne, Indiana 46896
(219) 447-4603

To help you find the model of your choice, the following list includes each gun found in the catalog section of **Shooter's Bible 1991.** A supplemental listing of **Discontinued Models** and the **Caliberfinder** follow immediately after this section.

BLACK POWDER

MUSKETS, CARBINES AND RIFLES

CVA

Squirrel	358
Blazer	358
St. Louis Hawken	358
Apollo 90	359
Hunter Hawken	359
Hawken	359
Kentucky	359
Pennsylvania Long	360
Express Double Barrel	360
Frontier Carbine	360
Over/Under Carbine	361
Ozark Mountain	361

Dixie

Second Model Brown Bess	365
Kentuckian Flintlock/Perc.	365
Hawken	366
Tennessee Mountain	366
Tennessee Squirrel	366
Pennsylvania	366
Pedersoli Waadtlander	366
Mississippi Rifle	367
Winchester '73 Carbine	367
Wesson	367
Tryon Creedmoor	367
1862 Three-Band Enfield	368
1858 Two-Band Enfield	368
1863 Springfield Civil War	368
1861 Springfield Perc.	368

Euroarms

Cook & Brother Confederate Carbine	370
J. P. Murray Carbine	370
Magnum Cape	370
London Armory Company (2-band)	371
London Armory Company Enfield Musketoon	371
London Armory Company 3-Band Enfield Rifled Musket	371
1803 Harpers Ferry Rifle	372
1841 Mississippi Rifle	372
1863 Zouave Rifle	372

Gonic

Model GA-87 (458 Express)	374

Lyman

Deerstalker Rifle	375
Great Plains Rifle	375
Trade Rifle	375

Modern Muzzleloading

Knight MK-85	377

Navy Arms

Parker-Hale Whitworth Military Target	383
Parker-Hale 451 Volunteer	383
Ithaca/Navy Hawken	383
#2 Creedmoor Target	384
Rolling Block Buffalo	384
Country Boy	384
1853 Enfield Rifle Musket	385
1858 Enfield	385
1861 Enfield Musketoon	385
Mississippi Model 1841	386
Rigby-Style Target	386
1863 Springfield	386
Henry Military	387
Iron Frame Henry	387

Henry Trapper	387
Henry Carbine	387
Flintlock Rifle	388

Shiloh Sharps

Model 1874 Business	389
Model 1874 Military	389
Model 1874 Carbine "Civilian"	389
Model 1863 Sporting	390
Model 1874 Sporting #1	390
Model 1874 Sporting #3	390

Thompson/Center

Pennsylvania Hunter	391
New Englander	391
Hawken	392
White Mountain Carbine	392
Renegade	393
Renegade Single Trigger Hunter	393
Cherokee	393
Scout Carbine	394

Traditions

Frontier Scout	395
Hunter	395
Hawken	395
Hawken Woodsman	396
Pennsylvania	396
Pioneer	396
Trophy	396
Trapper	397
Frontier	397

A. Uberti

Santa Fe Hawken	399

Ultra Light

Model 90	399

PISTOLS

CVA

Hawken	357
Kentucky	357
Colonial	357
Philadelphia Derringer	357
Vest Pocket Derringer	357
Siber	357

Dixie

Screw Barrel Derringer	363
French Charleville Flint	363
"Hideout" Derringer	363
Lincoln Derringer	363
Abilene Derringer	363
LePage Perc.	364
Queen Anne	364
Pedersoli English Dueling	364
Pennsylvania	364

Lyman

Plains Pistol	375

Navy Arms

LePage Flintlock	381
LePage Percussion	381
LePage Double Cased Set	381
Kentucky	382
Harper's Ferry	382

Thompson/Center

Scout	394

Traditions

William Parker	394
Trapper	397

REVOLVERS

Armsport

Models 5133/5136/5138/5120/5139/5140	352
Models 5145/5152/5153/5154/5155 Remington Buffalo	353

CVA

1858 Remington Army Steel Frame	354
1858 Remington Target	354
Colt Walker	354
New Model Pocket Remington	354
1861 Colt Navy	355
1851 Colt Navy	355
Colt Sheriff's Model	355
1860 Colt Army	355
Wells Fargo Model Colt	356
Remington Bison	356
Third Model Colt Dragoon	356
Colt Pocket Police	356

Dixie

1860 Army	362
Navy Revolver	362
Spiller & Burr	362
"Wyatt Earp"	362
Walker	363
Third Model Dragoon	363

EMF

Sheriff's Model 1851	369
Model 1860 Army	369
Model 1862 Police	369
Model 1851 Steel Navy	369
Second Model 44 Dragoon	369

Euroarms

Rogers & Spencer (Model 1005)	373
Rogers & Spencer Army (Model 1006)	373
Rogers & Spencer (Model 1007)	373
Remington 1858 New Model Army (Models 1020, 1025 & 1040)	373
Schneider & Glassick 1851 Navy Confederate	374
Schneider & Glassick 1851 Navy	374

Mitchell Arms

1851 Colt Navy	376
Spiller & Burr	376
Remington New Model Army	376
1860 Colt Army	376
Remington "Texas" Model	376

Navy Arms

1862 Police	377
Lemat (Army, Navy, Calvary)	378
Colt Walker 1847	378
Rogers & Spencer Navy	378
Reb Model 1860	379
Colt Army 1860	379
1851 Navy Yank	379
Stainless Steel 1858 Remington	380
Target Model Remington	380
Deluxe 1858 Remington-Style	380
Remington New Model Army	380
Army 60 Sheriff's	380

A. Uberti

1st, 2nd & 3rd Model Dragoons	398
1861 Navy	398
Walker	398
1851 Navy	398
1862 Pocket Navy	398
1858 Remington Army 44	399

DISCONTINUED MODELS

The following models, all of which appeared in the 1990 edition of Shooter's Bible, have been discontinued by their manufacturers or distributors and therefore do not appear in the 1991 edition.

BLACK POWDER

NAVY ARMS
Elgin Cutlass Pistol

THOMPSON/CENTER
Patriot

A. UBERTI
New Army Target Revolving Carbine

HANDGUNS

AMERICAN ARMS
Model 1 (30 Luger, 30 Mauser, 41 Action Auto, 9mm and 38 Special only)

EXCAM/TANARMI
Model TA 76M "Buffalo Scout"

THOMPSON/CENTER
Alloy II Contender

A. UBERTI
1873 Stallion Quick Draw SA
1875 Remington Outlaw

WALTHER
Model P-38 DA (22LR only)

RIFLES

BEEMAN/KRICO
Model 400

BROWNING
A-Bolt High Grade Big Horn Sheep (Limited Edition)
Model 65

BLASER
Model K77A Single Shot

CHURCHILL
Rotary 22

CLASSIC RIFLES
Standard Grade
Grades I and II

HECKLER & KOCH
Model 630
Model 770
Model 940

HOWA
Model 1500 Trophy Grade

IVER JOHNSON
L'il Champ Single Shot

MARLIN
Model 336 Lightweight

PARKER-HALE
Target Rifles (Models M87 & M84)

PRECISION SALES
Injek Net Projector

REMINGTON
Model 700 ("RS" & "FS")
Model Seven "FS"
Sportsman Model 78 Bolt Action

RUGER
Model M77RS Tropical

SAKO
Fiberclass (Short Action only)
Carbine (213 Rem., 270 Win., 30-06 only)
Fiberclass Carbine (243 Win. only)
Mannlicher-Style Carbine (222 Rem. only)
Laminated Stock (223 Rem. and all Left Hand Models only)
Safari Grade (300 Win. Mag. only)
Left Hand Custom Rifles (all Fiberclass Long Action Models)

SAUER
Model S-90 Supreme & Linx
Model S-90 Stutzen
Model S-90 Safari

VALMET
Hunter Model 412S Double Rifle (now distributed under Tikka label in 9.3×74R only)

A. UBERTI
Model 1866 Indian Carbine
Model 1875 Army Target Revolving Carbine
Buckhorn Revolving Carbine

WEATHERBY
Mark V Euromark (378 Wby. Mag. only)
Mark XXII Semiauto

SHOTGUNS

AMERICAN ARMS
Model RS/Combo O/U
Sterling Model O/U
Model AASB Single Barrel Models
Camper Special
Turkey Special S/S

ARMSPORT
Congress Combo Series O/U
Double Trigger O/U
Turkey Gun (Models 2782 thru 2785)

BERNARDELLI
Elio S/S
Model 120 O/U Combo

BROWNING
Recoilless Single Barrel Trap

CHURCHILL
Royal S/S
Windsor I S/S (10 ga. only)

FRANCHI
Elite Autoloader
Prestige Autoloader

KRIEGHOFF
Model Teck O/U
Model Ulm O/U

MERKEL
Models 47S, 147S, 247S, 447S
Boxlock Models 122E & 47E

MOSSBERG
Persuader 8-Shot (Speedfeed Model only)
Persuader 6-Shot Maxi-Combo

REMINGTON
Model 1100 Tournament Skeet

SILMA
Models 70 & 80

SKB
Model 3000
Model 1300 Slug Gun

VALMET
Models 412ST Trap & Skeet, Premium & Standard Grade (now distributed under the Tikka label)

WEATHERBY
Model 82 Automatic

CALIBERFINDER

How to use this guide: To find a 22LR handgun, look under that heading in the **Handguns** section. You'll find several models of that description, including Beretta Model 21. Turn next to the **Gunfinder** section and locate the heading for **Beretta** (pistols, in this case). Beretta's **Model 21,** as indicated, appears on p. 93.

BLACK POWDER

HANDGUNS

31

CVA New Model Pocket Remington, Wells Fargo Model Colt, Vest Pocket Derringer

36

Armsport Models 5133, 5135
CVA Models 1851 & 1861 Colt Navy Revolvers, Sheriff's Model, Pocket Police
Dixie Navy Revolver, Spiller & Burr Revolver
EMF 1851 Sheriff's Model, 1851 Steel Navy, Model 1862 Police
Euroarms Schneider & Glassick 1851 Navy & Navy Sheriff, Schneider & Glassick 1851 Navy Confederate Revolver
Mitchell Arms 1851 and 1861 Colt Navy, Spiller & Burr, Remington "Texas" Model, Remington New Model Army
Navy Arms 1862 Police Revolver, Reb Model 1860, Army 1860 Sheriff's Model, 1851 Navy "Yank" Revolver
A. Uberti 1851 Navy, 1861 Navy, 1862 Pocket Navy

38

Dixie Pedersoli Navy Target Pistol

41

Dixie Abilene & Lincoln Derringers

44

Armsport Models 5138, 5120, 5134, 5135, 5136, 5139, 5145, 5152
CVA 1861 Colt Navy, 1860 Colt Army Revolvers, Colt Walker, Third Model Colt Dragoon, Remington Bison, 1858 Remington Army Steel Frame Revolver (also Brass Frame)
Dixie Walker Revolver, Pennsylvania Pistol, Third Model Dragoon, Wyatt Earp Revolver
EMF Model 1860 Army, Second Model 44 Dragoon
Euroarms Rogers & Spencer Models 1005 & 1006, Remington 1858 New Model Army (and Target)
Mitchell Arms 1851 and 1861 Colt Navy, 1860 Army Model, Remington "Texas" Model, Remington New Model Army
Navy Arms Colt Walker 1847, Reb Model 1860 Revolver, Colt Army 1860 Revolver, Rogers & Spencer Navy Revolver, Target Model Remington Revolver, Stainless Steel 1858 Remington, Remington New Model Army, LeMat Revolvers, 1851 Navy Yank Revolver, Deluxe 1858 Remington-Style Revolver
Uberti 1st Model Dragoon, Walker, 1858 Remington

45

CVA Colonial, Philadelphia Derringer, Siber
Dixie Pedersoli English Dueling Pistol, LePage Dueling Pistol

Navy Arms LePage Percussion 7 Flint Pistols, Double Cased LePage Pistols
Thompson/Center William Parker Pistol
Traditions Trapper Pistol

50

CVA Kentucky Pistol, Hawken Pistol
Dixie Queen Anne Pistol
Lyman Plains Pistol
Thompson/Center Scout Pistol
Traditions Trapper

54

Lyman Plains Pistol
Thompson/Center Scout Pistol

56

Navy Arms Harper's Ferry Pistol

RIFLES (Black Powder)

308 Spitfire

Gonic Arms Model GA-87

32

Dixie Tennessee Squirrel
Navy Arms Country Boy
Thompson/Center Cherokee

36

CVA Squirrel
Modern Muzzleloading BK-89 Squirrel
Navy Arms Country Boy
Traditions Trapper, Frontier Scout

44

Navy Arms Henry Carbine, Iron Frame, Henry Military

44-40

Dixie Winchester '73 Carbine
Navy Arms Henry Carbine, Henry Trapper, Military, Iron Frame, Henry Military

45

Dixie Kentuckian, Hawken, Pedersoli Waadtlander, Tryon Creedmoor
Modern Muzzleloading Knight MK-85
Navy Arms Country Boy
Thompson/Center Hawken, Cherokee
Traditions Frontier, Frontier Scout, Pennsylvania, Uberti Santa Fe Hawken
Ultra Light Arms Model 90

451

Navy Arms Rigby-Style Target Rifle, Parker-Hale Whitworth Military Target, Parker-Hale 451 Volunteer

45-70

EMF Sharps Carbine/Rifle
Navy Arms Rolling Block Buffalo rifle, #2 Creedmoor Target
Shiloh Sharps Model 1874 Sporting Rifle #1 & #3/Business/Military/"Civilian" Carbine

45-90

Shiloh Sharps Model 1874 Sporting #1 & #3; Model 1874 Business/"Civilian" Carbine

45-120

Shiloh Sharps Model 1874 Sporting #1 & #3, Business

458

Gonic Model GA-87

50

CVA Frontier, Blazer, Kentucky, Pennsylvania Long Rifle, St. Louis Hawken, Apollo 90, Hawken, Hunter Hawken, Express Double Rifle & Carbine, Over-Under Carbine, Ozark Mountain
Dixie Hawken, Tennessee Mountain, Wesson
Lyman Great Plains, Trade Rifle, Deerstalker Rifle
Modern Muzzleloading Knight MK-85
Navy Arms Country Boy, Ithaca-Navy Hawken
Thompson/Center Renegade, Renegade Hunter, Cougar Hawken, Scout Carbine, Hawken, New Englander, Pennsylvania Hunter, White Mountain Carbine
Traditions Frontier Scout, Hunter, Hawken, Frontier, Pennsylvania, Hawken Woodsman, Trapper, Pioneer, Trophy
Uberti Santa Fe Hawken
Ultra Light Arms Model 90

50-70

Shiloh Sharps Model 1874 Business, Sporting #1 & #3, Military

50-90

Shiloh Sharps Model 1874 Business, Sporting #1 & #3

50-140

Shiloh Sharps Model 1874 Business, Sporting #1 & #3

54

CVA St. Louis Hawken, Hawken Mountain, Express Double Barrel, Hunter Hawken, Ozark Mountain
Dixie Hawken
EMF Sharps Carbine/Rifle
Euroarms 1803 Harper's Ferry
Lyman Great Plains, Trade Rifle, Deerstalker
Modern Muzzleloading Knight MK-85
Navy Arms Ithaca Navy Hawken
Shiloh Sharps Model 1863 Sporting
Thompson/Center Renegade, Renegade Hunter, Hawken, New Englander, Scout Carbine
Traditions Hunter, Hawken, Hawken Woodsman, Pioneer, Trophy
Uberti Sante Fe Hawken

557

Navy Arms 1853 Enfield Rifle Musket, 1858 Enfield Rifle, 1861 Enfield Musketoon

58

Dixie U.S. Model 1861 Springfield, Mississippi, St. Louis Hawken, 1863 Springfield Civil War Musket, 1862 Three-Band Enfield Rifle Musket, 1858 Two-Band Enfield rifle

Euroarms Model 2260 London Armory Company Enfield Rifled Musket, Models 2270 and 2280 London Armory Company Enfield Rifled Muskets, Model 2300 Cook & Brother Confederate Carbine, J. P. Murray Carbine, 1841 Mississippi, 1863 Zouave

Navy Arms 1863 Springfield, Mississippi Model 1841

75

Dixie Second Model Brown Bess Musket

SHOTGUNS (Black Powder)

CVA Trapper (12 ga.)
Dixie Double Barrel Magnum (12 ga.)
Euroarms Model 2295 Magnum Cape (single barrel)
Navy Arms Model T&T, Flintlock, Fowler (12 ga.)
Thompson/Center New Englander

HANDGUNS

22LR

American Arms Models PK & PX, Model P-98, Woodmaster
Anschutz Exemplar
Astra Constable
Beeman Unique 690 Target, Model PO8, Model 150 Free Pistol, Model 152 Electronic, Beeman/Hammerli Model 208 Target & Model 215 Target, Model 280,
Beretta Model 21, Model 89
Bernardelli Model PO10 Standard, Model 69, AMR, USA
Bersa Model 23
Browning Buck Mark 22
Charter Arms Pathfinder, Off-Duty
Chinasports Norinco Type EM-32
Davis Model D-22
EMF/Dakota Model 1873, Dakota Target, 1894 Bisley
Erma ESP 85A Sporting Pistol, Model 772 Match Revolver
F.I.E. Arminius, Cowboy, Model SSP, Model 722 TP Silhouette
Heckler & Koch Model P7K3
Iver Johnson Pocket Model, Trailsman Model TM 22
Llama Automatic (Small Frame)
Mitchell Arms SA Army Model (revolvers)
New England Firearms Standard Revolver, Ultra Revolver
North American Arms Mini-Revolvers
Rossi Model 511
Ruger New Model Single-Six, Mark II Pistols, Model SP101 Revolver
Smith & Wesson Models 17, 34, 63, 41, 422
Springfield Armory Model 1911-A2 SASS
Targa Model GT22T
Taurus Model 94
Thompson/Center Contender
A. Uberti 1871 Rolling Block Target Pistol, 1873 Cattleman Quick Draw
Walther Model P-38, Model TPH-DA, Models OSP & GSP, Model FP (Free Pistol), Model U.I.T.-BV

22 Rimfire Magnum

American Derringer Model 1
AMT 22 Automag II

Anschutz Exemplar
EMF/Dakota Model 1873
Grendel Model P-30
North American Mini-Revolvers
Ruger Government Target Model
Dan Wesson 22 Rimfire Magnum

22 Short

Beeman Unique 2000-U, Beeman/Hammerli Model 232 Rapid Fire
Beretta Model 950 BS
F.I.E. Arminius DA, Cowboy
North American Arms Mini-Revolvers
Walther OSP Match Rapid Fire Pistol

22 Hornet

American Derringer Model 1
MOA Maximum
Thompson/Center Contender
Uberti 1871 Rolling Block Target Pistol

22 Win. Mag.

F.I.E. Arminius, Cowboy
New England Firearms Ultra Revolver
North American Mini-Revolvers
Thompson/Center Contender
Uberti 1871 Rolling Block Target Pistol, 1873 Cattleman Quick Draw
Dan Wesson 22 Win. Mag. Revolvers

223 Remington

Remington Model XP-100, XP-100R Custom
Springfield Armory Model 1911-A2 SASS
Thompson/Center Contender, Hunter

223 Rem. Comm. Auto

American Derringer Model 1
Thompson/Center Contender

6mm BR

Remington XP-100 Long-Range Custom

25 Auto

Beretta Model 21, Model 950BS
Davis Model D-22 Derringer
F.I.E. Model E28
KBI/Kassnar Model PSP-25
Raven Arms Model P-25
Targa Model GT 26S

250 Savage

Remington XP-100 Long-Range Custom

270 Remington

Thompson/Center Contender

7mm BR

Remington Model XP-100
Springfield Armory Model 1911-A2 SASS

7mm T.C.U.

Thompson/Center Contender

7mm-08

Remington Model XP-100 Long-Range Custom

7-30 Water

Thompson/Center Contender, Hunter

30 Luger

American Derringer Model 1
Walther Model P-38

30 Carbine

IAI Automag III
Ruger Model BN-31
Thompson/Center Contender

30 Mauser (7.62 Tokarev)

American Derringer Model 1

30-30 Win.

American Derringer Model 1
Thompson/Center Contender, Hunter

32 Mag.

American Derringer Models 1, 3 & 7, Lady Derringer
Charter Arms Police Bulldog, Bonnie & Clyde
Walther 32 Magnum Six-Shot

32 Auto

Davis Models D-22 and P-32
F.I.E. Model SSP
Llama Auto (Small Frame)
Walther Models PPK & PPKS

32 H&R

Charter Arms Police Undercover
New England Firearms Ultra Revolver
Ruger New Model Single-Six SSM

32 S&W Long

American Derringer Model 7
Beeman/Hammerli Model 280
Erma Model 773 Match, ESP 85 Sporting
F.I.E. Arminius
Ruger New Model Single-Six SSM
Smith & Wesson Model 31
Taurus Model 73

32 S&W Wadcutter

Erma ESP 85A Sporting Pistol, Model 773 Match Revolver
Walther Model GSP-C

32-20

American Derringer Model 1
EMF/Dakota Model 1873
Thompson/Center Contender

35 Remington

Remington Model XP-100, XP-100R Custom
Thompson/Center Contender, Hunter

357 Mag.

American Derringer Models 1, 6
Astra 357 Mag. Big-Bore
Beeman Korth
Charter Arms Bulldog Tracker, Police Bulldog, Target Bulldog, Pit Bull
Colt King Cobra, Python
EMF/Dakota Target, 1894 Bisley, 1875 Outlaw, Model 1873, Model 1813 Premier SA, Custom Engraved S4
Erma Model 777 Sporting Revolver
F.I.E. Arminius
L.A.R. Grizzly Mark I
Llama Comanche III
Magnum Research Desert Eagle
Mitchell Arms SA Army revolvers, 1875 Remington Revolver
Rossi Model 971
Ruger Model GP-100, New Model Bisley, Blackhawk SA
Smith & Wesson Models 13, 19, 27, 65, 66, 586
Springfield Armory Model 1911-A2 SASS
Taurus Models 65, 66, 669

Thompson/Center Contender
Uberti 1875 and 1890 Remington Army Outlaw, 1871 Rolling Block Target pistol, 1873 Cattleman Quick Draw
Dan Wesson 357 Mag., 357 Super Mag.

357 Maximum

American Derringer Model 1
Thompson/Center Contender, Hunter

358 Winchester

MOA Maximum
Springfield Armory Model 1911-All SASS

38 Special

American Derringer 1, 3, 7, 11, Lady Derringer, DA 38 Double Derringer
Charter Arms Police Undercover, Police Bulldog, Off-Duty, Undercover 38 Special, Bonnie & Clyde, Pit Bull
F.I.E. Derringer D-86, Titan Tiger, Arminius
Rossi Models 68, M88, M951
Ruger Model SP101
Smith & Wesson Models 649, LadySmith
Taurus Models 66, 80, 82, 83, 85, 86, 669
Uberti 1873 Cattleman Quick Draw
Dan Wesson 38 Special

380 Auto

American Arms Model EP
American Derringer Models 1 and 7
AMT Model 380 Backup
Astra Constable
Beeman Model Mini-PO8
Beretta Models 84, 85, 86
Bernardelli Models AMR, USA
Bersa Model 383 DA, Model 85
Browning Model BDA-380
Colt Government Model, Mustang, Mustang Plus II, Mustang Pocket Lite 380
Davis P-380
F.I.E. Super Titan II, Model SSP
Grendel Model P-10
Heckler & Koch Model P7K3
Iver Johnson Pony Model PO380B
Llama Automatic (Small Frame)
Sig Sauer Model 230
Targa Model GT380XE
Taurus Model PT 58
Walther Model PPK & PPKS, 357 Super Mag.

38 Super

American Derringer Model 7
Auto-Ordnance Model 1911A-1 Thompson
Chinasports Type 54-1 Tokarev
Colt Combat Commander, Government Model
Llama Compact
Sig Sauer Model 220
Springfield Armory Model 1911-A1 Standard, Omega
Victory Arms Model MC5

38 S&W

American Derringer Model 7
Smith & Wesson Models 10, 13, 15, 36, 38, 49, 52, 60, 64, 65

9mm Federal

American Derringer Model 1
Charter Arms Target Bulldog

9mm Luger

American Derringer Model 1, DA 38 Double Derringer
Heckler & Koch Model P7M8
Smith & Wesson Model 5900 & 6900 Series
Thompson/Center Contender
Walther Model P-38
Wilkinson Arms Model "Linda" Pistol

9mm Parabellum

Action Arms Models AT-885, AT-88P, AT-88H
American Derringer Semmerling LM-4
Auto Ordnance Model 1911A-1 Thompson
Astra Model A-90
Beretta Model 92F
Bernardelli Model P018
Bersa Model 90
Browning 9mm Hi-Power
Charter Arms Pit Bull
Colt Combat Commander, Government
F.I.E. Model TZ75
Glock Models 17, 17L Competition, Model 19
Heckler & Koch Models P7M8 & P7M13, Model SP89
KBI/Kassnar Model 941 Jericho
Llama Automatics (Compact Frame), Model M-82, M-87 Comp
Ruger Model P-85
Sig Sauer Models 220, 225, 226, 228
Smith & Wesson Third Generation Pistols (Model 3900, 5900 and 6900 Series)
Springfield Armory Model 1911-A1 Standard, Model P9 DA
Star Models BKM, BM, Models 31P, 31PK, M43 Firestar
Tanarmi Models BTA90B & BTA90C
Taurus Models PT92 & PT99
Victory Arms Model MC5
Walther Models P-38, P-88DA, P-5DA

10mm

Colt Delta Elite, Delta Gold Cup, Double Eagle
Glock Model 20
IAI Javelina
L.A.R. Grizzley Mark I
Springfield Armory Omega, Model 1911-AI Standard
Victory Arms Model MC5

10mm Auto

Thompson/Center Contender

41 Action Express

Action Arms Models AT-88S, AT-88P, AT-88H
American Derringer Model 1
F.I.E. Model TZ75
Kassnar Model 941 Jericho
Tanarmi Model TA90B
Victory Arms Model MC5

41 Mag.

American Derringer Model 1
Magnum Research Desert Eagle
Ruger New Model Bisley, Redhawk, Blackhawk SA
Smith & Wesson Models 57, 657
Dan Wesson 41 Mag Revolvers

.410

American Derringer Models 1, 4, 6
Thompson/Center Contender Super "16"

44 Magnum

American Derringer Model 1
Colt Anaconda
Freedom Arms Premier & Field Grades
Llama Super Comanche IV
Magnum Research Desert Eagle
Mitchell Arms SA Army Model Revolvers
Ruger Redhawk, New Model Bisley, Blackhawk SA (S-45N), Super Blackhawk, Super Redhawk DA
Smith & Wesson Model 629
Springfield Armory Model 1911-A2 SA
Thompson/Center Contender, Hunter
Dan Wesson 44 Mag. Revolvers

44 Special

American Derringer Models 1 and 7
Charter Arms Bulldog Pug, New Police Bulldog, Target Bulldog
Smith & Wesson Model 629
Uberti 1873 Cattleman Quick Draw

44-40

American Derringer Model 1
EMF/Dakota Models 1873, 1875 Outlaw 1894, Bisley, Custom Engraved SP
Mitchell Arms 1875 Remington Revolver
A. Uberti 1873 Cattleman Quick Draw, 1875 and 1890 Remington Army Outlaw

45 Auto

American Derringer Models 1, 6, Semmerling LM-4
AMT Longslide & Government Models
Astra Model A-90
Auto-Ordnance Model 1911A-1 Thompson, Model 1927A-5
Chinasports Norinco Type M1911 Pistol
Colt Combat Commander, Lightweight Commander, Gold Cup National Match, Officer's ACP, Government Model, Double Eagle
Detonics Combat Master, Servicemaster, Scoremaster, Compmaster
L.A.R. Grizzly Mark I
Llama Automatics (Large and Compact Frames)
Sig Sauer Model 220
Smith & Wesson Third Generation (Model 4500 Series), Model 625
Springfield Armory Model 1911-A1 Standard, Commander, Omega
Star Model PD
Victory Arms Model MC5

45 Colt

American Derringer Models 1, 4, 6
EMF/Dakota Target, Models 1873, 1875 "Outlaw", 1894 Bisley, 1873 Premier SA, Custom Engraved SA, Hartford Models
Freedom Arms Premier & Field Grades
Mitchell Arms SA Army Model Revolvers, 1875 Remington Revolver
Ruger New Model Bisley
Smith & Wesson Model 25
Thompson/Center Contender Super "16"
Uberti 1873 Cattleman Quick Draw, 1875 and 1890 Remington Army Outlaw

45 Win. Mag.

American Derringer Model 1
IAI Automag III, IV
L.A.R. Grizzly Mark I
Wildey Pistols

454 Casull

Freedom Arms Casull Premier & Field Grades

45-70 Government

Thompson/Center Hunter

475 Wildey Mag.

Wildey Pistols

RIFLES

CENTERFIRE BOLT ACTION

Standard Calibers

17 Rem.

Kimber Model 84 Mini Mauser Sporter
Remington Model 700 BDL

Sako Hunter, Varmint, Deluxe
Ultra Light Model 20 Series
Winslow Varmint

22 Hornet

Ultra Light Model 20 Series

220 Swift

McMillan Super Varminter

22 PPC

Sako PPC Varmint, BR, Hunter, Deluxe

222 Rem.

Brno Models ZKK 600, 601, 602
Churchill Highlander
Kimber Model 84 Mini Mauser Sporter
Remington Model 700 BDL
Sako Varmint, Hunter, Deluxe
Steyr-Mannlicher Model SL
Ultra Light Model 20 Series

223 Rem.

Brno Model ZKK601
Browning A-Bolt
Howa Trophy Sporting, Varmint, Model 1500 Series
Kimber Model 84 Mini Mauser Sporter
Mark X Mini
McMillan Super Varminter
Remington Models 700 BDL, Seven
Ruger M-77 Mark II
Sako Hunter, Varmint, Deluxe, LS
Savage Model 110 Series
Steyr-Mannlicher Model SL
Tikka New Generation Rifles
Ultra Light Model 20 Series
Weatherby Vanguard Classic I, Weatherguard
Winchester Models 70 Featherweight, Sporter, Lightweight, Varmint

22-250

Blaser Model R84
Browning Short Action A-Bolt
Dakota Arms 76 SA Alpine
Heym SR20 Classic Sporter
Howa Trophy Sporting, Varmint, Model 1500 Series
Mark X American Field Mauser System
McMillan Super Varminter
Parker-Hale Models M81, 1200, 2100, 1100 LWT
Remington Model 700 ADL, Model 700 BDL, Model 700 AS
Ruger Models M-77RSI International, M-77V Varmint
Sako Deluxe, Varmint, Carbine, Hunter, Fiberclass, LS
Savage Model 110 Series
Steyr-Mannlicher Luxus Model L
Tikka New Generation
Ultra Light Model 20 Series
Weatherby VGX Deluxe
Winchester Model 70 Featherweight, Lightweight, VGX Sporter, Varmint
Winslow Basic

240

Weatherby Mark V Lazermark, Ultramark, Fibermark, Euromark

243 Win.

Beeman/Krico Models 600, 700
Blaser Model R84
Brno Model ZKK 601
Churchill Highlander
Dakota Arms Model 76 SA Alpine

Heym Model SR20, Classic Sporter Series, Trophy Series
Howa Trophy Sporting, Model 1500 Series (barreled actions)
Mark X American Field Mauser System
Mauser Model 66 & 99 Standard
McMillan Super Varminter, Benchrest
Parker-Hale Models M81, 1200, 1100 LWT, 2100
Remington Models 700 BDL, LS, AS & FS, 7400, 7600, 700 Mountain, 700 ADL Deluxe, Model Seven
Ruger Models RSI International, Model M-77RSI International, M77V Varmint, M-77 Mark II
Sako Varmint, Fiberclass, Hunter, Deluxe, LS, Mannlicher-Style Carbine
Savage Models 110 Series
Steyr-Mannlicher Models Luxus L, SSG Marksman
Tikka New Generation Rifles
Ultra Light Model 20 Series
Weatherby Vanguard Classic I, Classic II, Weatherguard VGX Deluxe
Winchester Models 70 Featherweight, Lightweight, Varmint, Sporter, Ranger Youth
Winslow Basic

6mm Rem.

Blaser Model R84
Dakota Arms Model 76 SA Alpine
McMillan Classic Sporter SA, Benchrest, Super Varminter
Parker-Hale Models 81, 1100 LWT, 1200, 2100
Remington Model Seven, Model 700 BDL
Ruger Model M-77 Varmint, M-77 Mark II
Steyr-Mannlicher Luxus Model L
Ultra Light Model 20 Series

250-3000 Savage

Dakota Arms Model 76 SA Alpine
Ruger Model M-77RSI International
Ultra Light Model 20 Series

257

Ruger Model M-77RL Ultra Light
Ultra Light Model 20 Series
Weatherby Mark V Lazermark, Fibermark, Euromark, Ultramark

6 PPC

McMillan Benchrest
Sako PPC Varmint, BR/Varmint, Hunter, Deluxe

25-06

Blaser Model R84
Browning A-Bolt
Churchill Highlander
K.D.F. Model K15 American
Kimber Model 89 Big Game (Featherweight)
Mark X American Field Mauser System
Mauser Model 99 Standard
McMillan Classic Sporter LA, Super Varminter
Remington Model 700 BDL, Classic Limited Edition
Ruger Models M-77V Varmint, 77RS
Sako Fiberclass, Hunter, Carbine, Deluxe, LS
Steyr-Mannlicher Model Luxus M
Winchester Model 70 Sporter Walnut
Winslow Basic

257 Roberts

Dakota Arms Model 76 Classic
Kimber Model 89 Big Game (Featherweight)
Ultra Light Model 20 Series
Winslow Basic

270 Win.

Beeman/Krico Model 720
Blaser Models R84
Brno Model ZKK 600
Browning A-Bolt
Churchill Highlander
Dakota Arms Model 76 Classic
Heym Model SR20, Classic Sporter Series, Trophy Series
Howa Trophy Sporting, Lightning, Model 1500 Series (barreled action)
KDF Model K15 American
Kimber Model 89 Big Game (Featherweight)
Mark X American Field Mauser System, LTW Sporter
Mauser Model 66 & 99 Standard
McMillan Classic Sporter LA, Alaskan LA, Titanium Mountain
Parker-Hale Models M81, 1100, 1200, 2100
Remington Models 700 LS, AS, FS & RS, 7400, 7600, 700 ADL Deluxe & BDL, 700 Mountain
Ruger Model M77 RS, RL Ultralight, 77RSI International
Sako Deluxe, Fiberclass, Hunter, LS, Fiberclass Carbine
Savage Model 110 Series
Steyr-Mannlicher Luxus Model M
Tikka New Generation Rifles
Weatherby Models Mark V Lazermark, Deluxe, Fibermark, Vanguard Classic I & II, VGX Deluxe, Euromark, Ultramark, Weatherguard
Winchester Models 70 Lightweight, Featherweight, Ranger, Winlite, Sporter
Winslow Basic

280 Rem. Win.

Blaser Model R 84
Browning A-Bolt
Dakota Arms Model 76 Classic
Kimber Model 89 Big Game (Featherweight)
McMillan Titanium Mountain, Classic Sporter LA, Alaskan LA
Remington Models 700 AS, Mountain, RS, 7400, 7600, 700 BDL
Sako Fiberclass, Hunter, LS, Deluxe
Winchester Models 70 Featherweight, Winlite, Lightweight
Winslow Basic

284 Win.

McMillan Classic Sporter SA
Ultra Light Model 20 Series
Winslow Basic

7mm Mauser

Remington Model 700 Mountain, BDL

7mm-08

Browning A-Bolt Short Action
Dakota Arms Model 76 SA Alpine
McMillan Classic Sporter SA, Super Varminter
Remington Model Seven, Model 700 Mountain, Model 700 BDL
Sako Hunter, Deluxe, LS, Varmint, Fiberclass
Ultra Light Model 20 Series
Weatherby Classic I, Weatherguard

30-06

Beeman/Krico Model 700, 720
Blaser Model R 84
Brno Model ZKK 600
Browning A-Bolt
Churchill Highlander
Dakota Arms Model 76 Classic
Heym Model SR20, Classic Sporter Series, Trophy Series

Howa Trophy Sporting, Lightning, Model 1500 Series (barreled action)
K.D.F. Model K15 American
Kimber Model 89 Big Game (Featherweight)
Mark X American Field Mauser System, LTW Sporter
Mauser Model 66 & 99 Standard
McMillan Classic Sporter LA, Alaskan LA, Titanium Mountain
Parker-Hale Models M81 Classic, 1100 Lightweight, 1200 Super, 2100 Midland
Remington Models 700 LS, BDL Deluxe, AS, 7400, 7600, Model 700 Mountain
Ruger Model M-77RS, 77RL Ultra Light, 77RSI International
Sako Carbine, Fiberclass, Hunter, Deluxe, LS
Savage Model 110 Series
Steyr-Mannlicher Luxus Model M
Tikka New Generation Rifles
Weatherby Fibermark, Lazermark, Euromark, Deluxe, Ultramark, Vanguard Classic I & II, Weatherguard, VGX Deluxe
Winchester Models 70 Featherweight, Winlite, Lightweight, Sporter Ranger
Winslow Basic

30-06 Carbine

Remington Model 7600 Carbine

300 Savage

Ultra Light Model 20 Series

308 Win.

Beeman/Krico Models 600, 640
Brno Model ZKK 601
Browning A-Bolt Short Action
Churchill Highlander
Dakota Arms Model 76 SA Alpine
Heckler & Koch Models HK SR-9
Heym Model SR20, Classic Sporter Series, Trophy Series
Howa Trophy Sporting, Model 1500 Series (barreled action), Varmint
Mark X American Field Mauser System
Mauser Models 66, 86 & 99 Standard
McMillan Classic Sporter SA, Super Varminter, Benchrest
Parker-Hale Models M81, 1100, 1200, 2100
Remington Models Seven, 700 Mountain, 7400, 7600, 700 ADL Deluxe & BDL
Ruger Models 77RSI International, 77V Varmint, M-77 Mark II
Sako Carbine, Varmint, Fiberclass, Hunter, deluxe, LS
Savage Model 110 Series
Steyr-Mannlicher Models Luxus L, SSG Marksman & Match UIT
Tikka New Generation
Ultra Light Model 20 Series
Weatherby Vanguard Classic I, Weatherguard
Winchester Model 70 Lightweight, Featherweight, Heavy Barrel Varmint
Winslow Basic

35 Whelen

Kimber Model 89 Big Game (Medium)
Remington Models 700 BDL & CL, 7400, 7600

358 Win.

Dakota Arms 76 SA Alpine
Ultra Light Model 20 Series
Winslow Basic

MAGNUM CALIBERS

222 Rem. Mag.

Kimber Model 84 Sporter
Steyr-Mannlicher Model SL
Ultra Light Model 20 Series

224 Weatherby Mag.

Weatherby Mark V Lazermark

257 Weatherby

Blaser Model R84
K.D.F. Model K15 American
Mauser Model 99
Steyr-Mannlicher Model S

264 Win. Mag.

Blaser Model R84
Steyr-Mannlicher Model S
Winchester Model 70 Sporter

270 Weatherby Mag.

K.D.F. Model K15 American
Winchester Model 70 Sporter

270 Win./Weatherby Mag.

Mauser Model 99
Sako Carbine
Weatherby Vanguard Classic II, VGX Deluxe

7mm Rem. Mag.

Blaser Model R84
Browning A-Bolt
Churchill Highlander
Dakota Arms Model 76 Classic
Heym Model SR20, Classic Sporter Series, Trophy Series
Howa Trophy Sporting
K.D.F. Model K15 American
Kimber Model 89 Big Game (Medium)
Mark X American Field Mauser System, LTW Sporter
Mauser Model 66 & 99
McMillan Classic Sporter MA, Alaskan, Titanium Mountain
Parker-Hale Model M81 Classic
Remington Models 700 LS & FS, 700 ADL Deluxe, AS
Ruger Models M-77RS, 77RL
Sako Fiberclass, Hunter, Carbine, Deluxe, LS
Savage Model 110 Series
Steyr-Mannlicher Luxus Model S
Tikka New Generation
Weatherby Mark V Fibermark, Euromark, Deluxe, Lazermark, Vanguard VGX, Classic I & II, Ultramark, Weatherguard
Winchester Model 70 Winlite, Sporter, Super Grade
Winslow Basic

8mm Rem. Mag.

Remington Model 700 BDL

300 Weatherby Mag.

Blaser Model R 84
KDF Model K15 American
Mauser Models 66 & 99
McMillan Classic Sporter Model MA, Safari, Alaskan MA
Remington Model 700 AS
Sako Hunter, Deluxe
Weatherby Mark V Fibermark, Ultramark, Euromark, Deluxe, Lazermark, Vanguard Classic II, VGX Deluxe

Winchester Model 70 Winlite
Winslow Basic

300 Win. Mag.

Browning A-Bolt
Blaser Model R 84
Churchill Highlander
Dakota Arms Model 76 Safari & Classic
Heym Model SR20, Classic Sporter Series, Trophy Series
Howa Trophy Sporting, Lightning, Model 1500 Series
KDF Model K15 American
Kimber Model 89 Big Game (Medium)
Mark X American Field Mauser System
Mauser Model 66, Classic Sporter Model MA, Alaskan MA
McMillan Titanium Mountain, Safari, Long Range
Parker-Hale Model M81 Classic
Remington Model 700 BDL
Sako Fiberclass, Hunter, Carbine, LS, Deluxe
Savage 110 Series
Steyr-Mannlicher Luxus Model S, Model S
Tikka New Generation
Weatherby Vanguard Classic II, VGX Deluxe
Winchester Model 70 Winlite, Super Grade, Sporter
Winslow Basic

300 H&H

Kimber Model 89 Big Game (Medium)
McMillan Alaskan MA, Safari
Steyr-Mannlicher Model S
Winchester Model 70 Sporter
Winslow Basic

308 Win. Mag.

Churchill Highlander
McMillan National Match

338 Win. Mag.

Blaser Model R84
Browning A-Bolt
Dakota Arms Model 76 Safari, Classic
Heym Classic Sporter Series, Trophy Series
Howa Trophy Sporting, Model 1500 Series
McMillan Classic Sporter MA, Safari
Kimber Model 89 Big Game (Medium)
Mauser Model 99
Remington Model 700 BDL
Sako Safari Grade, Hunter, Carbine, Deluxe, LS, Fiberclass
Tikka New Generation Rifles
Weatherby Vanguard VGX Deluxe, Classic II
Winchester Model 70 Winlite, Sporter, Super Grade
Winslow Basic

340 Weatherby Mag.

KDF Model K15 American
McMillan Classic Sporter MA, Alaskan MA, Safari
Weatherby Mark V Ultramark, Deluxe, Lazermark

35 Whelen

Remington Model 700 BDL

358 Win.

McMillan Alaskan MA
Winslow Basic

375 H&H

Blaser Model R84
Brno Model ZKK 602
Browning A-Bolt
Dakota Arms Model 76 Safari, Classic

Heym Model SR20, Classic Sporter Series,
  Trophy Series
K.D.F. Model K15 American
Kimber Model 89 Big Game Hunter & African
  Grades
Krieghoff Ulm & Teck
Mauser Model 66 & 99 Safari
McMillan Classic Sporter MA, Safari, Alaskan MA
Parker-Hale Model M81 African
Remington Model 700 Safari, BDL
Ruger Magnum
Sako Safari Grade, Carbine, Fiberclass, Hunter,
  LS, Deluxe
Steyr-Mannlicher Models S & S/T
Whitworth Safari Grade Express
Winchester Model 70 Super Express
Winslow Basic

378 Win. Mag.

McMillan Safari
Weatherby Mark V Lazermark, Deluxe

416 Rem./Weatherby Mag.

KDF Model K15 American
McMillan Classic Sporter Model MA Alaskan MA,
  Safari
Remington Model 700 Safari
Weatherby Mark V Euromark, Deluxe, Lazermark

416 Rigby

Dakota Arms African Grade 76
Kimber Model 89 African
McMillan Safari
Remington Model 700 BDL
Ruger Magnum

425 Express

Heym Model SR20 Classic Safari Series

458 Win. Mag.

Brno Model ZKK 602
Dakota Arms Model 76 Safari, Classic
Heym Model SR20 Classic Safari Series
KDF Model K15 American
Krieghoff Ulm & Teck
Mauser Model 66 Safari
McMillan Safari
Remington Model 700 Safari, BDL
Ruger No. 1 Tropical
Steyr-Mannlicher Model S/T
Whitworth Safari Grade Express
Winchester Model 70 Super Express Walnut
  Magnum
Winslow Basic

460 Win./Weatherby Mag.

Kimber Model 89 African
Weatherby Lazermark, Euromark, Deluxe

CENTERFIRE LEVER ACTION

218 Bee

Marlin Model 1894 Classic

22 Magnum

A. Uberti Model 1866, Model 1871 Rolling Block
  Baby Carbine, Model 1873

222 Rem./223 Rem.

Browning Models 81 BLR, 1885

22-250

Browning Models 81 BLR, 1885

243 Win.

Browning Model 81 BLR

25-20 Win.

Marlin Model 1894 Classic

257 Roberts

Browning Model 81 BLR

270

Browning Model 1885

284 Win.

Browning Model 81 BLR

7mm-08

Browning Model 81 BLR

307 Win.

Winchester Model 94, Big Bore Walnut

308 Win.

Browning Model 81 BLR

30-30 Win.

Marlin Models 336CS, 30AS
Winchester Models 94 Ranger, Win-Tuff

30-06

Browning Model 1885, 53 Ltd. Ed.

32-20 Win.

Marlin Model 1894 Classic

35 Rem.

Marlin Model 336CS

356 Win.

Winchester Model 94, Big Bore Walnut

357 Mag.

Marlin Model 1894CS
Rossi Puma (Model M92)
Uberti Models 1871 Rolling Block Baby Carbine,
  Model 1873

358 Win.

Browning Model 81BLR

375 Win.

Marlin Model 336CS

38 Special

Marlin Model 1894CS
Rossi Puma (Model M92)
A. Uberti 1866 Sporting, Model 1873 Carbine and
  Sporting

44 Special

Marlin Model 1894S

44 Rem. Mag.

Marlin Model 1894S

444 Marlin

Marlin Model 444SS

44-40

Uberti Model 1886, Model 1873

45 Colt

Marlin Model 1894S
Uberti Model 1873

45-70 Government

Browning Model 1885
Marlin Model 1895SS

7mm Rem. Mag.

Browning Model 1885

CENTERFIRE PUMP

38 Special

Action Arms Timber Wolf

357 Magnum

Action Arms Timber Wolf

SINGLE SHOT

22S,L,LR

Varner Favorite Hunter Model
Walther Running Boar, Model GX-1, UIT Match,
  Model KK/MS Silhouette

22 BR Rem.

Remington Model Bench Rest

22 Hornet

Thompson/Center Hunter

220 Swift

Ruger No. 1V Special Varminter, No. 1B Standard

222 Rem.

Remington Models 40-XB, Bench Rest
Thompson/Center Hunter

223

Remington Model Bench Rest
Ruger No. 1B Standard, No. IV Special Varminter
Thompson/Center Hunter

22-250 Rem.

Remington Model 40-XB Rangemaster
Ruger No. 1B Standard, Special Varminter
Thompson/Center Hunter

243 Win.

Remington Model 40-XB Rangemaster
Ruger No. 1A Light Sporter, No. 1B, No. 1 RSI
  International Standard
Thompson/Center Hunter

25-06

Remington Model 40-XB Rangemaster
Ruger No. 1V Special Varminter, No. 1B Standard

6mm BR Rem.

Remington Model Bench Rest

6mm Rem.

Remington Model Bench Rest, 40-XB
  Rangemaster
Ruger No. 1B Standard

257 Roberts

Ruger No. 1B Standard

270 Win.

Ruger No. 1A Light Sporter, No. 1B Standard, RSI International
Thompson/Center Hunter

280 Rem.

Ruger No. 1B Standard

7mm-08

Thompson/Center Hunter

30-06

Remington Model 40XB Rangemaster
Ruger No. 1A Light Sporter, No. 1B Standard, RSI International
Thompson/Center Hunter

300 Win. Mag.

Remington Model 40-XB Rangemaster

308 Win.

Remington Model 40-XB
Thompson/Center Hunter

7mm Rem. Mag.

Remington Model 40-XB Rangemaster

300 Weatherby/Win. Mag.

Ruger Medium Sporter

338 Win. Mag.

Ruger No. 1 Medium Sporter, Standard

375 H&H

Ruger No. 1H Tropical

458 Win. Mag.

Ruger No. 1H Tropical

AUTOLOADING

22 LR

Thompson/Center Contender
American Arms Model EXP-64, SM-64

22 Hornet

Thompson/Center Contender

22 Win. Mag.

Thompson/Center Contender

223 Rem.

Colt Model AR-15A2
Ruger Mini-14, Mini-14 Ranch
Thompson/Center Contender

30-30 Win.

Thompson/Center Contender

308 Win.

Springfield Armory SAR-8 Standard, Model SAR-4800 Bush Rifle, Compact & Sporter; MIA Standard, Match; MIA-A1 Bush

35 Rem.

Thompson/Center Contender

357 Rem. Max.

Thompson/Center Contender

44 Mag.

Thompson/Center Contender

45 Auto

Auto-Ordnance Thompson Models M1, 1927A1, 1927A3
Marlin Model 45

9mm

Marlin Model 9 Camp

RIMFIRE BOLT ACTION

22S,L,LR

Anschutz Match 54 & Match 64 Sporters: Models 1403D, 1416D, 1418D, 1516D, 54.18S, 54.18S-REP, 1803D, 1903D, 1907, 1910, 1911, 1913, 1808, Model 1700, Achiever, Model 1449
Beeman/Weihrauch Models HW60 Smallbore, HW 60J-ST, HW660 Match
Beeman/FWB Model 2600
Browning Model A-Bolt 22, A-Bolt Stalker
Kimber Model 82 (Sporting, Gov't Target)
Marlin Models 15YN "Little Buckaroo", 880, 881
Mauser Model 201
Remington Models 40-XR, 40-XC, 541-T
Ruger Model 77/22RS
Weatherby Accumark Classic 22

22 WMR

Marlin Models 25MN, 882, 883
Mauser Model 201

222 Rem.

Beeman/Weihrauch Model HW 60J-ST

RIMFIRE AUTOLOADING

22S,L,LR

Anschutz Model 525
Browning Model 22 (Grades I & VI)
Iver Johnson Targetmaster
Marlin Models 70P, 70HC, 75C, 60, 995
Mitchell Arms 22 Col. Military Style Rifles
Remington Model 572 BDL Fieldmaster
Ruger Model 10/22

RIMFIRE LEVER ACTION

22S,L,LR

Browning Model BL-22 (Grades I & II)
Iver Johnson Wagonmaster
Marlin Models 39TD, Golden 39AS
Mitchell Arms Reproduction Models (1858 Henry, 1866 Winchester, 1873 Winchester)
A. Uberti Model 1866
Varner Favorite Hunter
Winchester Model 9422

RIMFIRE PUMP ACTION

22 LR

Ruger Model M62 SAC, M62 SA

22 WMR

Winchester Model 9422

DOUBLE RIFLES

308

Krieghoff Models Ulm & Teck

30-06

Krieghoff Models Ulm & Teck

300 Win. Mag.

Krieghoff Models Ulm & Teck

375 H&H

Heym Model 88B Safari
Krieghoff Models Ulm & Teck

458 Win.

Heym Model 88B Safari
Krieghoff Models Ulm & Teck

470 N.E.

Heym Model 88B Safari

500 N.E.

Heym Model 88B Safari

RIFLE/SHOTGUN COMBOS

22 Mag./12 ga.

Heym Model 22S

22 Hornet/12 ga.

Heym Model 22S
Savage Model 24F

222 Rem./12 ga.

Churchill Regent
Heym Model 22S
Savage Model 389

222 Rem. Mag./12 ga.

Heym Model 22S

223 Rem./12 ga.

Churchill Regent
Savage Model 24-F (20 ga. also)

243 Win./12 ga.

Heym Model 22S

270 Win./12 ga.

Churchill Regent

308 Win./12 ga.

Churchill Regent
Savage Model 389

30-06/12 ga.

Churchill Regent

30-30/12 ga.

Savage Model 24F